Glee Club and Chorus

A Handbook of Organizing, Conducting,
and Maintaining Glee Club and Choral
Organizations, with Selected, Graded, and
Classified Lists of Octavo Music and Texts

By

Van A. Christy, M. A.

G. SCHIRMER, Inc.
New York

FOREWORD

This handbook has been prepared because there is a widespread need, especially in the schools, for complete and concise treatment of the problems of organizing, conducting, and maintaining glee clubs and choruses, as well as information concerning music materials.

The principal objectives of the book are:

1. To furnish a guide and method of procedure for the inexperienced choral director.

2. To furnish information, ideas, and suggestions, for the experienced choral director.

3. To furnish a basic text and a teacher's outline for instructors of choral conducting and choral methods. (See p. 3.)

4. To furnish a textbook for college classes in choral conducting, containing in one volume necessary information in relation to theory, method, practice, and materials.

5. To furnish an up-to-date, carefully graded and classified list of the most suitable octavo music and music books for the use of glee clubs and *a cappella* (unaccompanied) mixed choruses.

6. To furnish valuable information and to suggest vocal exercises to supplement standard texts or methods of class voice training (See *Principles of Vocal Production*, p. 40, and *Group Vocal Exercises*, p. 48).

7. To furnish suggestions of suitable vocal music for arrangers of radio programs.

8. To furnish suggestions of suitable vocal music for arrangers of supplementary vocal music for motion pictures.

9. To furnish carefully selected references for more detailed study of many topics here outlined.

PREFACE

If music is ever to take its rightful place in the lives of the men of America, it will be through neither the opera nor the recital nor any music form to which they listen— but that music which, with their fellows, they help to produce.

CLAYTON W. OLD
President of the Associated
Glee Clubs of America

The remarkable expansion of choral singing in the secondary schools and colleges of the United States during the past decade is one of the most significant trends in modern education. Choral music, for reasons which are not entirely clear, for a long time lagged behind instrumental music in both the type of music chosen and the standard of performance. However, performances of choral music on a symphonic level have now become fairly general, not only in colleges but in many high schools as well. Indeed, the quality of the secondary school work in some communities is superior to that done in the local colleges, a situation which suggests reorganization of college choral work to meet higher standards. The astonishing rise in both the number and quality of glee clubs and *a cappella* mixed choruses truly promises to make the America of the future the most musical of nations. This great choral movement, which has as its purpose the "betterment of America through song", deserves the whole-hearted coöperation and support of all those who are interested in the establishment of a happier and more stable society.

Several organizations and individuals have been very active in promoting the success of the movement. Much of the initial and present interest in men's glee-club singing is due to the vision and leadership of Dr. Archibald T. Davison of Harvard University. The tremendous spread and success of the glee-club movement is due largely to two associations: The Intercollegiate Musical Council, Inc., and the Associated Glee Clubs of America. Mr. and Mrs. Albert F. Pickernell and Marshall Bartholomew of the Intercollegiate Musical Council and Clayton W. Old of the Associated Glee Clubs of America have, by their untiring zeal and unselfish service, done much in organizing and promoting this movement on a nation-wide scope. The officers of the National Bureau for the Advancement of Music, of the National High School Chorus, and of the Chorus of the Music Educators National Conference have also contributed much of value to the extension of choral singing.

A number of pioneer directors of *a cappella* choirs and their disciples have, both through precept and through the example of the performances of their organizations, been largely instrumental in lifting high school music above the level of the commonplace. Fine concert choruses such as the St. Olaf's Choir, the Westminster Choir, the Smallman A Cappella Choir, the Denver A Cappella Choir, the Chicago A Cappella Choir, and such professional or semi-professional groups as the English Singers, the Russian Symphonic Choir, the Ukrainian Chorus, the Sistine Choir, the Don Cossack Choir, the Hall Johnson Chorus, the Vienna Boys Choir, and other worthy groups have provided notable stimulus to choral development.

There is no doubt that the organization of contests is responsible to a considerable extent for the heightened interest and the phenomenal spread of the movement. Since 1914 the men's glee-club contest has become a national event, with more colleges participating each year. There is a possibility in the future of national, perhaps international, contests or festivals for both men's and treble-voice glee clubs, and for *a cappella* mixed choruses. Already we see the seeds of this in the many regional and state contests and festivals, and in the National High School Chorus. The greatest single obstacle in the path of present progress is the financial problem.

Authors of text-books dealing with choral conducting, community music, and public-school music have made recent valuable contributions to the literature of the *a cappella* mixed chorus; but there has been little attention specifically given to the subject of the glee club. The available information is widely scattered and, even when combined, inadequate to clarify the many problems which confront the inexperienced director. This handbook is an attempt to compile in one volume, *in concise and yet comprehensive outline-form*, the practical and theoretical information which should be available to glee-club and choral directors. No claim to originality is made for many of the ideas expressed; the aim has been rather to compile in one volume the most useful beliefs and practices of experienced choral directors. Certain parts are discussed very briefly because the subject matter is readily available in worthy and well known texts. Parts covering subject matter not available in any other text are discussed at greater length. In all instances, *the object has been to give the essential facts, so organized and outlined that they may be quickly and easily accessible to the reader.*

Grateful acknowledgment is offered to the officers of the Intercollegiate Musical Council, the Associated Glee Clubs of America, and the National Bureau for the Advancement of Music; to the various choral conductors whose opinions have been solicited; to the fifty-four music publishers who have contributed by submitting music for examination; to Peter W. Dykema, Edwin J. Stringham, the late Robert Elwyn, and others of the music faculty of Teachers College, Columbia University.   V. A. C.

CONTENTS

PART I: Organizing, Conducting, and Maintaining Glee Clubs and Choruses

GLEE CLUB AND CHORUS

PART I
Organizing, Conducting, and Maintaining
Glee Clubs and Choruses

CHAPTER I

THE CONDUCTOR

(See also CHAPTER IV, REHEARSALS, and CHAPTER VII, CONTESTS AND FESTIVALS)

> *Our boys and girls must somehow come to prize good singing and playing not only as a classroom and concert-hall activity, but mainly as an everyday means of recreation and an enchantment of social life.*
>
> Amateur Music Report of the Music Education Research Council, 1933 Music Supervisors National Conference.

A. Opportunity

The demand for competent choral directors is continually growing. Aside from glee-club and chorus work in the schools, most communities present an opportunity to conduct local choral organizations. There are few communities so poor or so lacking in desire for musical expression that they cannot maintain a singing society. Much of the benefit of the music work now carried on in the schools is lost because it is not yet being carried over into adult life through adequate community extension. The time is now ripe for expanding choral music in the communities. The average adult is becoming surfeited with passive listening and will welcome an opportunity for personal expression. "A movement of vital importance to school music teachers is now being inaugurated under the combined sponsorship of the Associated Glee Clubs of America, Kiwanis International, National Recreation Association, and the Music Educators National Conference. It looks to the formation of Junior Glee Clubs of male voices consisting of graduates of high schools who have shown an interest in singing."[1]

The directors of school choirs must recognize that the organization of community choruses is a natural outgrowth and extension of their school work and that the moral responsibility for leadership is theirs.

B. Need for Adequate College Courses in Conducting

The normal schools, colleges, universities, and music conservatories have considerably improved the quality of training offered; nevertheless they continue to graduate music educators and solo performers many of whom do not succeed, because they are unable to direct choral groups satisfactorily. In many instances these failures are due not to weak personalities or poor musicianship but rather to insufficient or faulty training in this type of work. So much attention has been centered upon making classroom teachers and solo performers that the importance of training conductors to meet the demands of the present situation has been underestimated or neglected. A number of institutions have recognized

[1]Osbourne McConathy, "Junior Glee Clubs of Young Men", *Music Educators Journal*, March, 1935.

the need, and reorganized their choral conducting courses. However, it is only the rare institution that even approaches the needed efficiency in training its graduates to meet successfully today's demand for skilled directors of choral groups.

Music graduates in the majority of colleges are required to take only one or two, seldom three, semesters of classroom work in choral conducting, meeting one, two, or (rarely) three times a week. In most instances no further elective work is offered. The amount of classwork is not only meager but, on the average, poorly organized; the method is haphazard, and the subject-matter covered inadequate or irrelevant for practical needs. It is a common observation that music graduates not only know very little about the problems involved in organizing, conducting, and maintaining choral groups but also are deficient in their knowledge of suitable music materials and of the actual mechanics of conducting.

Although it is a fact that, regardless of training, only a select few can be expected to become really great conductors, it is equally true that the average music student can, through well directed college training, be taught the methods and techniques he needs to be an acceptable director of choral organizations. Is it not reasonable to ask that training institutions awake to this need, and give their graduates adequate training rather than allow them to go through a trying, often costly, and sometimes disastrous experience in the practice of their profession?

C. Training

1. Most Important Qualifications for Choral Conductors:
    a. Genuine love of music and joy in giving it personal expression.
    b. Good sense of pitch and rhythm.
    c. Sympathetic and imaginative interpretative sense.
    d. Mastery of the mechanics of conducting sufficient to indicate interpretative ideas satisfactorily.
    e. Commanding and pleasing personality. (A sense of humor, a cheerful attitude, and patience are qualities most necessary for the director of school and amateur groups.)
    f. Persistence in self-improvement and alertness to new ideas. (The ambitious conductor must avoid the insidious danger of becoming satisfied with his own efficiency. He must continually reexamine techniques and methods that might be improved.)
    g. Solo performance ability, preferably both vocal and instrumental.

2. Types of Training Most Valuable for Choral Conductors:
    a. Study of voice, conducting, solo instrument, harmony, and choral writing.
    b. Experience in singing in glee clubs, choirs, or choruses.
    c. Conducting any type of choral or instrumental ensemble.
        (Opportunity for the most gifted students to gain experience in conducting should be given in all high schools and even in the grades. It is significant that the National Solo and Ensemble Contests have sponsored a Student Conductors Contest. This is a move in the right direction, but still greater emphasis by music educators is needed.

The best way to ensure the quality of musical progress in the future is to develop the young conductor of today.)

d. A broad musical and general education.

D. Method of Conducting

A well trained choral director should be able to conduct skilfully either with or without a baton.   Interpretative ideas may be conveyed with definiteness and grace regardless of which method is used.   The expression of the face and the posture of the body assume more importance at times than the style and sweep of the conducting beat.   There is a growing tendency to discard the traditional baton when possible.   No hard and fast rule can be made.   However, the baton is usually preferable for large groups where the singers are so placed as to have difficulty in seeing the conductor, while it is better to discard the baton for small groups and, perhaps, for large well trained choruses so arranged that they can easily see the conductor.

A quiet, unobtrusive style is desirable.   The motions of the conductor should be both definite and graceful, "not the kind that attracts attention because of unusual superfluous motions, nor the kind that seems to be lacking in motion to the extent that the director seems to be afraid of exerting himself."[2]

Mechanically, the conductor must be able to indicate any of the following phases of music interpretation:

1. Tempo.
2. Rhythm or pulse (Sometimes the actual duration of a note).
3. Accent.
4. Power or dynamics.
5. Style.
6. Attacks.
7. Releases.
8. Phrasing. (The skilful conductor indicates the "shape" of the phrase and suggests by his method of beat where breath is to be taken.)

There are instances where one hand is inadequate to convey all necessary interpretative ideas.   It then becomes necessary to use both hands, the right engaged primarily in beating time, the left in indicating attacks, releases, phrasing, and in accentuating dynamic effects, *etc.*   The student of conducting should be coached carefully on the importance of using the left hand and arm *only when significant changes or effects are desired.*   The habitual use of the left arm merely to duplicate the functions of the right is a useless waste of effort.   It results in distracting from the significance of movements which are necessary and which indicate important effects.

E. Suggested Outline for Choral Conducting Classes

CONDUCTING I

A basic course in the fundamentals of conducting with special emphasis upon preparation for directing assembly and community singing.   Also a basic

[2]O. Irving Jacobsen, "A Self-Examination for the Choral Conductor", *Supervisors Service Bulletin,* March, 1932.

course for further work in instrumental conducting. (The material outlined here may be covered in one semester, the class meeting three times weekly; but it is preferable that Conducting I cover two semesters, the class meeting two or three times weekly.)

1. Practice:
    a. Time-beating in all standard meters. (The phonograph may be used in teaching the mechanics of time-beating.)
    b. Conducting. (The class may serve as a chorus, using most songs found in standard assembly or community song books.)
    c. Solving problems encountered in music of the above type, *e.g.*, preliminary beats, holds, attacks, releases, divided beats, using the left hand, and adapting methods to meet the practical requirements of unlike groups and different conditions.
    d. Conducting songs of the pupils' own choice.

2. Method and Theory:
    a. Psychological basis of conducting.
    b. Short historical background.
    c. Opportunity for the skilled choral conductor.
    d. Most important qualifications for choral conductors.
    e. Types of training most valuable for choral conductors.
    f. Method of conducting.
    g. Time- or meter-beating: kinds of meter most commonly used, normal accent, syncopation, conducting figures, preliminary beat, attack, release, divided beat, hold, recitative, and free rhythm.

    h. Musical terminology in most common usage.
    i. Fundamental rules for the conductor to observe.
    j. How to rehearse music.
    k. Interpretation: tempo, rhythm and accent, dynamics and climax, spirit or emotion.

Assigned Texts (to be purchased by the student):
    Christy, *Glee Club and Chorus*, Chapter I and the following parts of Chapters IV and V: Fundamental Rules for the Choral Conductor to Observe, How to Rehearse Music, Tempo and Rhythm, Dynamics and Climax, Spirit or Emotion.
    Gehrkens, *Essentials in Conducting*, Chapters I-VII, and IX.

Supplementary Readings (to be provided by the school library):
    Beattie, McConathy, and Morgan, *Music in the Junior High School*, pp. 95-121, 144-151, 176-200.
    Dann, *Conductor's Book*, pp. 1-39, 59-76, 100-111.
    Giddings and Baker, *High School Music Teaching*, pp. 18-116, 128-141.
    Playground and Recreation Association, *Community Music*, Chapters II, III, IV, VIII, and IX.
    *Schmid, *The Language of the Baton*, pp. 1-72.
    Zanzig, *Community and Assembly Singing*, pp. 5-49.

    *Especially recommended as supplementary reading for this chapter.

Suggested Music:

    Standard community or assembly song-books.

    Phonograph records illustrating the different meters.

Teaching Suggestions:

    Conducting is both a science and an art. To obtain proficiency in any art, technique and theory must be so thoroughly mastered that they can be forgotten. Time-beating and all common conducting indications should become so habitually established by practice that the student is able eventually to concentrate on interpretation and other matters.

    At least 75% of the recitation period should be devoted to practice by the student, the instructor helping by giving necessary illustrations, explanations, and corrections. Most of the mechanics of conducting may be taught by the "class" rather than by the "individual" method. A class period in choral conducting may well consist of the following activities:

1. Practice by the class as a unit in solving problems of conducting and in directing music furnished by the phonograph or piano. (Large classes may be divided into two sections, which alternate in conducting and in singing the music.)
2. Practice by individual students in conducting music sung by the class as a chorus.
3. Illustrations and explanations of specific problems by the instructor or by a selected student.
4. Class discussion of theory or method encountered in readings.
5. Helpful criticism—verbal or written—by the instructor and members of the class. (Criticism of the individual may deal with posture, appearance, method, style, authority, definiteness, and interpretative qualities.)
6. Review of appropriate materials for various choral groups.
7. Listening to fine choral interpretations on phonograph records, over the radio, or in concert. (It is a valuable aid to have the score for observation while the composition is being sung.)
8. Observing the methods and style of skilled conductors. (This can best be accomplished by singing with the chorus, in rehearsal and in concert. The ambitious student-conductor should welcome the opportunity to sing under various experienced conductors, striving to obtain the best ideas and methods from each.)

CONDUCTING II

    A continuation of Conducting I and an advanced course in choral conducting with special emphasis upon conducting glee clubs and choruses. (In order to be thoroughly mastered, the work outlined in Conducting II should be extended over two or more semesters, with classes meeting two or three times a week.)

1. Practice:
    a. Conducting glee-club and chorus numbers selected by the instructor.
    b. Conducting glee-club and chorus numbers of the pupils' own choice.
    c. Music in meters of five and seven, music in free rhythm, strict and free recitative.

2.   Method and Theory:
    a.   Organizing glee clubs and choruses, creating and maintaining interest, selecting members, advertising, obtaining cooperation, constitutions and by-laws, inducements to membership.
    b.   Rehearsals: objectives, activities, time, place, number, length.
    c.   Principles of vocal production: posture, breathing, diction, tone-quality, Latin diction.
    d.   Interpretation: balance, blending, intonation, unanimity. (Review elements of interpretation outlined in Conducting I.)
    e.   Program-building and suitable materials.
    f.   Contests and festivals: special rehearsal methods, posture, appearance, uniforms or robes, stage-grouping, conditioning.
    g.   Concert tours and radio broadcasting.

Assigned Texts (to be purchased by the student):
Christy, *Glee Club and Chorus*, Chapter I, Latin Diction; Chapter IV, parts not covered in Conducting I; Chapters II, III, V, VI, VII, and VIII.
Smallman and Wilcox, *The Art of A Cappella Singing*, entire book.

Supplementary Readings (to be provided by the school library):
Cain, *Choral Music and its Practice*, entire book.
Coward, *Choral Technique and Interpretation*, pp. 2-19, 69-88, 93-95, 97-98, 112-114, 166-200, 249-259, 261-279.
Greene, *Interpretation in Song*, pp. 37-145, 158-167, 169-172, 176-184, 195-198.
Wodell, *Choir and Chorus Conducting*, pp. 5-36, 52-168.
Schmid, *The Language of the Baton*, pp. 72-116.
Additional Reading (suggested but not required in a one-semester course):
Beach, *Preparation and Presentation of the Operetta*.
Dawson, *The Voice of the Boy*.
Earhart, *The Eloquent Baton*.
Elson, *Music Club Programs from all Nations*.
Jones and Wilson, *Musico-Dramatic Producing*.
Rogers, *English Diction*.
Scott, *Madrigal Singing*.
Taft, *The Technique of Pageantry*.
Westerman, *Modern Phonetization*.
Webster and Wetzel, *Scenery Simplified*.

Suggested Music:
Octavo music for mixed chorus, treble-voice glee clubs, and men's-voice glee clubs.
Music texts suitable for junoir and senior high school groups.

Teaching Suggestions:
At least 50% of the recitation period should be devoted to practice by the student, the instructor helping with illustrations, explanations, and corrections. The student should become familiar with all types of music suitable for use in the school and community. (Observe also activities suggested for the class period, under Conducting I, "Teaching Suggestions.")

F. Fundamental and Necessary Theoretical Knowledge

1. The Technique of Song-Leading:
    a. Time-Beating:[3]

    "The underlying essential in all song-leading is thorough understanding of time-beating, which is the comparatively mechanical and formal phase of getting all the singers together so that they are singing the same tune at the same time. Every song leader is likely to have his own method of conducting, but the fundamentals of time-beating will always remain the same. It may be well to begin by illustrating the different movements, for example, in three-four time, then executing them, counting them out and finally applying the movement to beating time for some song in three-four rhythm. The candidates should be taught that once they have mastered this routine and their application of it becomes subconscious, it is for them to preserve their own individuality so that in their leading they will not merely be imitators of their instructor.

    "Before the class is given detailed instruction in time-beating for any of the rhythms, the leader should take up the question of some of the technical details of musical structure, namely the make-up of the measure or bar, as it is frequently called. He will point out that between the strong accents which indicate the beginning of measures there are one or more less important, weaker accents which determine the measure-rhythm of a song.... Measures with one strong and one weak accent are *two*, double or march rhythm; those with one strong and two weak are *three*, triple or, usually, waltz rhythm. These two rhythms are the foundation of all others —*four, six, nine, twelve, five, seven. . . .* Abundant practice is needed in determining these measure-rhythms by ear. Every leader should constantly practise this and should consult the upper number of the time signature which appears at the beginning of all music merely as a means of testing and correcting himself.

    "The theory of the usual formal system of time-beating is that the strong or primary accent in any kind of measure-rhythm should normally be represented by a vigorous downbeat directly in front of the body."

    b. Preliminary Beat and Attack:

    The preliminary beat is a necessary signal to the performers, indicating exactly the speed of the following composition. It is the most important beat in starting a song, since precision of attack is impossible without a decisive preliminary beat. Considerable practice is necessary to enable the student to master properly this fundamental phase of conducting. We occasionally see a conductor beat a measure or two before beginning; but this procedure is a waste of energy, distracting and unnecessary if proper technique is habitualized in training. *One precise and assured preliminary beat is enough!*

    There are three fundamental principles to observe in relation to the preliminary beat:

[3]Playground and Recreation Association of America, *Community Music*, C. C. Birchard and Co., Boston. Quotations under the heading of "Time-Beating" are from Chapter IV, Training Leadership, and are reprinted here by special permission of the author of that chapter, Prof. Peter W. Dykema.

(1) *It should be confident and precise,* but not emphasized to the extent that performers want to start with it.

(2) *It should be in the exact tempo of the music which follows.* (The conductor should never start until he can imaginatively "feel" the proper tempo and "hear" the first phrase.)

(3) *It should travel in such direction that, when completed, the hand and arm will be in the proper position for the first notated beat.*

The two most common preliminary beats occur:

(a) When music begins on the first beat of the measure, *e.g.,* in "America."

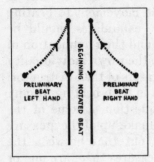

Instructions: Hands held slightly above the head and well apart. Direction of the preliminary beat from the outside upward. After the down-beat, the left hand is usually dropped at the side until it is needed again.

(b) When music begins on the last beat of the measure, *e.g.* "The Star-Spangled Banner."

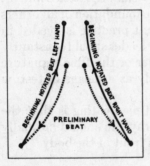

Instructions: Hands held well above the head and about 16 inches apart. Direction of the preliminary beat downward and outward.

These two types of preliminary beats should be thoroughly mastered by persistent practice.

When music begins other than on the down- or up-beat, the student may easily determine the direction of the preliminary beat by the application of the principle No. (3) previously stated. If music begins on a fraction of a pulse, the preliminary beat may be a divided beat or, perhaps, it may be a complete preceding beat plus the part of the beat in which the music begins. *Use lip motion to secure unanimity in attack in all instances where attack is difficult.*

c. Release:

It is a well known fact that the release is neglected more than the attack by the average conductor. Finished phrasing is impossible without skilful command of the release. Some of the most "telling" interpretative effects are accomplished through expert use of the release. The motion to indicate release may travel in any direction, *depending on what follows*. Its force is determined by the dynamics and the style of the music. Releases at the end of a verse or of a compositon are usually indicated with both hands. In music of several parts, the left hand is used generally to indicate attacks and releases of parts while the right' hand continues with time-beating.

A powerful interpretative effect for an ending *fortissimo* is obtained by a *crescendo* on the final chord. Move the hands gradually upwards and outwards to the highest point; then secure the release with a swift and forceful downward sweep. Extreme *pianissimo* releases should be definite but short in length. A lovely effect for an extreme *pianissimo* at the end of a composition (provided the final word ends on a vowel or a "humming" consonant) is obtained by a *decrescendo* to inaudibility. Drop the hands slowly and gradually as the *decrescendo* progresses, allowing the movement to end below the waist without giving any definite indication of release.

d. **Kinds of Rhythm in Most Common Usage, Normal Accent, and Conducting Figures:** (Classes in conducting should be thoroughly familiar with the theory and practice of conducting the various rhythms under this heading. The subject matter is fundamental, and essential to mastery of the mechanics of conducting. It is suggested that conducting classes supplement this by mechanical drill and by the conducting of music illustrating each of the rhythms. Most assembly or community song books will supply representative music for practice in the common rhythms. In the following illustrations the letters *d*, *l*, *r*, and *u* written above the notes indicate the general direction of the conductor's arm in beating time (*down*, *left*, *right*, and *up*); the accent marks indicate the notes upon which the *normal* accent falls; the size of the accent mark indicates the *relative force* of the accent; and the diagrams illustrate the approximate direction and "shape" of the conducting movement.)

(1) Double or Duple Rhythm: $\frac{2}{2}$, $\frac{2}{4}$, $\frac{2}{8}$.

Ex. 1

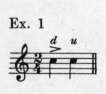

Conducting figure for all tempi.

(Note—The first beat, in order to be properly accented, should be performed with a forearm *rebound upward*. The short rebound is indicated in this and in all following illustrations. Dots are used to indicate approximately where each beat ends. Short dotted lines approximate the movement of the hand and arm in turning to the proper position for the succeeding beat. An illustration of the shape of a conducting beat, like that above, can be only relatively correct, since the exact shape must vary for different dynamics and interpretative effects. This explains minor disagreements among authorities in various textbooks regarding the shape of the conducting figures. For the sake of developing definiteness and precision, it is best for the student to learn first to make each beat—in this and in all rhythms which follow—*as if strongly accented*. The first music conducted should be of a strongly rhythmic character. *Legato* style is easily learned later.)

(2)   Triple Meter: $\frac{3}{2}$, $\frac{3}{4}$, $\frac{3}{8}$.

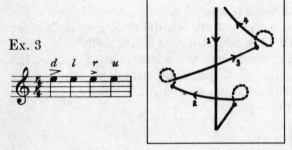

Ex. 2

Conducting figure for slow tempi. Standard waltz and all fast tempi are conducted one down-beat to the measure.

(3)   Quadruple Meter: $\frac{4}{2}$, $\frac{4}{4}$, $\frac{4}{8}$.

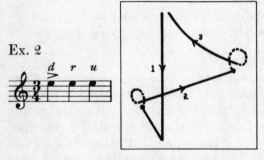

Ex. 3

Conducting figure for slow and moderate tempi. Fast tempi are conducted in a manner similar to that of duple rhythm, two beats to the measure.

(4)   Sextuple or Compound Duple Meter: $\frac{6}{2}$, $\frac{6}{4}$, $\frac{6}{8}$.

Ex. 4

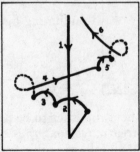

Conducting figure for slow tempi.

Fast tempi are conducted in a manner similar to that of duple rhythm, two beats to the measure. All compound rhythms have two or more methods of conducting in common usage. I have illustrated here one of the methods most favored. Many professional conductors simplify the beating of slow compound rhythms by using a down-beat for each pulsation except the last, giving the accented beats the most emphasis, particularly the first beat of each measure. This system is simple, gives good results, and eliminates the bother and time necessary to learn rather complicated and awkward figures. This "pulse" system is particularly recommended for slow Compound Triple and Compound Quadruple Meters, and for the Five and Seven Meters.

(5) Compound Triple Meter: $\frac{9}{2}$, $\frac{9}{4}$, $\frac{9}{8}$, $\frac{9}{16}$.

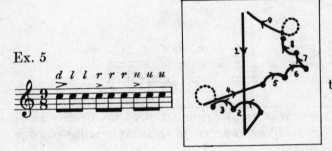

Ex. 5

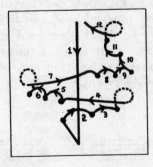

Conducting figure for slow tempi.

Conducted like Triple Meter in moderate and fast tempi.

Note—See "Pulse" method recommended under discussion of Sextuple Meter above.

(6) Compound Quadruple Meter: $\frac{12}{2}$, $\frac{12}{4}$, $\frac{12}{8}$, $\frac{12}{16}$.

Ex. 6

Conducting figure for slow tempi.

Conducted like Quadruple Meter in moderate and fast tempi.

Note—See "Pulse" method recommended for slow tempi, under discussion of Sextuple Meter above.

(7)   Five Meter: $\frac{5}{2}$, $\frac{5}{4}$, $\frac{5}{8}$, $\frac{5}{16}$.

Ex. 7

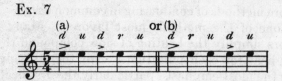

Conducted (a) like a measure of Duple followed by a measure of Triple Meter, or (b) like a measure of Triple followed by a measure of Duple Meter.   The accent of the words in each individual measure usually determines the accent of the music.

Note—See the "Pulse" method recommended under discussion of Sextuple Meter above.

(8)   Seven Meter: $\frac{7}{2}$, $\frac{7}{4}$, $\frac{7}{8}$, $\frac{7}{16}$.

Ex. 8

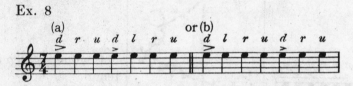

Conducted (a) like a measure of Triple followed by a measure of Quadruple Meter or (b) like a measure of Quadruple followed by a measure of Triple Meter.

Note—See the "Pulse" method recommended under discussion of Sextuple Meter above.

(9)   Free Rhythm:
Rhythm without a meter signature had best be conducted by the "Pulse" method described under discussion of Sextuple Meter above.

e. Divided Beat; Beating Note Values:
It is sometimes necessary for the conductor to beat actual note values in order to express marked accent or flexible changes in tempo.   It is desirable, at times, to divide the beat in order to indicate more exactly dotted-note values or entrances of parts on the last half of a beat.

A typical example of dotted-note rhythm is found in the old Welsh air "All Through the Night".

Ex. 9

In the first and second measures a conductor might indicate the dotted-note value as in illustration (a), and in the third measure as in illustration (b)

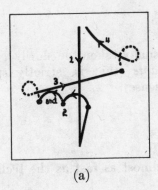

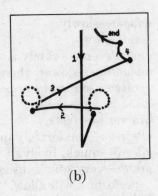

(a)   (b)

This principle of dividing the beat to indicate dotted-note values is a particularly useful device to assist weak groups, but is in bad taste when used with able choruses in obvious places where it is not necessary. Most conductors use more physical energy than is needed. Wild fanning of the air, tossing of the hair, affectations, and mannerisms are not favored by the leading conductors today. The more able the chorus, the less time-beating should be necessary. Fine choral organizations need *more suggestion and inspiration* and less conducting in order to achieve the highest artistic results. Time-beating, as such, may well be practically eliminated in conducting a well-trained, responsive choral organization. *The conductor must become versatile in adapting the method of conducting to the various powers of each choral group.*

2. Musical Terminology in Most Common Usage.
   a. In relation to force or dynamics.
      (1) Common gradation from soft to loud:
          ppp (double *pianissimo*)—as soft as possible.
          pp (*pianissimo*)—very soft.
          p (*piano*)—soft.
          mp (*mezzo piano*)—medium soft.
          mf (*mezzo forte*)—medium loud.
          f (*forte*)—loud.
          ff (*fortissimo*)—very loud.
          fff (double *fortissimo*)—as loud as possible.
      (2) Other terms of dynamics:
          cresc. or ———— (*crescendo*)—increasing gradually in volume.
          dim. or ———— (*diminuendo*)—diminishing gradually in volume.
          morendo—gradually dying away in volume.
          mezza voce—in half-voice, half-power.
          fp (*forte piano*)—loud followed at once by soft.
   b. In relation to tempo or time.
          tempo primo—in the original tempo.
          a tempo—return to the tempo that obtained before the last change.
          moderato—moderate tempo.
          accel. (*accelerando*)—gradually quickening.
          rit. (*ritardando*)—gradually slowing.
          rall. (*rallentando*)—gradually slowing.

    adagio—slowly.

    lento—slowly.

    andante—moderately slow (usually taken too slowly).

    andantino—slower than *andante* (that is, strictly speaking; but often used in the opposite sense).

    meno mosso—slower.

    più mosso—faster.

    allegretto—moderately quick.

    allegro—quick, lively.

    presto—very quick, usually almost as fast as the technique of the performer will allow.

    stringendo—gradually hastening the tempo to a climax.

c. In relation to style of interpretation.

    agitato—agitated.

    sostenuto—sustained, legato.

    legato—connected, smooth, flowing.

    marcato—accented in a broad style, not detached.

    staccato—accented, distinct, detached.

    sf or *sfz* (*sforzando*)—strongly accented.

    cantabile—in a singing, melodious manner.

    ad libitum—at the pleasure of the performer.

d. In relation to both tempo and style of interpretation.

    animato—with spirit, lively.

    vivace—lively and animated.

    grave—very slow and serious.

    largo—very slow, majestic, and broad.

    larghetto—somewhat less slow and broad than *largo*.

e. In relation to diction.

    "Pronunciation—The utterance of words with regard to sound and accent.
Enunciation—The manner of utterance as regards fullness and clearness.
Articulation—The action of speech organs in the formation of conso-
vowels, syllables, and words.

    Correct pronunciation, clear enunciation, and distinct articulation in singing constitute good diction."[4]

3. Latin Diction:[5]

    Music critics are generally agreed that much of the charm of early Church music is lost if it is sung in English rather than in Latin. It is almost impossible to substitute an English translation that retains both the pure tonal beauty and the charming rhythmic effects of the Latin.

    However, the "Italianized" Latin as sung in the modern Catholic Church is preferred to the academic Latin. In "Italianized" Latin all the vowels are *pure*. For this reason many directors prefer to use selected music with Latin text rather than vocalises for the building of correct vocal habits. The

[4]Quoted from an *Outline of Theory* made and adopted by the American Academy of Teachers of Singing.

[5]The author is indebted to Max T. Krone for permission to use material under this heading from his forthcoming book, the Teacher's Manual for Vol. VI of the *A Cappella Chorus Series*, published by M. Witmark and Sons.

following brief rules and illustrations will serve as a guide to proper pronunciation of "Italianized" Latin.

a. Vowels:
   Vowels are always pure and brilliant in quality:
   a as *ah*, *e.g. ma'la* = mah'-lah.
   e as *a* in "day", *e.g. le'one* = lay'-o-nay.
   i as *ee* in "meet", *e.g. fi'lii* = fee'-lee-ee.
   o as *oh* in "oh!", *e.g. no'bis* = noh'-beess.
   u as *oo* in "boot", *e.g. a'gimus* = ah'-gee-moos.
   au as *ow* in "fowl", *e.g. au're* = ow'-ray.
   œ and *œ* as *ay* in "say", *e.g. sœ'cula* = say'-koo-lah.

b. Consonants:
   c as *ch* before *œ, œ, e,* and *i*; otherwise as *k*.
   g as *j* before *œ, œ, e,* and *i*; otherwise as in "gate".
   gn as *ny*, *e.g. a'gnus* = ah'-nyoos.
   h as in English, except in the words *mi'-hi, ni'-hil,* and words derived from them, in which it is pronounced as *k*.
   j as *y*, *e.g., ja'nua* = yah'-noo-ah.
   sc as *sh* before *e, i, œ,* and *œ, e.g. ascen'dit* = as-shayn'-deet,
      as *sk* before other vowels, *e.g., scu'tum* = skoo'-toom.
   xc as *k-sh* before *e* and *i, e.g. excel'sis* = ayk-shayl'-seess.

c. Accents:
   All accented syllables are sung with a little additional force. Accent gives the word vitality. The primary accent (marked ´) is the most important; secondary accents are marked `. Latin accents are brief and never heavy or ponderous in effect.

Reference List for Further Reading

Technique of Conducting:
   Bartholomew and Lawrence, *Music for Everybody*, Abingdon Press, New York.
   *Earhart, *The Eloquent Baton*, Witmark, New York.
   *Gehrkens, *Essentials in Conducting*, Ditson, Boston.
   Kendrie, *Handbook on Conducting*, Gray, New York.
   *Playground and Recreation Association, *Community Music*, Birchard, Boston.
   *Schmid, *The Language of the Baton*, G. Schirmer, Inc., New York.
   *Stoessel, *The Technic of the Baton*, Carl Fischer, New York.
   *Zanzig, *Community and Assembly Singing*, National Recreation Association.

Musical Terminology:
   *Baker, *A Dictionary of Musical Terms*, G. Schirmer, Inc., New York.
   *Gehrkens, *Music Notation and Terminology*, Laidlaw, Chicago.
   *Grove, *Dictionary of Music and Musicians*, Macmillan, New York.
Readings for Choral Conducting Classes:
   *Beach, *Preparation and Presentation of the Operetta*, Ditson, Boston.
   *Beattie, McConathy, and Morgan, *Music in the Junior High School*, Silver Burdett & Co., New York.

Bedford, *An Essay on Modern Unaccompanied Song*, Oxford University Press, London.

*Cain, *Choral Music and Its Practice*, Witmark, New York.

*Coward, *Choral Technique and Interpretation*, Novello, London.

*Dann, *Conductor's Book*, American Book Co., New York.

Dawson, *The Voice of the Boy*, Kellogg, New York.

Drew, *Notes on the Technique of Song Interpretation*, Oxford University Press, London.

Ellis, *Pronunciation for Singers*, Curwen, London.

Elson, *Music Club Programs from All Nations*, Ditson, Boston.

Fellowes, *The English Madrigal*, Oxford University Press, London.

*Giddings and Baker, *High School Music Teaching*, Earl L. Baker Co., Appleton, Wisc.

*Greene, *Interpretation in Song*, Macmillan, New York.

Hanslick, *The Beautiful in Music*, Novello, New York.

Jeppeson, *The Style of Palestrina and the Dissonance*, Oxford University Press, London.

*Jones and Wilson, *Musico-Dramatic Producing*, Gamble Hinged Music Co., Chicago.

Parry, *Style in Musical Art*, Macmillan, London.

Rogers, *English Diction*, Mrs. C. K. Rogers, Boston.

Schoen, *The Effects of Music*, Paul, London.

*Scott, *Madrigal Singing*, Oxford University Press, London.

*Smallmann and Wilcox, *The Art of A Cappella Singing*, Ditson, Boston.

Taft, *Technique of Pageantry*, Barnes, New York.

*Umfleet, *School Operettas and Their Production*, Birchard, Boston.

Webster and Wetzel, *Scenery Simplified*, Eldridge Entertainment House, Franklin, Ohio.

Weisman, *School Choirs*, Oxford University Press, London.

*Westerman, *Modern Phonetization*, Edwards Bros., Ann Arbor, Mich.

*Witherspoon, *Singing*, G. Schirmer, Inc., New York.

*Wodell, *Choir and Chorus Conducting*, Presser, Philadelphia.

*Especially recommended as supplementary reading for this chapter.

CHAPTER II

ORGANIZATION

The true musicality of a community is determined, not by the number of public concerts and recitals it supports, but rather by the degree in which music is integrated into the every-day life of every man, woman and child.

EDGAR B. GORDON.

Young people like a great deal of business and ceremony; it makes them feel more grown-up and important, and it is a valuable part of their education. Since choral organizations are maintained largely for the pleasure and benefit of their members, it is but just and democratic that they be so organized that many duties are discharged by officers and members of the group rather than by the musical director. This plan has two important advantages: first, glee-club[6] members, if given a voice in the management, will naturally have a greater personal interest and pride in the organization and will work harder for the advancement of its interests; second, proper organization will relieve the director of much detail-work, allowing him more time and thought for the selection of music, planning of rehearsals, and attention to musical objectives.

The director should be a leader and adviser, not a dictator. However, he must realize that glee club officers need supervision in the performance of their duties. School boys and girls are flattered with the distinction conferred upon them when elected to an official position, but they often do not realize the responsibility involved. This results in neglect or in slip-shod work unless the director keeps in touch with their work and insists that it be well done. Even in more mature groups, the director needs to check the work of officers if he wishes to guarantee a smooth-running organization.

It is true that some able directors prefer to do all the work themselves rather than be worried with officers who fail to perform their duties on time or in the proper manner. But such instances are the exception rather than the rule. In any case, matters of organization should not be permitted to become so lengthy or involved that the rehearsal is robbed of its main purpose—the development of joy and skill in singing beautiful music.

Before listing the duties of glee club officers, it may be well to enumerate the duties and powers which most directors do not care to have transferred to officers of the club. Many choruses elect committees to consult with the director on the following matters, but the final decision usually rests with the director:

1. Final decision regarding membership and the assignment of members to their proper voice-section.
2. Selection of soloists, quartets, octets, accompanists, and voice-section leaders.
3. Selection of music, and final decision regarding concerts and programs.
4. Decision regarding time, place, number, length, and conduct of rehearsals.
5. Final decision regarding all social functions which involve the reputations of the club and the director.

[6]The terms "glee club" and "chorus", used in a general way, are intended to be synonymous. A distinction will be made whenever necessary.

The director of school groups may well keep all of the foregoing duties as his own prerogatives, but he should also seek the opinions and advice of the more experienced members on these and other matters. If the officers of the club are well chosen, they should be the best qualified members to consult on the policies and undertakings of the group. Well organized adult choruses sometimes desire to determine membership and all of the policies of their own club, leaving the duties of the director strictly confined to an advisory and musical capacity.

A. Glee Club Constitutions[7]

1. Officers:
    a. Elections—Officers of the preceding year should serve until new officers are elected. Elections should be held as soon as new members have had a chance to become acquainted. Announcement that elections are to be held should be made at least a week preceding the date, in order to allow wise consideration. A good choice of officers is important in determining the spirit of a glee club. Later administrative trouble or confusion may be avoided if the duties and qualifications of officers are clearly understood. It is a good plan to present each member with a mimeographed or printed sheet containing this information at the time elections are announced.
    b. Qualifications aud Duties:
        (1) *President.*
            Qualifications: Good speaking-voice, knowledge of parliamentary procedure, likable personality, popularity, dependability.
            Duties: Presiding at all meetings, assessing fines, appointing committees, acting as adviser to the Director and other officers and as social representative of the club, making announcements in assembly, *etc.*
        (2) *Vice-President.*
            Qualifications: Same as those for President.
            Duties: To assist the President, and to serve in his capacity in the event of his absence.
        (3) *Secretary-Treasurer.*
            Qualifications: System, accuracy, interest in business methods, honesty, and dependability.
            Duties: Keeping the roll, marking absence and tardiness, acting as business representative of the club, collecting fines, keeping and disbursing funds when authorized by the President, keeping an accurate record of the minutes at business meetings, and giving a correct account to the club of all receipts and disbursements. (Note: In large clubs an appointed member in each section may well assist in getting necessary information about absent and tardy members.)
        (4) *Advertising Manager.*
            Qualifications: Interest in writing, newspaper work, and advertising; good personality, dependability, and promptness.

[7]There is considerable divergence among existing glee clubs in the manner of organization, the names, number, qualifications, and duties of the officers. Some groups prefer a committee system. The list of officers given here is intended to be merely suggestive. It was formulated with the program of an ambitious college men's glee club in mind.

Duties: Writing articles for newspapers; taking charge of programs, tickets, photography, cuts, posters, circulars, and all other advertising in connection with the glee club; acting as advance agent in obtaining contracts for glee club tours; assisting Secretary-Treasurer in arranging transportation, board, and lodging on trips. (Note: The Advertising Manager's work is done under the supervision and with the advice and assistance of the Director.)

(5) *Librarian.*

Qualifications: Interest in the glee club and in orderly care and cataloging of the music; dependability.

Duties: Cataloging music; arranging music for distribution; passing out and collecting music at rehearsals; keeping record of music lent to members; reporting the loss or mutilation of music to the Secretary-Treasurer for the assessment of fines; keeping the music library in an orderly condition. (New members are often elected to this position. The duties of the Librarian, however, are exacting and vital to the orderly and efficient progress of the rehearsal. The Librarian may select assistants if they are needed.)

(6) *Student Director.*

Qualifications: Musical training and mechanical technique sufficient to direct the club creditably in appearances where a student director is desirable or required; ability to direct school songs in concerts and in "pep" meetings; ability to take charge of the rehearsal in case the Director is absent; pleasing personality; dependability.

Duties: Assisting and cooperating with the Director; directing the glee club as indicated above. (The Student Director is best elected by popular vote after trial of several students.)

(7) *Accompanist.*

Qualifications: Ability to play in a creditable manner the grade of accompaniments used in glee club concerts; facility in playing from vocal scores for rehearsal.

Duties: Playing accompaniments and vocal parts; assisting the glee club soloists and other members to learn their parts. (The Accompanist is usually chosen by the Director. The ability to play piano solos is desirable but not necessary. In men's glee clubs, a good woman accompanist is preferable to a poor man accompanist. Either the Student Director or the Accompanist may, if necessary, hold one of the other elective positions; but it is desirable to keep these two members free for their own duties.)

2. Formulation of Constitutions:

When a glee club is to function as either a student or a social activity, it is desirable to have a constitution for the guidance of members. If the club is just being organized, it is necessary for the members to appoint a committee to work with the director in formulating a constitution. The director should have the subject well in mind in order to guide the committee wisely. After the constitution has been drafted, it is ready to be brought before the club to be discussed, possibly enlarged, and voted upon, point by point, before adoption. Any objectionable item may be rejected or amended according to the wishes of the majority of the club.

After the constitution has been adopted, it is suggested that at least the section pertaining to rules of conduct and fines be printed or mimeographed and given to each member of the club so that there may be no excuse for not knowing the regulations. *The time taken to formulate a constitution will be wasted unless the director and officers see that the rules are strictly enforced.* Better have no constitution than one that does not function in practice. Any item which proves poor in practice should be rejected or amended. New rules may be added if conditions require them.

a. Content:

A glee club constitution may be formulated according to the following plan:

(1) A preamble stating the objectives of the club.

(2) A section giving rules for elections, committees, the types of officers, their qualifications and duties.

(3) A section outlining procedure with regard to membership, conduct, absence, tardiness, care of music, fines, and assessments.

b. Typical Example:

"X" UNIVERSITY MEN'S GLEE CLUB CONSTITUTION

Preamble

We, the members of "X" University Men's Glee Club, in order to raise the standard of glee-club performance and conduct, to maintain a more democratic and pleasurable type of activity, and to promote the musical enjoyment and interest of the glee-club members, students, and patrons of the school, do hereby form the following constitution.

Membership

1. Only upper-classmen (sophomores, juniors, and seniors) are eligible for membership.

2. All members must be *bona fide* students of "X" University, doing work of a passing grade in at least twelve semester hours.

3. Candidates for membership must be approved by the Director, following a voice-trial or other proof of fitness.

4. Active membership of any individual in the glee club may be terminated at any time by the Director or by a majority vote of the members.

Officers and Duties

1. Election of officers shall be held early each year at a time designated by the Director.

2. Any glee club officer elected by the club may be removed by a two-thirds vote of the club.

3. The Director has the right to retain or reject any member and to put him in any section of the club he (the Director) chooses. The Director shall have the final power of decision and veto in all matters pertaining to the glee club and its activities.

4. Officers of the club are to be elected by a majority vote.
5. The officers and their duties are as follows: (Note—See duties and powers of the Director, p. 17, and "Officers: Elections, Qualifications, and Duties", p. 18. Reprinting is omitted here to save useless repetition. Note—A "Points and Merits Committee" may be desirable in some high schools.)

Rules of Conduct

1. Members of the club shall act like gentlemen at all times, avoid unnecessary noise and needless confusion in rehearsals and concert, and give immediate attention to the wishes and directions of the Conductor.
2. Members pledge themselves to be on the lookout for desirable new members and to encourage interest in glee club work.
3. Any member having (a) three unexcused absences, (b) five unexcused tardinesses, or (c) an unexcused absence from one concert, is dropped automatically from membership until such absence or tardiness is excused by the Director and all fines are paid.

Fines and Assessments

1. Members may be assessed a sum not in excess of $2.00 at the beginning of the year in order to purchase music and to meet other necessary expenses.
2. Fines are to be assessed and collected as follows:

Unexcused absence from rehearsal.......................... .25
Unexcused absence from concert.......................... $1.00
Unexcused tardiness at rehearsal.......................... .10
Unexcused tardiness at concert............................ .50
Delaying glee club unnecessarily on concert trip............. $1.00
Failure to bring music to rehearsal........................ .10
Music lost...full value
Music mutilated...........................Librarian's estimate

(Fines are usually desirable for community or paid groups but may not be advisable for some school groups.)

B. Community Extension

(Note: See also "Opportunity", p. 1)

The organization of community glee clubs or choruses may proceed in the same general fashion as previously indicated. However, members of adult choruses should have more responsibility in determining policies, membership, and even the music to be sung. Community choruses are social as well as musical organizations and need to be conducted with this in mind. A board of directors or committee is often found useful. It is desirable that committees on membership, selecting music, rehearsals (times and places), concerts (dates and places), social affairs, rules, assessments, fines, etc., take much responsibility from the Musical Director. From three to five committees are enough, e.g., one committee may take care of the activities connected with membership, rules, assessments, and fines; a second ("music") committee may serve in selecting music, determining concert dates and places, and arranging the times and places for rehearsals; and a third ("social") committee may arrange a schedule of desirable social activities. The Director advises and cooperates with the various committees, but frequently does not have the power of final decision as with school groups. John Stark Evans, speaking on "Conducting Community Choral Groups" before the Vocal Music Section of the 1933 Music Supervisors National Conference, made the following acute observations in regard to organization, financing, and community service:

"*Organization*—Opinions may differ in matters of organization, and different set-ups may suit different localities, but it is pretty clear that a great deal of argument and possible controversy may be avoided if a board of directors—seven is ideal—are elected by the whole group and all matters of business, including election of officers, left to them. These men need to be of real influence, not only within the organization but throughout the community at large.

"*Financing*—Money isn't everything, but careless financing is the rock on which many an otherwise good organization has been wrecked. First, the active members themselves must pay annual dues, though nominal in amount. They will manifest a keener interest when they pay than when they do not. Early budgets must be small, but music must be purchased and be the property of the group. The director and accompanist should be paid; and, in larger groups, it may be found desirable to pay the librarian and secretary as well. There should be an associate membership list, a card to which should cost about five dollars, this fee providing for at least two tickets to at least two concerts, the remainder of the sum constituting a small donation. The more influential your board of directors in the community, the easier it will be to have a large associate membership list. The longer this list, the better the financial results, of course; but, more than that, the wider the public interest —and public interest is a very stimulating factor in the life of such a group.

"*Community Service*—The public interest leads to the next point which is a matter of service—community service. Herein is the real strength of the organization, for a group that contributes nothing to the community life cannot expect to gain very wide public support. It should be prepared for and welcome invitations to sing for large gatherings of general community concern—conventions, mass meetings, or any large concourse to which the community is playing host. It is by providing such features gratis that a singing group makes itself an integral part of the civic life, and public appreciation will show itself in many ways. As the singing improves, the group can extend its sphere a little and visit other communities, carrying the same good-will abroad that it has been developing at home. It should be emphasized in word and in practice that it is organized for community service and not for profit."

C. Ten Commandments for the Chorister

The following "Ten Commandments for the Chorister" may be incorporated in the constitution if desired. As an aid in properly directing attitudes and thought-processes, they have proved of remarkable value in speeding up the process of seasoning new members or in quickly developing an amateur group. They should be printed or mimeographed and put in the hands of each member. A little discussion may help to "drive home" the points. A correct attitude at the beginning towards the conductor and towards choral work in general is the most important factor in the success of the organization.

TEN COMMANDMENTS FOR THE CHORISTER

A fine chorus is like a chain—no stronger than its weakest link. Every individual's excellencies or deficiencies have a noticeable bearing upon the character of the ensemble. A single voice can mar the beauty of a delicately balanced chord by incorrect pitch, vowel color, or dynamics.

The most complete joy in singing and the highest artistic results can be obtained only when each member earnestly and intelligently strives to attain *perfection of ensemble*. Even soloists ultimately receive more aesthetic satisfaction if willing to "tone down" and merge their voices and personalities in the group. The best choral singing is achieved only through individual excellencies blended into a thrilling cooperative effort. More than any other factor, the intelligence and effort expended by the individual in practising the following fundamental choral rules will determine the ultimate degree of perfection attainable. *How far are you willing to go?*

1. BE PROMPT AND REGULAR IN ATTENDANCE. Be in your place and *ready to sing* when the Director takes his place. When possible, come to rehearsals a few minutes early and help in any necessary preparations.

2. TAKE PRIDE IN ESTABLISHING HABITUALLY PROPER POSTURE DURING REHEARSALS. Singing will be accomplished more easily and correctly, and much useless repetition of music will be avoided.

3. ESTABLISH THE HABIT OF WATCHING AND LISTENING TO THE DIRECTOR CAREFULLY. All conversation should cease when the Conductor comes to the stand. Give strict attention to announcements and directions. Be keenly alert in following interpretative indications. Strive to remember—and make an earnest effort to duplicate—effects obtained in previous rehearsals. (Much rehearsal time is wasted needlessly because of lazy minds and eyes.) Always carry a soft-lead pencil for making needed directions on the music score. Mark the staff at the beginning if you have difficulty in following your part.

4. READ ALOUD THE TEXT OF THE MUSIC, attempting to realize to the fullest its emotional content, accent, and dramatic significance.

5. SING WITH THE SAME NATURALNESS, CLARITY OF DICTION, AND DRAMATIC EMPHASIS THAT YOU HAVE WHEN READING. It is necessary to give considerably more emphasis to percussive consonants (such as "p", "d", and "t") in singing than in speaking. It isn't enough that the audience be *able* to understand your words: *they must hear them easily*.

6. LEARN MUSIC AS QUICKLY AS POSSIBLE. This is the easiest way. Very little progress can be made with a chorus whose chief effort and attention is devoted to reading the text and music. It is *best* to memorize; but, in any case, the music should be so familiar that only an occasional glance is necessary.

7. PRACTISE THE MOST DIFFICULT PARTS OF YOUR SCORE FIRST; make them the best-known parts; master difficult attacks.   Do not sing loudly when learning new music.   *Music is learned with the head, and not with the throat.*

8. LEARN TO SING YOUR PART WITH THE SAME CARE YOU WOULD GIVE TO A SOLO; observe proper phrasing, dynamics, *etc.* You have not learned a part well until you can hear mentally the complete musical phrase *before* it is sung.

9. USE YOUR EYES, YOUR EARS, AND YOUR INTELLIGENCE. Sing confidently, but softly enough to enable you to listen and adjust your voice to blend and balance with the other voices in pitch, vowel color, and dynamics.   Better err on the *piano* side than on the *forte*.   Remember that dynamic terms are relative, never absolute, and not nearly as important in ensemble singing as the *balanced chord;* that when there is a melody it should be the most prominent part; that altered notes and moving parts should receive more tonal emphasis; that the first word in a contrapuntal attack should usually be somewhat *accented* and louder than the printed dynamics; that, for the most consonant effect, the fifth of the chord should not be sung as loudly as the root or the third; that low tones should be thought "high and brilliant" and high tones "easy"—on the same level of difficulty as the notes which precede them; that initial consonants should have the same pitch as the vowel which follows; and that the mental approach to a tone should be *from above*, not from below.

10. FEEL FREE, ESPECIALLY DURING FINAL REHEARSALS, TO CALL THE ATTENTION OF THE DIRECTOR TO ANY MISTAKES NOTED.   Members of the chorus can help even the most skilful and competent director by making excellent practical suggestions.   A sensible conductor will realize this and not resent suggestions made in the right spirit.

D.   The Second Glee Club

There are numerous reasons why it is best, when possible, to organize two choruses.   After the try-outs have been held, those with the best voices and the most experience should be enrolled in the first group and the remainder in a "feeder" group.   However, the second glee club should never be considered as existing merely to provide trained members for the first group.   It should be worth while as an activity in itself, of prime importance in the educational scheme, singing at times in public on appropriate occasions, and having an organization and social program similar to that of the first group.   The two groups may well be combined for all social occasions and may even sing together at times when a larger chorus is desirable.   In small schools the first group may consist merely of a sextet or octet.   "Each club should be known by a name rather than by 'first glee club' or 'second glee club', for the inexperienced members should not be permitted to feel that they are inferior."[8]

One requirement for membership in the first chorus may well be at least one semester of experience in the second group.   Exceptions may be made for members of unusual talent and ability which the students themselves recognize.

[8]Grace Ullemeyer, "An Idea for Motivation", *The Supervisors Service Bulletin*, Jan., 1934.

In most cases facility in the use of the voice and proper habits of choral thought must be gained during the first year of chorus work—after the singer enters the second chorus. This second group is the proper place to improve music reading, learn good singing habits, and stress intelligent listening while singing. Careful discrimination in such matters as pitch, blend, and balance is properly initiated here. The best way to guarantee a high level of musical achievement for the first glee club is to have a well organized second chorus doing interesting work on its own level of ability.

E.   Types of Choral Groups in the Schools

What type of choral organization shall I develop first in my school? This matter frequently requires careful consideration. A few suggestions may help:

1. Every high school or junior high school needs, first of all, a general mass chorus which reaches every pupil. This should certainly be required in the freshman year and perhaps in the sophomore. Regular assembly singing is taken for granted.

2. The elective choral organization which seems to promise the richest and most valuable musical experience is the *a cappella* mixed chorus.

3. Small schools, unable to maintain more than one elective choral organization, will find that the mixed chorus (preferably of the *a cappella* type) is usually most practical and desirable.

4. In a small school, a girls' glee club is easier to maintain successfully than a boys' glee club.

5. In addition to general chorus, assembly singing, and voice-training classes, the large school may well maintain an *a cappella* mixed chorus, a boys' glee club, and a girls' glee club.

6. Care must be exercised in changing a traditional "set-up".

F.   Voice Training Classes

(Note—See also "Fundamental Vocal Exercises for Choral Groups and
Voice Classes", p. 49)

The success of voice training in groups is no longer questioned. Not only do voice classes give the pupil ability in solo singing, but they furnish uniform, systematic training in vocal fundamentals that saves valuable time in chorus rehearsals—time that otherwise needs to be spent on vocal drills. Schools that have given voice class work a fair trial are unanimous in their reports that it improves the quality of massed choral work considerably. Raising the standard of individual excellence inevitably raises the level of group achievement.

G.   Voice Try-outs

The problem of selecting membership in the smaller schools is usually slight, for a host of other activities compete with the glee club for membership among a small body of students. The director of a glee club having a small number of applicants cannot afford to be too particular about the quality of membership. Only the most hopeless voices and those not able to carry a tune need be refused. These should be encouraged to participate in some other activity.

Make the glee club or chorus easy to join. Formal try-outs are, in many instances, a barrier repelling many perhaps talented students who would like to try to sing. The important objective in the beginning is to *get everybody who is interested to singing and enjoying it.* Allow new members to use their own judgment in choosing the section in which they wish to sing until try-outs are made. If selective or competitive try-outs are necessary, they can usually be delayed. *Under no circumstances should they be made to appear formal or difficult.*

The results of a standard test of native musical ability and musical achievement given to each freshman class on entrance may prove helpful in selecting promising material. The data from this test make it possible to classify students into those who might prove (a) desirable, (b) questionable, (c) undesirable.

Contrary to a rather common belief, one does not necessarily have to be able to read music to become a valuable member of the average chorus or glee club. The principal requirements are a love of music, ability to carry a tune, desire to sing, and a fairly quick and accurate ear. Many beginning glee clubs have all their music taught at first by rote. Strangely enough, members who cannot read music often memorize the text and music before their more experienced fellows. A glee club composed for the most part of individuals who cannot read music may well be expected to give musically worth-while public concerts.

1. Individual Voice-Trial Method:

In large schools where the glee club has become a popular activity, the selection of members becomes a problem that deserves careful consideration. The Collective, Quartet, and Individual voice-trial methods are used, depending on the requirements of the situation. Some directors contend that it is eventually worth the time and effort to hear personally each voice, rank it on a voice-record sheet or card, and select members largely on this basis. When combined with the Quartet method, the director not only can select and reject candidates more fairly than otherwise, but can assign voices to sections more accurately and meanwhile secure a valuable permanent record for future reference. Voice-record sheets may be printed or mimeographed in any desired number. A typical example for a college club is illustrated on the following page; a similar sheet may be easily prepared to meet the requirements of any other group. All but the last section is to be filled out by the applicant. A voice may be accurately tested and ranked as indicated in as little as five to seven minutes. An effort should be made to dispel nervousness of prospective members by making them feel that the test is not an ordeal to be feared, but rather an easy and natural requirement. If for any legitimate reason the applicant appears at a disadvantage in the first try-out, he should be given another opportunity later to qualify.

It is suggested, for the sake of simplicity, that the examiner use the letters A (excellent), B (average), and C (poor). Departures from these estimates may be indicated by plus or minus signs. Tonal memory and accuracy of pitch may be estimated by having the applicant first listen to an interval or melodic phrase and then sing it. These two qualifications are important and

VOICE-RECORD SHEET*

Name... Age.............. Class..........

Address.. Telephone No.....................

Former experience in glee clubs or choruses:

No. of years in High School?.................... Where?.................................

No. of years in College?.................... Where?.....................................

Experience in church choirs, *etc.,*...

Instrumental training:

What instruments do you play?...

How long have you played?.......... How long have you taken lessons?............

With what organizations have you played?...

Vocal training:

Have you ever taken vocal lessons?.......... Private or class lessons?...........

With whom have you studied?..

How long?..........Have you ever sung solos?.......... Where?...............

Can you sing easy music of the hymn type at sight?.............................

Voice Record: (To be filled out by examiner)

Type of Voice.............. Section assigned.............. Could also sing............

Total compass.......... Easy compass.......... Quality.......... Power..........

Control.......... Tonal memory.......... Accuracy of pitch..........

Solo ability..

Diction.. Sight-reading..........................

General remarks:**

....

....

....

*All except the last section is to be filled out by the applicant *previous* to the try-out.
**The general remarks should include notes on the candidate's appearance and personality.

Suggested Record for Applicants at Try-Outs

should be tested by several examples of varying difficulty. It may be desirable to use the accompaniment to encourage some of the more nervous or unmusical applicants. The candidate should be asked to sing several phrases of a song which he himself selects in order to furnish a basis for judging his solo ability.

If an unusually large number try out, the director may need assistance. Voice-instructors, or perhaps experienced members of the club, can help in this. It is not necessary to try out mature voices with whose ability you are already familiar; but when dealing with immature voices, particularly young boys' voices still in the process of change, it may be necessary to reclassify the voices and reassign sections several times during the school year. In all cases, changes in vocal ability, address, and telephone number should be kept up-to-date for every member.

2. Quartet Voice-Trial Method:

When an accurate individual record is not deemed necessary, the Quartet (or small group) Method of Voice Trial may be used. Groups must be kept small enough so that the director or judges can easily hear each individual voice and consider its comparative merits. Many directors prefer this method, pointing out the following advantages:

a. The fact that there are several in the group lessens to a great extent fear and self-consciousness during the try-out.
b. It is much quicker than the Individual Voice-Trial Method.
c. It gives opportunity to judge intonation, blending, and vocal skill *when the individual is singing with a group.*

When only a few positions in the club are open, it is a good plan to have each applicant sing in turn with a nucleus of select voices chosen from the club membership. Both familiar music and sight-reading material may be used in the trial. Familiar music may be distributed before the test to those who wish to review it. If records for comparison of applicants are desired— and they become necessary when many applicants are involved—the director and judges may use a form and rating somewhat similar to that suggested for the Individual Voice-Trial Method. (See p. 26.)

3. Collective Voice-Trial Method:

If the size of the club need not be restricted and mere classification of the voices is the principal aim, then students may be assigned to their respective sections by the Collective Voice-Trial Method. This method is speedy, but it requires a more quick and accurate ear on the part of the examiner.

All are asked to sing a double octave scale or arpeggio together, the director determining the quality and type of voice and assigning individuals to sections by standing closely in front of the group and listening successively to each voice. A double octave from low G to high G is a suitable range for all groups except the Junior Boys' Glee Club (for ages 11 to 15, when voices are changing). The double octave from B flat, second line in the bass clef, to B flat, third line in the treble clef, will be found more suitable for this group. As the director classifies voices in this manner, it is well to have one or more assistants write down the name and voice section of each individual as they are assigned. The group should be directed to sing easily on a syllable such as "ah" or "oh" and, only when the pitches are comfortable and easy, to join in again when the exercise returns to their range. The piano may be used quietly, if necessary, to keep the exercise going. Too much emphasis cannot be placed on the principle that *classification of voice depends not upon range but upon quality of the voice in the most freely produced register*.

As a rule, immature and undeveloped voices that sing the pitches indicated below *with characteristic quality for that voice* may be safely classified as shown:

Men's Glee Club

Ex. 10

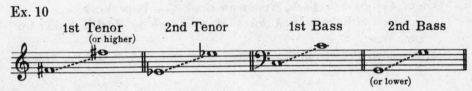

Note—All changed male voices written in the treble clef sound an octave lower than written.

Girls' or Women's Glee Club

Ex. 11

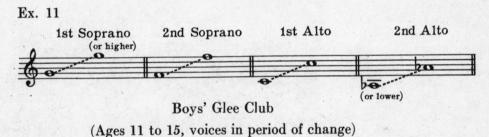

Boys' Glee Club

(Ages 11 to 15, voices in period of change)

Ex. 12

Note—In boys' glee clubs with voices of the above ranges, 1st tenor is treated as high alto, 2nd tenor as low alto. Their voices sound at the pitches indicated and *not* an octave lower, as does the changed male voice when written in the treble clef.

Reference List for Further Reading

Musical Aptitude and Achievement Tests:

Beach, *Standardized Music Tests*, Bureau of Educational Measurements and Standards, State Normal School, Emporia, Kansas.

*Gildersleeve, *Music Achievement Tests*, Teachers College, Columbia University, New York.

Hutchinson, *Music Tests*, Public School Publishing Company, Iowa City, Iowa.

*Kwalwasser and Dykema, *K-D Music Tests*, Victor Talking Machine Co., published by Carl Fischer, New York.

*Kwalwasser and Ruch, *Tests of Musical Accomplishments*, Extension Division, State University of Iowa, Iowa City, Iowa.

Seashore, *Music Talent Tests*, Columbia Phonograph Co., New York.

Torgeson and Fahnstock, *Music Tests*, Public School Publishing Co., Bloomington, Illinois.

Methods and Procedure of Organization:

Beattie, McConathy, and Morgan, *Music in the Junior High School*, Silver Burdett and Co., New York.

*Cain, *Choral Music and Its Practice*, Witmark, New York.

*Dann, *Conductor's Book*, American Book Co., New York.

*Giddings and Baker, *High School Music Teaching*, Earl L. Baker Co., Appleton, Wisc.

McCauley, *Professionalized Study of Public School Music*, Joseph Avent, Knoxville, Tenn.

*Especially recommended as supplementary reading for this chapter.

CHAPTER III

AROUSING AND RETAINING INTEREST

The secret of success is constancy of purpose.
SAMUEL C. ARMSTRONG

A. Advertising

A successful choral director must be efficient in more than the musical aspects of his profession. He must be wide awake as an organizer and as an advertiser; and he must be ready to seize or to make opportunities for the purpose of arousing or retaining the interest and cooperation, not only of the chorus-members, but also of the community, fellow instructors, and other departments of the school.

If anything today is to be successful, it has to be well advertised. There are usually so many activities bidding for the membership, time, and interest of the pupil that some activities must suffer from lack of sufficient members. The conductor is under a disadvantage from the start if only a few try out for the glee club. This situation allows little choice as to the quality of membership and prevents stimulating competition for places in the concert or contest club. We can scarcely imagine a successful football team if only eleven members reported for practice. It is equally important to a glee club or chorus that enough members be enrolled at the beginning of the season to make membership an object of competition.

However, a small turn-out does not necessarily mean that the season will be unsuccessful. After all, the quality and not the number of members is the most important factor. Very fine clubs are developed by competent directors under unfavorable conditions, but in such cases an even better directed and more concentrated type of work is demanded in order to overcome the handicaps.

In order to secure and retain the most effective membership, the activities, advantages, and values of the glee club must be kept before the student body and the community. Advertising may be local (school and community) and sectional (outlying districts from which the school draws its student body).

"One way to create interest is to have attractive, 'snappy' posters located in the most conspicuous places in the halls and class rooms. They should be of sufficient size to be seen from a distance; and they should be interesting, original, and have an interesting cartoon or picture placed so that the entire poster will attract the attention of students."[9]

Articles in the school bulletins and papers, community newspapers, Chamber of Commerce bulletins, church bulletins, and occasional "write-ups" in large city newspapers, help to impress both pupils and patrons with the fact that the glee club is an active and worthy organization. The material for newspaper articles, bulletins, circulars, *etc.*, may be selected very largely from the following:
1. Local news concerning glee club officers, director, social and musical activities, new music, soloists, quartet or octet.
2. News concerning concert programs, concert tours, festivals or contests.

[9]Grace Ullemeyer, "Arousing New Interest", *The Supervisors Service Bulletin*, Sept., 1933.

31

3. Articles dealing with the value and advantages of the glee club.   (These must be written in such a way that they are good advertising without giving the impression that they were written for that purpose.)
4. General news concerning other glee clubs, sectional and national contests or festivals, and significant developments in glee club work.

After the club has been organized and the officers elected, the advertising manager should prepare the newspaper articles and other advertising.   The director may need to give suggestions regarding topics and an outline covering the ideas or subject-matter to be included.   *All advertising*, including newspaper articles and concert programs, *should be submitted to the director for approval before publication.*   This rule will prevent many mistakes and items likely to create false impressions from appearing in print.   Some clubs regularly prepare one or more small articles in each weekly issue of the school or local community paper. The wide-awake director will have something ready to publish in case the advertising manager fails in the assignment.   This plan will do as much as anything else to create and retain a vital interest in choral work.

B.   Obtaining Cooperation

It is a sound procedure to state definitely the objectives for the year's work at the beginning of the season.   Members of the chorus and—especially—the superintendent, principal, and other faculty members should know these plans. Make sure that the time set for rehearsals is clear, in order that all are aware when students are being called to rehearsals, and can plan to cooperate in the project. Insist that other organizations respect this rehearsal time in setting the dates for extra rehearsals or performances.   Demand promptness at rehearsals and be particularly careful about prompt dismissals as well.   *Music directors too often neglect to be definite and considerate,* thus frequently causing inconvenience to other departments or instructors.   Resentment and lack of cooperation is the natural result.

Let other instructors know that you and the club are ready to cooperate with them in return for a like consideration   In large school systems it is important that there be cooperation within the music department itself.   The choral director frequently depends upon the piano department for the training of the student accompanist, upon the instrumental department for orchestral accompaniments, and upon voice instructors for the training of soloists and the coaching of individual glee-club members or voice-sections to sing their parts more effectively.

In schools where there are both boys' and girls' glee clubs, each may greatly assist the other in helping advertise and "put over" concert programs.   They may also be effectively combined and quickly trained to do excellent work in presenting mixed-chorus music for special occasions, operettas, cantatas, and oratorios.   Picnics, banquets, and other social affairs are usually more successful and enjoyable for all concerned with both clubs participating.   Each club may well act as sponsor for the other's home concerts, selling tickets, ushering, etc. Soloists or quartets may even be borrowed back and forth in order to make the programs of each more interesting and varied.

It is desirable and sometimes necessary that the director of the chorus and the directors of other school activities cooperate, both in setting the times for practice so that there will be less conflict, and in making demands upon the time and energy of students who take part in several activities. Athletics and dramatics are especially likely to conflict with the glee club; yet both of these activities frequently need the assistance of the music department or of the music students. Athletic coaches realize the value of the band in keeping up spirit on the athletic field, and of the glee club in singing school songs for "pep" programs. The dramatic department may profitably use pupils from the music department to furnish incidental music between acts in dramatic presentations. Surely cooperation between the choral director and the directors of athletics and dramatics would result profitably for all concerned.

That the public success and, to some extent, the artistic success of a glee club is due to its advertising cannot be denied. For this reason, directors of choral organizations need to be especially considerate of editors and reporters of school and local newspapers. Their good-will is worth cultivating. It is a sound policy to have an understanding with local editors early in the season. The newspaper needs news which will be of interest to the readers; the glee club director proposes to furnish well written articles regularly to help fill that need. (A feature department of either school or local newspapers may well be devoted to choral activities of the community.) The editor may have to be "sold" on the fact that the glee club deserves the cooperation of the press. If any complimentary tickets are given to choral concerts, they should be given first of all to editors and music critics of newspapers.

C. Announcements

Announcements in school assemblies should be both carefully prepared and well presented. If the president of the glee club is popular with the student body and has a good speaking voice and an attractive stage presence, he is the logical person to make the announcements.

Announcements on bulletin boards should be concise and definite, preferably typewritten and signed by the director or some officer of the club. A special music bulletin-board is often advantageous.

Announcements in school catalogues should be prominently placed and written so as to appeal to students. Mention of the type of work done, the activities, advantages and rewards received by members, and the method of achieving membership may be included.

D. Inducements

The various rewards or inducements which may be offered to glee club or chorus members are as follows:
1. Musical pleasure derived.
2. Cultural benefits.
3. Activity credit.
4. Scholastic credit. (Note: Some administrators believe that elective glee-club or chorus work should be kept strictly on an extra-curricular basis with no scholastic credit allowed. The point is debatable.)
5. Concert trips with part or all of expenses paid.
6. Participation in sectional, state, or national contests or festivals.

7. The honor of belonging to an important school organization.
8. Glee club pins, charms, rings, sweaters, or school letters.
9. Social activities, *e.g.*, picnics, banquets, parties, and dances.
10. Valuable musical training for future membership in church choirs, select adult choral groups, and perhaps professional groups.

It is the duty of the choral director to determine which of the above inducements are desirable and practical in his school system, and to endeavor to make them achievable.

E.   Programs at School Assemblies, Club Meetings, Banquets, *etc.*

The best devices for creating interest are short programs by the club or by club representatives that create a favorable impression upon the student body and the school patrons. A very good procedure is to give such a program at the beginning of the school year to interest new members. If the glee club is broken up by graduation, and the members remaining are not able to give a creditable performance, a quartet, duet, or a solo from one of the members or the director will serve. However, *such a program should not be given unless it is of a nature to please and excite the interest of the listeners;* otherwise it defeats its purpose. Such a program offers an excellent opportunity to extend an invitation to those interested in joining the club and to explain requirements, time of rehearsal, *etc.*

There are many demands from civic clubs, churches, other organizations, and even individuals for programs by the glee club or some of its members. The director must realize that it is the duty of school groups to render community service, but he needs to exercise good judgment in knowing where to draw the line. Furnishing a limited amount of free entertainment to civic organizations is usually good advertising for the club's home concerts. However, local interest will be lessened if the club appears in public too frequently. The whole glee club should be used sparingly or not at all for community programs or civic club banquets unless these events are of special importance to the community as a whole. The services of the glee club will not be highly valued if the group is at the beck and call of every minor civic function. Representatives from the chorus—an octet, a quartet, a duet, or a soloist—may be used for such occasions. These representatives may well be students primarily interested in music as a major study. The additional training that this experience gives them is a valuable part of their education.

When giving entertainment at civic club banquets, the director may well expect and insist on courteous treatment for himself and his group. The director and small groups such as quartets should have their place at the table along with the other guests, preferably at the speaker's table. Arrangements should be made to have a proper introduction of the club. *Do not allow any singing to begin until attention and quiet is secured. If music is worth having it is worth hearing.* Songs should be between and not during courses. Insistence on the above principles will create a greater respect for the director, for the club, and for the dignity of music.

CHAPTER IV

REHEARSALS

(*See also* CHAPTER II, ORGANIZATION, *and* CHAPTER VII, CONTESTS AND FESTIVALS, SPECIAL REHEARSAL METHODS.)

> *If we want to derive spiritual and aesthetic nourishment from any piece of music, if we want music study to be a satisfaction of a deep natural hunger, if we want to build our work on an assured psychological foundation, then we should remember that one can acquire infinitely more musical insight and delight from one piece beautifully learned than from ten miserably learned.*
>
> JAMES MURSELL*

A. Objectives

1. To promote a greater joy in hearing music and in participating in making it.
2. To raise the standard of music appreciation.
3. To learn the assigned music—prepare for concert, contest, or festival.
4. To improve the interpretative and technical powers, and the general musicianship of the individual members and of the club as a whole.
5. To gain the interest of members and to attract others.

B. Activities

1. Learning new music, either in a group or in sectional rehearsals.
2. Practising to perfect interpretation of songs already learned.
3. Singing, for the fun of it, known songs of which the interpretation is already satisfactory.
4. Listening to music. (This may well be glee club music sung by a select quartet or octet, or played on the phongraph or piano, or by a quartet of instruments. Music is learned much more rapidly if it can first be heard.)
5. Hearing the text read, and commenting on its meaning.
6. Improving by vocal exercises blending, balance, tone quality, control, range, sight-reading power, and general musicianship.

C. Time, Place, Number, and Length

1. Time—The time for rehearsals of the chorus depends upon the particular school system. In some schools, rehearsals must be held at the time allotted for all extra-curricular activities. This system makes the glee club compete for membership with other organizations. As a result, the chorus may suffer from lack of numbers; but, on the other hand, it may benefit from a relatively better quality of membership. It is, of course, desirable to set a time for rehearsals when there are no other interfering activities or classes regularly scheduled. After glee-club rehearsals become established at a definite time,

*"We Need Music", *Music Supervisors National Conference Yearbook, 1932*

35

pupils who are interested will make out their programs so that there are no conflicts. Once the rehearsal time has been determined and properly advertised, *the director will find that he needs to be steadfast in opposing any encroachment upon rehearsal time by other organizations or events.* Firmness in this respect is necessary.

An examination of the school's activity and classroom schedule may disclose a suitable time. Whenever possible, the director should meet with executives responsible for arranging the schedule and endeavor to have a suitable time set aside for choral activities. In a particularly difficult situation, it may be necessary to meet all that are interested in glee-club membership and, by a show of hands, determine the greatest number or the most desirable group that can come to rehearsals at a given time. A system of "staggered" rehearsals has been worked out in some schools where it is impossible to schedule rehearsals either during the school day or after school hours. The club meets during the first period for the first rehearsal, during the second period for the second rehearsal, *etc.* If the glee club meets three times weekly in a school system which has six scheduled periods for daily recitation, this would mean absence from any one scheduled class but twice a month.

A rehearsal time between 7:00 and 10:00 p.m. is usually most practical for community groups. Rehearsals immediately after working hours are favored in some industrial centers where a short working day leaves much of the afternoon free. The preference of chorus members should be consulted in all cases before a rehearsal time is decided. Community groups have more difficulty in planning frequent rehearsals. Therefore longer rehearsals are favored; one two-hour rehearsal a week with a fifteen-minute intermission seems to be the usual plan.

2. Place—A clean and attractive room encourages good singing. An auditorium or stage in a large room is best for general rehearsals. Clubs that do all of their practising in smaller rooms are very liable to be confused by the different acoustic effects in large rooms or auditoriums. Small rooms may be used to advantage and are especially desirable for rehearsing sections and learning new music. The rehearsal room should be well lighted, of good acoustic properties, and equipped with a good piano and a stage large enough to accommodate the club.

3. Number and Length—Two separate one-hour rehearsals are better than one continuous two-hour rehearsal. The length of time between rehearsals should be spaced as evenly as possible. Three one-period rehearsals on Monday, Wednesday, and Friday are favored in many school systems. The best results are possible where the chorus is given regular academic credit and meets normally for five periods a week.

D. Methods of Creating and Retaining Interest

1. Promptness, order, and discipline: Begin rehearsals on time, even if only a few of the group are there, and end the rehearsal promptly. A haphazard and loosely disciplined method of rehearsal can be expected to result in a lack of interest and pride in the organization and in a loss of respect for the director.

The director must be strict but also sensible, human, sympathetic, and ready to laugh at funny incidents or tell a good joke on occasion. *It is well to remember that rehearsals are to be enjoyed*, but fun should never be the excuse for lax discipline in matters that are essential. *The director must insist that each club-officer and member do his part promptly and efficiently.*

2. Definite rehearsal program: Well planned and executed rehearsals have helped many a mediocre conductor to surpass in results many conductors with much greater musical insight and technical skill. Give glee-club members definite information and objectives for work; have the numbers to be rehearsed and the order in which they are to be practised written on the board previous to the start of the rehearsal; inform the singers of the objectives to be accomplished in each practice and, as soon as possible, of the numbers to be memorized and the places and dates for concerts. Plan the rehearsal, and conduct it so that the proper amount of time is given to each phase of the work.

3. Occasional singing of old songs that the chorus likes: An interest in glee club work, an *esprit de corps*, and an ability to follow closely the rhythmic and interpretative directions of the conductor may be best established in the beginning through singing familiar numbers. It is well to have interesting and perhaps new interpretative effects worked out in order that members may quickly learn to respect the musical leadership of the director.

4. Singing new and easy numbers for recreational purposes: Most amateur clubs are greatly attracted at first to light, easy numbers with humorous texts. The more serious numbers are not greatly appreciated by the average chorus member during the first few rehearsals, but appreciation tends to grow as interpretative power and familiarity with the music increase. Conversely, appreciation tends to decrease for the light, humorous, and obvious numbers that seemed so attractive at first. Many directors plan to start each season with some new and especially attractive music.

5. Keeping all sections busy during rehearsals: Sections that would otherwise be idle, when special drill is being given to one part, should be kept busy by having them attempt to hum quietly along in an effort to learn their own part better. Easy parts can often be learned in this manner without the group's giving specific attention to them. When any one section needs a considerable amount of individual attention, part-rehearsals in separate rooms are best.

6. Praise, criticism, and practice-objectives: Praise frequently; criticise indirectly and do not be so severe in your criticism that the club becomes discouraged. *Criticism should be of a nature to produce stimulation, not discouragement.* Be careful about continually criticising one section and praising another; develop each member's pride in his own section. Don't attempt to correct all mistakes at the first few rehearsals; concentrate upon the most obvious and serious faults and ignore the others.

E. Rehearsal Technique and Musical Considerations

1. Fundamental Rules for the Choral Conductor to Observe:[10]

[10]A number of the ideas expressed under this heading were suggested by a pamphlet issued by the National Bureau for the Advancement of Music, *Twenty Points for Song Leaders*, by Kenneth S. Clark.

a. Maintain discipline. Plan your rehearsal so that it "moves" rapidly without any unnecessary pauses. "Remember that the Devil finds work for idle fingers and voices."[11] Demand respect and attention, from the first rehearsal to the last. The first few rehearsals are the logical ones to settle most disciplinary matters; *the longer discipline is delayed, the harder it is to obtain.* Unnecessary noise during rehearsals should not be permitted. Do not be mean, harsh, and vindictive, but even-tempered, just, and firm. Simple silence during which the director looks at the offender is often sufficient rebuke. When disturbances are made to appear in the light of offenses against the wishes and welfare of the group, they usually cease. In extreme cases it may be necessary to ask individuals to leave the rehearsal until they feel that they can give the proper attention. The best plan is to have the group take care of disciplining its own members through efficient organization for this purpose.

b. Systematize the rehearsal: Determine the objectives, prepare the plan, and apportion the time for the several activities of the rehearsal beforehand. Plan all routine procedures such as distribution of music, order of practice, and vocal exercises, so that no time is wasted. Signals to indicate rising and sitting, sustaining a chord, singing by designated sections, repeating of phrases or chords, and producing various interpretative effects, should be prearranged and understood by the group. Such a plan at the beginning will save a great deal of time by eliminating the necessity for repeated explanations and unnecessary talking by the director.

c. Select the accompanist carefully; his or her attitude, interest, and skill are extremely important factors in determining the success of the club.

d. Always be sure that the accompanist is in a position to see the conducting beat.

e. Make sure that both *you* and the accompanist are familiar with the music *before* it is rehearsed by the club. Find the difficult places and be prepared to approach and practise them in an effective manner; determine the probable tempo, style, dynamics, and general effects you wish to obtain.

f. Always maintain variety in the choice of songs, and divide long rehearsal periods into several activities.

g. Select songs for both the beginning and end of the rehearsal period that are especially attractive to the club. *First and last impressions are the most important.*

h. When a choral group becomes restless or tired, change the activity or vary the method.

i. The more the responsibility can be placed upon the group itself, the better the ultimate progress will be. *Use the piano or sing with your group as little as possible.*

j. Act and speak confidently; be sure that your directions are plainly worded, distinctly articulated, and spoken loud enough to be understood. Do not "baby" your group by repetition of directions which have been plainly given. Let them get into trouble and then you have a real cause for effective criticism.

[11]Max T. Krone, "Music of the XVI Century for the H. S. Choir", *The Supervisors Service Bulletin,* March, 1934.

k. Demand clean-cut attacks and releases, satisfactory diction, and uniform phrasing; remember that a clean-cut release is no less important than a decisive attack.

l. Make the conducting beat plain and direct; avoid any affected or fancy style. Endeavor to maintain good posture and graceful beat, but not at the expense of definiteness. *Adapt your method and style of conducting to the ability of the group.* The ideally trained chorus should receive very few indications from the conductor regarding such elementary matters as strict tempo, rhythm values, easy attacks, or ordinary releases. However, inexperienced groups need a great deal of help at first on even the most elementary phases of interpretation.

m. Demand full attention and correct posture from the singers, and silence from the audience, before beginning a song in concert. *This moment of silence helps create a proper atmosphere in the beginning and is an extremely important factor in good interpretation.*

n. In unaccompanied singing, be sure that the correct pitch for each section is well sounded and understood before beginning. Groups need considerable practice in the technique of taking the pitch quickly and accurately, and retaining it. *Always take the pitch in the same manner for the same composition.* Sometimes a single note is enough; at other times it is best that the full chord be hummed before beginning. Two or more pitch pipes may be used in large choruses by specially selected members of the group located in the back row; the pitch is more easily heard coming from the back up through the group.

o. Develop the technique of taking pitch unobtrusively in concert; do not make it a diverting or formal ritual. The giving of pitch for *a cappella* choruses may be concealed by the following method: pitch for the first number is taken offstage, before marching on, or before the curtain is drawn. This needs to be practised, for keen concentration on the pitch is necessary if a considerable interval ensues before singing. Applause, even if only perfunctory, can usually be depended on after each number is completed. During this period, while the director is recognizing the applause, the pitch for the next number is given by one or more members of the chorus—preferably members located unobtrusively in the back row. This technique for giving pitch is seldom either seen or heard by the audience. This method avoids disturbing the artistic atmosphere, it speeds up the program, and is a most effective device for creating a favorable impression on judges of contests or festivals.

p. Remember that the purpose of both praise and criticism is to *stimulate your group to do better work.*

q. Treat all members of the club courteously and considerately; and demand attention, respect, and courtesy in return.

2. How to Rehearse Music: (See also "Special Rehearsal Technique" in Chapter VII.)

a. When learning new music, use the "Whole Method" followed by the "Part Method" of memorization. First get a good general idea of the whole compositon by singing through it a number of times; then take up the memorization of sections or parts. Do not make the mistake of breaking it up into too many individual phrases, but rather work on larger units of several phrases at a time.

b. Practise from the beginning *all* the music to be used in the succeeding program or concert. The less time there is to prepare the concert the more important it is that you follow this rule.

c. Nothing but a very serious blunder should halt a chorus when going through a number for the first time.

d. Sing through a number *several times* before stopping to correct minor mistakes. Do not make the mistake of many conductors—too much *telling* and not enough *singing*. Stopping a group frequently will dull the interest and perhaps create resentment. First give your chorus a chance to solve the problem on their own initiative. If the mistake is not corrected by simple repetition, help them individually and collectively to become more intelligent and capable singers by *first asking them where and what the trouble is*. The conductor who wisely places the initiative for correction upon the group will reap a reward of heightened attention and an increased interest, love, and understanding of the music which will reflect itself in better interpretation. The aesthetic and educational values of this procedure to the singers are correspondingly great.

e. Do not stop choruses frequently at any time. *A few wisely chosen suggestions at the end of a section, followed by repetition of the whole, will be found to be the best plan.* A phrase should never be broken for correction except when the difficulty it presents fails to improve through normal treatment.

f. Concentrate on the most difficult parts until they are the best known sections.

g. Be careful that technical aspects of the work are not overemphasized to the point that the singing impulse is injured or destroyed. John Dewey's "We learn by doing" is a most vital truth to keep in mind. It is largely the social aspect of the chorus or glee club which first appeals to boys or girls—*they come to sing together*. Any form of vocal drill must be judiciously handled and *should have immediate application* to music being sung. The purpose of a vocal exercise should be understood and the improvement it achieves should be noted by the group.

h. Use a favorable vowel or a neutral syllable when concentrating on the musical aspects of a new composition. Words may interfere with speedy learning of the desired effect.

i. If there is any doubt about the correctness of the inner parts, have them sung through alone. Other parts may hum along quietly, but never loudly enough to interfere. The inner parts are the most difficult to hear, and they are also the parts most likely to throw chords out of tune or balance. It is only the director with an unusually keen ear who can afford to dispense with the procedure of hearing inner parts alone.

3. Principles of Vocal Production:

The underlying principles of vocal training are the same for the group as for the individual. However, the method must be varied to suit the particular needs and common problems of the group. Many principles and practices of correct posture, proper breathing, easy and pleasing vowel production, good diction, and vocal coloring or shading can be taught to the group more easily and thoroughly than to the individual. *Groups must be trained, moreover, in the very important factors of voice blending and dynamic balance between sections.*

The director who is ambitious to achieve the best musical results with his club will find that training on some or all of the following points is invaluable. Most of these principles are best taught in voice classes, where this method of organization is possible; otherwise, it needs to be given during the rehearsal period of the chorus.

a. Breathing:[12]

"The correct practice of singing in itself tends to develop and establish the mastery of breath." However, the student will develop more rapidly and correctly if taught how to breathe. Breath should be inhaled easily and deeply with an accompanying sensation similar to that of sighing. The proper method is known scientifically as "diaphragmatic-costal" breathing, colloquially as "deep breathing".

"In inhalation the upper abdomen expands, owing to the descent of the diaphragm, and the ribs expand; in exhalation the abdomen tenses and contracts, owing to the pressure of abdominal muscles and to the gradual ascent of the diaphragm, and the ribs contract. Thus the greatest observable effect in both inhalation and exhalation is in front and at the sides in the region of the waist line."

Either the mouth or the nose may be used in inhalation, preferably both in most instances. Take only enough breath to sing the phrase easily; too much is a detriment. Difficult phrases should be marked and a habit established of breathing always in the same places. Most choirs are unable to sustain tone well to the ends of phrases. Much of this trouble is due to poor breath support. Any group can be taught in a short time to inhale properly, but suspension of the breath "at the waist-line" and control of the manner and speed in which breath is vocalized must be learned gradually and practised continually. All good choirs have the ability to sing long phrases on one breath.

The best way to obtain proper phrasing and develop breath support is to insist from the first on correct phrasing. It may be necessary on long phrases for individual members of the chorus to breathe alternately, but the group effect of a legato sustained to the end of the phrase must not be broken. As the singer's familiarity with the composition and efficiency in tonal production increase, he will gradually gain in ability to sustain long phrases on one breath. Proper exercises (See p. 49), holding tones or chords a considerable time while members of the chorus breathe alternately, will do much to speed the process of learning correct phrasing and easy breath support.

Proper thought-processes in relation to breath support are, of course, vitally important. The following method of inducing them will result in immediate and remarkable improvement in both tone quality and ability to sustain long phrases:

[12]Quotations are from *An Outline of Theory*, made and adopted by the American Academy of Teachers of Singing, Dec. 9, 1925.

First, be sure the singers have correct posture. (See Dr. Hollis Dann's "pulling the string" suggestion, p. 43.) Second, give the following four directions to your group and endeavor, by continually checking on the matter, *to guarantee that they habitualize the thought-processes involved.* (Note—After the thought-process is consciously habitualized, it becomes automatic and will not interfere with spontaneity in interpretation.)

(1) *Sing as freely and as naturally as you talk.*

(2) *On all attacks start the tone "deep, from the feet."* ("Contrary to general practice, which instructs the singer to think *upward* as the tone is made, far more desirable results will be realized by asking the singers to continually think *downward,* . . . especially when singing high tones."[13]

(3) Use the "pulling the string" idea you have utilized in obtaining good posture also: (a) *on the attack of each new phrase:* pull the string from the toes; (b) *on sustained notes:* pull the string steadily; (c) *for accents:* on *sforzando* accents pull the string suddenly and powerfully; (d) *on sustained fortissimi:* pull the string steadily and powerfully; (e) *on sustained pianissimi:* pull the string steadily and gently.

(4) Do not think of the diaphragm as a *pulling* or pumping muscle but as a *resisting* muscle, which has an expansive, pushing-out feeling around the waist-line rather than a contracting and pulling-in feeling. *There should be no appreciable sinking of the abdominal muscles as the tone begins.*

Do not condemn this method of obtaining good tone and steady breath-support just because you have been taught to think differently—instead, *try it.* "The proof of the pudding is in the eating."

There are three phases of breathing:

Inhalation: The chest assumes a comfortably high position; the ribs and back slightly expand; the abdomen, impelled by the downward movement of the diaphragm, moves downwards and outwards.

Suspension: This occurs the moment after inhalation ceases, and before exhalation begins. It induces proper laryngeal position and makes possible an easy and correct attack with the breath-impulse. This moment of suspension is a vital factor in breath support and therefore in artistic singing. It may well be taught to groups.

Exhalation: The physical manifestations are the reverse of inhalation. The objectives should be *steadiness of control without undue tension* and the vocalization of tone *without waste of breath.* The chest should never collapse at the end of exhalation. A moment of support after the tone ceases prevents an unpleasant wavering ending or perhaps a grunt. Before the next inhalation there should be a moment—sometimes very slight if a quick breath is necessary—of recovery and relaxation.

[13]Harold Sheldon Dyer, "Effective Rehearsal Technic that Builds Better Choirs", *Educational Music Magazine* (*The Supervisors Service Bulletin*), Jan., 1935.

Trained singers learn to make this moment very short and thus avoid being out of breath or tense on the next phrase.

The effort expended in breathing must be in proportion to pitch and intensity. It is easy to overweight low tones with too much breath-effort; it is difficult to get enough strength and endurance of breath-support for extremely high *forte* tones in sustained singing. The secret of both delicate *pianissimo* and robust *forte* singing lies largely in a steady and adequate supply of breath. *Fortissimo* singing must come as a gradual result of growing strength and control of the muscles which govern breathing. It is of utmost importance for both the soloists and the members of a choral group to develop the power of "holding or supporting the breath at the waist".

Fine *pianissimo* singing demands an even steadier control of the breath than does *fortissimo*, as well as a more vivid conception of tone and diction. A *pianissimo* tone should be sung well forward to the front teeth and lips of a nearly closed mouth: the throat should be relaxed but *not expanded;* and the tone, although small, should be as clear and vital as a *forte*. *The focusing of attention upon clear-cut articulation is most valuable in obtaining resonant pianissimo effects and accurate intonation.*

b. Posture:

"The singer should stand comfortably erect, with the chest medium high, and with a feeling of flexibility and well being."[14] The shoulders should be back and down and the head neither thrust forward nor thrown back unnaturally, but balanced evenly on the spinal axis. In order to produce a firm and easy posture when standing, one foot may well be slightly in front and to the side of the other. *The weight should always be forward* for either the standing or the sitting position. The body should not be allowed to slump down, and the legs should never be crossed when seated. "The arms may be either dropped loosely at the sides or clasped loosely in front. It is usually not a good practice to have the hands clasped behind the back, as it throws the body out of line and cramps the breathing muscles, and also presents an awkward appearance. *The singer should always give the impression of being perfectly at ease.*"[15]

Dr. Hollis Dann's suggestion to his choral groups to induce balanced posture is well worth repeating. Imagine a string attached to the upper *back* part of the head; assume the posture that a firm and steady pull on this string would produce. A similar effect may be achieved by directing the pupil to *keep his chin down* and imagine himself growing steadily taller. If this advice is followed, it results not only in the proper vertical position of the spine but also in proper head- and chin- position. It will correct the tendency of many singers to stretch the neck forward and tilt the head upwards.

c. Diction:

The director who carefully analyzes the text with a view to discovering where indolent or incorrect diction is most apt to occur is fore-

[14]American Academy of Teachers of Singing, *An Outline of Theory.*
[15]Carol M. Pitts, "Spring Festival Preparations", *The Supervisors Service Bulletin*, March, 1934.

armed in both detection and correction of mistakes. Diction in itself is a study that will well repay the director. *Proper attention to this one element alone can make a surprisingly good chorus from mediocre talent.* Faults in diction should receive immediate attention in beginning rehearsals.

Good singing consists of correct pronunciation, clear enunciation, and distinct articulation. *Words in singing should be pronounced exactly as in correct speaking.* Consonants should be uttered plainly but *rapidly.* They should never be prolonged to the extent that they interfere with the flow of tone on the vowel (except humming consonants, for unusual interpretative effects). With most amateur groups, the consonant "r" is a particular offender. It is growled or gurgled with a very ugly effect in such words as "father", "never", "her", *etc.*, because singers insist on trying to sing *on it* instead of pronouncing *with it.* Groups may be instructed to think and sing the "er" as "uh-r" and the "ar" as "ah-r". The syllable is thus sung on the vowel, with the "r" quickly articulated or "rolled" at the end.

Initial and final consonants, such as *h, d, t, k,* and *p,* are often omitted or slighted to such an extent that audiences wonder whether the song is being sung in English. These are the sounds most necessary to make words understandable. Conductors who are careless in requiring them, or who do not make decisive motions for attacks and releases, are usually to blame for poor percussive consonants. The most common weakness of even well-trained choral groups is their frequent failure to "get the words across". It is not enough that they be barely heard: A CHORUS SHOULD BE HEARD AND UNDERSTOOD EASILY.

No word should be pinched off, stopped with a stroke of the glottis, or allowed to end indefinitely. In order to ensure audibility and satisfactory interpretation, it is especially necessary to aspirate the vowels and to exaggerate all consonants of: (a) accented words, (b) the subject and predicate of a sentence, (c) the last word at the end of a phrase. Many consonants, when articulated with proper force, produce an effect that at first may seem radically exaggerated at close range, but does not seem so to an audience in the average auditorium. Even the softest vowel sound will carry to the back of a large hall, but consonants do not have the carrying power of vowels. Therefore, they must be articulated with more force than seems necessary. If soloists or choruses want to be heard, they must accustom themselves to a *pianissimo* conception of the vowel with perhaps, at the same time, a medium *forte* conception of the consonant.

Linking over the consonants to the following word is common, *e.g.,* "Let us now pray" sounds like "Le tus snow pray"; "Feet of them" becomes "Fee tuv them"; and "With her", "Wither". Substitutions such as *g* for *k* (*gall* for *call*), *b* for *p* (*bower* for *power*), *v* for *f* (*vine* for *fine*) and *d* for *t* (*dire* for *tire*) are forms of lazy or careless diction that need continual correction among untrained groups.

The letters *s, c,* and *z* (the sibilants), are frequently anticipated and unpleasantly hissed when they come as the inital letter of a word starting a musical phrase. The beginning of the Christmas carol, "Silent Night", offers an excellent example of a place where this type of mistake is most likely to occur. These sibilant letters are also hissed too long at the ends of words or phrases. Sopranos, for some reason, seem to be the worst offenders in this respect. *Difficulty with both the percussive and the sibilant consonants is greatly lessened if the attacks and releases of the conductor are precise and assured.*

Careless enunciation of diphthongs or vowel combinations are common. The word "fountain" too often sounds like "fahtun", "mountain" like "mahtun", "gladness" like "gladnuss", and "silent" like "silunt". The long "i" combination-vowel (as in the words "die" or "by") and the long "a" (as in the words "day" or "pray") are sung by amateur groups with an offensive lingering on the "ee" sound at the end. The ending sound in double vowel combinations of this type should be articulated as rapidly as a consonant.

An ugly, mewing sound, making such words as "down" sound like "dee-own" and "now" like "nee-ow", is prevalent in some sections. A hard, unpleasant "a" sound in such words as "can't", "and", "glad", and "that" is habitual in the speech of many Americans. This fault causes much harshness in singing unless detected and corrected.

Although under-definition is the most universal sin in diction, we occasionally hear the other extreme, over-definition. In this case the articulation of consonants is exaggerated to the point of interfering with the "flow" and length of tone properly belonging to the vowel. Such rare examples constitute another form of "bad" diction and are due either to an improper conception of *legato* or to an insufficient technique for producing a good, flowing tone and distinct speech in song at the same time.

d. Tone Quality: (See also "Breathing", p. 41).

"Good vocal tone depends upon a conception of beautiful sound and upon a sensitive and educated ear. It results from a consequent coordination of the following:

(1) Controlled breath;
(2) A larynx whose normal position, neither raised nor lowered locally, is ensured by correct inhalation, and allows freedom of action of the tongue, to which it is attached;
(3) Vocal chords in unhindered vibration. These three produce a fundamental tone, proportionately reinforced by
(4) The resonance chambers of the chest and head (mouth and nasal cavities), and issuing through
(5) A free throat;
(6) Tongue, palate, lips, and jaw, all freely active in pronouncing, without rigidity, and with no locally specialized effort for supposed aid to tone.

"This tone, easy, flowing, smooth, permits and favors every variety of expression in singing. Its inception, following inhalation, is the Attack, that is, the immediate application of breath to the vocal chords, after pitch and vowel adjustment of the whole vocal apparatus."[16]

[16]American Academy of Teachers of Singing, *An Outline of Theory.*

Good tone depends upon a pure, vital, and resonant vowel. Any exercise to procure better tone should be a means to an end and not an end in itself; singers should never be drilled in such a manner that they become technique- and tone-conscious to the detriment of spontaneity and naturalness of expression. *Never sacrifice voices for the sake of interpretative effects.* It is unnecessary to "drive" the voices on music of too severe vocal requirements, for much good music of a suitable degree of difficulty is now available.

The *pianissimo* should have the same vital brilliance as the *forte*. A common fault of the amateur chorus is the production of dark, breathy, devitalized, under-pitch *pianissimi*. The remedy is, first, a proper conception of *pianissimo* tone; second, proper posture and steady breath support; third, sufficient practice to establish confidence; fourth, and by no means least, *clear-cut diction.*

The tone-quality of a chorus may be developed by having one section sing its tone in a specific chord until the desired quality is obtained. Then each of the other parts may sing its tone in like manner. Finally, all parts are combined in the full chord. The first essential is *listening* and *discriminating* between the good and the bad and, later, between fine shades or textures of tone for varying interpretative effects.

e. Balance:

Grade the possible degree of *piano* or *forte* according to the powers of the weakest section; otherwise chords and imitative melodic parts will be out of balance. Tonal balance does not depend so much upon numbers in individual sections as it does upon the comparative resonance, power, and quality of the voices. No definite rule can be made for the relation of numbers in the different sections, since conditions vary with different clubs and even with different compositions or different arrangements of the same composition.

It may be said, in general, that for harmonic and physical reasons, more voices are needed in the sections singing the lowest part and the part next to the highest: *e.g.*, in a men's glee club the second bass and the second tenor sections. It is best, when possible, to have enough singers in the second bass section to obtain a satisfactory tonal balance without the necessity of using full voice or straining in the least to achieve it. Both quality of tone and intonation are benefited in choruses where this condition prevails. However, in high schools more first tenors than second tenors are sometimes needed on account of the immaturity of high tenor voices at this age.

In men's glee clubs and in *a cappella* mixed choruses, the baritones (first bass) are apt to overshadow the power of the second bass section; in mixed-voice choirs, first sopranos are usually too numerous (some leading directors favor fewer singers for the first soprano than for any other part); in women's glee clubs there are usually too few second altos. Some experimentation in assigning parts and in variations of dynamics between sections may be necessary before a satisfactory balance is secured. The ear of the director or of other competent critics listening *at a distance* is the best guide. From the standpoint of the listener, overstrong inner voices are most objectionable because they upset the chordal balance.

One of the most frequent problems confronting the director of high-school mixed choruses or of men's glee clubs is to obtain enough high first tenors. This problem rarely exists in schools having established voice-training classes, a fact which indicates that *there are enough tenors in the average school system if they are developed by proper training*. Fortunately, nature has arranged that one mature tenor voice, owing to a stronger and more penetrating quality, is able to balance four to six ordinary sopranos or altos and two to four second basses. It must be remembered, however, that the best effect is obtained by the tenor through quality rather than through quantity of tone.

There is little cause to disband the mixed chorus if first tenors cannnot be developed. If altos are available who can sing down to *g*, the problem is solved. Most tenor parts written today for high school groups do not carry the range below *g*, fourth space, bass clef (usually written second line, treble clef, but sounding an octave lower than written). This pitch is easy for the low altos, and there is no reason except tradition for their not singing this part if necessary, or at least supporting the first tenors to create a proper balance when more resonance is needed. From the standpoint of sound, low alto voices make better first tenors than immature high school boys' voices do. Few members of concert audiences ever detect the difference, and it is doubtful whether the average judge of choral contests would know the difference if blindfolded.

Boy altos are frequently useful on high tenor parts, and may be used more appropriately in men's glee clubs than girl altos. Where *enough* boy altos are available, the director need not fear to attempt men's glee-club music with extremely high first-tenor parts. However, it is unwise to place too much dependence on the boy alto, since his voice is usually in the process of change and may become unmanageable at the very time when it is most needed.

A perfect balance is not always artistically desirable, for the melody (if one is present) and striking harmonic parts need to be made prominent. It is frequently a good effect on *pianissimo* repetitions of the chorus to allow the bass part to be prominent. The skill and judgment of the director in bringing out or revealing the beauty of certain parts contributes greatly to the interest, variety, and perfection of interpretation.

f. Blending:

Good blending is the result of similar tone-quality from all individual voices and all harmonic parts. Choral organizations must learn to sing vowels with a homogeneous quality, since poor ensemble is frequently caused by *variations in the quality of vowel color* and not by a deviation from pitch or a lack of dynamic balance between sections. All vowel sounds should be vocalized *easily* and *clearly*. Dark, guttural vowels, thin, white, pinched tones, and breathy, raspy sounds will not blend properly. Any one section, or voice, can spoil the blend by varying from the pitch or singing "off-color". Sopranos spoil the blend when they shriek on top tones, contraltos when their voices become breathy, hollow, or "hooty"; tenors and baritones must be watched for open, "shouty" tones in the upper register, and basses for a somber, guttural, and inflexible lower register.

A highly trained, resonant solo voice is usually a "sore thumb" in a group of untrained voices. The vowel production is so much clearer and the voice so much more powerful that it continually stands out from the ensemble. The soloist is generally an obstacle to the ensemble of untrained voices unless he is willing to merge his personality with that of the group for the time being, singing so softly that the voice is not prominent.

The effect of good blending in the easy registers should be made the object of study by both the director and the chorus in an attempt to extend the same desirable effects into more difficult registers.

4.   Group Vocal Exercises:

Many directors feel that the most valuable activity of the rehearsal is the short period at the beginning devoted to vocal study. Others believe that such exercises are a waste of precious time, and that all necessary technique can be obtained in the process of rehearsing the music to be used. We hear groups who sing beautifully under both systems of training. What is the answer?

First, choral groups differ in the amount and quality of their former vocal training and in their experience in group singing; second, directors vary greatly in their skill and understanding in obtaining technical perfection through either direct or indirect methods. In defense of the direct method, it is safe to assume that there are comparatively few directors ingenious enough to take the average unskilled group and speedily weld it into a chorus with commendable technical power without recourse to definite vocal exercises as part of the rehearsal program. Furthermore, most successful directors believe that vocal exercises are essential for untrained voices and, properly selected and applied, valuable to even the most skilled professional organizations.

The members of a chorus or glee club do not resent giving a reasonable amount of time to vocal drills, especially if well presented and used directly to help increase interpretative power. In fact, joy in singing increases directly in proportion to growth in ease, power, beauty, and control of the voice. Proper exercises for the development of strength and flexibility of control are just as necessary for the development of the vocal organs as they are for the development of any muscle, or set of muscles, in athletics. However, vocal exercises are deadening, uninteresting, and inefficient unless they are undertaken with definite objectives in mind and accompanied by intelligent comment, analysis, and comparison. Too often, indeed, group vocal exercises are nothing more than warming-up drills, killing precious rehearsal time without sufficient justification. Directors using such drills are frequently good teachers of voice in private lessons, but weak in adapting their knowledge to group needs. They fail first, perhaps, to recognize the most vital factors in group performance and, second, to select and adapt vocal exercises to the requirements of the group.

Granted that vocal exercises are desirable for the efficient training of most choruses or glee clubs, these questions arise: What are the minimum technical essentials needed by a chorus or glee club? And what types of vocal exercises are adapted to attaining them quickly and efficiently? Analysis of the technical equipment of excellent choral groups leads to the conclusion that the most vital essentials, in the order of their importance, are:

   a. Smooth and even *blending* of voices.

   b. *Balance* of power between voice sections.

   c. Satisfactory *tone quality* and *pitch*.

   d. Vocal *range* and *technique* sufficient to interpret music sung by the group.

The following exercises are recommended as being well adapted to choral groups in attaining the above essentials. Even the best adult choruses will derive considerable benefit from an intelligent use of some of the exercises illustrated.

(Note: Many leading music educators believe that the principal emphasis of voice classes in high school during the first year of training should be upon *developing skill in the use of the voice in ensemble*. This seems reasonable in view of the fact that the majority of students taking voice-class work continue their vocal experience in after-school life as members of church choirs, glee clubs, or choruses; only a few of them become soloists appearing regularly before the public. Proper training for ensemble singing furnishes also the ideal basic training for solo singing. The exercises described in the following section will be found useful in themselves and as a supplement to the various text-books for voice-class training).

FUNDAMENTAL VOCAL EXERCISES FOR CHORAL GROUPS AND VOICE CLASSES

General directions:

1. Benefit from an exercise is obtained only by intelligent and *continued* practice, and by constant effort to achieve progressive improvement. It is well to remember that there is comparatively little benefit in vocal exercises themselves; the benefit comes from *intelligent use of them*.

2. Apply added technique gained through the vocal exercises immediately to improve interpretation in music being sung by the group. These exercises may also be used as a vocal specific after trouble has been encountered and a need for improvement is felt.

3. If the full value of the exercises is to be realized, it is best that they be sung *unaccompanied*.

4. When one section is singing, it should sound like a single voice rather than so many separate voices; when all sections are singing in harmony, they should produce a rich balance and blend of tone similar to that of a fine pipe organ. This effect will be best achieved at first in *pianissimo*. *Make every effort to retain the same quality as tonal volume is increased.*

5. Use all vowels: *ah*, *ā* (as in "late"), *ē* (as in "me"), *ī* (as in "ice"), *ō*, and *ōō* (as in "moon").

6. Start with the best vowel as a pattern for comparison. For most groups this will be an *ō*—an *ō* brilliant in quality produced with an upward inflection. The *ah* and the *ōō* are best for relaxing the jaw and developing a rich, somber

quality. The *ā* and the *ē* are best for developing brilliance and pronounced head resonance.

7. Endeavor to obtain a clear, easy, resonant, and pure "Italian" vowel color on all pitches. Try to keep a similar brilliance of color and sensation of resonance for all vowels. *Most singers change the physical adjustment far too much when singing different successive vowels.*

8. Put the exercises on a blackboard, if one is available; or dictate them to the students.

9. Emphasis must constantly be placed upon the importance of proper posture and of analytical listening on the part of the singers in an effort to make the voices blend and the parts balance.

EXERCISE I.

Objectives:

1. To develop a keen sense of voice blending, pitch, balance, and tonal beauty in ensemble.
2. To teach breath control on sustained notes.
3. To develop a beautiful, easy, and homogeneous vowel production.
4. To teach intelligent interpretation of dynamic indications.

Ex. 13

Directions:

1. Make *crescendos* and *decrescendos* smoothly.
2. Never let the *forte* become so loud that the tone is raucous or forced; in part-singing, the power of the weakest section must determine the degree of the *forte*.
3. Give specific help to voices that do not blend; first ask them to sing softly or to listen.
4. Gradually extend the length of time the note is held and the extent of the *crescendo* and *diminuendo*. Practise sustaining the note over a considerable period of time, individuals breathing alternately (see pp. 40 ff.)
5. Vary the exercises by singing sustained notes at the same degree of loudness throughout, *e.g., ppp, pp, p, mp, mf, f, ff,* and *fff.* Do not expect to get all these gradations at first; with undeveloped voices use extreme *forte* very little, or not at all.
6. Vary the exercises by singing different vowels (*ah, ā, ē, ī, ō, ōō*) one after the other on the sustained note, never breaking the flow of tone when changing.
7. Transpose the exercise to different degrees in both major and minor keys.

(Note: When choral groups can sing major and minor chords and scales in tune they are well on the road to singing music with good intonation.)

EXERCISE II.

Objectives:

1. To develop *legato* style of singing.
2. To teach ease of vowel-production, control, and correct intonation on changing pitches.
3. To extend the voice range.

Ex. 14

(Note—the octave scale in both major and minor may follow the five-tone scale.)

Directions:

(Note—Directions 1, 2, and 3, of Exercise I should also be observed.)

1. Use all vowels and degrees of loudness as in Exercise I.
2. Use only in medium ranges for the whole group; signal parts or voices to drop out as the exercise is extended either above or below their suitable range.
3. Vary the tempo from slow to fast.
4. Vary the exercise by using different vowels on different pitches, by using consonants (*l, n,* or *m*) before the vowels to loosen up the tongue and jaw action, and by putting the exercise into minor.
5. Extend the exercise to a six-note scale; to the octave scale, in major and all three forms of minor; and to the chromatic scale.

EXERCISE III.

Objectives:

1. To develop a technique for an accented or detached style of singing; to teach proper *staccato* and *sforzando* attack.
2. To develop the ability to sustain a tone properly after a *sforzando* attack.
3. To develop strength and flexibility of the diaphragm.

(Note: This exercise cannot be done properly without generous diaphragm action. It is usually most difficult for the less flexible voices of the basses and altos, but highly beneficial for them as well as for the lighter voices.)

Ex. 15

Directions:

1. Vary the speed from slow to fast.
2. Use all vowels as in Exercise I.

3. It will help in inducing the right attack to think an *h* before the vowel and to strive for a sensation similar to that experienced when laughing, "ha!"

4. Vary the exercise by using a consonant (*l*, *n*, or *m*) before the vowel to loosen tongue and jaw action.

EXERCISE IV.

Objectives:

Same as those of Exercise I, as well as to develop ability to maintain satisfactory blending and balance *in moving harmonies.*

Directions:

1. Disregard time-signatures at first, holding each chord until the proper corrections of blending, balance, or pitch have been made.

2. Sing the cadences with different vowels and dynamics, as in Example I.

(Note: The exercises illustrated are for men's voices. It must be remembered that men's changed voices written in the treble clef sound an octave lower than written. Cadences using the same and different progressions may be easily constructed by the conductor for other groups; select keys and arrange parts so that they are effectively spaced and remain within the effective range of the voices.)

Ex. 16

ah, ā, etc.

Reference List for Further Reading

Methods:
    *Cain, *Choral Music and its Practice*, Witmark, New York.
    *Coward, *Choral Technique and Interpretation*, Novello, London.
    *Greene, *Interpretation in Song*, Macmillan, New York.
    *Roberton, *Mixed Voice Choirs, Female Voice Choirs, Male Voice Choirs*,
        Paterson, London.
    *Smallman and Wilcox, *The Art of A Cappella Singing*, Ditson, Boston.
    Weisman, *School Choirs*, Oxford University Press, London.
    *Wodell, *Choir and Chorus Conducting*, Presser, Philadelphia.

Collective Voice Training:
    *Clippinger, *Class Method of Voice Culture*, Ditson, Boston.
    *Granville, *Voco Study Plan*, Gamble Hinged, Chicago.
    *Haywood, *Universal Song*, G. Schirmer, Inc., New York.
    *Maybee, *Vocal Ensemble Exercises*, G. Schirmer, Inc., New York.
    *Pierce, *Class Lessons in Singing*, Silver Burdett and Co., New York.
    *Taylor, *Group Voice*, G. Schirmer, Inc., New York.
    *Witherspoon, *Twenty Lessons in Singing*, G. Schirmer, Inc., New York.

Voice Culture and Diction:
    *Ellis, *Pronunciation for Singers*, Curwen, London.
    Fillebrown, *Resonance in Singing and Speaking*, Ditson, Boston.
    Muckey, *The Natural Method of Voice Production*, Scribner, New York.
    *Proschowsky, *The Way to Sing*, Birchard, Boston.
    *Rogers, *Clearcut Speech in Song*, Ditson, Boston.
    *Rogers, *English Diction*, Mrs. C. K. Rogers, Boston.
    *Waters, *Song, the Substance of Vocal Study*, G. Schirmer, Inc., New York.
    Westerman, *Modern Phonetization*, Edwards Bros., Ann Arbor, Michigan.
    *Witherspoon, *Singing*, G. Schirmer, Inc., New York.

Psychology of Learning:
    Hall, *Adolescence*, Appleton, New York.
    James, *Psychology*, Henry Holt, New York.
    *Mursell, *Human Values in Music Education*, Silver Burdett, New York.
    *Mursell, *Principles of Musical Education*, Macmillan, New York.
    *Mursell and Glenn, *The Psychology of School Music Teaching*, Silver Burdett
        and Co., New York.
    Seashore, *Psychology of Musical Talent*, Silver Burdett and Co., New York.
    *Taylor, *Psychology of Singing*, Macmillan, New York.
    Thorndyke, *Educational Psychology*, Columbia University Press, New York.

*Especially recommended as supplementary reading for this chapter.

CHAPTER V

INTERPRETATION

(See also CHAPTER IV, REHEARSALS, *and* CHAPTER VII, SPECIAL REHEARSAL METHODS.)

How sour sweet music is
When time is broke and no proportion kept!
SHAKESPEARE

Good interpretation in song depends principally upon three elements: *clean-cut diction*, *adequate technique*, and *spirit* or *emotion*. Interpretation should begin with the *first* rehearsal of a composition; otherwise habits may be formed which will be difficult to break later. Several of the technical elements of interpretation —tone-quality, diction, breathing, posture, balance, and blending—have been discussed in the previous chapter on "Rehearsals". Other important elements are:

A. Tempo and Rhythm

It may be necessary in some new compositions to experiment with the tempo in order to find the most effective rate. The rate depends also upon the technical powers of the group. As a rule, *amateur groups should take tempo markings faster than indicated;* professional groups, on account of their better control of *sostenuto* and tonal nuance, may at times take tempos slower than indicated. Conductors of amateur choruses will do well to remember Dr. Thaddeus P. Giddings' advice: "If a tempo has to be incorrect, let it be fast rather than slow."

Never stop the march or movement of a song. "When the pulse stops the rhythm is dead."[17] The pulse may be quickened or retarded and the music may stop with rests or holds, but the rhythmic pulse which throbs in the consciousness must continue unbroken to the final beat. "Not that every throb should be communicated, but it should be in the consciousness of the singers and the conductor. The absence of the consciousness of pulsation is responsible for much of the dead singing that we hear."[17]

Tempo rubato, desirable in some instances, is no excuse for playing fast and loose with rhythm on the presumption that there is no fixed law in this matter. What has been borrowed must be paid back. In this respect it should be regarded as altogether different from variations in tempo such as *ritardando* or *accelerando*. *Tempo rubato* allows accent, stress, and flexibility; but, in the strict sense of its meaning, it does not alter the general speed of the fundamental tempo.

Failure of choral groups to sing intervals correctly when learning new music is, in many instances, due to a fundamental difficulty with the rhythm. If the rhythmic problems in new music are solved first, the reading of the intervals often becomes easy. Inaccuracies in rhythm should therefore be corrected immediately in the beginning rehearsals. "Consonants, remember, are rhythm-

[17]Sir Hugh Roberton, *Mixed Voice Choirs, Female Voice Choirs, Male Voice Choirs*, Paterson Sons and Co., Ltd.

54

makers, the percussive elements in singing. They fulfil the same function as tonguing, lipping, striking, and plucking in instruments."[18] *Consonants must be precise and confident if vocal music is to have rhythmic vitality.*

B. Phrasing

Although musical phrasing is generally determined by the text, there are occasional musical settings that necessitate the taking of breath at places other than those indicated by the words. Musical phrases intended to be sung on one breath should be followed carefully. Since the phrase determines the place of breathing, singers should be aware of the demands of the phrase before beginning. The musical phrase need never be sacrificed; if the group is not able to deliver the phrase on one breath, it is possible to obtain the desired effect by allowing sections or individuals within a section to take an unobtrusive catch-breath at different times. Compositions that present problems in phrasing should be marked as to breathing during the first rehearsal; it is best to establish proper breathing habits at the very beginning as it is very difficult to correct improper habits once they have become established.

Pleasing effects may sometimes be obtained by singing two phrases on one breath. This opportunity occurs most frequently on the last return of the first theme, or on the joining together of the last verse with the chorus in songs of the ballad type. However, a striking bit of phrasing merely for its own sake should never be encouraged. Unusual phrasing must always add charm to style in order to be acceptable.

Good phrasing includes more than breathing. Artistic shape, nuances of color and intensity, similarity or contrast between phrases, life of melodic line, and proper stress are necessary considerations. *It is most important that all members of the chorus make all changes of color and intensity simultaneously.*

Probably the best training in artistic phrasing can be obtained through intelligent singing of the old Italian and English motets and madrigals. The beauty and charm of this style of music depends, in particular, upon part-clarity and beauty of phrasing.

C. Dynamics and Climax

The general degree of loudness best calculated for satisfactory interpretation is marked ordinarily by the composer. In some of the choral music of the masters, however, the dynamics are not indicated by the composer; they have, in most instances, been indicated according to the best judgment of the editor. Unfortunately, that judgment is not always good. In any case, there are many small variations of loudness not marked, the observance or lack of observance of which means the difference between good and mediocre performance.

The less trained the choral group, the more necessary that the conductor indicate even the slightest shadings in dynamics. Choruses should be taught from the beginning to produce a number of degrees of tonal force and to follow carefully when these are indicated in the music or by the conductor.

[18]Sir Hugh Roberton, "Adjudicators and Adjudication", *Supervisors Service Bulletin*, May, 1934,

One of the most common and distressing faults of choral organizations is the habit of singing *pianissimo* phrases at a slower tempo than preceding phrases, a tendency which has a deadening effect upon vitality of interpretation.

There are two types of climax, the dynamic climax and the emotional climax. They may be and usually are achieved at the same time. *Pianissimi are much more effective in some instances for emotional climaxes than are fortissimi. Most directors miss very fine interpretative effects through not realizing the degree of* pianissimo *which choral groups are capable of achieving.*

A *fortissimo* climax is frequently the danger-point, straining the technique of the group and spoiling the finish of an otherwise good interpretation. *A fortissimo should never be louder than the group can sustain with good vocal quality, proper chordal balance, and sure intonation.* The secret of obtaining a good *fortissimo* climax lies not in striving to obtain a louder tone, but rather in obtaining a softer tone *before* the climax. "A tone attacked with a *fortissimo* should always be the loudest, if it cannot be maintained, at the *release*. In this connection, it might be well to emphasize the fact that a *crescendo* cannot be obtained from a *fortissimo*. This is a truism which many conductors fail to understand."[19]

Dynamic climaxes are obtained very largely by a skilful working-up of tonal intensity, although height of pitch, climax of meaning in the text, and force of diction are important contributing factors. The director may often wisely disregard dynamic markings in order to favor the technical powers of his group. After all, dynamics in music, in so far as they relate to effective interpretation, are a relative matter of contrast, varying with the powers of each singer and each choral group. The objective, in any case, should be to obtain pleasing contrasts and to avoid the weakening effect of too many climaxes. *One major dynamic climax is enough in most songs or short choral compositions.*

D.   Attack and Unanimity

(Note: See also Chapter I, "The Preliminary Beat and Attack", p. 7)

A confident, inspiring start wins half the battle. Prerequisites for the ideal attack are: Breath properly taken and suspended, a feeling of bodily ease, and a correct conception of pitch, word, dynamics, and vowel color. Choruses often have difficulty in making a good attack if the first word of the phrase starts with a consonant. In such cases the consonant should be *clearly* but *quickly* articulated in order to arrive as soon as possible at the singing tone, the vowel.

Much of the charm in listening to choruses depends upon unanimity. Unanimity requires precision of attack, release, accent, dynamics, tempo, phrasing, and sureness of diction, pitch, rhythm, and interpretative effects.

E.   Pitch or Intonation

The greatest aids to intonation are intelligent *listening* and *tuning* the voice to the general ensemble. It is better in unaccompanied singing to be in tune harmonically rather than to stick conspicuously to the right pitch. Although deviations from the pitch are at best deplorable, there is such a thing as artistic flatting or sharping.

[19]Archie N. Jones, "The Basis of Choral Interpretation", *The Supervisors Service Bulletin*, Jan., 1932.

When concentration is overly intense and the chorus is nervous, as in a contest, the pitch tends to rise; when concentration is weak and the chorus tired, bored, or inattentive, the pitch tends to fall. Flatting is by far the more common. *It is chiefly due to inertia*, to a lack of physical and mental alertness. There may be one or several reasons for a chorus's singing off pitch. An able director is quick at analyzing the reasons and is prepared with a method of correcting the difficulty.

Singing off pitch may be traced to one or several of the following causes:

1. Poor diction. Much of the lifeless, mechanical, and off-pitch singing we hear is due to careless diction. "Whenever your pitch is waning, vitalize your words."[20]

2. Poor ventilation and improper temperature. Never sing in a stuffy, overheated, or smoky room if it can be avoided.

3. Failure to think of beginning consonants on the same pitch as the vowel which follows. This fault is responsible for much of the "crooning" slurs, poor *sostenuto*, and flatting that one hears.

4. Incorrect posture. It is most difficult to sing on pitch if the head is out of balance or the body allowed to slump or sag.

5. Poor breath support. This is most frequent on long phrases and in *pianissimo* passages. Soft passages require a greater concentration upon breath support and clear diction than do loud passages.

6. Lack of attention to music or conductor. This failure to concentrate is sometimes due to physical fatigue but is often the result of plain mental laziness.

7. Tempo too slow and "draggy". Most conductors have a tendency to take tempos too slowly and they thus increase the chances for flatting.

8. Lack of familiarity with the music. Inadequate memorization results in insecurity of breath support, poor diction, poor tone quality, dragging tempo, and sagging of pitch. It is always easier to maintain pitch after the music is memorized.

9. Lack of concentration on the pitch. Insist on the habit of striving to hear the entire musical phrase before the attack. Intervals must be thought correctly before they can be sung correctly. *Think of approaching the tone from above, rather than from below.* The practice of singing a neutral syllable or humming quietly allows greater concentration upon melodic line and sometimes clarifies the sound of difficult intervals. Courage in thinking ahead must be established; the director must discourage the habit common among untrained singers of waiting until someone else hits the pitch before attacking the tone.

10. Failure to keep a clear and vital conception of the tone in low registers and in *pianissimo* passages. Flatting results unless singers maintain a conception of resonant, brilliant, and freely produced vowels, accompanied at the same time by clean-cut articulation of consonants.

11. Fatigue of the vocal organs, or improper vocalization. Fatigue is due either to overuse or to misuse of the voice. It is difficult in the ordinary length of a rehearsal to fatigue a voice that is properly produced. The director must, however, be careful about long practice periods in difficult

[20]Sir Hugh Roberton, "Adjudicators and Adjudication", *Music Supervisors Journal*, May, 1934.

ranges. The tone quality of a club and its ability to sing on pitch can be seriously impaired if rehearsals are made too strenuously fatiguing. Attempts to sing too loudly in the extreme upper and lower registers is a common fault. No section should be forced beyond its limit of easy and pleasing *forte* in order to balance the power of other sections; the adjustment must be in the other direction. The habitual singing of vowels with a breathy, dark, or sombre quality is a frequent cause of flatting. This fault is closely allied with singing too "big", meaning, for example, a tenor who thinks like a baritone and attempts to sing with the characteristic quality and large vowel form of that voice. The natural and individual clarity of the voice must be retained.

12. Failure of the low voices to keep solidly in tune. If the bass (low) part is kept in tune, the other parts are not likely to fall from pitch and will recover if they do so. Low notes should not be forced beyond an easy *forte* and should be thought bright and high in order to counteract the tendency to sing breathily, or to darken and flat the tone. It is extremely dangerous to ask for a big *fortissimo* in low registers unless the low voices are powerful and mature. Descending scalewise passages and upward leaps of a fourth are progressions most liable to be flatted by low voices.

13. Registers too high or too low for sustained practice. In order to avoid fatigue of the voice in rehearsals, it is sometimes best to transpose momentarily to an easier key. In part-rehearsals, high parts may be dropped an octave until learned. Extremely low parts for second bass or low alto may likewise be transposed upwards or sung an octave higher during the process of learning the music.

14. Failure to observe proper breathing-places, with a consequent lack of breath to sustain phrases properly to the end. The whole of the musical phrase should be in the consciousness of the singer when taking breath. Phrases which present problems in breathing should be marked carefully in beginning rehearsals.

15. Wrong classification and placement of voices. A baritone among tenors, even though he can reach the high pitches, will have a tendency to pull the tenors down, on account of singing with a "bigger" and darker vowel-quality. This trouble will not arise if voices are classified properly and assigned to sections according to the characteristic timbre and not the possible range of the voice. It usually brightens the ensemble and improves the pitch to step a few voices down, *e.g.*, using first tenors on second tenor parts or first sopranos on second soprano parts, but the opposite procedure is nearly sure to result unsatisfactorily. In the average school system there are an adequate number of all types of voices; *the problem of the director is to find them and develop them*. Failure to develop a good chorus or glee club is the fault either of the director or of the organization of the particular school and not of a genuine lack of material.

16. Difficult intervals or progressions. Intervals most likely to give difficulty are: Intervals in extreme ranges, descending half steps, raised ascending tones, augmented seconds, ascending fourths, and all intervals involving chromatically altered tones. In the singing of chords, the offending interval is usually the *third*. The conductor may quickly detect and overcome

such difficulties if he carefully analyzes each part and notes intervals or progressions most likely to give trouble.

17. Repeated tones. It is difficult to sustain the pitch in *legato* singing on repeated tones. If the singers will think of the tone as gradually ascending with each attack slightly higher in pitch, most of the difficulty in singing sustained repeated tones will be overcome.

18. Chronic "flat-ers" or "sharp-ers". The problem may be solved by placing the offender in front of or between members who sing with assurance and accuracy. However, such voices sometimes need psychological help outside the rehearsal room. If they do not improve with proper training, they must be removed. One voice out of tune is sufficient to spoil the pleasure of the remainder of the club, by marring the beauty of ensemble and perhaps dragging the whole chorus off pitch. Singers who have colds, sore throats, or bronchial trouble are usually unreliable in their control of pitch. It is dangerous to risk using a chronic "flat-er" or "sharp-er" in a contest.

19. Nervousness or tenseness. High voices have a habit of sharping when nervous or tense. The remedy is found in concentrating the attention on the music, gaining more experience by singing in public, and strengthening confidence through growth in technical skill. However, excitement is frequently the spur needed to cause clubs that habitually sing flat in rehearsal to sing on pitch in concert.

20. Growing "stale". This is usually the result of too much concentrated practice on one number. Drop the piece for a while, change the key, or radically change the method of rehearsal. Experienced directors are familiar with the fact that changing the notated pitch of an *a cappella* number frequently causes a group to sing on pitch. This is particularly true after long rehearsals on one number.

F. Spirit or Emotion

Clayton W. Old, President of the Associated Glee Clubs of America, states: "Technically many of our glee clubs do marvelous work. In attack, tone-quality, diction, phrasing, and rhythm, little is lacking. But when technical perfection is attained, it is after all but a means to an end." Singing must be an emotional expression if it is to be worth while, and choral singing can only be great when there is understanding, sympathy, and unanimity in expressing emotions. *Singing must intensify the meaning of the spoken text or it has no excuse for existing.* The greatest pleasure in singing, to both the performer and the listener, comes when every singer is in sympathy with the spirit of the text and is thrilled emotionally by a unified vocal expression of that feeling. "When the music is so wedded to and woven out of the thought and meaning of the poem that the singers can catch the great emotional and musical meaning, it is only a short step from singing that is commonplace to singing that is unusual in its breadth and beauty."[21]

The great distinction and charm in the singing of Negro choruses lies very little in the supposed superiority of their voices, but is the direct result of a lack of self-consciousness, a naturalness of expression, and an earnest emotional feeling.

[21]Harper C. Maybee, "The Soul of the Vocal Ensemble", *The Supervisors Service Bulletin*, March, 1933.

Anglo-Saxons must strive for these qualities which the Negro seems to possess by nature.

Self-consciousness is best eliminated by centering attention on the message of the music, by losing oneself in an earnest attempt to tell its story. In order to do this one must concentrate his thoughts on the text and its emotional meaning. "Whenever singing is rich in emotional power, it is significant in diction."[22]

We must not only understand the meaning of the text but be emotionally stirred by its mood. The general mood of a song should be felt before a note is sung. The reading and discussion of the text during rehearsals will help to establish a feeling for mood. However, it is the responsibility of the conductor further to inspire his group through facial expression, posture, and manner of conducting. This practice, like all good things, can be overdone to the extent that it becomes undignified, sentimental, or even funny. Emotionalism controlled is a great asset, while emotionalism uncontrolled may interfere with techniques necessary for satisfactory performance and thus defeat its purpose.

It must not be forgotten that the most moving interpretations in song are possible only through the presence of adequate technique, the servant of expression. However, if too much time is spent on technical detail and not enough on singing the music as a whole in an attempt to discover its spirit and charm, then rehearsals become a series of tiresome drills, pleasure and enthusiasm wane, and the chorus suffers, or perhaps fails, because of lack of interest. "Always be more concerned with the matter of what you are doing than with the manner of doing it."[22] In choral music we may well encourage the attitude that music is a beautiful vehicle for the conveyance of ideas and emotions expressed by the words, but that if the vehicle is halted when its journey is obstructed by technique, then the message cannot arrive.

"Remember, finally, that an act of art is an act of love."[22]

Reference List for Further Reading

(Note references regarding Methods at end of Chapter IV, especially recommended, and in addition:)

Carrit, *Theory of Beauty*, Macmillan, New York.
*Drew, *Song Interpretation*, Oxford University Press, London.
Fellowes, *English Madrigal*, Oxford University Press, London.
*Guilbert, *How to Sing a Song*, Macmillan, New York.
Hanslick, *The Beautiful in Music*, Novello, New York.
Jeppeson, *Style of Palestrina and the Dissonance*, Oxford University Press, London.
Parker, *Principles of Aesthetics*, Silver Burdett, New York.
*Parry, *Style in Musical Art*, Macmillan, New York.
Schoen, *The Effects of Music*, Paul, London.
*Scott, *Madrigal Singing*, Oxford University Press, London.

*Especially recommended as supplementary reading for this chapter.

[22]Sir Hugh Roberton, "Adjudication and Adjudicators", *Music Supervisors Journal*, May, 1934.

CHAPTER VI

CONCERT TOURS AND RADIO BROADCASTING

Only a small percent of us have any valid excuse for appearing as soloists, but in having our part in concerted singing we possess enormous possibilities.

D. A. CLIPPINGER*

Many college clubs have a habit of making yearly concert tours through the territory from which the school draws its student body. A few more ambitious clubs have even travelled through Europe. Most concerts of the average club are near home and can be reached after school hours or over the week-end. Extensive tours of one to four weeks or longer must usually be arranged during vacations. However, some clubs take yearly concert trips during school time. Concert trips which cause the members to be absent from a considerable number of classes and make it difficult or impossible for students to make up all the work missed are, naturally, disadvantageous. In spite of this drawback, many educators are convinced that the contacts and experiences of glee-club or chorus members while on tour are of far more educational value than the classwork missed at the time. Objections to making concert tours during school time are lessened where the policy is maintained of allowing only members of high academic standing to make the trips.

A.   Value of Well-Conducted Concert Tours

1.   Value to the school: The school receives much favorable advertising of a nature that tends to attract not only a greater number but also a better type of students. Through glee club tours the school establishes a more intimate and personal contact with the people in its territory. Glee club members are, as a rule, the more refined and intellectual members of the student body. When they are brought in contact with people in outside districts through giving concerts, being entertained in homes, *etc.*, the effect is usually the creation of a friendly attitude towards the school the glee club represents. Some school executives capitalize the advertising value of their choral groups and arrange the concert itinerary with this in mind. However, if the advertising is to be advantageous rather than detrimental to the school, the glee club must be well disciplined and well behaved. Rules regarding behavior on concert tours should be thoroughly understood by the members and strictly enforced. Any member who proves difficult or unmanageable should be sent home immediately.

2.   Value to the community: In small communities a good glee-club concert is often the most enjoyable musical event of the year. Both the standard of performance and the type of music chosen have improved to the extent that it can now be said truthfully that the best school glee clubs and choruses

*"On Becoming Musical", in the Yearbook of the 1933 Music Supervisors National Conference.

present programs of a high musical quality. Through sponsoring a glee-club concert, civic organizations, churches, societies, *etc.*, are often able to raise needed funds for their own organization. Young people are quite frequently influenced to attend college as a result of hearing a glee-club concert and meeting members of the club.

3. Value to chorus members: The experiences and contacts made through travelling and associating with a congenial group are extremely valuable in building character and personality. Timid, backward members "come out of it" because of their experiences on concert tours. Meeting other people in new communities, forming new friendships, seeing different sights, observing different customs and practices, assimilating new ideas—all have refining, socializing, cultural, and educational value for the individual. Intimate friendships, bonds of comradeship, and outside contacts are formed that continue on through school and after-life. No college graduate has fonder memories of school days than does the glee club member of his experiences on concert tours. The musical and practical experiences thus obtained are of special benefit to those who expect to make music their profession.

B. Advertising

A concert tour must be well advertised if it is to be successful. The advertising manager, with the advice and assistance of the director, should be responsible for the advertising material and tickets to be sent to communities giving the concerts. All the preliminary work in preparing this material must be done long before, and the advertising must be sent in plenty of time—usually two weeks or more preceding the concert—to be most effective. This is an exacting job that requires intelligence, good judgment, and efficiency. The following methods of advertising concerts are suggested:

1. Window Cards. Pasteboard window cards may show pictures of the club, director, and soloists, and give the place, date, and price of the concert. Cards may be of varying size: the larger the card the greater the expense of cuts, printing, and material, but the more effective the advertising. Cards should be put on bulletin boards, in shop windows, and in other conspicuous places about two weeks preceding the concert. When advertising material is sent to an organization sponsoring a concert, suggestions should be included as to the most effective manner of using the material.

2. Circulars. Circulars may contain pictures of the club, director, soloists, quartet, *etc.*, together with information about their training and experience. Remarks concerning either past or present concert programs by the group and information about the college and its music department are often included. Circulars should be sent to influential people and those most likely to be interested; they may also be given out with the programs at the concert. Sometimes it is better to combine the concert program and circular than to print and issue the two separately. It is often a good policy to invite several of the most influential citizens in a community to act as patrons or patronesses for the concert.

3. Bill-Board Posters. Bill-board advertising may perhaps yield financial returns when a concert is to be given in a large hall in a city.

4. Newspaper Advertising. Most local newspapers will be glad to print the program and give an account of the coming concert as a news feature. Circulars, programs, and former complimentary newspaper write-ups should be sent to the editor as a basis for information. It is tactful also to send two or more complimentary tickets.
5. Motion-Picture Slides. Slides giving the place, date, and price of the concert may prove effective advertising when shown in local moving-picture theatres.
6. Short Musical Programs. Some clubs, while on tour, make a practice of appearing in school assemblies to sing one or two short numbers on the day of the concert. Sometimes only a soloist or a quartet representing the club will appear. This practice attracts many pupils and parents who otherwise would not attend the concert.

C. Advance Contracts

Ordinarily the director or advertising manager makes the contracts. However, it is frequently better to allow a student living in the community in which a concert is desired to make the arrangements. The one who "signs up" the club for the concerts should be a good salesman and, if possible, well known in the community. He should be acquainted with the club and its program and have sufficient advertising material with him to convince the possible sponsors of the desirability of the concert.

Some clubs have two territories for regular concert trips; each territory is visited every other year. Tentative arrangements are made after each concert for another to be given in two years at the same place. Names and addresses of organizations or individuals most likely to sponsor concerts should be kept in a permanent file for future reference. When writing to a new locality concerning concert dates, it is advisable to consider such organizations as schools (senior classes, parent-teacher associations, music organizations), churches and civic organizations (Y. M. C. A., Y. W. C. A., Chamber of Commerce, music clubs, business houses, lodges, and women's clubs).

The terms of the contract should be definitely understood by both parties. Contracts for clubs on tour should cover the following points:
1. Arrangements concerning money guarantee (or the percentage of profit to go to the club) and the date and time of the concert. (The sooner the date of the concert is advertised, the less probability of conflict with other events.)
2. Agreement concerning room and board for the club.
3. Provision for a suitable concert hall and a place to rehearse, if desired. (Clubs usually need to rehearse during concert tours.)
4. Provision for a good piano, properly tuned. A poor piano can ruin a concert.
5. An understanding regarding the advertising material to be furnished—posters, circulars, programs, tickets, *etc*.

Some clubs prefer to make a flat-rate contract wherever they go; others like a percentage; many prefer a flat rate plus a percentage of the profits. The latter plan has several good features: first, organizations usually work harder to advertise a concert when they have to guarantee a definite amount; second, the glee club is certain of the amount of the guarantee at least; third, the club realizes more profit from large audiences when there is a split of the proceeds. It is advisable to have a common policy for all contracts. However, it is necessary sometimes to alter the contract to accommodate the traditional practices of a community or school sponsoring the concert.

The contract price for concerts depends upon several factors: precedent, popularity of the club, traveling expenses, and occasion (*e.g.*, short programs for school assemblies, banquets, *etc.*, may well be given at reduced fees). Small clubs can afford to charge much less than large clubs. When glee club members are guaranteed entertainment in private homes, the contract can be made for a nominal sum. When board and room are furnished by the sponsors, clubs have travelled and made expenses on receipts as low as $35.00 to $75.00 per concert.

D. Travelling Expenses

Large clubs are liable to suffer a loss from extensive tours unless the tours are well advertised, large receipts are assured, and expenses are cut to a minimum. It is often very difficult to secure favorable places and suitable terms for contracts. especially when concerts must be given each day in order to make the trip financially possible. Before making the contracts for a concert tour, the approximate cost of travel and living expenses should be estimated carefully. Glee-club members are usually willing to pay for their meals in order to make the trip, but they should not be expected to pay for their rooms. The average club cannot make a concert tour unless it can at least break even on expenses and receipts. The following suggestions may help those who need to economize:

1. Reduce traveling and other expenses. Club members or patrons are sometimes willing to drive their own cars on cross-country trips if expenses are paid. Six or seven double-seated cars will carry a club of average size. This number of cars can often be secured for short trips. Usually, buses can be chartered at a reasonable rate for extended trips. One large modern bus is sufficient for the average chorus. Glee clubs that come from great distances to participate in the National Men's Glee Club Contest charter special railroad coaches at a rate far less than regular fare. Traveling expenses can be reduced by arranging the concert itinerary so that there are only short trips between concerts. Some clubs make a practice of giving a concert every night and, in addition, one or more concerts at school assemblies while on the road during the day. A small admission fee of 10 cents to 25 cents is usually charged for these short assembly concerts. The receipts from this source may amount to enough to pay transportation expenses.

2. Raise the guarantee price of concerts. This can often be done if the club is popular and has been a financial success to the organization sponsoring previous programs.

3. Reduce living expenses. In smaller communities or towns it is often favorable to both parties of the contract to have room and board for club members provided at private homes. This allows all money realized in concerts to be applied to transportation expenses. Reduced rates for hotel rooms and meals can usually be obtained if arranged-for previously.

4. Take fewer members on trips. When only one trip is made, this practice is obviously unfair to deserving members left at home. It is a last resort, for as many should be taken as possible. But some clubs travel with as few

as sixteen members.   Attendance at rehearsals and academic standing may
be a convenient basis for cutting the membership, with possible disciplinary
benefits.   It is sometimes practical to make two or three short concert trips,
each of several days' duration, allowing every member to take at least one
trip.

E. Uniforms and Choir Robes

Uniforms or robes not only add greatly to the appearance of a chorus
but actually have a favorable psychological influence upon its ability to give
unified interpretations.   Uniforms have the power of subordinating the personality of the individual and emphasizing the unity of the group.   However, uncomfortable or conspicuous costumes should be avoided.   A uniform may be
conspicuous because it is ugly, ill-fitting, too florid, ornate, or elaborate.   A quiet
and dignified color-scheme is preferable.   The tuxedo has been pretty generally
adopted as the traditional glee club uniform for young men.   Some adult male
choruses still cling to the full-dress suit.   A good informal outfit for warm weather
consists of white flannel or white duck trousers, a soft white shirt, and a light-
weight dark-colored coat.   Women's glee clubs have no standard uniform; individual clubs adopt a common type of costume, or at least dress with a harmoniz-
ing color scheme.

There seems to be no generally accepted standard regarding costumes for
mixed choruses.   Some directors prefer that both men and women have a similar
type of costume; others prefer a contrast in color-scheme between the two.   Robes
of a uniform color are usually preferred for the *a cappella* choir.   Uniforms or
robes may be purchased in lots at very great savings.   In some localities, it is
even possible to borrow enough robes from churches.   However, it is preferable
either to purchase or to make the robes in order that they may be uniform and
readily available when needed.   Robes or uniforms should be the property of the
school or of the choral organization, and should be carefully cleaned and stored
in a safe place until issued to individual chorus members.

Measurements for a robe may be made as follows:
1. Measure the arm-length from the cuff of the extended arm to the armpit.
2. Measure the expanded chest.
3. Estimate the length by subtracting fifteen inches from the student's height.
    The remaining length will be proper for the robe, giving a five-inch clearance
    of the floor.

F. Radio Broadcasting*

School groups and amateur choruses have increasing opportunity to be heard
over the radio.   The present-day possibilities for being heard, not only in local
programs but also over national chains before vast audiences, places an added
responsibility upon the director of school groups to be well prepared for this work.
It also presents an opportunity, in favorable situations, for the conductor of fine
choral organizations to make his chorus and himself locally and perhaps nationally
famous.

*Two articles by Ernest La Prade in the Music Educators National Conference Yearbook of 1938
are especially recommended as references: "The Broadcaster and Music Education", p. 210, and "Problems
in Microphone Placement", p. 226.

There are no alibis over the air.   To the listener the music is either interesting enough to listen to, or it isn't.   School groups must be good enough to compete with professional groups in order to obtain a hearing.   The task is not hopeless. Professional groups must prepare many programs during the season.   Therefore, individual programs are frequently prepared on short order without the advantage of thorough consideration and preparation which the amateur group may enjoy.

"Participation in the radio program presents us with a challenge to endeavor in a new field.   So suddenly has the challenge come upon us that few directors have been prepared to meet it. . . . The first and most important thing to remember is that when school musicians broadcast there is only one appeal to the listening public—that through the ear. . . . In the ordinary concert, most any audience will listen to children because the very sight of youngsters on the platform produces a friendly, sympathetic attitude. . . .

"It must be remembered that radio reception and broadcasting are, at best, imperfect.   What the listener hears on the receiving set is by no means the same thing that his ears would receive if he were in a concert hall.   Inaccuracies in pitch, lack of tonal balance among performers, peculiarities of tone production, may be either buried or unheard in public audition, but in a broadcast all tonal discrepancies are unerringly picked up and often magnified. . . .

"An *a cappella* choir should remain an *a cappella* choir, singing the music it carefully rehearses in a manner befitting that music. . . . A difficult number may well be used in rehearsals because of its educational value.   If the director then decides to program it because it will look well in print, regardless of how it must sound, he is misguided; but if he then yields to vanity and performs it over the air, he is just plain silly. . . .   Incidentally, *a cappella* choirs will do well to perform occasionally some light and frivolous number which is far removed from early church music.   On the air, a little early church music goes a long way and should be reserved for Christmas, Easter, and other seasons when people's minds are naturally fixed on religious matters."[23]

The choral director will do well to keep the following dozen points in mind when broadcasting over the radio:

1.   A radio program must be entertaining to be successful.

   (Note: This requirement excludes only a certain type of contrapuntal and classical music.   The very best choral music is entertaining *if properly interpreted*.)

2.   The program should be accurately timed, item after item, and be well arranged from the standpoint of variety and interest.
3.   The director should know what to do if, in spite of all precautions, something happens to cause the planned program to run over or under the scheduled time limit.
4.   Take no chance on faulty memories.   Provide music for those who do not know their parts thoroughly.
5.   Either write your own continuity or give suggestions you wish included to the announcer of the station who arranges the continuity.   Let someone else do the announcing, unless tests have proved that you have a good radio speaking voice.

[23]John W. Beattie, "School Music on the Air", *Music Educators Journal*, November, 1934.

6. Send a list of the numbers you intend to broadcast, including title, composer or arranger, and publisher, to the manager of the station from which the broadcast is to be made. Send this information in plenty of time for the broadcasting company to obtain permission to perform the numbers if they do not already have the legal right. Copyright laws are very strict in this respect, and it is possible that some numbers may have to be omitted if the terms of the owners of the copyright are not met by the broadcasting company.

7. Prepare your group for a successful broadcast by arranging for a rehearsal time in the studio, when matters of grouping, position of the microphone or microphones, and various technical effects may be satisfactorily adjusted by experimentation.

8. Warn your group about disturbing noises, such as the rattling of turning pages, shuffling of feet, coughing, labored breathing, *etc.* The performance should sound relatively effortless.

9. Remember that the voices which are nearest the microphone will "take" best. Select a balance of your best voices and arrange them near the microphone. A small group of select voices will usually sound better over the air than a large group. The microphone, although improved, remains kind to the small group and unjust to the mass qualities of a large chorus. The larger the group, the more difficult to obtain a realistic transmission of its vocal effects. Large choruses broadcasting in small rooms may find that two or more balanced microphones are preferable to one. Mechanical improvements are being made continually, but for large choruses there is still much to be desired in respect of realism of effect and clarity of diction.

10. If you do your own announcing, be natural and cheerful, never pedantic or ponderous. The radio fan cannot be compelled to subject himself to unnecessary punishment.

11. Remember that enunciation, especially that of percussive consonants, must be even more clear over the air than in concert. The radio audience cannot guess at the words through reading the lips of the singers; articulation must be clean-cut.

12. Avoid over-difficult, contrapuntally involved, or over-long compositions. A variety of well chosen short numbers is superior in holding a radio audience. Do nothing that is not well within the technical ability of all the participants. The microphone is unfailing in emphasizing technical insecurities, poor intonation, and tonal peculiarities.

CHAPTER VII

CONTESTS AND FESTIVALS

Always be more concerned with the matter of what you are doing than with the manner of doing it. In other words, having learned the notes and the time and the general run of the piece, forget them and go out for the music; for notes are not music any more than ribs are a man.

SIR HUGH ROBERTON*

A. Adjudication and Contest Procedures

The value of contests in promoting the spread of choral singing in the United States has been referred to in the preface to this volume. I shall endeavor to explain some features of three outstanding glee-club contests and festivals, in the belief that such information may prove of value to those organizing other contests and to directors whose groups are participating in contests.

The Intercollegiate Musical Council, Inc., 119 West 57th St., New York City, sponsors two contests: a national contest for college men's-glee-clubs and a contest for boys of high-school age in preparatory schools. The Associated Glee Clubs of America, 1 Parade Place, Brooklyn, N. Y., promotes a triennial meet-convention and prize competition for community men's-glee-clubs. Further information concerning contests and membership in these organizations may be obtained by writing to the above addresses.

In the national contest for college men's-glee-clubs, each club sings three numbers in competition:

1. A required prize-song, to be sung unaccompanied, counting 50% out of a total of 100% for all three songs.
2. A choice-song, to be sung unaccompanied, counting 30%.
3. A school-song, counting 20%.

In addition, each club learns one or more numbers which all clubs sing together.

The Inter-Preparatory-School Contest for boys of high school age is conducted in similar fashion. However, to encourage glee clubs to learn more songs of a better type and to curb undue concentration on the three contest numbers, four prize-songs are designated at the beginning of the year; a month before the contest two of these are eliminated by lot; and on the day of the contest one of the remaining two songs is chosen as the prize-song for the contest. The three prize numbers that were eliminated are sung, however, by all clubs in ensemble. In the Inter-Preparatory-School Contest, the prize-song counts 60% and the choice-song 40%, while the school-song, although sung, is not graded. A special prize is given for the best school-song—an attempt to encourage the composition and adoption of better school-songs.

"There are usually three judges, chosen for outstanding musical ability and experience, who mark independently and do not discuss their musical opinions

*"Adjudicators and Adjudication", *Music Supervisors' Journal*, May, 1934.

during the contest. The points of judgment are: Pitch, tone-quality, diction, ensemble, and interpretation—20% for each, totaling a possible 100 points. Each club sings three times—prize-song, choice-song, and school-song respectively. The final judgment therefore is a matter of mathematical calculation, arrived at by totaling the scores of the three judges on each song and dividing by three, to arrive at the average total of each song. To arrive at the grand total, the relative importance of the prize-song, the choice-song, and the school-song is figured out, and the club emerging with the largest score is the winner."[24]

1. Contest Scoring Sheets:

Reproductions of the scoring sheets used by the judges in the Intercollegiate Contest and in the Associated Glee Clubs of America are given on ensuing pages. (These two illustrations indicate that even experts are not entirely agreed as to the relative importance of the different points in scoring.)

2. Festival Rating Sheets:

A Festival Rating Sheet that has also proved satisfactory to both adjudicators and participants is given on a page following the reproductions of scoring sheets used by the Intercollegiate Musical Council and the Associated Glee Clubs of America. Adjudicators should be given the following directions in the use of this rating sheet:

"The enclosed Festival Rating Sheet has been evolved to save you time, to help point your thinking, and to secure greater uniformity of results in adjudication. If you are pressed for time, use the numbers 1, 2, 3, 4, and 5 instead of the terms Excellent, Superior, *etc.* Plus and minus signs may be used if you choose. *Please be sure to fill in the 'General Estimation of Performance' and the four main headings under 'Detailed Estimation of Performance.'*

"Fill in as much of the details under the four general headings as you care to, or as much as time will allow. You may use your preference in regard to using the indicated rating scale here or in writing in other remarks after the detailed headings. Endeavor to make criticisms as constructive as possible."

It is suggested that four judges be used, if possible, each judge giving his "General Estimation of Performance" but thereafter concentrating on just one section of the "Detailed Estimation of Performance". One judge should be selected to act as chairman and to make general remarks in relation to the performances. Public comparison, with specific remarks regarding the merits or shortcomings of individual schools, is undesirable, since this procedure exemplifies more the contest than the festival idea. The judges' rating sheets should be given or sent later to the various participants, but it is best for their contents not to be revealed by the remarks of the chairman.

The immense value of contests in stimulating public interest and in elevating the standard both of musical taste and of finish in performance is universally recognized. There is little doubt that the contest has furnished a motivation for steady improvement in selection and performance of music. However, the prevailing opinion today among music educators seems to be

[24]From an article by Marshall Bartholomew in the March, 1928, issue of *The Keynote*, official bulletin of the Associated Glee Clubs of America.

JUDGE'S SCORE

INTERCOLLEGIATE MUSICAL COUNCIL

119 West 57th Street, New York City

Scoring of .... Contest ....

Place .... Date ....

INSTRUCTIONS — Score as indicated below. Place your mark in spaces indicated, rating on basis of ten points in each subdivision. Auditing Committee will add totals at the end of each group.

GROUP

Auditing Committee will reduce Judge's total on Choice Group to 3/5 and in College Group to 2/5. Computing tables on reverse side.	Ensemble	Interpretation	Tone	Enunciation	Pitch	JUDGE'S TOTAL	REDUCED TOTAL	No reduction is made on total for Prize Song.
Total possible points in each subdivision in this group	10	10	10	10	10	50		REMARKS
1								
2								
3								
4								
5								
6								
7								
8								
9								
10								
11								
12								
13								
14								
15								

NOTE—This sheet must be signed and given to the Auditing Committee as soon as the Group is finished.

Judge's Signature ....

Reproduction of Scoring Sheet Used by Intercollegiate Musical Council (*front*)

Reducing Table to be used by Auditing Committee in computing
proper totals for Choice and College group:

	CHOICE SONG 3/5	COLLEGE SONG 2/5
50	30	20
49	29.4	19.6
48	28.8	19.2
47	28.2	18.8
46	27.6	18.4
45	27	18
44	26.4	17.6
43	25.8	17.2
42	25.2	16.8
41	24.6	16.4
40	24	16
39	23.4	15.6
38	22.8	15.2
37	22.2	14.8
36	21.6	14.4
35	21	14
34	20.4	13.6
33	19.8	13.2
32	19.2	12.8
31	18.6	12.4
30	18	12
29	17.4	11.6
28	16.8	11.2
27	16.2	10.8
26	15.6	10.4
25	15	10
24	14.4	9.6
23	13.8	9.2
22	13.2	8.8
21	12.6	8.4
20	12	8
19	11.4	7.6
18	10.8	7.2
17	10.2	6.8
16	9.6	6.4
15	9	6
14	8.4	5.6
13	7.8	5.2
12	7.2	4.8
11	6.6	4.4
10	6	4

CHOICE SONG COUNTS — 30 POINTS
PRIZE   "   "   —50   "
COLLEGE "   "   —20   "

Reproduction of Scoring Sheet Used by Intercollegiate Musical Council (*back*)

ASSOCIATED GLEE CLUBS OF AMERICA

TRIENNIAL-MEET CONVENTION

PRIZE COMPETITION

NEW YORK CITY

ADJUDICATORS RECORD

Contestant Number_____   Class_____

_____   Test Song_____

ACCURACY (Value 25%)				QUALITY (Value 25%)				INTERPRETATION AND GENERAL EFFECT (Value 50%)		
Correctness of Pitch and Rhythm	Unanimity in Attack and Release	Correctness of Notes and Words	Consistency in following leader's direction	Beauty of Tone	Dynamic Effects	Enunciation	Tempo and Phrasing	Expression and Nuance	Spontaneity	Legitimate Individuality

_____

_____

_____

JUDGES

Reproduction of Scoring Sheet Used by Associated Glee Clubs of America

FESTIVAL RATING SHEET

Name of Participant...

Description of Gradations in Rating:
1. Excellent—(Ranks favorably with best work done anywhere.)
2. Superior—(Distinctly better than average.)
3. Average—(Usually indicates worthy work.)
4. Poor—(Not consistently good; may be good in places.)
5. Very Poor—(Consistently below standard in most respects.)

Individual Rating of Participants:

General Estimation of Performance = ...

Detailed Estimation of Performance:

I. APPEARANCE = ...
   (a) Efficiency in getting on and off the stage........................
   (b) Posture...
   (c) Neatness and uniformity of dress................................
   (d) Stage alignment or grouping....................................
   (e) Alertness, and attention to the director.......................

II. DICTION = ...
   (a) Pronunciation..
   (b) Articulation...
   (c) Enunciation...
   (d) Word emphasis...

III. ENSEMBLE = ...
   (a) Blend..
   (b) Balance...
   (c) Tone..
   (d) General pitch...
   (e) Variation from exact pitch....................................

IV. INTERPRETATION = ...
   (a) Mood..
   (b) Unanimity in attacks, releases, and effects...................
   (c) Correctness of notes and effects..............................
   (d) Vocal proficiency...
   (e) Tempo...
   (f) Phrasing..
   (g) Dynamics..
   (h) Spontaneity...
   (i) Responsiveness to director....................................
   (j) Individuality...

Note—General remarks will be found on the back of this page.

Adjudicator's Signature...........................

Suggested Scoring Sheet for a Contest or Festival

that the contest, as it has been traditionally conducted, has outlived its use-fulness in many communities. "What are now contests should become festivals, where groups from different nearby schools can hear each other perform in friendly rivalry, cheering each other to their mutual inspiration and motivation."[25] The general tendency seems to be towards retaining a rating scheme with the written comments of the judges as a corollary, but to subordinate the competitive feature.

Dissatisfaction with past results in adjudication have occurred, and numerous suggestions for betterment have been advanced. A practical suggestion is made by Ralph L. Baldwin: "It is very difficult for any judge to mark accurately all the points in a musical performance with unerring judgment and fairness. It might be a better plan to have one judge mark general ensemble and diction, a second pass upon pitch accuracy and tone quality, and the third be the arbiter of matters of interpretation. The judges might well be selected with these factors in view." There is also a strong sentiment towards obtaining just one especially eminent judge, whose non-partisanship and competence are unquestionable.

If a club has done its best but has lost the contest, it is a mistake for the director to reproach and criticize the members for the unintentional mistakes they have made. To do so will add a deeper hurt to an already keen dis-appointment and may perhaps result in a loss of interest in the glee club that will seriously injure the future of the organization. If the desire to sing the music beautifully is placed on a lower level than the desire to win, the club is very likely to be disappointed in both respects. If the reverse is true, however, there will be considerable satisfaction, even if someone else wins the contest, in knowing that they gave their best in earnest effort to create a lovely and moving interpretation.

The conductor will find that it pays to be a good sport if his club loses, and magnanimous if it wins. He should foster the same spirit among the members of the club. Never publicly criticize or object to the judges' decisions at the time they are made. Talk it over quietly with the club later on if you disagree, but avoid the common alibi of blaming it all on unreasonable or in-competent judges. Remember that they were chosen because of experience and eminence in their profession, and that their opinions are probably honest and as good as your own, or perhaps even better.

B. Special Rehearsal Methods

1. Selecting music: All clubs participating in a contest or festival must use the number or numbers chosen by the contest committee, regardless of whether or not these numbers are well adapted to their technical equipment. In the choice-song, however, the director has an opportunity to select a number that will reveal the powers of his club to the greatest advantage, and perhaps entirely conceal its weaknesses. Many contests are won by a wise selection of the choice-song—a selection that not only brings out the ability of the best voice sections in the club, but also is of a musical character calculated to please the judges. The ideal choice-piece is one which demonstrates most effectively

[25]Ralph M. Holmes, "The Evaluation of Musical Performance", *Music Supervisors Journal*, Nov., 1932.

all of the things which the chorus can do well, offering, at the same time, considerable contrast to the prize-song. The director who is thoroughly familiar with the powers and weaknesses of his group and is well acquainted with the best available music has the advantage.

If your club has good tenors and weak basses, select a choice-song which has an easy bass part and shows the tenors to good advantage. If the inner voices are superior to the outer voices, select a number that keeps the melody in the inner voices—in other words capitalize the strength of the best sections.

Some clubs are unfortunate in having a poor, weak, or borrowed school-song, while others struggle with poor or commonplace arrangements. One of the first duties of a choral director whose club is singing the school-song in a contest should be to determine whether the song is musically good, and *whether it is effectively arranged for contest purposes.* If the song needs arranging, the work should be done by someone who can do it well; if the song is poor or the music borrowed, perhaps someone in the school or community can be encouraged to compose a satisfactory original school-song. A number of colleges have adopted new school-songs in the last few years because contests have revealed that their song was poor, or because it was borrowed. There has been considerable agitation to eliminate the school-song from consideration in judging the winners of a contest on the ground that good clubs are often at an unfair disadvantage because of a poor school-song. However, it has been retained in college contests because it was felt that such a requirement furnished the needed stimulus to promote the composition and adoption of better school-songs.

2. **Correlation with School-Music Class-Work:** It is frequently possible and desirable to correlate the glee club or chorus with other music class-work. Individual voice pupils, vocal classes, sight-singing classes, and appreciation classes may well use contest or festival music as part of their regular study. The value of such correlation is readily apparent.

3. **Selecting Voices:** Voices must be selected with much greater care for festival and contest work than for ordinary glee club or chorus routine. Singers of exceedingly nervous temperament and those who frequently sing off pitch are dangerous elements in a contest group. A small club of select voices is much safer than a large group with several voices of doubtful dependability. The mistakes of one individual frequently spoil for the remainder of a fine club their chances of winning a contest. Individuals who sing off pitch, and those who have voices that "stick out" at times or exhibit striking peculiarity of tone quality, should be eliminated from the contest group. It is not at all uncommon for one of the best solo voices to offend the ensemble seriously by persistence in singing too loudly. The general musical effect of the club is improved by the removal of such soloists unless they can be taught to "tone down" their voices and join with the ensemble in striving for a unified blending of the voices.

Large groups may be improved by eliminating voices in a process of shifting the voices downward: *e.g.,* in men's glee clubs, only the higher first tenors sing first tenor parts, the best of the lower-voiced first tenors sing second tenor with selected second tenor voices, some of the best lower-voiced first basses sing with selected second basses.   The use of first tenors on second tenor parts and of first soprano on second soprano parts usually produces a surprising improvement in pitch, tone quality, and general ensemble. *It is especially desirable in contests that some of the best voices and some of the best musicians be assigned to the more difficult inner parts.*

4. Humming and Special Instrumental Effects: Some choral directors regard the hum as an instrument of the devil resorted to by arrangers when they do not know what else to do.   Some even assert their belief that it is injurious to the voice and difficult, even impossible, to sing with good intonation when humming.   It is true that the device of humming has been excessively and often inappropriately used by many modern arrangers.   However, anyone familiar with the work of the fine Russian choirs can testify that the hum, correctly produced in a suitable musical setting, can be very beautiful and thrilling in effect.   Neither is *properly resonated* humming injurious to the voice nor any more liable to be out of tune than a vowel.

There are three types of humming sound—the *m*, the *n*, and the *ng*. There is little difference in effect, the *n* and the *ng* being slightly more brilliant because the lips remain partly open.   In either case the hum should be *freely produced in the throat and resonated in the head*.   It should never be the thin, pinched, or choked sound often heard.   Humming is intended to produce a contrasting, instrumental-like effect, similar to that of stringed instruments.   A tonal characteristic of stringed instruments is *nasality*. The director need not fear in humming that a nasal quality of tone with an extreme amount of frontal head resonance will spoil the effect—it is appropriate and necessary to free the tone and give it dynamic vitality.   *Like the bowing of stringed instruments, the hum should usually be attacked on each new phrase with an accented "bite" to the tone.*   An inducing *h* (*hm, hn*, and *hung* or *hng*) is a valuable aid to this effect, and the hum is often so written.   The most suitable type of hum is not always indicated in the music.   However, experimentation with another type may give more satisfactory results.   The *hm* type is usually preferable.

A successful method of obtaining a free, ringing hum may be described as follows: While singing a major chord using the word "sing", instruct the chorus to sustain the *ng*, keeping the tone as free, resonant, and ringing as the vowel.   This produces the *ng* type of hum in its proper placement.   From the position of the *ng* type of tone described, the *n* is easily and correctly produced by lowering the base of the tongue and bringing the tip firmly upward against the base of the teeth; the *m* is produced by closing the lips and allowing the tongue to lie loosely in the mouth.   Another easy and successful method of teaching a resonant hum is to alternate the hum with a freely produced vowel, *e.g., ah- m- ah- m- ah- m, etc.*, keeping the tone flowing continuously from vowel to hum, and retaining the same free relaxed throat sensation throughout.   Some singers may be unsuccessful at first, but with practice they will soon learn to produce a free resonant tone from the softest *pianissimo* to a fairly good *forte*.   Encourage the chorus to develop the sensation of frontal nasal resonance to the fullest extent.   The type of humming placement described is also an excellent vocal exercise to induce more brilliant head resonance.

Modern composers and arrangers, in seeking for new expression, frequently use instrumental effects. These must be recognized when encountered, and treated instrumentally. When there is a main melodic line or solo part, it should be allowed to have prominence, while the "instrumental" parts furnish a suitable background of accompaniment.

5. Stage Grouping:

Seating and standing arrangements can often make or spoil the ensemble, affecting pitch, balance, blending, *etc*. The grouping of a chorus on the stage depends on the size and shape of the stage, the number in the chorus, and the relative strength of the voices in the several sections. It is particularly difficult to obtain good balance and blend with a large group when all singers are on floor-level; singing-stands or some system of elevating singers in the rear rows should be used. Weak sections are benefited by being placed in a prominent front- or end-position. A particularly strong voice, or a voice that for any reason is likely to stand out, should never be placed on the ends or in the front row, where it will be more prominent to both eye and ear. It is usually desirable in amateur groups to keep members of the same section, and the best voices within sections, together. As a rule, the more compact the group, the better the pitch and the ensemble. Singing on pitch can sometimes be best obtained by arranging the club in three or four rows rather than the conventional two. Whatever the seating or standing arrangement, *singers should turn so as to face the conductor, and not the audience.*

6. Stage Appearance:

The manner of coming on the stage is important, from the standpoint not only of appearance but also of musical performance. A club that comes upon the stage in a solemn, timid, slow, or "draggy" manner cannot very well be in the proper mental and emotional condition to sing well, for the way in which a person acts largely determines his emotional state. On the other hand, one can expect a creditable musical performance from a group that comes upon the stage in a confident, cheerful, and alert manner, taking their places quickly, smoothly, and accurately. A quasi-military efficiency without its obvious formalism and exact precision may well be the goal. It is well to remember that a proper start is half the battle.

If a club appears nervous or unduly tense, the director may wisely indicate through a prearranged signal that they are to relax and draw several deep breaths before starting. Some conductors prefer that their chorus sing while seated. There are good reasons, especially in long and taxing concerts of an intimate type of music, for this preference. Most conductors, however, believe that a greater range of dynamics and a more finished interpretation of dramatic music is possible in the standing position. In any case, groups should be rehearsed and accustomed to singing well in either standing or sitting position. Choruses sing with much better appearance and intonation if platforms (sometimes called "chorus-stands") are provided. A collapsible type is available, and is very desirable and useful for many purposes.

7. Lighting:

Lighting should be adequate but not brilliant or colored. Avoid the use of footlights; they create unnatural lighting, and are distressing and con-

fusing to the singers. Conductors are divided in their preference as to
house lights. Most directors prefer that the audience be in semi-darkness,
in order that attention be centered on the stage and that there be less
chance of distraction for members of the chorus.

8. Sectional Rehearsals:

Sectional rehearsals are especially important in preparing for the exact
singing which contests and festivals demand. In most clubs the less able
singers will never properly learn their parts without sectional rehearsals.
The common plan is to use the first part of the rehearsal period for sectional
rehearsals, each section meeting separately in smaller rooms, and to use the
latter part of the period for singing together those numbers that have been
practised separately. It is necessary that each section have a competent
leader. This can usually be accomplished if the director takes one section,
the student director another, the accompanist another, and the best musician
or best pianist the remaining section. It may be possible to induce other
faculty members or local musicians to take charge of a sectional rehearsal
before an important contest. The director should personally take the section
that needs the most assistance, but should hear each section alone several
times.

The purpose of part-rehearsals is to teach each section to sing its part
with the proper notes, good diction, blending, tone-quality, pitch, and musicianship throughout. The most important objective is to obtain a blending of
voices so that the whole section sounds like one big voice instead of many
separate individual voices. The piano may be used to teach a part or to
check a pitch, but should never be played along with the voices as a device
for keeping them together or preventing them from singing off pitch. *Choruses
must become independent of the piano in these respects.*

9. Special Rehearsal Technique: (See also Chapter IV, "How to Rehearse
Music", p. 39.)

Pronunciation, enunciation, and articulation should be as nearly perfect
as possible. Exercises similar to those illustrated in Chapter IV for the
improvement of breath-control, vowel-purity, pitch, blending, and balance
become an especially important part of the rehearsal. *Listen to the club at a
distance;* mistakes that would not be noticed near at hand will then become
more apparent. Ask members of the chorus and others who are invited to
the final rehearsals to give helpful suggestions and criticisms. No director
is so perfect that he cannot receive valuable ideas from others. He cannot
afford to harbor false pride or over-sensitiveness in this respect.

The objective in teaching contest music is not primarily to give the members growth of skill and independence in music reading, but rather to *teach
the music as quickly, accurately, and thoroughly as possible.* The following
suggested steps for the rehearsal of contest music are adapted to a group
whose sight-singing and general musicianship are weak; but most of the
steps are equally well adapted to the training of the most capable choral
organizations.

a. Start each rehearsal with a few minutes of carefully selected *group vocal exercises*. Strive to improve breath- and tone-control, vowel-purity, diction, pitch, blending, and balance.

b. *Introduce new music through reading and discussing the text.* Ask for discussion concerning the ideas and mood of the text. Explain words, sentences, or allusions that may be confusing.

c. *Have the chorus observe the vocal score and text as they listen.* The vocal parts may be sung by a selected few, or played on the phongraph or piano, or performed by several instruments (brass, string, or woodwind ensembles are very effective in teaching choral music, *providing the instruments play the vocal score at the pitch as written for voices*). An accompanist who can play vocal scores well is a treasure. It may be necessary for the vocal score to be reduced or rewritten before it can be played by the accompanist. This is especially true of male glee-club music, for tenor parts must be played an octave lower than they are usually written, as it is in this lower octave that they actually sound. It is of fundamental importance that the first impression the club receives of the music be a correct and pleasant one.

   After the music has been heard once, attention may be called to climaxes, changes of mood and style, dynamics, and other outstanding features. The group may well listen to the music several times as they follow their parts with both eye and ear. After several hearings they may *lightly* hum or sing along with the performers of the music. Place the entire attention here upon the melodic progression, remembering that music is learned with the head and not with the throat.

d. *Have the chorus sing the whole number through with the words.* Use the accompaniment, if necessary, with weaker groups. Try to achieve the correct tempo and observe as many of the musical markings as possible. Do not stop to correct mistakes unless the club or an essential vocal section gets completely lost. Sing again, and perhaps a third or fourth time, noting places where the part-leading or the harmony is insecure.

e. *Sing the number in large sections*, using a vowel or neutral syllable. It is unwise to break a song into small units such as single phrases, unless that is the only way to correct a mistake. The learning of intervals, melodic lines, blending, and balance of parts is accelerated if the attention is not distracted by words but can be fully concentrated upon the musical aspects. Give particular attention to the weak places revealed in the previous step, d. Chord-progressions that are particularly difficult should be sung slowly, each chord being held until mistakes in pitch, blending, and balance can be recognized and corrected. If the group has sufficient technical power to learn the music without the assistance of the piano, so much the better. However, it is sometimes desirable with particularly weak choruses to use the piano or a group of instruments to teach the difficult parts of the music. *In any case, the use of the piano should be dispensed with as soon as possible.* This rule applies in rehearsal not only to unaccompanied music but to accompanied music as well.

f. *Sing again with the words* after the music has been learned. All mistakes and weaknesses in diction should be corrected. Work for improvement in phrasing, attacks, releases, tonal colorings, dynamics, balance, and blending. All dependence on the piano should be eliminated.

g. *Practise in sectional rehearsals* for more exact part-singing. (Note: See "Sectional Rehearsals", p. 78.)

h. *Practise singing in quartets or smaller groups.* Each singer is assigned to a small group whose members can find a time that is suitable for all to rehearse. It is well for each group to choose a leader who is responsible for calling rehearsals and directing the practice. The director hears each group as frequently as possible, using this opportunity to help individuals, and to check up on those who can and those who cannot sing their parts satisfactorily. This brings considerable pressure to bear upon each member to learn his part well and is an especially valuable procedure in large glee clubs where there is competition for contest positions. It is most desirable to encourage these small groups to continue singing together on other music, as well as on that assigned. It is the duty of the choral director to encourage small ensemble singing in the school and community and to suggest suitable music. (Note: See also Chapter VIII, "Suitable Music for the Choral Library", p. 87.)

A successful method for securing good ensemble is as follows: Select a model group composed of the best voices in each section. When this group has been taught to sing the contest music satisfactorily, the remainder of the club may listen and endeavor to imitate. Members of the club are gradually added to the nucleus of the small group until all are able to obtain the desired effect.

i. *Memorize the words and the music.* This should be easy after the preceding steps. The club should be notified some time beforehand when the music is to be memorized. After that time, no music need be allowed in the hands of members except for occasional necessary reference. *The conductor, by all means, must thoroughly memorize both words and music so that complete* attention may be devoted to stimulating the club to the best interpretation of which it is capable.

j. *Sing contest numbers publicly.* Appearances in assemblies and local gatherings and on concert trips are the best possible experiences for the preparation of contest or festival music. Some clubs regularly arrange their concert tour so that they participate in a contest on the latter part of the tour. However, it is necessary to have opportunity for rehearsals during the tour in order to correct any weak features of technique or interpretation that are revealed. *Points of danger in a composition should be rehearsed until they become the best-known portions.*

It is sometimes best to have the accompanist play a difficult progression until it becomes impressed upon the ear. It may then be sung until it becomes habitually correct. Before considering the technical elements of interpretation satisfactory, the director may well question and attempt to improve any or all of the following: tempo, rhythm, word-accent, diction, phrasing, pitch, dynamics, contrast, climax, blending, and balance.

k. *Final interpretative touches.* Technique should be so well established by this time that it can be forgotten, allowing full attention to be given to refining the emotional qualities of the interpretation. A moving interpretation must project emotion, mood, and atmosphere through the medium of words and music. Suggestions from club members and others concerning improvement in the technique, interpretation, and appearance of the chorus should be carefully considered.

C. Training the Student Conductor
(Note: See also Chapter I, "The Conductor")

The National Intercollegiate Musical Council, Inc., has made a ruling that all members of college glee clubs competing in the national contests must be *bona fide* undergraduate students carrying regular college work. This ruling makes it necessary for clubs to sing without a conductor or to use a student conductor. Most of them choose the latter although they realize that it is highly improbable that a choral group will be able to rise above its conductor. This rule has been criticized by those who feel that far better musical results would be obtained by the faculty director; that an injustice is done to fine clubs in contests because of very poor student directors; and that this practice places far too much emphasis upon the ability of a single, and often inexperienced, student director and not enough upon the collective ability of the club when properly conducted.

In its favor, however, this ruling has two very important points: it has encouraged the study of directing by many college students, and has given them a much needed opportunity to develop through practice.

It is often impossible, especially in the smaller colleges, to find a student who has both experience and ability in choral conducting. The director of glee clubs in such a situation is faced with the task of finding and developing one or more student conductors to direct the club in contests. These students may, in some instances, receive all their training in conducting in the incredibly short time of one or two school-semesters of coaching by the director. Although excellent progress may sometimes be made under these conditions, we cannot expect anything but unskilled and insecure conducting. It may even be preferable to attempt training the club to sing without a conductor—an extremely difficult task for music of the type used in contests.

It is most important that the student director be carefully chosen and well trained. He should be self-reliant, confident, controlled, and free from self-consciousness, but willing to accept and act upon the suggestions of the director. A natural leader who is well liked by the club and has a slight knowledge of music is often a wiser choice for student director than one who is better equipped musically but lacks the initiative necessary for compelling leadership. The student conductor must be ambitious to learn conducting and willing to give his time to the necessary drill required for mastering the mechanics of beating time, the method of indicating attacks, releases, dynamic changes, and phrasing. He must become sensitive to the limitations and abilities of the club and efficient in controlling interpretative effects. To learn all this, even for two or three numbers, requires careful and intelligent coaching from the director and faithful practice on the part of the student.

The student conductor should take supplementary class-work in choral conducting if it is offered in the school. After being coached by the director on the specific problems of each number, the student should in imagination conduct the contest numbers many times before attempting to direct the chorus.   Progress will be more rapid if an accompanist plays the parts as the student director conducts.   However, with all the practice and study that an inexperienced student director is able to devote outside the rehearsal, it is still necessary that considerable time in the rehearsal be used for teaching him, if he is to conduct satisfactorily.   The words and music must be thoroughly memorized, and all technical features of conducting the contest numbers should become natural and mechanical reactions by the time of the contest.

In some instances, it is better to have two or three student directors in training, selecting eventually the most skilled of these by popular vote.   It is also possible, when the prize-song, choice-song, and school-song present striking contrasts of style and emotional content, to allow different students to conduct them. A student may be selected whose personality and style best fit him to conduct a particular number.

D. Conditioning

It should be impressed upon the chorus members' minds that it is not enough to start conditioning two or three days, or even a week, preceding a contest. *First-class singing demands first-class physical and mental condition from both the individual and the group.*   This can be realized only through proper training over an extended period of time.   Regular habits promoting vitality of mind and body are necessary.   Desirable habits of eating, sleeping, and exercising must be observed if the members of the club are to be in the best physical condition. Colds and sore throats are the bane of a singer's existence.   Many directors prohibit dancing during the week or two before a contest because of the danger of taking cold.

People who have habitual colds should be not pitied but censured; they are a menace to society.   Colds should be avoided like poison, for they are frequently dangerous, contagious diseases.   Doctors generally agree that the most insidious ailment that afflicts mankind is the common cold—an infection that in itself may not seem dangerous but that may cause organic weakness and serious trouble later on.

It is difficult to cure a cold once it has been contracted, although recovery may be hastened by proper treatment.   *However, colds, influenza, and many cases of hay-fever can be prevented.*   The best preventive is, of course, good physical condition. In addition, sanitary measures to clean and protect the mucous membranes of the nose and throat will assist in preventing infection in these organs.   However, *sprays and gargles should be used as preventives before the cold is caught* if they are to be truly effective.   When there is danger of infection, they should be used as a sanitary measure more regularly and religiously than the tooth-brush.

The following ten rules, if you are willing to take the trouble to observe them, will guarantee better health and enable the prevention of that distressing and objectionable disease, the "Common Cold":

1.   Avoid close contact with others suffering from colds. Avoid crowds and hot, "stuffy" rooms during epidemics.
2.   Do not use drinking glasses, dishes, or towels used by cold-sufferers.

3. Avoid long exposure to wet or cold, sudden changes of temperature, and *overeating;* and keep out of draughts. All these things lower resistance.

4. If feet or clothing get wet, change to dry shoes and stockings and garments as soon as possible. Clothes wet through with perspiration are as dangerous as if wet through by rain.

5. Exercise regularly, breathe deeply of fresh air, bathe frequently, and secure a regular and sufficient amount of sleep daily.

6. Dress sensibly—that is, suit your clothing to the weather.

7. Have infected teeth, tonsils, and adenoids removed. If you have a continuous source of infection in the nose because of an enlarged turbinate bone or a deviated septum, it is best to have it corrected by a nose specialist as soon as possible.

8. Use a good antiseptic gargle twice a day, and more frequently if you have a sore throat or a cough. A warm salt-water solution is safe and fairly effective. Do not believe advertising in connection with commercial antiseptics; instead, obtain your doctor's recommendation.

9. Clean the nasal passages with a warm salt-water solution (or any suitable gentle alkaline solution) twice a day. This may be done with a spray, a nose douche, or by "snuffing" the liquid up the nose.

10. After cleaning the nasal passages with an alkaline solution, use a *gentle* protective oil spray. Consult your doctor if in doubt, as *many highly advertised oil sprays are too strong for use as a preventive.*

Although practically everyone understands the principles of proper eating and sleeping, few people follow them. There is some misconception, however, as to what a singer's exercise should be. This depends somewhat upon the individual; but for the majority, *exercise should be exhilarating but not too violent;* such games as golf, tennis, handball, and volley-ball are good if they are not engaged in too strenuously. Deep breathing, setting-up exercises, and walks in the open air are excellent. Strenuous wrestling, boxing, basketball, football, swimming, and rigorous gym classes are often detrimental to the singer. Swimming and diving, while offering the best of exercise, have proved detrimental to many singers because water, especially strongly treated water, may irritate the mucous membrane of the nasal passages and cause congestion, and perhaps even sinus trouble.

Experts agree that a singer should be as regular in his habits as a well-trained athlete, and even more careful of his diet. Heavy and unwise eating affects the quality and control of the voice to a very noticeable extent; the abdominal muscles —which largely control breathing, and therefore singing—cannot function properly if the stomach is too full. A period of at least two hours should intervene between eating and singing. However, a person with a full stomach will usually sing better than one who has mistakenly fasted and whose energy, as a result, has been lessened and the tendency to nervousness increased.

Food should be nourishing but not too bulky: most vegetables (with the exception of potatoes and beans), eggs and toast, fish, or a small cut of roast beef are satisfactory as a diet before a contest. Sweets and excessive starches should be avoided. Water, milk, or any other beverage should be drunk sparingly before singing. Good sleep and rest are especially desirable on the night before a contest.

The chorus should be thoroughly alive and energetic before going on the stage. Avoid waiting in a hot, stuffy room, or standing for long periods before going on the stage. If the chorus members appear nervous or tense after they get on the stage, the director should signal them to take several deep breaths and relax before taking the singing position. It is a mistake to allow impassioned speeches to be made to a nervous chorus before a contest; it is better for a chorus to be too calm than worked up into a frenzy of nervous excitement. Tell them funny stories or talk to them seriously if need be, but do not excite them with a "do or die, the old school is depending on you to win" speech. Never tell a chorus that they are sure to win; tell them that they have a chance if they keep calm, follow the director, use their musical intelligence, and *confidently interpret the music.*

CHAPTER VIII

PROGRAM BUILDING AND MATERIALS

In this determination to exceed anything we have done before lies the secret of success, if it be backed by intelligent effort and the willingness to work—no matter how hard.

CAROL M. PITTS

A. Size of the Club

There is no fixed limit upon how large or how small a group may be and still call itself a glee club. However, in men's glee-club contests for colleges and high schools the minimum size of a club has been placed as low as sixteen while the maximum is usually designated as thirty-six. Community groups are frequently much larger. As a rule, smaller clubs should sing music of a quieter, more lyric and personal type. Faults will be more audible in small groups, unless the members know and interpret their music better than the larger clubs. On the other hand, smaller clubs may be the result of higher selectivity, while the conductor can also give more help and personal attention to the members, thus achieving, perhaps, a higher standard of musical excellence.

Large clubs may more safely select the more sonorous, dramatic, and *forte* type of music, but should never entirely neglect the opposite kind. Immature voices of a limited range and technique, regardless of the number in the group, should sing chiefly the more lyric and vocally less taxing type of music. Larger groups, as a rule, may do mostly *a cappella* music; but smaller, less experienced groups need to depend more on music with accompaniment.

B. Community Standard of Appreciation

The director is constantly faced with the problem of selecting a type of program which will attract patrons to a concert and send them away pleased. The likes and dislikes of an audience should affect, but never rule, the building of a concert program. The conscientious musician endeavors to elevate the public taste by introducing both old and new music which is worth while but not generally known. "In many communities the audience needs education more than the students. Such a task must be approached with great care and judgment, and with no such motive being apparent, as it would be greatly resented."[26]

C. Glee Club Standard of Appreciation and Technical Limitations

The director must not underestimate, baby, or coddle his choral groups; nevertheless he must realize that much of the music he would like to use is beyond the powers of many amateur untrained groups. Better do easy music well, rather than difficult music poorly. This does not necessarily mean that untrained groups are obliged to sing music of a low standard, for some of the finest

[26]Carol M. Pitts, "Elements of Success in Mixed Chorus Activities", *Educational Music Magazine*, Sept., 1934.

choral literature is technically of an easy grade; but it does mean that the director needs to be better acquainted with choral literature in order to be able to select music that is both of a high degree of excellence and also appropriate to the technical limitations of his group.   No number should be used in concert that is beyond a reasonably pleasing interpretation by the club.   Many of the finest choral compositions demand a degree of interpretative insight and technical skill beyond the limitations of ordinary clubs, *e.g.*, much of the best men's glee-club music is not practical for the average school club because the vocal ranges are too extreme for immature voices; the same is true of many four-part arrangements for women's voices which carry the second alto part too low.

The director should not choose the program strictly on the evidence of the club's ability as shown in the first few rehearsals.   Growth in appreciation and technical skill may be expected.   He should wisely choose some music on the assumption that, though too difficult at the beginning of the year, it will be within the eventual technical and interpretative powers of the club.   With the large amount of good music of all degrees of difficulty that is now available, there is little excuse for the director to purchase music of an unworthy character for the concert program.

D.   Selecting and Arranging the Concert Program

Careful thought and sound judgment are required in selecting and arranging a good concert program.   The comparative worth of each number and its order and relation in the group and in the program must be considered.   The more experienced conductor, with his wider knowledge of suitable materials and audience preferences, has the advantage here.   The ideal program would appeal to both the musician and the average layman; it would represent several schools of composition and maintain the interest of the listener through planned unity, tasteful variety, and constant change—change of some or all of the following elements: key, mode, tempo, meter, mood, type, style, composer, and, perhaps, language. *A concert program should seldom be over one hour in length.*   Better send an audience away anxious to hear more than allow them to become weary and surfeited.

It is perhaps easier to advise the inexperienced director what not to do rather than what *to* do in arranging the concert program:

1. Do not fail to select especially effective numbers for both the beginning and the close of a concert program; the first and last impressions are most important in shaping the total judgment of the listener.   A lovely opening invocation and a "rousing" ending-number give the program dignity and appeal.

2. Do not fail to separate ensemble groups, solos, and instrumental numbers judiciously.

3. Do not place the music most difficult to appreciate at the close of the program.

4. Do not place a number or group of numbers at the beginning of the program that taxes the strength or voices of the group too severely.

5. Do not fail to consider, at least to some extent, the preferences and standard of taste of the audience and of the chorus.   Do not make the opposite mistake, however, of underestimating the capacities of either group.   The

music chosen should be challenging to the best efforts of the chorus, and much of it should be *new and stimulating to the audience.*

6. Do not be content to be a follower; be a pioneer and a leader. Have the courage to include on the program and interpret new music which your judgment says is good rather than simply to copy numbers which some other conductor has introduced successfully.

7. Do not make a practice, when commenting on or advertising a program of the club, of magnifying the importance of the soloists instead of the ensemble; *the chief emphasis should be upon the ensemble work.*

8. Either do not make a practice of singing encores, or use only those that are somewhat in the spirit or style of the preceding music.

9. In general, do not place comic or humorous songs of a trivial nature in the same group with serious music; contrast should be striking *between* rather than *within* groups.

10. Do not leave the supervision and proof-reading of program-printing to someone else. Well-arranged, neatly spaced, and attractive printing affects the attitude of an audience to a surprising degree. A striking slogan or music quotation may well be adopted and used to head each program given by the club.

E. Choral Libraries

1. Material Now Available:

We hear less and less the formerly common opinion of instrumental musicians that there is little available choral material of high musical value practical for school and amateur groups. It is true that the market is still flooded with mediocre music and popular trash, but the wide-awake choral conductor is also aware that there is a large and constantly increasing amount of excellent music, much of it written and arranged by recognized master-musicians of the past and present.

A number of song-books for glee club and chorus have become deservedly popular, but the material in any one text, especially if it is widely used, soon becomes hackneyed for concert purposes. School clubs should have two or more good texts in their permanent library from which they may secure music for holidays, special occasions, and—to a limited extent—for concerts. However, glee clubs should never be limited to the material found only in books, for the great wealth of choral music is published only in separate octavo form. All choruses should endeavor to maintain a constantly growing library of octavo music; *the director should build his own library of single octavo copies to which he may refer each year in selecting suitable music.*

2. Suitable Music for the Choral Library:

How may we choose good music? The criteria on p. 92 represent an attempt to solve this problem. It may be well to state in this connection that most S. A. B. arrangements are considered by leading conductors to be neither practical nor musically satisfactory; they should be used, if at all, only until the chorus has developed sufficient skill to do four-part music.

Vocal music should not have to compete at a disadvantage with instrumental music. *Choral settings of works composed originally for instruments had best not be sung.* There are very few exceptions to this rule.

A cappella music is now sweeping the country, and in a way this is a good thing, because singing without accompaniment demands choirs that can really stand on their own feet musically, and much worthy music is being brought to light. There is also little doubt that there is more educational value to the individual in the singing of unaccompanied music. However, the pendulum in favor of *a cappella* music threatens to swing too far, to the neglect of the vast amount of artistic and colorful music which the composers considered most effective with accompaniment such as the piano, organ, or orchestra. After all, the great operas and oratorios, in fact the majority of the great choral works from Bach down to Honegger, have accompaniments of one form or another. *A chorus or glee club should not limit itself to either unaccompanied or accompanied music.* Let us not take the position that *a cappella* music is, *ipso facto*, superior music; let us not make the mistake of choosing poor *a cappella* music instead of good accompanied music, for *it is not the form and manner that are most important, but the spirit.*

The chorus or glee club should be, first of all, a place to gain vital musical experience. This can best be achieved through acquaintance with representative literature from all the great periods and schools, including the present. There is a prevailing tendency in the *a cappella* mixed chorus to overemphasize the use of contrapuntal music of the Old English and Italian Schools. This is perhaps more unfortunate for the listener than for the chorus, since the average person, after hearing several madrigals or motets, can distinguish little difference in other numbers from the same school. *One group of numbers of this type is enough on the concert program.* These numbers should also be chosen with unusual care if they are to be sung publicly by a *large* chorus. The "English Singers" have ably demonstrated that most of the music of the Old English Madrigal School is most charmingly presented by a small "chamber" group of six to eight performers. This is music of such an intimate nature that clarity demands a small, flexible group for ideal interpretation. It was composed for singing in the home and remains essentially "home music" —better for participation in by small, intimate groups than for the listener's consumption. This is ideal music for the small vocal ensemble now being so vigorously encouraged by music educators. It is just as reasonable to have music intended for a string quartet played by the whole string orchestra as it is to present most of the music of this school with large *a cappella* choirs. Large choruses should have the fine educational and inspirational advantage and the enlarged technical equipment that singing this type of music confers, but the experience is most fittingly gained in the rehearsal and in the small ensemble group.

Concert programs will gain in appeal without lowering their musical standards through the inclusion of more music from other schools: the modern English and American Schools (the modern English School of composers has produced lovely music and clever arrangements, ideally adapted to the potentialities of the modern many-voiced *a cappella* chorus; the present-day American School has few outstanding composers, but boasts a number of skilled arrangers); the Russian School (some of the most effective, deeply moving, and noble music in existence is now translated and conveniently arranged for school and amateur groups); the Classic School; and the Romantic School (a surprising amount of suitable choral music, some of it unaccompanied, was produced by the great composers of the Classic and Romantic Schools; much of this music is now available in good translations).

(Note: The author is aware that the foregoing observations will draw "fire" from some of the most able directors. This matter of suitable music deserves more careful investigation and further discussion by music educators.)

Should the school chorus present a yearly operetta or oratorio? That all depends on the school. If these larger works can be done without neglecting other musical experiences which may be more important, and without causing unreasonable effort on the part of the participants, well and good. It is desirable that each member of the high school glee club or chorus have at least one experience during his school life in the presentation of a larger dramatic work. The giving of a good light opera or operetta every fourth year is perhaps desirable in the average high school, but the wisdom of more frequent productions is questionable.

3. Care of the Choral Library:

A good library may soon be built up in the schools if a policy is maintained of adding several select numbers each year. Such libraries need to be carefully catalogued and well taken care of by the director and the librarian. If possible, a music filing-case should be provided. Each copy of the music to be used may be taken from this cabinet by the librarian, and assembled in separate numbered packages or folios. The music itself should be numbered so that an accurate record may be kept if it is necessary to issue music to members for practice outside rehearsals. Copy No. 1 of the music may be put in folio No. 1, *etc*.

Replacement of lost or worn-out music must be made, or the library becomes valueless. It is an excellent investment to have all music hinged at the time of purchase; the additional cost is slight in view of the ultimate benefits. School executives, music committees, and others in charge of financing the purchase of music will spend money much more cheerfully and generously if assured that an attractive and permanent library is being built up. As time passes, the usefulness of such a choral library becomes increasingly evident.

4. Financing the Purchase of Music:

Newly organized clubs must find some plan of financing the purchase of music. Some school administrators are willing to include the purchase of music for choral groups of the school as an item in the activities budget, but in many cases the director must adopt a temporary plan of financing. This can be done by borrowing—money to be paid back with receipts of concerts—or, preferably, by levying a membership fee large enough to take care of the purchase of music. Objections by pupils to purchasing their own music can be met by pointing out that the total cost of music for the whole year is no more per member than that of a small textbook for classwork. Some directors prefer this as a permanent plan, pointing out that each member is then responsible for his own music and that long waits and possible reductions in the music budget by the Board of Education are thus avoided. It is true that this plan saves the director considerable trouble, but it also prevents the building up of a useful library of which the school may be justly proud, and it may hinder some talented student from singing because of inability to pay the music fee. A combination of the two plans may prove feasible, the school purchasing all glee-club or chorus books, the members of the club paying a small fee to purchase supplementary octavo music.

PART II

Recommended Materials

EXPLANATORY REMARKS

There has been tremendous activity in the last few years among composers, arrangers, and publishers of glee-club and choral music, resulting in a constantly growing wealth of worth-while music especially appropriate for school and amateur use. The discovery, selection, grading, and cataloging of the best available music—published by many different firms and mixed with a confusing amount of poor and mediocre material as it is—is a task for which the average director has not time or energy.

This volume attempts to solve this problem for the director, listing, classifying, grading, and giving helpful comments and desirable information about much of the best and most suitable music now published for men's glee club, women's glee club, and for *a cappella* (unaccompanied) mixed chorus. All publishers were invited to submit their music to the author for consideration, and they were very generous indeed in their response.

Particular attention has been given to the listing of *music of an easy grade*—music which is well worth while artistically, and at the same time so reasonable in its demands upon range and vocal technique that immature voices and untrained groups may perform it successfully. Music of the contemporary English and American Schools and of the Russian School is generously represented. However, the author's hope is that directors will not be permanently satisfied with the music recommended here, but will continue to search on their own account for worthy material.

It is recognized that the personal tastes and preferences of any reviewer must necessarily be reflected in the type of music chosen. The author, therefore, has endeavored to lessen this tendency by applying the following criteria for selecting choral music to be recommended:

a. *Literary worth and suitability of the text*, including consideration of poetic value, clarity of idea, power of imagery, suitability for singing, and appropriateness of content.

b. *Reasonable range and difficulty of the parts*, including consideration of prohibitive extremes and pleasantness of part-leading in the individual voices.

c. *Worth of the music*, including consideration of originality, charm, taste in adaptation, usefulness, skill in arrangement, and probable permanency.

d. *Appeal to both singers and audience*, including consideration of type, mood, variety, and purpose.

The above criteria naturally eliminate the great mass of transient popular music and all other music concerning the lasting value of which there is serious doubt. However, they do not exclude choice songs of the humorous or rollicking type. The following list of music is intended primarily as a guide to the most attractive and practical music for school and amateur groups; but even the best adult groups will find that there is much material, even in the music ranked as "easy", that is fine enough musically to be included in their concert programs. The most difficult music recommended is not beyond the excellent high school or good college chorus, while all of the music marked "easy" and most of it marked "medium difficult" is within the powers of a good high school group.

KEY TO ABBREVIATIONS OF PUBLISHERS*

(Note: The abbreviations, not the names of the publishers, are in alphabetical order)

A —Augsburg Publishing House.
AM —Associated Music Publishers.
AP —Arthur P. Schmidt Co.
Ar —Edward Arnold & Co.
Au —Augener Ltd.
B —Boston Music Co.
BH —Breitkopf & Härtel.
Bo —Boosey & Co.
Bs —Bosworth & Co.
C —Carl Fischer, Inc.
CC —C. C. Birchard & Co.
CH —Chappell Harms, Inc.
D —Oliver Ditson Co.
De —H. F. Deane & Co.
E —Elkin & Co., Ltd.
EC —E. C. Schirmer Music Co.
Ed —Educational Music Bureau, Inc.
F —Harold Flammer, Inc.
Ga —Galaxy Music Corp.
GH —Gamble Hinged Music Co.
GS —G. Schirmer, Inc.
H —R. L. Huntzinger, Inc.
HF —H. T. FitzSimons Co.
Ho —Raymond A. Hoffman Co.
HM —Hall & McCreary Co.
HW —H. W. Gray Co.
J —J. Fischer & Bro.
JC —J. Curwen & Sons, Ltd.
JCh —John Church Co.
JF —John Franklin Music Co.
JK —Joseph P. Katz.
JW —J. & W. Chester, Ltd.
JWm—Joseph Williams, Ltd.
K —Kay & Kay Music Co.
M —Miessner Music Co.
MW —M. Witmark & Sons.
N —Novello & Co., Ltd.
O —Oxford University Press.
Pa —J. A. Parks Co.
Pn —Paterson Publications, Ltd.
Pr —Theo. Presser Co.
R —G. Ricordi & Co.
RC —Rodeheaver Co.
Ro —R. D. Row, Inc.

*Publications of all houses may be obtained from G. Schirmer, Inc., 3 East 43rd St., N. Y. C.

SB —Silver Burdett & Co.
Sc   —Schott & Co.
SF —Sam Fox Publishing Co.
SP —Shattinger Piano and Music Co.
St   —Stainer & Bell, Ltd.
Su —Clayton F. Summy Co.
U   —Universal Edition
W   —Willis Music Co.
Wo —B. F. Wood Music Co.
WS —White Smith Music Publishing Co.

Publications of all houses may be obtained from G. Schirmer, 3 East 43rd St., N. Y. C.

Key to Other Abbreviations

Grade of difficulty:

    1 = Easy for good high-school and average college choruses.

    2 = Medium difficult for good high-school and average college choruses.

    3 = Difficult for good high-school and average college choruses.

General abbreviations:

Ac.	=Accompaniment	No.	=Number
Arr.	=Arrangement	Oct.	=Octavo
Bar.	=Baritone, Bass I	Ob.	=Obbligato
S.	=Soprano	Or.	=Orchestra
A.	=Alto	P.R.	=Piano part for rehearsal
T.	=Tenor	U.	=Unaccompanied, *a cappella*
B.	=Bass		

Range of Voices:

When the highest or lowest note indicated in the voice columns is followed by a number (*e.g.*, 4) the number indicates how many times this note (the extreme in range for the composition) appears in the course of the music.

Tenor notes in the treble are indicated by the actual pitches at which they *sound*, and not an octave above, where they are written. The following system of notation is used in referring to the recommended music, in order that there may be no confusion as to the exact meaning of part ranges.

Ex. 17

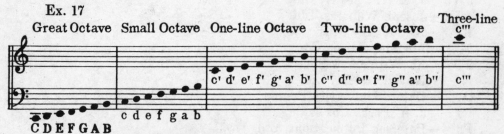

The following criteria have been used in the range listings:

1. If the extreme range is reached more than six times, no numeral follows the letter.

2. An extreme range is not counted when an easier optional note is indicated, or when the progression is doubled in octaves as in counter bass parts.

3. Extreme ranges in solo voices are not counted.
4. Extreme ranges are counted again on an obligatory D. C. or D. S., but are counted only for the first verse in instances where a number of verses are printed under one musical setting.
5. The number given indicates the number of times an extreme range is reached in the phrase, not the actual number of times the extreme note is printed. Thus a succession of four or more high b flats for soprano occurring in one phrase would be counted b♭"1.

The following lists of octavo music and texts are by no means intended as complete and final. However, they are representative of the *choicest* numbers in the huge mass of material sent for review by the fifty-four publishers listed. If careful reviewing, selecting, grading, and classification of this material can be of help to those unfamiliar with what is available of the best music literature, the task of compilation will seem to have been worth while.

All the music in these lists can be purchased from G. Schirmer, Inc., 3 East 43rd St., New York, the publishers of this volume; but they do not guarantee the accuracy of the data supplied. Every effort has been directed by the compiler towards making all the information given correct. However, prices change, grades of difficulty differ with each chorus, performance time varies with the tempo chosen, *etc.*, and the readers should consider all the information given as only approximately exact.

1. MUSIC FOR MIXED VOICES

Remarks on the List of
Recommended *A Cappella* Octavo Music for Mixed Voices

1. For two-part music with piano accompaniment suitable for mixed voices, see "One- and Two-Part Music with Descant" and "Two-Part Music", p. 132.

2. For the sake of brevity, music is listed under only one heading—where it seems most appropriate. It may be necessary to look under a number of different headings to find all music by a certain composer or arranger.

3. It must not be presumed that all music listed under such headings as "Humorous Encore" or "Novelty" is of a lower musical quality than that listed under other headings; most of the music listed under such headings is good enough to be regularly programmed.

4. This list features secular music; only those sacred compositions especially suitable for secular performance as well are included.

5. The music listed is for unaccompanied (*a cappella*) mixed voices with piano reduction for rehearsal; several numbers with instrumental obbligato parts or string-quartet accompaniment are exceptions; piano is optional in a number of instances. Information in this regard will always be found in the "General Remarks" column.

6. Music is listed alphabetically under the different headings by composer (or arranger).

7. In case the same composition is published in arrangements of equal worth by two different firms, the lower-priced issue is listed; if the prices are the same, both issues are listed.

8. A key to abbreviations of publishers will be found on p. 93; to grade-of-difficulty estimates, exact pitch indications, and other abbreviations, on p. 94.

9. The performance-time indicated is an estimate; it is not to be considered exact for purposes of radio or concert.

10. It is suggested that directors seeking suitable new music for their groups will save time and receive the greatest value from the music catalogued here by proceeding in general as follows:

    a. Find the sections which list the type of music in which you are most interested.

    b. Determine from the grade of difficulty, the composer-arranger, the title of the composition, and general remarks, which music seems most promising. In most cases, single copies may be secured on approval.

    c. Select by careful review from these "On Approval" copies the music which seems most suitable for your group.

RECOMMENDED *A CAPPELLA* OCTAVO MUSIC FOR MIXED VOICES

Composer; Title; Arranger (or, Arranger; Title)	Octavo No.; Price; Publisher	Number of Parts	Grade of Difficulty	Length in Minutes	General Remarks (Note—All music *a cappella* with piano reduction [P.R.] unless noted otherwise)
MUSIC OF THE FIFTEENTH, SIXTEENTH, SEVENTEENTH, AND EIGHTEENTH CENTURIES (Madrigals, Motets, Glees, Chansons, Canzonets, Chorales, etc.)					
ENGLISH					
Bateson, Down the hills Corinna trips	2; 24¢; O	5	1	2½	(SSATB) Rollicking
Bennet, All creatures now are merry minded	14405; 15¢; D	5	1	2½	(SSATB) Lively; from "Triumphs of Oriana"
——Let go, why do you stay me?	1140; 18¢; EC	4	2	1½	Humorous madrigal, T. to g'
Byrd, Ave verum corpus (Hail, O hail, True Body)	393; 18¢; EC	4	1	3	Motet; Latin & Eng.
——Bow Thine ear	61; 16¢; O	5	2	2½	(SATBB) or (SATTB); Easy except T. to g'
De Pearsall, When Allen-a-Dale went a-hunting	2538; 12¢; GS	4	1	2	Madrigal
Dowland, Awake, sweet love	2036; 20¢; R	4	2	3	Easy except T. to g'
——Come again, sweet love	2264; 9¢; GS	4	1	3½	Madrigal
——Come, heavy sleep	3143; 15¢; St	4	1	1½	U; T. to g' 1*
Ford, Since first I saw your face	2037; 12¢; St	4	1	3	
Gibbons, Hosanna to the Son of David	242; 15¢; Wo	6	2	2	(SSAATB)
——The silver swan	7789; 10¢; GS; or 14409; 10¢; D	5	2	1½	(SATBB) or (SSATB)
Morley, April is in my mistress' face	14623; 15¢; D, or 1612; 15¢; EC	4	1	1½	Madrigal
——Dainty, fine, sweet nymph	1607; 16¢; EC	5	1	2½	(SSATB)
——Fire, fire, my heart	2266; 12¢; GS	5	2	2	(SSATB) Alto to g, Bass to F
——My bonny lass	1162; 16¢; EC; or 322; 20¢; CC	5	2	2½	(SATTB) or (SATBB)
——O grief, even on the bud	7; 12¢; St	5	1	1	(SATTB) or (SATBB)
——Shoot, false love, I care not	1141; 16¢; EC	5	1	1	(SSATB)
——Sing we and chant it	2633; 10¢; MW	5	1	1½	(SSATB)
——What saith my dainty darling?	82; 15¢; N	5	2	1	(SSATB)
Pilkington, O softly singing lute	24; 30¢; St	6	2	3½	(SSAATB) Alto to low d 1*
——Rest, sweet nymphs	1144; 18¢; EC	4	1	2½	
Purcell, In these delightful, pleasant groves	1106; 16¢; EC	4	1	2	
——The Mavis	12; 15¢; JWm	4	1-2	1	
Ward, Die not, fond man	515; 10¢; GS	6	1	4	(SSAATB)
Stevens, Ye spotted snakes	2300; 10¢; GS	4	1	5	Text by Shakespeare
Weelkes, Methinks I hear	58; 20¢ O	6	3	3	(SSAATB) T. to a'
——Strike it up, Tabor	1611; 15¢; EC	3	1	1	(SSB) or (SAB)
Wilbye, Adieu, sweet Amarillis	1143; 16¢; EC	4	2	2½	T. to g' 3*
——Alas! what hope of speeding	956; 20¢; CC	4	2	3	T. to g' 3*
——Flora gave me fairest flowers	1180; 18¢; EC	5	1	3½	(SSATB)
FLEMISH					
Waelrant—Hard by a fountain	14584; 10¢; D	4	1	1	Madrigal
FRENCH					
Binchois, Dear love whom I adore [*Saar*]	4561; 15¢ C	4	1	2	Chanson; T. to g' 4*
Janequin, Chanson (Oh, follow, follow)	7138; 15¢; GS	4	2	2	T. to a' 6*; Eng. & Fr.
Letevre, The pain of love [*Damrosch*]	5786; 10¢; GS	4	2	2½	B. to high eb' 2*
Sermisy, Chanson (Roaming the wood)	7133; 10¢; GS	4	1	2	Eng. & Fr.
Tessier, To lovely groves	6576; 10¢; GS	4	1	1½	Eng. & Fr.; T. to g' 2*
GERMAN					
Bach, J. S., All breathing life (from motet "Sing ye to the Lord")	7470; 16¢; GS	4	3	2½	Brilliant fugue
——Four chorales (from "Jesu, priceless treasure")	7603; 12¢; GS	....	2	4½	(SSATB)
1. Jesu, priceless treasure		4			
2. In Thine arm I rest me		5			
3. Hence with earthly treasure		4			
4. Hence, all fears and sadness		4			

* Such numerals indicate the number of times an extreme note occurs.

Composer; Title; Arranger (or, Arranger; Title)	Octavo No.; Price; Publisher	Number of Parts	Grade of Difficulty	Length in Minutes	General Remarks (Note—All music *a cappella* with piano reduction [P.R.] unless noted otherwise)
MUSIC OF THE FIFTEENTH, SIXTEENTH, SEVENTEENTH, AND EIGHTEENTH CENTURIES—(*Cont'd*) (Madrigals, Motets, Glees, Chansons, Canzonets, Chorales, etc.)					
GERMAN—(*Cont'd*)					
Bach, J. S. (*cont'd*)					
——If by His spirit (from "Jesu priceless treasure")	7605; 9¢; GS	5	2	2	(SSATB)
——My Savior dear, what woe of soul [*Lundquist*]	5503; 15¢; W	4	1	3	Chorale
——Now let all the heavens adore Thee (from cantata "Sleepers, wake")	14563; 10¢; D	4	1	2½	
Bach, W. F., No blade of grass can flourish [*Frank*]	5677; 8¢; GS	4	1	2	
Bruck, Know'st thou then, poor Judas?	7559; 18¢; GS	6	2	4½	(SSATBB)
Eccard, Presentation of Christ	2618; 12¢; GS	6	1	2	(SSATBB)
Gluck, De profundis (Out of the deep)	1223; 18¢; EC	4	1	3½	Latin & Eng.
Hassler, Love's captive (Liebeskrieg) [*Cain*]	17; 20¢; Ho	8	2	3½	For double chorus; Eng. & Ger.
Lundquist, Now that the sun is beaming bright	327; 15¢; Wo	4-8	1	2	Latin Hymn, Fifth Century
Niedt, In mirth and in gladness	7540; 18¢; GS	4	2	2	
Schütz, Song of praise	7648; 18¢; GS	8	3	4	For double chorus
ITALIAN					
Anerio, Christus factus est (Jesus once for our salvation)	349;15¢; EC	4	1	2½	Latin & Eng.
De Wert, The love bird [*Schindler*]	6573; 12¢; GS	5	1	2½	(SSATB) Eng. & Fr.
Festa, Down in a flowery vale	2265; 8¢; GS	4	2	3½	
Lotti, Crucifixus	6396; 9¢; GS	8	2	3	Latin
——Crucifixus (arrangement of the preceding number [*Baldwin*]	9035; 9¢; GS	4	2	3	Latin
——Surely He hath borne our griefs	1124; 15¢; EC	3	1	1½	(SAB) or (STB)
Marenzio, Spring returns	1642; 18¢; EC	5	2	2	(SSATB)
Palestrina, Ah! you would see	14411; 15¢; D	4	2	2½	Canzonet
——Alla riva del Tebro (By the smooth flowing Tiber)	1147; 18¢; EC	4	1	3	Madrigal; Latin & Eng.
——Ave Maria	4332; 12¢; GS	5	2	2½	Latin (SSATB)
——Exultate Deo (Sing and praise Jehovah)	7672; 16¢; GS	5	2	2	Latin & Eng. (SAATB)
——O bone Jesu	1166; 12¢; EC	4	1	1½	Latin
——Tenebrae factae sunt	361; 15¢; EC	4	2	2½	Latin
——When flowery meadows	2350; 9¢; GS	4	1	1½	
——Who is she that looketh forth	3360; 15¢; J	5	2	2½	Motet (SSATB)
Vecchi, Let every heart be merry	14412; 15¢; D	4	1	1½	
NETHERLANDISH					
Arcadelt, Now Spring in all her glory	2439; 10¢; GS	4	2	2	T. to g♯′ 1*
Gombert, Canon apertus (Neath a shady linden tree) [*Damrosch*]	7135; 20¢; GS	6	1	2½	(SSAAAT) Eng. & Fr.
Lasso, Chanson (Let us all flee love's desire)	7128; 10¢; GS	4	2	1½	T. to a′ 2*; Eng. & Fr.
——Chanson (Night falls, cold and gloomful)	7129; 12¢; GS	4	2	2	Eng. & Fr.
——Echo song (Double chorus)	5802; 15¢; GS	8	2	2½	Eng. & Latin
——I know a young maiden wondrous fair	1606; 16¢; EC	4	1	1	Eng. & Latin; Madrigal
——Matona, lovely maiden	2421; 12¢; GS	4	1	3½	Madrigal
——My heart doth beg you'll not forget	1145; 16¢; EC	4	1	1½	Madrigal; Latin & Eng.
——O eyes of my beloved	1146; 16¢; EC	4	1	1½	Latin & Eng.
Regnard, Gay little nymph	1150; 16¢; EC	4	2	2	Eng. & Fr.
Sweelinck, Arise, oh ye servants of God	2619; 12¢; GS	6	2	2½	Fr. & Eng. (SSATBB)
——All thine alone, John	1152; 20¢; EC	5	2	2½	Fr. & Eng. (SSATB)
SPANISH					
Morales, Me ye have bereaved (The lamentation of Jacob)	1650; 18¢; EC	5	1	3	Motet (SSATB)
Vittoria, Ave Maria	9039; 8¢; GS	4	1	3	Latin
——Jesu dulcis Memoria	9040; 6¢; GS	4	1	1	Latin
——O magnum mysterium (O wondrous nativity)	7626; 15¢; GS	4	1	4½	Latin & Eng.
					* Such numerals indicate the number of times an extreme note occurs.

RECOMMENDED *A CAPPELLA* OCTAVO MUSIC FOR MIXED VOICES

Composer; Title; Arranger (or, Arranger; Title)	Octavo No.; Price; Publisher	Number of Parts	Grade of Difficulty	Length in Minutes	General Remarks (Note—All music *a cappella* with piano reduction [P.R.] unless noted otherwise)
MUSIC OF THE NINETEENTH AND TWENTIETH CENTURIES					
AMERICAN					
Berwald, Far, far away	6870; 15¢, J	4	1	2	
Brockway, Matins song	5586; 16¢; GS	8	2	1½	
——Wings of a dove	2610; 15¢; GS	8	1	2	
Cadman, The wind of March	1033; 15¢, HF	8	1	2	
Cain, Calm be thy sleep	972; 15¢; GH	7	1	3	(SSAATBB)
——How do I love thee	7910; 15¢; GS	4-8	2	3½	S. to a″ 3*
——Hymn to the night	68; 12¢; Ho	8	1	2	
——Offering of the soul	46; 20¢; Ho	8	3	3½	
——Say thou lovest me	7875; 12¢; GS	8	3	2½	S. to a″ 2*; Bass to D 2
——The night has a thousand eyes	81063; 15¢; F	4-8	2	2½	Bass to D 2*; dissonant
Calver, Echoes	206; 12¢; AP	4	1	2	
Chadwick, O lady weave thy silken thread	12; 15¢; GH	4-8	2	3½	Madrigal
Charles, Clouds [*Treharne*]	7846; 12¢; GS	6	2	2½	Alto solo
Childe, From Oberon in fairyland	219; 15¢; AP	4-8	3	4	
Christiansen, Beautiful Savior	51; 10¢; A	8	2	3	
——Hosanna	57; 18¢; A	8	2	3	
——Lost in the night	119; 15¢; A	7	2	3	(SSAATBB)
——Sunbeam out of heaven	140; 15¢; A	4-5	1	2	
——Vistas of song	141; 15¢; A	4-8	2	4	First S. to bb″ 2*
Clokey, Blow, blow, thou winter wind	31; 10¢; CC	4	1	1½	
——If I but knew	6148; 15¢; J	6	1	1½	
——Lullaby	502; 10¢; CC	6	1	2	(SSATBB)
Cowles, O come, soft rest of cares	7193; 12¢; GS	4-6	1	2	(SATTBB)
Cross, A dream within a dream	7990; 12¢; GS	8	1	2	
Dett, O holy Lord	6579; 16¢; GS	8	2	4	Spiritual style
Dunham, What the chimney sang	2012; 15¢; Su	4-6	2	5	Bass to E
Dunn, Song of the night	5394; 15¢; J	8	2	4½	
Ferrari, In the great hall	7030; 15¢; GS	4-5	2	1½	(SATBB) Short Bar. solo
Fischer, The song of Mary [*Kranz*]	784; 12¢; R	7	2	3	
Foote, The bells	10; 8¢; CC	4-6	1	1	(SSAATB)
Foster, Come where my love lies dreaming [*Treharne*]	5462; 15¢; W	8	2	3	
——Old Black Joe [*Jones*]	4587; 12¢; C	8	3	2	
Gaul, A chant for Chloë	14094; 15¢; D	4-8	2	3	
——Daybreak	9005; 12¢; GS	4-6	1	5	
Hadley, It was a lover and his lass	21098; 15¢; Pr	4	1	1½	
Hawke, Song of the winds	1007; 18¢; GH	4-5	1	3	(SSATB)
Josten, Crucifixion	7022; 20¢; GS	4-8	3	5	Short Bass solo
Kountz, The sleigh [*Mueller*]	7796; 12¢; GS	8	3	1	
Loomis, The harp and the willow	1086; 16¢; GH	4-8	3	3½	Short Bar. solo, optional acc.
Lundquist, Sing ye stars of light	91; 15¢; Ho	4-8	1	3½	
Lutkin, Cargoes	215; 15¢; HW	5	2	2	(SATBB)
MacDowell, Dance of the gnomes	270; 15¢; AP	4	2	1	
Macfarlane, Nymph and swain	11; 15¢; GH	4	2	1½	Madrigal
——A rondel (Echo is a timid maid)	4410; 12¢, GS	4	1	2	
McCollin, Madrigal (A song of four seasons)	7100; 18¢; GS	4-6	1	3½	Madrigal
Mueller, Daybreak	7936; 12¢; GS	8	2	2	
——Envoy	7998; 15¢; GS	8	2	3	S. to b″ 1*: T. to a′ 2
Noble, Come, O thou traveler unknown	4842; 10¢; GS	4-8	1	3½	
——Fierce was the wild billow	5283; 12¢; GS	4	2	2½	
——Go to dark Gethsemane	501; 15¢; HW	4-7	1	3	T. to ab′ 1*; S. to ab″ 1*
——Hail, gladdening light	5281; 10¢; GS	4	1	3	
Noss, Sing we merrily unto God	47; 20¢; Ho	8	3	4	
Protheroe, The birds	1824; 15¢; B	4-8	1	3	
Righter, Matins	2539; 15¢; MW	4	1	1½	
Thompson, O fons Bandusiae, splendidor vitro (The fountain of Bandusia)	1626; 20¢; EC	4-5	2	4	Modern madrigal; Latin only
Woodbury, Stars of the summer night [*Cain*]	7997; 12¢; GS	8	2	2½	T. to a′, S. to a″; solo for medium voice

*Such numerals indicate the number of times an extreme note occurs.

Composer; Title; Arranger (or, Arranger; Title)	Octavo No.; Price; Publisher	Number of Parts	Grade of Difficulty	Length in Minutes	General Remarks (Note—All music *a cappella* with piano reduction [P.R.] unless noted otherwise)
MUSIC OF THE NINETEENTH AND TWENTIETH CENTURIES—*(Continued)*					
BOHEMIAN					
Dvořák, Around us hear the sounds of even......	4734; 12¢; GS	8	1	4	Optional Bass to D
——Full many a song........................	4733; 9¢; GS	4	1	2	
ENGLISH					
Bainton, I love the jocund dance.............	1596; 15¢; St	4	2	1	Lively
——In the wilderness......................	720; 24¢; O	4	3	2	T. to a♭' 3*
Bantock, The moon has risen.................	3; 25¢; BH	8	1	3½	Double chorus
——On Himalay......................	1062; 15¢, N	8	2	2	
Baynon, Dream, baby, dream.............	74; 20¢; St	4-5	2	2	(SAATB)
Bax, I sing of a maiden that is makeless........	440; 40¢; O	5	3	4	T. to g' 6*; very dissonant (SAATB)
Benjamin, He is the lonely greatness...........	710; 16¢; C	5	2	2	(SSATB)
——I see his blood upon the rose........	701; 24¢; O	5	2	2	(SSATB) S. and T. solos
Bishop, Home, sweet home [*Nyvall*]...........	1021; 12¢; HF	8	1	3	Humming introduction, short Alto solo
Blower, Evensong...................	1480; 15¢; N	5	2	5	(SATBB) easy except T. to a' 2
Calcott, How sweet the moonlight.............	2412; 9¢; GS	5	2	2½	(SATBB) easy except Bass I
Challinor, By the sea.................	5049; 12¢; GS	4-7	1	2½	(SSAATTB)
Coleridge-Taylor, By the lone sea shore......	699; 15¢; N	4-5	2	2½	T. to g' 1*; Bass to e' 1
——The lee shore.................	1231; 15¢; N	4-8	2	2½	Dramatic
D'Erlanger, The arrow and the song........	33951; 35¢; Sc	4-8	3	3½	
——Sleep.............................	33952; 35¢; Sc	4-8	3	3½	
Dunkley, The bonnie bell.................	20; 20¢; JWm	4	1	1½	
Dyson, Evening........................	503; 16¢; Ar	4	1	2	T. to g' 1*
Elgar, As torrents in summer.............	276; 12¢; Wo	4	1	2	
——Fly, singing bird.................	1150; 30¢; N	4-5	1	4	Two violins and piano acc.
——Death on the hills..............	1299; 40¢; N	4-7	1	3½	
——Deep in my soul.................	1057; 30¢; N	4-7	2	2½	Features bass
——Go, song of mine..............	1164; 30¢; N	8	3	4	
——My love dwelt in a northern land..........	2366; 12¢; GS	4-7	2	3	(SAATTBB)
——Serenade (Dreams all too brief).............	1301; 30¢; N	4-5	1	2	
——Yea, cast me from heights of the mountains..	1396; 12¢; N	4-6	2	1	(SAATTB)
Faning, Moonlight...................	2566; 9¢; GS	4-5	1	4	(SATBB)
Finzi, Clear and gentle stream.............	——; 20¢; O	4	3	3	Modern madrigal style
——I praise the tender flower..............	——; 12¢; O	4	3	1½	Modern madrigal style
Fletcher, How beautiful this night........	60996; 20¢; JC	4-8	3	4	
Geehl, My lady.............	518; 16¢; Ar	4	2	2	Modern madrigal style
German, O peaceful night.............	937; 15¢; N	4	1	2½	
Jacob, The song of spring.............	767; 20¢; O	4-8	3	2½	S. to b♭'' 1*
Jenkins, Hymn to the soul.............	61009; 15¢; JC	6	2	3	(SSATBB)
Mackenzie, My soul would drink those echoes....	1197; 30¢; N	8	3	4	Modern; dissonant
Mackinnon, Lord Christ came walking........	796; 15¢; HW	4-6	1	3½	Short Bar. solo
Margetson, Why weep ye by the tide, ladie?.....	4578; 15¢; C	4-8	3	2½	Ballad; Scotch dialect
Marks, Blow, ye gentle breezes, blow...........	615; 12¢; N	4	1	2	
Murrill, Love not me for comely grace...........	768; 12¢; O	4	1	1	Modern madrigal style
Parry, Never weather-beaten sail...........	1128; 16¢; CC	5	3	3	(SSATB) Modern motet
——There is an old belief.................	1127; 16¢; CC	6	3	3½	(SSATBB) Modern motet
Richardson, How calm, how beautiful...........	1515; 16¢; Pn	4	1	4½	
Roberton, All in the April evening.............	8100; 10¢; GS	4-5	1	3	(SATBB)
——Celtic hymn..............	61090; 10¢; JC	4-8	2	3	
——Nightfall in Skye.................	8099; 10¢; GS	4-8	1	2½	Humming throughout
Shaw, An evening's pastorale...................	61079; 10¢; JC	4	1	2½	
Stanford, The blue bird...................	27; 15¢; St	4-5	2	2	(SAATB)

*Such numerals indicate the number of times an extreme note occurs.

Composer; Title; Arranger (or, Arranger; Title)	Octavo No.; Price; Publisher	Number of Parts	Grade of Difficulty	Length in Minutes	General Remarks (Note—All music *a cappella* with piano reduction [P.R.] unless noted otherwise)
MUSIC OF THE NINETEENTH AND TWENTIETH CENTURIES—(*Continued*)					
ENGLISH—(*Cont'd*)					
Thiman, Go, lovely rose.....................	1537; 20¢; E	4-8	1	3	
——Now sleeps the crimson petal..............	1099; 12¢; N	4	2	1½	
West, How eloquent.......................	1253; 15¢; N	4-8	3	3½	
Williams, C. L., Song of the pedlar........	1006; 15¢; N	4	1	2	Humorous
Wood, Hail, gladdening light................	1141; 20¢; CC	8	2	3	Double chorus
——Song for a dance.......................	1125; 15¢; CC	4	1	1½	Lively glee
FRENCH					
Saint-Saëns, By trees and flowers..............	2408; 10¢; GS	4-5	2	2	T. to g#'; S. to g#''
FRENCH CANADIAN					
Willan, How they so softly rest..............	488; 15¢; HW	4-8	2	3½	Longfellow text
——In youth is pleasure.....................	1045; 12¢; N	4	2	2½	
BELGIAN					
Gevaert, Coletta (Ronde villageoise)...........	324; 15¢; EC	5	1	1½	(SATBB)
GERMAN					
Abt, Away to the forest......................	2330; 10¢; GS	4	1	2	Piano optional
Beethoven, Elegy (Elegischer gesang)..........	1630; 20¢; EC	4	1	4	String quartet acc. Ger. & Eng.
——'Tis the evening's holy hour..............	50; 10¢; A	4	1	2	
Brahms, The hunter......................	963; 12¢; N	4	2	2	Easy except T. g' 3
——Lullaby (Cradle song)...................	2232; 8¢; GS	6	2	1½	Eng. & Ger.
——The maiden..........................	6; 20¢; R	4	2	2	Short S. solo; Eng. & Ger.
——O cast me not away from thy countenance..	7505; 16¢; GS	4	2	2½	Eng. & Ger.; Fugal motet
——Serenade............................	2257; 9¢; GS	6	2	1½	(SAATBB)
——Song from Ossian's "Fingal" [*Christy*]......	8372; 20¢; GS	4-8	1	4½	Accomp. *ad lib.*; horn and harp parts obtainable
——Thy heart so mild.....................	14406; 10¢; D	4	1	1½	Eng. & Ger.
——Vineta..............................	4764; 12¢; GS	6	2	4	(SAATBB)
——Where'er I go (All' meine Herzgedanken) ...	562; 20¢; B	6	1	3	(SAATBB) Eng. & Ger.
Kollner, Daybreak in the woods (Waldmorgen)..	1020; 18¢; F	4	2	5	Eng. & Ger.; No P. R.
Liszt, Ave Maria [*Cain*]...................	15; 15¢; Ho	4	2	5	Eng. & Latin
Mendelssohn, Farewell to the forest...........	2382; 8¢; GS	4	1	3½	No. P. R.
——The nightingale [*Luvaas*]................	1029; 12¢; GH	4	1	1½	
——On the sea [*Baldwin*]...................	9009; 12¢; GS	4	1	2½	
——Psalm 91............................	235; 20¢; CC	8	1	3	
——Winter's done [*Luvaas*].................	2621; 15¢; MW	4	1	2½	
Mozart, Adoramus te, Christe................	14445; 10¢; D	4	1	1½	Latin; motet
Reger, Dawn of spring.....................	10; 20¢; BH	6	3	4	(SAATBB)
——Evening song.........................	11; 20¢; BH	6	3	4	(SAATBB)
——My little sweetheart...................	400; 16¢; EC	4	2	1	Eng. & Ger.
——Silence..............................	9; 25¢; BH	6	3	4	(SAATBB)
Schubert, By the sea [*Smith-Aschenbrenner*]......	4593; 15¢; C	4-8	3	2½	
——Death and the maiden [*Smith-Aschenbrenner*].	4610; 15¢; C	4-8	1	2	Ger. & Eng.
——The fishermaiden [*Root*]..................	2036; 10¢; Su	4	2	2½	Short S. or T. solo
Shuetky, Send forth thy spirit...............	150; 15¢; CC	4-8	2	3½	
Schumann, Summer song....................	4397; 10¢; GS	4	1	2	
HUNGARIAN					
Kodaly, A birthday greeting.................	10444a; 20¢; U	4	1	1	
——Evening.............................	1135; 25¢; U	8	3	4	
——The aged............................	10696; 25¢; U	4-6	3	4½	
——Too late............................	10695; 25¢; U	4-5	2	2	
Kun, Hungarian lullaby....................	412; 10¢; HW	4	1	1½	

Composer; Title; Arranger (or, Arranger; Title)	Octavo No.; Price; Publisher	Number of Parts	Grade of Difficulty	Length in Minutes	General Remarks (Note—All music a cappella with piano reduction [P. R.] unless noted otherwise)
MUSIC OF THE NINETEENTH AND TWENTIETH CENTURIES—*(Continued)*					
ITALIAN					
Mascagni, Light Divine (Scene and prayer from "Cavalleria Rusticana" [*Rix*])	5959; 15¢; GS	7	2	5	(SSAATBB) S. to b'' 1*
Pinsuti, The caravan	263; 10¢; GS	4	2	3½	Easy except Bass
——The crusaders	2542; 9¢; GS	4	2	2	T. to g' 2*
——Eldorado	4655; 9¢; GS	4	2	2	T. to g' 5*
——In this hour of softened splendor	502; 12¢; N	4	1	2½	T. to f'
——The sea hath its pearls	2544; 9¢; GS	4	2	2	Easy except T.
Verdi, Our Father (Pater Noster)	493; 20¢; B	5	2	5½	
RUSSIAN					
Arensky, Cherubim song	1301; 15¢; B	8	2	3½	
——Serenade	4619; 9¢; GS	4	1	1½	'Cello Obbl.
——The steaming rill	4621; 15¢; GS	4	1	1½	'Cello Obbl.
Arkhangelsky, Evening on the Sava	5212; 12¢; GS	4-7	2	3	
——Incline thine ear, O Lord [*Kibalchich*]	2689; 12¢; MW	4	1	2½	
Bortnyanski, Cherubim song	2560; 8¢; GS	4	1	2½	
Cui, Cloud messengers	398; 16¢; EC	4-8	2	1½	
——Nocturne	913; 15¢; B	5-6	3	2	Easy except Bass II to low C
——Spring delight	2559; 10¢; GS	8	1	1	
——Two roses	2558; 10¢; GS	4-8	3	3	Bass to low D; otherwise easy
Gretchaninoff, Autumn	2555; 12¢; GS	4-8	3	3½	No. P. R.
——Cherubic hymn	1; 12¢; HW	4-8	2	3½	
——Cherubim song [*Cain*]	12; 20¢; Ho	4-8	1	2½	
——O gladsome light	4135; 20¢; J	8	3	3½	
——Praise the Lord, O my soul	8; 15¢; HW	4-8	3	4	Double chorus at end
——Sun and moon (Lullaby)	5217; 15¢; GS	4-8	1	6	
Kastalsky, O gladsome light	1065; 15¢; B	4	1	2	
Kopyloff, Hear my cry, O God [*Clough-Leighter*]	13804; 12¢; D	4-8	1	2	
——The elder blossoms [*Baldwin*]	9033; 8¢; GS	4	1	1½	
Lvovsky, Hospodi pomilui (Have mercy, O Lord)	2635; 12¢; MW	4	1	1½	A study in dynamics
Nikolsky, Praise Ye the Name of the Lord	1123; 20¢; B	7	2	3	
Ornstein, Russian winter	65; 30¢; AM	4-8	2	4	
——Russian lament	64; 30¢; AM	4	1	2	
Taneyef, From land to land	584; 35¢; B	8	3	5	Double chorus
——Sunrise	2623; 15¢; GS	4-8	2	3	
Tcherepnin, Cherubim song [*Clough-Leighter*]	1619, 18¢; EC	4-8	2	4	
——Oleg's men	1322, 20¢; B	4-8	2	2½	
Tchaikovsky, Cherubim song, No.3	2561; 12¢; GS	8	1	4	
——A legend	2378; 8¢; GS	4-8	1	1½	No P. R.
——The nightingale	12849; 12¢; D	4-8	1	3	Short T. or S. solo; No. P. R.
——Oh, blest are they [*Cain*]	3024; 15¢; GH	4-8	1	2½	
——Pilgrim's Song [*Christy*]	8373; 16¢; GS	4-8	1	3½	Piano *ad lib.*
Tschesnokoff, As a flower sorely fadeth	1; 15¢; Ga	4-8	1	2	(SSATTBB)
——Cherubim song	56; 15¢; Ho	4-7	2	3	
——Let thy blessed spirit	4497; 12¢; J	7	1	2	
SCANDANAVIAN					
Grieg, Ave, Maris stella (Hail, O star)	880; 10¢; CC	4-8	2	2	Eng. & Italian
——Solvejg's song [*Andrews*]	6835; 12¢; GS	4-6	2	3	S. or T. solo
——Springtide [*Baldwin*]	9029; 12¢; GS	8	2	3	Piano *ad lib.*
Palmgren, Lullaby (Finnish song)	5782; 8¢; GS	4-7	1	1½	(SAATTBB)
——Sorrow	5783; 8¢; GS	4-7	1	1½	(SAATTBB)
——The swing	5784; 9¢; GS	4-7	1	1½	(SSAATTB) B. melody
Sibelius-Row, Vale of Tuoni	311; 15¢; Ro	4	1	1½	Eng. & Finnish
SPANISH					
Nicolau, At Montserrat is sorrow	7503; 20¢; GS	6	3	6	(SATTBB)

*Such numerals indicate the number of times an extreme note occurs.

RECOMMENDED *A CAPPELLA* OCTAVO MUSIC FOR MIXED VOICES

Composer; Title; Arranger (or, Arranger; Title)	Octavo No.; Price; Publisher	Number of Parts	Grade of Difficulty	Length in Minutes	General Remarks (Note—All music *a cappella* with piano reduction [P.R.] unless noted otherwise)
FOLK-SONGS					
American					
Arranger:					
Brockway, The dying soldier (Brother Green)....	130; 12¢; HW	8	3	3	Harlan Co., Ky.
Buchanan, The Hebrew children...............	6749; 15¢; J	4	1	2	Southern Mt.
Clokey, He's gone away	6210; 15¢; J	6	2	3½	Southern Mt. (SSATBB)
——Our master hath a garden	1014; 10¢; CC	6	1	3	Traditional (SSATBB)
Harper, Ten miles away from home [*Holmes*]....	81; 15¢; Ho	4-8	1	3	Old Okla. song; piano *ad lib.*
Horton, Madam, I have come a-courting.........	80; 12¢; Ho	4	1	2	Humorous
——Pretty little miss.....................	53; 15¢; Ho	6	1	2	Kentucky Mt.
Loomis, The sunworshippers [*Mitchell*]......	82; 20¢; CC	4-6	1	2	American Indian
Malin, The gypsy laddie..................	3022; 15¢; GH	4-6	1	3	Southern Mt. Ballad
——The inconstant lover....................	3021; 15¢; GH	4-8	2	2½	Solo for medium treble voice; Southern Mt.
——The true lover's farewell...............	3027; 15¢; GH	4-8	1	2½	Southern Mt.
Powell, Rosemary and thyme.............	995; 20¢; CC	8	1	2½	Arkansas folk-song
——The weak and rambling one..............	919; 15¢; CC	4-6	1	1½	Arkansas folk-song
Treharne, Jenny fair, gentle Rosemarie	5378; 15¢; W	4-6	3	3	Virginia
——The three farmers...................	5505; 15¢; W	4	1	2½	Virginia, humorous
Armenian					
Levenson, The spinning wheel.................	2774; 12¢; MW	4	2	1½	
Treharne, Singing in the tree-tops............	1845; 15¢; B	4	1	3	
Australian					
Treharne, Corroboree (Festival night)..........	1927; 15¢; B	4	1	3½	
English					
Andrews, John Peel	49; 15¢; HW	4	1	2½	Old English hunting song
Bantock, The three ravens..............	64; 15¢; BH	4	1	2	
Christy, The old woman and the peddler........	8368; 20¢; GS	4	1	3½	Humorous
Davis, The cobbler's jig.................	1632; 18¢; EC	4	1	2	Piano optional
Holst, I love my love.....................	8117; 15¢; GS	4-6	2	4	Cornwall
——I sowed the seeds of love...............	61083; 10¢; JC	4-8	2	1½	T. to a' 1, S. to a'' 1; Hampshire folk-song
——Swansea town.......................	8097; 15¢; GS	4-5	2	3	Hampshire
Jacob, The bailiff's daughter of Islington........	F21; 24¢; O	4	1	2	
Matthews, The shepherd's holiday..............	7570; 15¢; GS	4-6	1	1½	
Rowley, The sweet rose in June..............	507; 16¢; O	4	1	1½	
Vaughan Williams, An acre of land	F26; 16¢; O	4	1	3	
——Just as the tide was flowing..............	130; 20¢; St	4	2	2	
——The dark eyed sailor...................	128; 20¢; St	4	1	2	Humorous
——The turtle dove......................	8105; 10¢; GS	4-6	1	2	Bar. solo
Whitehead, Song of the London watchman (The London waits).........................	4574; 15¢; C	4	1	2½	
Williams, G., The farmer's daughters............	8116; 15¢; GS	4-6	1	2	Ballad
Flemish					
Treharne, The snow-white dove................	1912; 15¢; B	8	1	2½	
French-Canadian					
Crist, Air de chasse.....................	4550; 15¢; C	4	1	3	Vigorous; Eng. text
Grant-Schaefer, Come dance with me...........	65; 10¢; Ho	4	1	2	
Whitehead, Gay is the rose..................	1758; 15¢; B	7	2	2	Eng. & Fr.
German					
Brahms, In stilly night (Suabian folk)...........	2612; 6¢; GS	4-5	2	1½	
Blech, Thy mouth, fair maid, is a rosebud red....	394; 16¢; EC	4-6	2	2	Eng. & Ger.
Rontgen, Song of the watchman [*Cain*].........	19; 15¢; Ho	4	1	1½	Eng. & Ger.
Treharne, On the mountains...................	1844; 15¢; B	4	1	2½	

* Such numerals indicate the number of times an extreme note occurs.

Composer; Title; Arranger (or, Arranger; Title)	Octavo No.; Price; Publisher	Number of Parts	Grade of Difficulty	Length in Minutes	General Remarks (Note—All music *a cappella* with piano reduction [P.R.] unless noted otherwise)
FOLK-SONGS—(*Continued*)					
IRISH					
Davis, Has sorrow thy young days shaded?......	1660; 16¢; EC	4	1	1½	T. solo and chorus
Grainger, Irish tune from County Derry........	7232; 12¢; GS	6	3	2	Humming throughout
Molloy, Kerry dance..........................	51; 12¢; JF	4	1	2	Piano *ad lib.*
Sheridan, Erin...............................	57; 10¢; JF	4	1	1½	Alto melody
Treharne, The Galway piper...................	1896; 15¢; B	4-7	1	2	
Vine, The lark in the clear air................	F30; 12¢; O	4	1	2	
RUSSIAN-UKRAINIAN-JUGO SLAV					
Arkhangelsky, Evening on the Sava...........	5212; 12¢; GS	4-6	2	3	
——Round the good father's door (Oh Danube, my Danube).........................	5213; 9¢; GS				
Christy, No wind bends the slender tree tops.....	8366; 16¢; GS	4-8	1	3	
Dargomyzhsky, The three cavaliers [*Schindler*]...	6688; 20¢; GS	4-6	2	1	
Gnotov-Krone, Nina..........................	2664; 15¢; MW	4-8	2	2½	Mezzo-S. solo
Koshetz, The chicken lady....................	2677; 20¢; MW	8	1	2½	
——The cossack...........................	2688; 12¢; MW	4-6	2	3	
——The cossack's march...................	2724; 12¢; MW	4-5	1	1	
——Cossack romance......................	2700; 15¢; MW	4-5	1	3	Bar. solo
——Lullaby..............................	2697; 12¢; MW	4-7	2	3½	Instrumental effects
——O give thanks unto God................	2696; 12¢; MW	4	1	1½	Mezzo-S. solo
——Praise the Lord.......................	2695; 12¢; MW	4-7	1	2	Old Ukrainian church melody
——from The Passion trilogy:		4-6	2	2	Old Ukrainian church melody
(1) The trial before Pilate...............	2771; 15¢; MW				
(2) Crucifixion....................	2773; 12¢; MW	4-6	3	3	Difficult rhythm
——Violin singing in the street............	2694; 12¢; MW	4	1	3	
Nikolsky, Little duck in the meadow...........	6669; 10¢; GS	4-5	1	3	
Rubetz, Two Russian folk-songs:	5817; 12¢; GS	4-6	1	1½	Humorous
(a) Volga boat song...................					
(b) In the fields.....................		4-8	1	2½	
Smith, The peasant and his oxen [*Aschenbrenner*]..	4595; 15¢; C	4	1	1	
Treharne, Song before dawn..................	1926; 15¢; B	4-8	1	2½	Humorous; Jugo-Slav
		4	1	2½	Serbian; piano *ad lib.*
SCANDINAVIAN					
Christy, The dove and the lily...............	8367; 15¢; GS	4-8	2	3½	Plaintive
Lundquist, Our loving God and Father..........	344; 15¢; Wo	4	1	1½	Norwegian
Luvaas, Norwegian cradle song................	998; 15¢; CC	8	1	1½	S. solo
Treharne, A lovely white rose.................	1846; 15¢; B	4	1	3	Finnish
SCOTCH					
Bantock, O can ye sew cushions?...............	1283; 15¢; N	4	1	1½	Old cradle song
——Dumbarton's drums......................	61021; 15¢; JC	4	2	2	
Bartholomew, Ca', dearie, hame..............	——; 15¢; Ga	5	1	1½	(SSATB)
Davis, Turn ye to me.......................	1633; 18¢; EC	4	1	2	Piano optional
McLeod, Loch Lomond......................	610; 16¢; Pn	4-6	1	2	
Roberton, Ay waukin' O....................	61057; 10¢; JC	4	1	2½	
Vaughan Williams, Alister McAlpine's lament ...	60997; 15¢; JC	4	2	2½	
——Ca' the yowes........................	61128; 15¢; JC	4-6	2	4½	
Treharne, The piper of Dundee................	1977; 15¢; B	4	1	2	
WELSH					
Treharne, In the Cambrian hills...............	1902; 15¢; B	4-7	1	5	Choral fantasia on Welsh folk-songs
YIDDISH					
Parson, Eili Eili...........................	271; 15¢; C	4-6	2	2½	Piano optional
Schindler, Avrahm, Avrahm (Prayer to the patriarchs).................................	6689; 16¢; GS	4-8	3	2	

RECOMMENDED *A CAPPELLA* OCTAVO MUSIC FOR MIXED VOICES

Composer; Title; Arranger (or, Arranger; Title)	Octavo No.; Price; Publisher	Number of Parts	Grade of Difficulty	Length in Minutes	General Remarks (Note—All music *a cappella* with piano reduction [P.R.] unless noted otherwise)
NEGRO SPIRITUALS AND MELODIES					
Arranger:					
Aschenbrenner, Jesus on the water side.........	1032; 15¢; HF	4-8	1	3	
Bron-Wright, Hail the crown...................	980; 16¢; CC	4-6	1	3	
——I wish I'se in heav'n set'in' down........	979; 15¢; CC	4-6	1	2	
——Steal away...........................	976; 15¢; CC	6	1	2½	(SSATBB)
Burleigh, Didn't my Lord deliver Daniel.......	6505; 16¢; GS	4-6	1	2½	
——Ezekiel saw de wheel...................	768; 15¢; R	4-5	1	2	
——Father Abraham.....................	6503; 9¢; GS	4-5	1	2	
——My Lord, what a mornin'...............	412; 15¢; R	4-7	2	2½	
——O Lord, have mercy on me..............	987; 15¢; R	4-8	3	2½	
——So sad.............................	6504; 12¢; GS	4	2	2½	Easy except Bass to E♭
——Two negro spirituals..................	5815; 12¢; GS	4-7	1	5	
(a) Dig my grave (b) Deep river					
——Were you there?.....................	423; 15¢; R	4-6	2	2½	(Also published in four parts)
Cain, Chillun' come on home..............	21; 15¢; Ho	4-9	2	2½	
——Couldn't hear nobody pray.............	7765; 15¢; GS	4-8	3	3½	
——Go down, Moses!.....................	7575; 16¢; GS	4-8	2	4½	
——I got religion.......................	7698; 15¢; GS	4-8	2	3	
——It's me, Oh Lord.....................	24; 20¢; Ho	4-8	1	3	
——Roll, chariot!.......................	81052; 16¢; F	4-11	2	3	
——Swing low, sweet chariot..............	1012; 15¢; HF	4-7	2	1½	
——Tell me, where was you?..............	81062; 16¢; F	8	3	3	
——The glory train.....................	48; 20¢; Ho	4-8	2	3	
——Wade in the water...................	7697; 15¢; GS	4-8	1	2	
——Walk together, chillun...............	3023; 15¢; GH	4-8	1	3	In Spiritual style
Clokey, (a) Mary wore three links..........	6201; 20¢; J	4-6	1	1½	
(b) 'Zek'l saw de wheel..............	....	...	...	2	
(c) Cross it yourself...............	....	...	...	1½	
——De sheepfol.......................	449; 10¢; CC	4-5	3	2½	Alto solo
Dawson, I couldn't hear nobody pray........	2008; 15¢; HF	4-7	2	3½	Soprano solo
——King Jesus is a-listening.............	2004; 15¢; HF	4	1	1½	
Dett—Don't you weep no more, Mary.........	7396; 15¢; GS	4	1	2½	
——Let us cheer the weary traveler...........	2809; 15¢; JCh	4-6	1	2½	
——Listen to the lambs...................	5956; 15¢; GS	8	2	4	
——Weeping Mary.......................	4434; 15¢; J	4-6	2	2½	T. to a' 1*
Fisher, He's the lily of the valley...........	14627; 10¢; D	4-5	1	3½	
Huguelet, Swing low, sweet chariot [*Aschenbrenner*]	4597; 15¢; C	4-8	3	2½	
Huntley, Swing low, sweet chariot..........	7150; 12¢; GS	4	1	1½	
James, Dark water....................	5509; 15¢; W	4-8	1	2	In Spiritual style
Loomis, Daniel in the lion's den..............	443; 15¢; CC	4-8	3	2	
——On Canaan shore....................	94; 15¢; CC	4	1	2	Solo voices
Pitcher, Water boy....................	821; 10¢; CC	4	1	2½	Negro work-song
Roberton, Deep river..................	1035; 12¢; HF	4	1	3	
——Negro dirge (Massa's in de cold, cold ground).	61093; 15¢; JC	4	1	3	Foster melody
——When your lamp burn down..............	1533; 12¢; Pn	4	1	2½	
Spaeth, Oh, Yes!.....................	1723; 15¢; B	4-8	1	3	
Treharne, Tell Bruddah 'lijah..........	5452; 15¢; W	4-8	1	3	
White, I'm goin' home...................	4543; 15¢; C	4-6	1	1½	
OPENING AND CLOSING CHORUSES; ENCORES; HUMOROUS SONGS; NOVELTIES					
OPENING AND CLOSING CHORUSES (Especially suitable)					
Composer:					
Arensky, To thee we sing..................	1289; 8¢; B	4	1	½	T. to g' 1*; Bass to F 1*
Bach, Now let every tongue adore Thee........	354; 15¢; EC	4	1	2	From cantata "Sleepers, Wake"
Bainton, To music.....................	501; 12¢; Ar	4	2	1	T. to a♭' 3
					* Such numerals indicate the number of times an extreme note occurs.

Composer; Title; Arranger (or, Arranger; Title)	Octavo No.; Price; Publisher	Number of Parts	Grade of Difficulty	Length in Minutes	General Remarks (Note—All music *a cappella* with piano reduction [P.R.] unless noted otherwise)
OPENING AND CLOSING CHORUSES; ENCORES; HUMOROUS SONGS; NOVELTIES—(Continued)					
OPENING AND CLOSING CHORUSES—(Cont'd)					
Cain, Calm be thy sleep	972; 15¢; GH	4-6	1	3	
——Wake up, sweet melody	7576; 16¢; GS	4-10	3	3½	
Dickinson, Music when soft voices die	32; 10¢; HW	8	1-2	1	
Elgar, Angelus	1167; 30¢; N	4-6	1	3½	
——How calmly the evening	779; 12¢; N	4	1	2	
Franz, Dedication (Widmung) [*Cain*]	7937; 10¢; GS	8	1	1½	Eng. & Ger.
Herts, Music, when soft voices die	1025; 12¢; GH	4	1	1	
Jenkins, Out of the silence wake me a song	61035; 25¢; JC	6-8	2	3	
Lasso, In hora ultima (Sweet music)	7618; 15¢; GS	6	2	2	Latin & Eng.
Miessner, Ode to music	1034; 12¢; HF	4-8	1	2½	
Mueller, Lo, God is here	7627; 15¢; GS	4-8	1	2½	
Praetorius, Sing we all now with one accord	7543; 8¢; GS	4	2	½	
Regnart, Pain at parting [*Cain*]	16; 15¢; Ho	4	1	4	Ger. & Eng.
Saar, A note of golden song	1038; 15¢; HF	4-9	1	2½	Piano optional
——Ye singers all	9; 12¢; GH	4-8	3	2½	Modern madrigal; No P.R.
Schvedof, With joyful song	1669; 16¢; EC	4-5	2	2	
Tcherepnin, Praise ye the name of the Lord	1621; 16¢; EC	4-8	....	1½	
ENCORES; HUMOROUS SONGS					
Brahms, The hump-backed fiddler	389; 20¢; R	4	1	2	Rhenish folk-song; Ger. & Eng.
Bullock, What can a young lassie do wi' an auld man	F1; 20¢; O	4	2	1	Humorous
Christy, Ain't it a shame	8371; 15¢; GS	4-8	1	2	Humorous negro song
Dargomyzhsky, The three cavaliers [*Schindler*]	6688; 20¢; GS	4-8	2	2	Humorous Russian folk-song; Short S. solo
Davis, The old woman and the pedlar	1679; 25¢; EC	4	2	2½	Eng. folk-song
De Lamarter, The de'il's awa'	2035; 12¢; Su	4-7	2	1½	
Grant-Schaefer, The little gray hen	66; 8¢; Ho	4	1	3	French-Canadian folk-song
Hadley, Bonnie sweet Robin	6782; 12¢; GS	4	1	1	
Haydn, Eloquence (Die Beredsamkeit)	2714b; —; U	4	2	2½	Ger. & Eng.; No P.R.; Humorous
——Harmonious wedlock	2714a; —; U	4	1	2½	Ger. & Eng.; No P.R.; Humorous
Horton, Pretty little miss	53; 15¢; Ho	4-6	1	2	Humorous Ky. Mt. Tune
Huber, Be on thy guard [*Cain*]	18; 15¢; Ho	4-5	1	3½	Humorous Ger. folk-song; Ger. & Eng.; No P.R.
Jones, Faith	4569; 10¢; C	4-5	1	1	Modern idiom
——Out of the dusk	4570; 10¢; C	4-8	1	1	Modern idiom
Josquin des Prés, Chanson	7134; 15¢; GS	6	2	2	Humorous chanson
Koshetz, The goldfinch's wedding [*Schindler*]	6670; 20¢; GS	4-8	2	2	Humorous Russian folk-song
——Marusia	2701; 15¢; MW	4-6	2	2	Humorous Ukrainian folk-song
——The ploughing farmers	2726; 12¢; MW	4-5	1	3	Humorous Ukrainian folk-song
Lassus, Chanson	7128; 10¢; GS	4	2	1	Humorous madrigal; Eng. & Fr.
——Chanson (Though you may be rather lean) [*Damrosch*]	7131; 10¢; GS	4	1	1½	
——Farmer, what's in your bag	5810; 9¢; GS	4	1	2½	Eng. & Ger.
——I know a young maiden	1606; 16¢; EC	4	1	2	Humorous madrigal; Ger. & Eng.
Luvaas, Ho-la-li	1056; 20¢; CC	6	2	2½	(SSATBB) Bavarian folk-song
Macfarren, Robin Goodfellow	2632; 12¢; MW	4	1	2	
Mueller, Grow old along with me	7744; 12¢; GS	5	1	1½	(SATBB)
Roberton, Mice and men	61232; 10¢; JC	4	1	2	Humorous Scotch dialect
Rowley, Fair Sally	1042MT; 12¢; N	4	2	1½	Humorous

RECOMMENDED *A CAPPELLA* OCTAVO MUSIC FOR MIXED VOICES

Composer; Title; Arranger (or, Arranger; Title)	Octavo No.; Price; Publisher	Number of Parts	Grade of Difficulty	Length in Minutes	General Remarks (Note—All music *a cappella* with piano reduction [P.R.] unless noted otherwise)
OPENING AND CLOSING CHORUSES; ENCORES; HUMOROUS SONGS; NOVELTIES—*(Continued)*					
ENCORES; HUMOROUS SONGS—*(Cont'd)*					
Saar, Lullaby	5480; 15¢; GS	6	2	2	(SSATB); S. or T. solo to high b♭ 1; Eng. & Ger.
Smith, I won't kiss Katy [*Aschenbrenner*]	4596; 15¢; C	4-8	1-2	2½	Humorous Jugo-Slav folk-song
——The peasant and his oxen [*Aschenbrenner*]	4595; 15¢; C	4-8	1-2	2	Humorous Jugo-Slav folk-song
Thiman, Oh, no John	1052; 12¢; N	4-5	2	1½	Humorous Eng. folk-song
Thompson, Cousin Jedediah [*Clokey*]	6209; 12¢; J	6	1	1½	Humorous Early American
Treharne, Mother and daughter	1847; 15¢; B	3-6	1	3½	Humorous Hungarian folk-song
——The monkey's wedding	5377; 20¢; W	4	1	3	Humorous Tenn. folk-song
Williams, L., Song of the pedlar	1006; 15¢; N	4	1	2½	Text from Shakespeare
NOVELTIES					
Archer, Ave Maria	999; 20¢; CC	8	1	2	Humming cho. with S. obbl.
Bantock, Milking song	61062; 10¢; JC	6	1	1	Hebridian air; Alto solo
Benelli, Song of the drummer	805; 20¢; R	4	1	1½	Baritone solo
Christy, Scotch bagpipes (The Campbells are comin')	7904; 12¢; GS	5	1	2	Descriptive novelty (SATBB)
——The frogs	7905; 12¢; GS	4	1	1	Old round extended
Chopin, Choral nocturne [*Mueller*]	7810; 10¢; GS	8	1	2	Humming chorus
Dett, Music in the mine	6580; 20¢; GS	4	1	5	Tenor solo to a♭'; Modern idiom
Fontaine, Some like dogs [*Christy*]	7906; 12¢; GS	1-5	1	1½	(SSATB); Humorous round extended
Grainger, I'm seventeen come Sunday	6098; 18¢; GS	4-5	1	3	Brass band acc. optional
Holst, Matthew, Mark, Luke, and John	61085; 10¢; JC	4-7	1	1	Bagpipe effect in humming acc.
Knyvett-Stewart, The bells of St. Michael's Tower	2472; 15¢; GS	5	2	2½	Descriptive; humorous
Lasso, Audite nove [*Widmann*]	5809; 9¢; GS	4	1	2½	Humorous
Malin, Jenny Nettles	1069; 20¢; CC	6	2	2	Scotch folk-song; bagpipe effect (SSATBB)
Martini, The tickling trio	2750; 10¢; MW	3	1	1	(SAB); No P.R.
Rimsky-Korsakoff, Spinning top	12847; 15¢; D	1-4	2	½	Bass to e♭ 4; descriptive
Stanford, The train	28; 15¢; St	4-8	2	1	Modern idiom
Tchaikovsky, Andante cantabile [*Mueller*]	7815; 20¢; GS	7	3	5	S. to d''' 1*; humming chorus from String Quartet, Op. 11
Van Der Stucken, Laughing song	5110; 15¢; GS	4	3	1½	Humorous
Venables, Bells of Aberdovy	2171; 12¢; GS	4-6	1	2	Welsh air
SONGS FOR SPECIAL OCCASIONS (CHRISTMAS; EASTER; MAY DAY OR SPRING FESTIVAL; PATRIOTIC HOLIDAYS—THANKSGIVING; ARMISTICE DAY; DECORATION DAY; Etc.)					
CHRISTMAS					
Bach, Break forth, O beauteous heav'nly light	302; 8¢; EC	4	1	½	Chorale from "Christmas Oratorio"
——I stand beside the manger	7555; 10¢; GS	4	1	3	
——Planets, stars, and airs of space	7554; 10¢; GS	4	1	2	
Baird, Ancient carol of the shepherds	2617; 15¢; MW	4-6	1	1	S. and A. solos
Barnes, When Christ was born of Mary free	7300; 12¢; GS	4	1	2	Old Fr. melody
Bornschein, Christmas folk-song	6617; 15¢; J	4-6	2	2½	
Burleigh, Go tell it on de mountains	817; 15¢; R	4-5	1	3½	Organ or piano optional; spiritual
					*Such numerals indicate the number of times an extreme note occurs.

RECOMMENDED *A CAPPELLA* OCTAVO MUSIC FOR MIXED VOICES

Composer; Title; Arranger (or, Arranger; Title)	Octavo No.; Price; Publisher	Number of Parts	Grade of Difficulty	Length in Minutes	General Remarks (Note—All music *a cappella* with piano reduction [P.R.] unless noted otherwise)
SONGS FOR SPECIAL OCCASIONS (CHRISTMAS; EASTER; MAY DAY OR SPRING FESTIVAL; PATRIOTIC HOLIDAYS—THANKSGIVING; ARMISTICE DAY; DECORATION DAY; Etc.)—(Continued)					
CHRISTMAS—(Continued)					
Christiansen, In dulci jubilo	90; 15¢; A	8	2	2½	From 14th century
——Lullaby on Christmas eve	136; 15¢; A	4-8	2	1½	S. solo
——Night, and a lonely star	85; 18¢; A	8	3	3½	
——Sighing soul, hear	77; 6¢; A	4	1	1½	
——Today there is ringing	63; 10¢; A	4-5	1	1½	
Cornelius, Christmas song	2557; 8¢; GS	4	1	2	Alto or Bar. solo
Curtis, Dar's a star in de east	1002; 20¢; H	6	2	2	Negro Christmas song
——Mary's baby	1001; 20¢; H	7	2	3	Negro Christmas song
Davis, In the bleak mid-winter	1647; 18¢; EC	4	2	2	
——Noël of the Bressen waits	1668; 18¢; EC	4	1	3	Old Fr. melody; Alto solo
——Out of your sleep arise and wake	1659; 16¢; EC	4	2	1½	15th century carol
——Pat-a-pan	1616; 18¢; EC	4	1	2	Burgundian air; Fr. & Eng.
Dett, Wasn't that a mighty day?	7712; 16¢; GS	4	3	3½	Spiritual
Dickinson, The angels and the shepherds	111; 12¢; HW	3-7	1	1½	Traditional Bohemian
——Holy angels singing	163; 12¢; HW	4	1	2½	Russian
——O nightingale, awake	179; 15¢; HW	4	1	1½	Swiss folk-song
——The shepherds' story	30; 15¢; HW	8	2	3	S., T., and Bar. solos
Eccard, From heaven's heights I come to you	14; 10¢; C	5	1	1	16th century (SSATB)
Fischer, The song of Mary	7659; 15¢; GS	7	3	3	(SSATTBB)
Franck, The Virgin by the Manger [*Christy*]	8374; 16¢; GS	4-8	2	3	Plaintive
Ganschow, Sleep, holy babe	2042; 16¢; HF	8	2	3½	Alto solo
Gevaert, A joyful Christmas song	5075; 15¢; GS	2-4	1	3	
——The sleep of the Child Jesus	2610; 12¢; MW	4	1	1½	
Graham, A carol	922; 15¢; R	4-8	1	2	S. solo
Grieg, By the cradle	9028; 10¢; GS	4-8	2	2	
Hassler, Angelus ad pastores (The angel said unto the shepherds)	1227; 18¢; EC	4	2	3	16th c. motet; Latin & Eng. (SSATTB)
Herzogenberg, Christmas song	2553; 12¢; GS	6	2	2	
Ippolitov-Ivanov, Russian Christmas Hymn [*Christy*]	8431; 12¢; GS	4-8	1	2½	Novel humming chorus
Jüngst, While, by my sheep [*Christy*]	8370; 15¢; GS	4-8	1	3	17th c. hymn; echo effect
Koshetz, Out of the darkness	2739; 15¢; MW	4	1	1½	Ukrainian church
——Let the world rejoice	2723; 12¢; MW	4-6	3	1½	Ukrainian carol
Lutkin, All my heart this night rejoices	2021; 20¢; HF	4-6	2	5½	Motet for two choirs
——The waits are singing in the lane	917; 10¢; HW	4-5	1	2	
Luvaas, Hark, now, O shepherds	840; 15¢; CC	4-8	1	1½	Moravian melody
Nunn, Bring a torch, Jeannette, Isabella	364; 12¢; EC	4	1	1½	Old Fr. melody
Percival, The stork she rose on Christmas Eve	864; 12¢; CC	4	1	2	Yorkshire carol
Praetorius, Lo, how a rose e'er blooming	2484; 6¢; GS	4	1	1½	
Rowley, Man, be merry	A23; 16¢; C	4	1	2	
Saar, Come in, dear angels	369; 10¢; C	4-5	1	½	Swiss folk-carol
——Joseph dearest, Joseph mild	370; 16¢; C	4	1	2½	S. or T. solo; violin obbl.
——My heart I here would give thee	368; 10¢; C	4-5	1	1	Claussen hymn 1653
——O Jesu, so fair	362; 10¢; C	4-8	1	1½	Early 17th century
Schumann, Mary's cradle song of the twelfth day	——; 15¢; A	4-7	1	3	Ger. & Eng.
Shaw, How far is it to Bethlehem	245; 12¢; N	4-6	1	1½	
Skinner, The Christ-Child lay on Mary's lap	993; 12¢; CC	4-7	1	1½	Phrygian mode
Somervell, The Grasmere carol	513; 16¢; O	4	1	2	
Thiman, The holly and the ivy (Old English carol)	1018; 12¢; N	4	1	2½	
Vardell, Christmas evocation	1189; 15¢; HW	4-8	2	3½	
Warrel, Bethlehem night	759; 16¢; O	4-8	2	2	
Westbrook, In dulci jubilo	363; 16¢; EC	4	2	3½	Ancient Ger. carol
Whitehead, The croon carol	354; 16¢; C	4	2	3½	S. or A. solo; old Ger. carol
——A Flemish Christmas cradle song	379; 15¢; C	4-6	1	4	S. solo
——Masters in this hall	281; 18¢; C	4	2	3	Fr. carol
——Now Christmas day is come	420; 15¢; C	4-5	2	1½	Irish carol
——This endris night	353; 12¢; C	4-5	1	1½	Eng. carol
——When Caesar Augustus	355; 15¢; C	3-4	1	3	Eng. carol
——Whence, O shepherd maiden	1756; 20¢; B	8	2	2½	S. solo; Fr.-Can. folk-song
Willan, The three kings	718; 20¢; O	3-8	2	3	

Composer; Title; Arranger (or, Arranger; Title)	Octavo No.; Price; Publisher	Number of Parts	Grade of Difficulty	Length in Minutes	General Remarks (Note—All music *a cappella* with piano reduction [P.R.] unless noted otherwise)
SONGS FOR SPECIAL OCCASIONS (CHRISTMAS; EASTER; MAY DAY OR SPRING FESTIVAL; PATRIOTIC HOLIDAYS—THANKSGIVING; ARMISTICE DAY; DECORATION DAY; Etc.)—(*Continued*)					
EASTER					
Aichinger, He is risen (Regina coeli)	7706; 12¢; GS	4	1	2	16th century Ger.
Bach, Up, up! My heart with gladness	1640; 16¢; EC	4-5	1	2	Eng. & Ger.
Brahms, O Savior, burst the heavenly bound	3025; 25¢; GH	4	2	3½	Motet based on Ger. folk-lyric
Christiansen, Easter bells	173; 15¢; A	4-8	3	3	Short S. solo
Dickinson, In Joseph's lovely garden	135; 15¢; HW	4	1	3	S. solo; trad. Spanish air
Gallus, Ascendit Deus (God goes up on high)	83; 20¢; AM	5	2	2	Latin & Eng.
Gaul, The three holy women	12597; 12¢; D	4	1	1½	Norman carol
Goldsworthy, The King of sorrow	940; 15¢; R	4	2	3	Piano optional
Handel, Then round about the starry throne [*Christy*]	8369; 16¢; GS	4-8	2	3	From "Samson"; piano *ad lib.*
Leisring, Ye sons and daughters of the King	379; 16¢; EC	8	2	1½	Double chorus
Lundquist, Old Latin hymn (Kyrie Eleison)	5500; 10¢; W	4	1	1½	
Makarov, An angel said to Mary	1203; 16¢; EC	4-7	1	2	
Marryott, The world itself is blithe and gay	1312; 15¢; HW	4-8	1	5	Ger. melody
Koshetz, Legend (Canticle)	2725; 12¢; MW	4	2	3½	Bar. solo; Ukrainian folk-song
——Crucifixion	2773; 12¢; MW	4	1	3	Ukrainian folk-song
Olds, Sunrise on Easter morning	473; 15¢; C	4-8	1	1½	Brass choir *ad. lib.*
Schubert, Christ is arisen	CM 187; 10¢; C	4	1	5	
Thompson, Spring bursts today	1223; 15¢; HW	4-7	2	2	Two S. solo voices
Treharne, O blest Redeemer	1887; 20¢; B	8	3	2½	14th century Latin hymn
Wetzel, Knight of Bethlehem	961; 12¢; GH	4-8	2	2	
Willan, Rise up, my love, my fair one	5; 15¢; O	4	3	1	
Wood, 'Tis the day of Resurrection	1171; 25¢; CC	8	2	4	Modern motet
SPRING FESTIVAL; MAY DAY					
Arcadelt, Now spring in all her glory	2439; 8¢; GS	4	2	2	T. to a' 1*
Byrd, This sweet and merry month of May	5; 24¢; O	6	2	2	Madrigal (SSATTB)
Davies, When summer's merry days come in	61013; 15¢; JC	4	1	1½	
Grieg, Springtide [*Baldwin*]	9029; 12¢; GS	4-8	1	4	
Jores, An April song	7705; 10¢; GS	4	1	2½	
Macfarlane, A May carol	532; 20¢; GH	4	3	4	
Mendelssohn, Winter's done [*Luvaas*]	2621; 15¢; MW	4	1	2½	
Morley, Now is the month of Maying	2267; 6¢; GS	5	2	1	(SATTB); Old Eng. ballet
Sinigaglia, All hail, O May	310; 16¢; EC	4	3	1½	Eng. & Fr.
MOTHER'S DAY					
Roberton, The old woman	1536; 10¢; Pn	4	1	½	
NEW YEAR					
Koshetz, On New Year's Day	2752; 15¢; MW	4-6	3	3	Ukrainian carol
Praetorius, Now is the old year passed away	7541; 15¢; GS	4	1	2	
FUNERAL ANTHEMS (Especially Suitable)					
Ingegneri, Behold and see [*Lundquist*]	5504; 15¢; W	4	1	4	
Palestrina, O gentle death (Soave fia il morir)	5600; 12¢; GS	5	1	3½	
PATRIOTIC (Memorial Day, Armistice Day, Thanksgiving, *etc.*)					
Davis, Morning comes early	1667; 16¢; EC	4	2	1½	Thanksgiving; Slovakian reapers' song
Forsyth, The new dawn	219; 12¢; HW	4-6	2	2½	
Grainger, Recessional	7520; 15¢; GS	5-8	2	6	Acc. optional
Loeffler, For one who fell in battle	5536; 25¢; GS	8	3	10	
Lutkin, The Lord bless you and keep you	1089; 8¢; Su	4	1	1½	Benediction
Sibelius, Our native hills [*Ross*]	77; 15¢; AM	4-5	1	3	From "Finlandia"
Stringham, The pilgrim fathers	443; 15¢; HW	4-8	2	3	
Treharne, How sleep the brave	81006; 16¢; F	4	1	2	*Such numerals indicate the number of times an extreme note occurs.

RECOMMENDED COLLECTIONS FOR MIXED VOICES

Note: The majority of the following books are for *a cappella* chorus with accompaniment included for rehearsal; some texts have partially *a cappella* and partially accompanied material. Books are listed according to the date of their publication.

1. "The Art of A Cappella Singing" by John Smallman and E. H. Wilcox. Oliver Ditson Co., Inc., 1933. Price $2.00, cloth-bound.
   A combination text-book and song-book. The problems of each chapter are illustrated by appropriate music, fourteen four- or five-part choruses of easy to moderately difficult grades being included. Phonetically spelled text in the musical examples especially good for teaching correct diction.

2. "Master Choruses" selected by Hugh Ross, John Smallman and H. Alexander Matthews. Oliver Ditson Co., Inc., 1933. Price $1.00, for vocal parts, board-bound—$3.00 for complete edition, cloth-bound.
   Contains 49 sacred choruses of moderate to difficult grade, carefully selected and edited: 15 *a cappella*; 34 with organ or piano accompaniment. For the more advanced chorus. (Orchestra parts available for the accompanied numbers.)

3. Program Choruses
   (a) "Red Book of Program Choruses", carefully compiled and edited by Noble Cain, Walter H. Butterfield, Walter Goodell and Glenn H. Woods. Hall & McCreary Co., 1933. Price 35c., paper-bound; 80c., cloth-bound.
   Contains 79 choruses, majority easy to moderately difficult: 35 *a cappella* choruses for mixed voices; 18 choruses for mixed voices with accompaniment; 12 choruses for treble voices; 8 choruses for male voices; 6 unison choruses. Adapted to junior high schools, high schools, colleges, and adult choirs.
   (b) "Green Book of Program Choruses", carefully compiled and edited by George Oscar Bowen, Noble Cain, Walter Goodell, Richard W. Grant, R. Lee Osburn, and Glenn Woods. Hall & McCreary Co., 1930. Price 35c., paper-bound; 80c., cloth-bound.
   Contains 76 songs adapted to junior high schools, high schools, colleges, and adult choirs: 18 *a cappella* mixed choruses; 24 choruses with piano or instrumental accompaniment; remainder of book devoted to 2-, 3-, and 4-part arrangements for male and for treble voices. Majority of numbers easy to medium difficulty.

4. "The A Cappella Chorus Book" edited by Dr. F. Melius Christiansen and Noble Cain. Oliver Ditson Co., Inc., 1932. Price $1.00, board-bound.
   Contains 27 choruses of easy to moderate difficulty, carefully selected and edited: 16 secular and 11 sacred, in 4 to 8 parts.

5. "The Junior A Cappella Chorus Book" edited by Olaf C. Christiansen and Carol M. Pitts. Oliver Ditson Co., Inc., 1932. Price $1.00, board-bound.
   Contains 38 choruses, carefully selected and edited, especially suitable for junior or senior high schools or beginning choral groups: 9 two- and three-part choruses; 27 four-part; 2 five-part.

6. "The A Cappella Chorus" edited by Griffith J. Jones and Max T. Krone. M. Witmark & Sons, 1931 and 1932. Carefully selected and edited, in a graded course. Price 60c. per volume, paper-bound.
    Volume III. (SAB.) 16 easy to difficult three-part songs.
    Volume IV. (SATB.) 12 easy to moderately difficult four-part songs.
    Volume V. (SATB.) 10 easy to moderatey difficult four-part songs.
    (Slightly more advanced than Volume III.)

7. "Choral Miscellany for Mixed Voices", The Boston Music Co., 1929. Chorus book. Price $1.00, cloth-bound.
    9 *a cappella* and 7 accompanied four-part choruses, easy to moderately difficult.

8. "Standard Part Songs for Schools, Colleges and Choral Societies" edited by Hollis Dann. H. W. Gray Co., 1928. Price $1.50, board-bound.
    22 easy to moderately difficult choruses: 13 *a cappella*; 9 accompanied; orchestral parts available for some choruses.

9. Small, inexpensive collections suitable for *a cappella* choruses, published by Hall & McCreary Co.
    (a) "Forty Spirituals" arranged by Walter Goodell; easy four-part; price 12c.
    (b) "Four Noble Cain Choruses" (O Watchers of the Stars; Almighty God; O Lord Send the Fire; The Crystal Hunters); 4-8 part, medium difficulty; price 12c.
    (c) "Four-Part Choruses" No. 13. Nine easy four- or five-part choruses arranged by Noble Cain. One number by Walter Goodell. Price 12c.
    (d) "Madrigals and A Cappella Choruses". Thirteen easy four-part choruses edited by Noble Cain. Price 20c.
    (e) "Select A Cappella Choruses". Fourteen easy to medium difficult four- to eight-part choruses edited by Noble Cain. Price 20c.
    (f) "The Dett Collection of Negro Spirituals" by R. Nathaniel Dett; four groups, Nos. 13, 14, 15, and 16 of the H. & M. Auditorium Series; each group has 14 to 28 arrangements of spirituals, mostly easy; price 20c. each.

10. Negro Spiritual collections: (Note—See also No. 9f, above).
    (a) "Thirty-six South Carolina Spirituals", collected and harmonized by Carl Diton; unaccompanied, mostly easy, four-part; price $1.50; G. Schirmer, Inc.

2. MUSIC FOR MEN'S VOICES

Remarks on the List of Recommended Octavo Music for Men's Voices

1. For two-part music with piano accompaniment, suitable for male voices, see "One- and Two-Part Music with Descant" and "Two-Part Music", p. 132.
2. For the sake of brevity, music is listed under only the one heading under which it seems most appropriate. It may be necessary to look under a number of different headings in order to find all music by a certain composer or arranger.
3. It must not be presumed that all music listed under such headings as "Humorous Encore" or "Novelty" is of a lower musical quality than that listed under other headings; most of the music listed under such headings is good enough to be regularly programmed.
4. This list features secular music; only those sacred compositions especially suitable for secular performance as well are included.
5. The music listed includes both accompanied and unaccompanied with piano reduction for rehearsal, unless otherwise noted. Unaccompanied (*a cappella*) music is identified in the "General Remarks" column by the abbreviation "U".
6. Music is listed alphabetically under the different headings by composer (or arranger).
7. In case the same composition is published in arrangements of equal worth by two different firms, the lower-priced issue is listed; if the price is the same, both issues are listed.
8. A key to abbreviations of publishers will be found on p. 93; to grade-of-difficulty estimates, exact pitch indications, and other abbreviations, on p. 94.
9. When extremes of range are reached more than six times, no numeral follows the letter.
10. The performance-time indicated is an estimate; it is not to be considered exact for purposes of radio or concert.
11. It is suggested that directors seeking suitable new music for their groups will save time and receive the greatest value from the music catalogued here by proceeding in general as follows:
    a. Find the sections which list the type of music in which you are most interested.
    b. Determine from the grade of difficulty, the composer-arranger, the title of the composition, and general remarks, which music seems most promising. In most cases, single copies may be secured on approval.
    c. Select by careful review from these "On Approval" copies the music which seems most suitable for your group.
12. Every effort has been directed by the compiler towards making all the information given correct. However, prices change, grades of difficulty differ with each chorus, performance-time varies with the tempo chosen, *etc*. The reader should consider all the information given only as approximately exact.

RECOMMENDED OCTAVO MUSIC FOR MEN'S VOICES

Composer; Title; Arranger (or, Arranger; Title)	Octavo No.; Price; Publisher	Number of Parts	Grade of Difficulty	Highest Tenor Note (Above e') Number of Times	Lowest Bass Note (Below G) Number of Times	Length in Minutes	General Remarks
MUSIC OF THE SIXTEENTH, SEVENTEENTH, AND EIGHTEENTH CENTURIES (Madrigals, Motets, Glees, Chansons, Canzonets, Chorales, etc.)							
ENGLISH							
Arne, When icicles hang by the wall [*Barratt*]	14; 10¢; JF	4	2	g'	......	2	
Bartlett, When from my love I look for love [*Malin*]	1059; 10¢; CC	4	1	g'1	......	2	U
Byrd, Sacerdotes Domini [*G. W. W.*]	906; 15¢; EC	4	3	bb'1	......	2	U; Latin
Dallio, Willow song [*Barratt*]	3; 10¢; JF	4	2	a'2	......	2	U *ad lib.*
Dowland, Come again, sweet love [*Davison*]	35; 12¢; EC	4	2	ab'2	F 2	2½	U
Handel, He saw the lovely youth [*Dawe*]	8019; 20¢; GS	4	2	ab'3	......	3	From "Theodora"
Johnson, Full fathom five thy father lies [*Barratt*]	15; 10¢; JF	4	1	g'1	......	1½	
Morley, April is in my mistress' face [*Davison*]	939; 15¢; EC	4	3	ab'3	F 2	1½	U
——Dainty, fine, sweet nymph [*Davison*]	43; 12¢; EC	4	2	a'3	......	2	U
——Fire, fire, my heart [*Davison*]	71; 16¢; EC	4	3	g'	F	3	U; Bar. to f'
——My bonny lass [*Davison*]	20; 12¢; EC	4	2	g'	......	2	U
Paxton, How sweet, how fresh this vernal day [*Davison*]	924; 15¢; EC	4	3	ab'3	F 6	1½	U
Purcell, Let the fifes and the clarions	377; 12¢; O	2	1	f#'	......	2	From "The Fairy Queen"
——Passing by [*Burleigh*]	754; 15¢; R	4	2	g'3	F	1½	U
Weelkes, The nightingale [*Davison*]	49; 15¢; EC	3	1	f'6	......	2	U
GERMAN							
Bach, Grant us to do with zeal [*Davison*]	29; 8¢; EC	4	2	a'2	......	1	U
——Jesu, joy of man's desiring [*Davison*]	96; 16¢; EC	4	2	bb'1	E 3	2½	Flute obbl. *ad lib.*
——Song of death [*Schumann*]	4969; 10¢; GS	4	2	a'1	F 2	2	U
Bach, W. F., No blade of grass can flourish [*Frank*]	5678; 5¢; GS	4	2	ab'6	Eb 4	1½	U *ad lib.*; Eng. & Ger.
Schütz, Since Christ our Lord was crucified [*Davison*]	88; 15¢; EC	4	3	a'3	E 1	2½	
Walther-Bach, Out of the depths I cry to Thee [*G. W. W.*]	904; 12¢; EC	4	2	a'3	F 1	2	
ITALIAN							
Allegri, Miserere mei Deus [*Davison*]	27; 15¢; EC	4	1	f'2	......	1½	U; Latin
Anerio, Christus factus est [*Davison*]	922; 15¢; EC	4	3	ab'3	Eb 1	2½	U; Latin
Caldara, O glade so friendly (Selve Amiche) [*Madrone*]	2548; 15¢; MW	4	2	g'2	F 1	2	U; Eng. & Latin
Lotti, Vere languores nostros [*Davison*]	70; 15¢; EC	3	1	g'1	......	2½	U; Latin
Palestrina, Adoramus te [*Davison*]	44; 15¢; EC	4	2	g'1	F	3	U; Latin; Antiphonal
——Ecce, quomodo moritur [*Davison*]	45; 15¢; EC	4	2	g'		3	U; Latin
——Improperia [*Davison*]	46; 15¢; EC	4	2	g'2	F 2	3	U; Latin
——O bone Jesu (O holy Father)	527; 10¢; EC	4	1	g'2	F 3	1	U; Latin & Eng.
Viadana, O sacrum convivium [*Davison*]	78; 15¢; EC	4	3	g#'4	F# 4	2	U; Latin
NETHERLANDISH							
Arcadelt, Ave Maria	526; 12¢; EC	4	2	g'5	......	2	U; Eng. & Latin
Lasso, Echo song [*Davison*]	69; 20¢; EC	8	2	g'1	......	1½	U; Double chorus; Antiphonal
——Matona, lovely maiden [*Davison*]	26; 16¢; EC	4	3	ab'3	Eb 4	2½	U

Composer; Title; Arranger (or, Arranger; Title)	Octavo No.; Price; Publisher	Number of Parts	Grade of Difficulty	Highest Tenor Note (Above e') Number of Times	Lowest Bass Note (Below G) Number of Times	Length in Minutes	General Remarks
MUSIC OF THE NINETEENTH AND TWENTIETH CENTURIES							
AMERICAN							
Andersen, O Captain, my Captain!....	4005; 15¢; HF	4-5	2	a'2	F# 1	2½	U
Andrews, Now sleeps the crimson petal.	7049; 10¢; GS	4	2	a'1	....	1	U
——The splendour falls	4739; 10¢; GS	4	2	a#'1	....	2	U; no P.R.
Bliss, Red man's death chant	2269; 12¢; JCh	4	3	bb'1	F 3	2	
Brooke, The mountain pine	810; 10¢; GH	3	1	f'4	....	1½	
Buck, Twilight	1019; 15¢; GS	4	3	a'3	F 3	4	U; no P.R.
Bullard, Winter song	12945; 12¢; D	4	1	g'1	....	3½	U *ad lib.*
Cadman, The builder [*Treharne*]	2011; 16¢; F	4	1	g'	....	3	
——The master of the forge	82063; 16¢; F	4	1	g'5	....	4	Bar. solo
Cain, Indian serenade	55; 20¢; Ho	4	3	a'5	F# 6	5	U
Candlyn, Dream-pedlary	2159; 15¢; C	4	1	f#'1	....	2	U
Charles, My lady walks in loveliness [*Treharne*]	7868; 12¢; GS	4	1	ab'1	Eb 1	2	
Curran, Dawn [*Deis*]	9065; 10¢; GS	4	2	ab'1	E 1	2	U; optional bb'
Clokey, The wind	3067; 8¢; Su	4-7	3	bb'1	F	1	U
Del Riego, Homing [*Lucas*]	1014; 15¢; CH	4	2	f#'1	....	2½	
Flagler, Boots	82078; 18¢; F	4	1	......	....	3	Kipling's text
Foster, Come where my love lies dreaming [*Spicker*]	5137; 12¢; GS	4	2	a'1	F	3	U
——Swanee river [*Roberton*]	1560; 12¢; Pn	4	2	a'1	E 1	2	U; Tenor melody
Gaines, The night has a thousand eyes.	5595; 12¢; GS	4	2	ab'2	F	1	U
Gaul, Poe's Fordham prayer	—; 15¢; R	4	2	a'2	E 1	3½	U
Hageman, Christ went up into the hills [*Saar*]	2135; 15¢; C	4	2	a'1	....	3½	Tenor solo
Hastings, Miller's song	5365; 12¢; GS	4	2	a'2	F#2	1½	U; Bar. solo
Huhn, Invictus [*Lynes*]	369; 12¢; AP	4	2	g'3	F# 2	1½	
Kountz, Cossack love song [*Treharne*]	7871; 12¢; GS	4	2	bb'2	......	2	Lower tenor part optional
——Fair maiden	2009; 15¢; F	4	1	......	F 6	1	U
——The sleigh [*Baldwin*]	9070; 12¢; GS	4	2	g'	....	½	Optional high bb'
Lester, The arrow and the song	6886; 10¢; GS	4	2	a'1	......	2	U; no P.R.
——The northland	3054; 12¢; Su	4	2	a'1	....	3½	
Macfarlane, Hymn to the night	7677; 12¢; GS	4	3	ab'4	F 2	2	U; High tenor solo
Merwin, Blow, blow, thou winter wind.	702; 20¢; R	4	3	b'2	E# 1	4	
Miller, Boats of mine [*Treharne*]	2013; 15¢; F	4	2	g'5	....	3	
Nevin, Little Boy Blue [*Treharne*]	1855; 15¢; B	4	1	f#'2	....	2	U
——The rosary	233; 15¢; B	4	2	ab'1	Eb 1	2	U; T. or S. solo
——Venetian love song [*Humphries*]	2569; 12¢; JCh	4	2	ab'3	Eb 4	3	U
Protheroe, Allah	4017; 15¢; HF	4	2	g#'2	....	3	
——Daphne's cheeks	4108; 15¢; HF	4	2	ab'3	....	2½	U
——Song of the western men	4001; 12¢; HF	4	1	g'1	....	1½	
Redding, The silver lanterns of the night	6874; 10¢; GS	4	2	a'1	F 1	1½	U
Speaks, Morning [*Baldwin*]	9076; 15¢; GS	4	2	a'2	....	2	
——Sylvia [*Gaines*]	9078; 12¢; GS	4	2	g'	....	3	
Test, Winds [*Huntley*]	1067; 16¢; GH	4	3	a'1	....	1½	
Townsley, The windy night [*Stevens*]	864; 15¢; R	4	1	gb'1	F 6	1½	
Warren, Eleanor, Autumn sunset in the Canyon	438; 15¢; HW	4	3	a'1	Eb 1	2½	
Werrenrath, Cavalier's song	5668; 12¢; GS	4	2	ab'3	F 1	1½	U
Woodman, At the wind's call	6222; 12¢; GS	4-6	3	bb'2	Eb 2	2	U
BOHEMIAN							
Dvořák, Around us hear the sounds of even [*Davison*]	36; 16¢; EC	4-5	3	g'	Eb 2	3½	U; Bass to low D optional
——Goin' home [*Fisher*]	13696; 15¢; D	4-5	2	ab'1	Eb 3	4½	T. and Bar. solos
ENGLISH							
Balfe, Excelsior [*Smith*]	6183; 20¢; Pr	4	2	a'3	......	2½	Short T. solo
Bantock, Lock the door, Lariston	1566; 12¢; Pn	4	3	bb'1	F 2	1½	U; Scotch traditional border ballad

Composer; Title; Arranger (or, Arranger; Title)	Octavo No.; Price; Publisher	Number of Parts	Grade of Difficulty	Highest Tenor Note (Above e′) Number of Times	Lowest Bass Note (Below G) Number of Times	Length in Minutes	General Remarks
MUSIC OF THE NINETEENTH AND TWENTIETH CENTURIES—(*Continued*)							
ENGLISH—(Continued)							
Bantock, Lucifer in starlight	516; 25¢; N	6	3	b′3	F	3½	U
——O Zeus the King	615; 20¢; O	4	1	f#′1	......	1½	U
——Requiem	448; 15¢; CC	4	2	g♭′	F 1	3	U
——Silent strings	1455; 15¢; Bo	4	1	g′1	......	2½	
——Through eastern gates	8118; 25¢; GS	4	3	a#′2	......	3	
——Twilight tombs of ancient kings	50595; 25¢; JC	4	3	bb′2	E♭ 1	5	U; Bar. solo
——War song of the Saracens	50575; 25¢; JC	4-8	3	b′1	......	3	U
——Zeus, Lord of Heaven	30; 30¢; AM	4-8	3	b′1	F 2	1½	U
Cowen, Border ballad [*Pitcher*]	991; 16¢; CC	4	1	f#′1	......	2	Vigorous
Davies, Hymn before action	329; 15¢; N	4	2	g#′1	F 1	2½	U
Elgar, After many a dusty mile	364; 20¢; N	4	2	a′1	F 5	1½	U
——As torrents in summer	641; 12¢; N	4	2	a′2	......	1½	U
——Feasting I watch	366; 20¢; N	4	3	a′3	......	1½	U
——It's O! To be a wild wind	365; 12¢; N	4	2	f′2	E 2	½	U
——Yea, cast me from heights of the mountains	362; 15¢; N	4	2	a′1	F 2	1	U
Fletcher, The lee shore	602; 15¢; N	4	3	bb′1	F# 3	2½	U
Forsyth, I was a king in Babylon	2068; 25¢; C	4	2	bb′1	F 3	3½	Optional Bass to D
——Tell me not of a lovely lass	159; 10¢; HW	4	1	f′5	F 4	1½	
Gardiner, Sir Eglamore	555; 15¢; N	4	3	bb′3	F	3	U
German, O peaceful night	370; 15¢; N	4	2	g′2	F	2½	U
Gibbs, The old soldier	50620; 16¢; JC	4	2	a′5	F 3	2½	U
——The silver penny	50621; 16¢; JC	4	3	bb′1	F 1	1½	U
——Tiger, tiger	3072; 15¢; Bo	4	3	a′2	E 2	2	U; modern
Holst, Hymn to Soma	292; 10¢; HW	4	2	a′2	F 1	1½	
Jenkins, Battle of Ivry	50532; 25¢; JC	4-8	3	a′1	F 3	3½	U
Jones, Silent strings	1530; 15¢; Bo	4	2	ab′4	F 1	3½	
Lyon, Men of Eric	50608; 25¢; JC	4	3	a′	F 1	2½	U
Maunder, Border ballad	—; 15¢; N	3-4	2	g′	F 2	2½	
Rhodes, Bring from the craggy haunts	603; 20¢; O	4-6	2	a′2	......	1½	U
Roberton, All in the April evening	50666; 10¢; JC	4	2	ab′1	E♭ 3	2½	U
——The miller's daughter	1561; 10¢; Pn	4	2	a′2	E 4	1½	U
——Remembrance	8115; 10¢; GS	4	2	g′4	D 1	2	U
——The winter it is passed	50651; 10¢; JC	4	1	g′6	......	2	U
Shaw, Hey Robin, jolly Robin	—; 20¢; JWm	4	2	ab′4	......	1½	
Stephen, He is gone on the mountain	1576; 16¢; Pn	4	2	a′2	......	2	U *ad lib.*
Sullivan, The long day closes	7276; 9¢; GS	4	2	a′1	E 1	3	U *ad lib.*
——The lost chord [*Brewer*]	1509; 12¢; GS	4	2	a′2	E 2	5	Organ, strings, and flute *ad lib.*
Vaughan Williams, Fain would I change that note	603; 12¢; N	4	2	a′4	F 2	2½	U; Canzonet
Willan, Border ballad	2153; 15¢; C	4	3	a′5	......	2½	
Williams, G., Come, shepherds, follow me	601; 24¢; O	4	3	a′	E 1	1½	U
FRENCH							
Franck, Chorus of camel drivers [*Davison*]	63; 25¢; EC	3-4	2	ab′3	......	4	From "Rebecca"
——Far o'er the bay	64; 16¢; EC	4	3	bb′1	......	3½	S. or T. solo
Gounod, By Babylon's wave [*Bergen*]	—; 25¢; GH	4	2	g′	E♭ 3	4½	
——Chorus of Bacchantes [*Davison*]	37; 16¢; EC	4	1	g′3	......	2	
——Soldiers' chorus [*O'Shea*]	266; 12¢; CC	4	1	gb′3	......	3	Simplified arr.
Hahn, Rapturous hour [*Gilbert*]	6651; 15¢; J	4	2	ab′4	......	1½	Fr. & Eng.
Massenet, The monks and the pirates	1330; 6¢; GS	4	3	bb′2	F	5	U; no P.R.
GERMAN							
Abt, The silent waterlily	7469; 12¢; GS	4	2	a′4	E 3	1½	U; no P.R.
Beethoven, The vesper hymn	1219; 8¢; GS	4	3	bb′4	F	3½	U; no P.R.

Composer; Title; Arranger (or, Arranger; Title)	Octavo No.; Price; Publisher	Number of Parts	Grade of Difficulty	Highest Tenor Note (Above e') Number of Times	Lowest Bass Note (Below G) Number of Times	Length in Minutes	General Remarks
MUSIC OF THE NINETEENTH AND TWENTIETH CENTURIES—(Continued)							
GERMAN—(Continued)							
Brahms, Beware	468; 6¢; GS	4-5	2	g'	F# 6	1½	U; no P.R.
——Four love songs [Davison]	58; 35¢; EC	4	1-2				Four-hand piano acc.
(a) Was once a pretty tiny birdie						2½	
(b) In wood embowered, neath azure skies						2	
(c) No, there is no bearing with these spiteful neighbors						1½	
(d) Secret nook in shady spot						1½	
——Six love songs	59; 40¢; EC	4	2-3				Four-hand piano acc. with violin obbl.
(a) Tremors in the branches						2	
(b) Nightingale, thy sweetest song						1	
(c) Bird in air will stray afar						½	
(d) From yon hills the torrent speeds						2	
(e) Locksmith, ho! a hundred padlocks						1	
(f) Now, ye muses, be hushed						½	
——I hear a harp	57; 20¢; EC	3-4	2	g'4		2	Piano or harp, horn obbl.
——My little maid has lips of rose [Patterson]	863; 15¢; R	4	2	g'3	E 4	1½	
——Like sweetest music [Lefevre]	684; 15¢; R	4	2	a'6	E 3	2	Bar. solo
——Lullaby [Riegger]	82067; 15¢; F	4	1	g'2		1½	U; no P.R.
——Lullaby [Zander]	1359; 8¢; GS	4-6	2	ab'		1½	Optional counter B.
——The trysting place [Davison]	928; 18¢; EC	4	2	bb'1	F 2	2	Eng. & Ger.
Bruch, Media vita (Battle hymn of the monks)	4820; 12¢; GS	6	3	bb'1	D 1	3	U; no P.R.
Haydn, Serenade [Schultz]	1087; 6¢; GS	4	2	g'	F	1½	U; no P.R.
——She never told her love [Barratt]	13; 10¢; JF	4	1	f#'1		2½	
Henschel, Morning hymn [Davison]	40; 12¢; EC	4	2	a'1		1½	U
Isenmann, The singer's harp	5626; 15¢; GS	4-5	2	a'		4	U
Liebe, In the night	5625; 12¢; GS	4	3	bb'2	Eb1	2	U
Mair, Suomi's song	2147; 15¢; C or 2049; 15¢; F	4-8	3	bb'2	D 1	1½	U
Mendelssohn, The cheerful wanderer	5120; 20¢; GS	4	2	a'1		1½	U
——In the woods [Roberton]	1579; 12¢; Pn	4	2	a'2.	E 1	1½	U
——On the water	6567; 8¢; GS	4	2	g'3	F# 5	1½	U
Othegraven, By moonlight [Bartholomew]	7865; 12¢; GS	4	2	bb'1	F 5	1½	U
——Summer morning	4858; 10¢; GS	5-6	3	b'2	D 1	4	U; no P.R.
Röntgen, Dirge	7290; 20¢; GS	4	3	b'1	E 1	6	
Rubinstein, Shine on, oh star [Smith]	67; 20¢; Ho	4	2	g#'2			
Schubert, Bard's song	1412; 12¢; O	3	2	ab'1		1½	U; no P.R. (TBB)
——By the sea [Tschirch]	1155; 9¢; GS	4	1	g'		3	
——Forgotten, forgotten	1406; 12¢; O	3	1	f'6		2½	U; no P.R. (TBB)
——Longing	4318; 5¢; GS	4	2	a'2	E 1	3½	U
——Night in the forest	1143; 15¢; GS	4	3	a'	F# 6	4½	
——O Lord, our God	1144; 15¢; GS	4-8	3	bb'2	F	9	U ad lib.; Chorus and quartet
——Serenade [Vogrich]	1184; 12¢; GS	4	1	g'3	F 2	2½	
——The omnipotence [Liszt]	1228; 15¢; GS	4	2	a'1		4	T. solo to bb'1
Schumann, Evening song [Vogrich]	1094; 12¢; GS	4	3	a'b	Eb 2	3	U; Bar. solo; Eng. & Ger.
——The dreaming lake	437; 10¢; B	4	1	f#'6		1	U; no P.R.
——The lotus flower	14110; 10¢; D	4	3	ab'4		3	U
——The rose stood in the dew	2109; 10¢; C	5	2	a'1	F 1	2	U; no P.R. (TTBBB)
——The two grenadiers [Robinson]	12663; 16¢; D	4	2	g'5		3	Short T. and B. solo parts
							* Such numerals indicate the number of times an extreme note occurs.

Composer; Title; Arranger (or, Arranger; Title)	Octavo No.; Price; Publisher	Number of Parts	Grade of Difficulty	Highest Tenor Note (Above e')	Number of Times	Lowest Bass Note (Below G)	Number of Times	Length in Minutes	General Remarks
MUSIC OF THE NINETEENTH AND TWENTIETH CENTURIES—(*Continued*)									
GERMAN—(*Continued*)									
Wagner, Dreams (Träume) [*Scherer*]...	436; 15¢; HW	4	2	g'1		E♭ 3		3	
——Two pilgrim-choruses............	1085; 9¢; GS	....	....					....	U; no P.R.
(a) Chorus of departing pilgrims..	....	4	2	g'1		F♯ 2		3	
(b) Chorus of returning pilgrims..	....	4	3	a'1		E 1		2½	
ITALIAN									
Pinsuti, Good night, good night, beloved [*Bliss*]......................	20332; 8¢; Pr	4	2	a'3		F		3	U
Bossi, Noon quiet in the Alps.........	6065; 9¢; GS	4-8	3	a'2		E 4		2½	U; Eng. & It.
RUSSIAN									
Arensky, The crystal brook [*Davison*]..	52; 20¢; EC	4	3	a'4		......		1½	U with 'cello obbl.
Bortniansky, Lo, a voice to heaven sounding [*Whitford*]...............	532; 16¢; EC	4	1	g'1		E 4		2½	U
Cui, Nocturne (Radiant stars) [*Davison*]	95; 16¢; EC	4	3	b'1		E 3		1½	U
Gretchaninoff, Autumn [*Davison*]......	66; 20¢; EC	4	3	a♯'1		D 1		4½	U
——Dusk [*Baldwin*].................	1656; 10¢; B	4-6	3	a'2		D♯ 4		2½	U; B. melody feature
Moniuszko, The cossack.............	9192; 10¢; GS	4	2	bb'1		......		2	U
Rachmaninoff, The harvest.........	962; 15¢; R	4-8	3	a'6		D 5		3	Counter B. *ad lib.*
Smith-Aschenbrenner, Bless the Lord.	476; 20¢; C	4	2	a'1		......		1½	U; Composer unknown
Tchaikovsky, One who has yearned alone [*Riegger*].....................	7711; 15¢; GS	4	1	ab'1		F 1		2½	
SCANDINAVIAN									
Bull, Shepherdess' Sunday [*Gilbert*]....	6826; 15¢; J	4	3	bb'1		D 1		1½	U; Bar. solo; hum acc.
Faltin, Fight (Student song of Finland).	74; 15¢; HW	4	2	ab'1		F 3		1½	U
Grieg, Land-sighting...............	1013; 15¢; GS	4	2	a'1		F		4	Short Bar. solo
Kjerulf, Night on the Fjord [*Gaines*]..	7083; 15¢; GS	4	3	bb'2		F		2½	U; Bar. or T. II solo
——Sing, nightingale, sing [*Gaines*]....	7235; 12¢; GS	4	2	g♯'2		E 2		2	U; T. or S. solo
Sibelius, Broken melody.............	5781; 10¢; GS	4	3	bb'1		F 5		1	U
——Finlandia [*Baldwin*].............	9198; 10¢; GS	4	2	a'2		......		2½	U

FOLK-SONGS
(**Note**—Some of the most attractive folk-song material will be found under "Encores, Humorous Songs, and Novelties")

Composer; Title; Arranger (or, Arranger; Title)	Octavo No.; Price; Publisher	Number of Parts	Grade of Difficulty	Highest Tenor Note (Above e')	Number of Times	Lowest Bass Note (Below G)	Number of Times	Length in Minutes	General Remarks
AMERICAN									
Arranger:									
Kun, Get along little dogies...........	918; 15¢; R	4	2	a'2				1	U
Malin, Cindy......................	3121; 15¢; GH	4	3	a'		E 1		1½	U; Ky. Mt. Ballad
——Sourwood Mountain.............	3120; 15¢; GH	4	2	a'2		F		2½	U; Humorous Ky. Mt.
Treharne, Dogie song (Cowboy tune)..	5372; 15¢; W	3	1	......		......		2	(TTB) or (TBB)
——There was an old soldier.........	5374; 15¢; W	3	1	......		......		2½	(TTB) or (TBB)
CZECHO-SLOVAKIAN									
Taylor, D., Waters ripple and flow.....	5671; 15¢; J	4	2	a'1		E 6		3½	Short T. and Bar. solos
ENGLISH									
Bartholomew, My Johnny was a shoemaker..............................	7215; 6¢; GS	4	2	......		E 1		1½	U; Easy except Bass
(a) Shall I, wasting in despair?...	7413; 12¢; GS	4-5	2	ab'1		E♭ 5		2	U
(b) Drink to me only............	....	4	2	a'1		E 3		1½	U
Bingham, Gently, Johnny.............	314; 15¢; HW	4	2	g'		......		2	U
Malin, I saw three ships.............	1058; 15¢; CC	4	1	f'		F 2		2	U
Moffat, Haste to the bower of Robin Hood.............................	461; 12¢; AP	4	2	g'2		F 4		2	Acc. *ad lib.*
Taylor, D., My Johnny was a shoemaker	4834; 15¢; J	4	2	g'2		......		1½	

Composer; Title; Arranger (or, Arranger; Title)	Octavo No.; Price; Publisher	Number of Parts	Grade of Difficulty	Highest Tenor Note (Above e¹) Number of Times	Lowest Bass Note (Below G) Number of Times	Length in Minutes	General Remarks
FOLK-SONGS—(*Continued*) (**Note**—Some of the most attractive folk-song material will be found under "Encores, Humorous Songs, and Novelties")							
Arranger: ENGLISH—(*Cont'd*)							
Vaughan Williams, An acre of land....	636; 20¢; O	4	1	....		2½	Acc. *ad lib.*; T. and Bar. solos
——Bushes and briars................	447; 12¢; N	4	2	ab'2	F	2½	U
——Down among the dead men.......	——; 20¢; JWm	4	2	g'6		3	U
——The jolly plowboy..............	448; 12¢; N	4	2	f'	F	1½	U
——The turtle dove.................	50570; 10¢; JC	4	2	gb'2	Eb 4	2	U; Bar. solo
Whitehead, Flowers in the valley......	2177; 15¢; C	4	2	g'	F 5	2½	U
FRENCH							
Donovan, Le beau galant.............	1; 20¢; O	4	2	g'2	F 2	2½	Eng. & Fr.
Schumann, G., Fare thee well........	5024; 8¢; GS	4	2	ab'6	Eb 3	2	U
Taylor, D., Before the shrine (Disons le chapelet)........................	4831; 15¢; J	4	2	g'		2½	Eng. & Fr.
FRENCH-CANADIAN							
MacMillan, The fair Françoise.......	1762; 20¢; B	4-6	3	a'6	D 1	3	U; Eng. & Fr.
——In all the country round........	1759; 15¢; B	4	2	g#2	F# 3	1	U; Eng. & Fr.; Humorous
——White as cometh the snowflake....	1760; 30¢; B	4	3	a'	C# 1	4	U; Eng. & Fr.
GERMAN							
Bartholomew, Alas, to whom dare I complain?	7227; 6¢; GS	4	3	ab'4	C 2	3½	U; no P.R.; Bar. Solo; Eng. & Ger.
——At parting...................	7233; 12¢; GS	4	1	g'2	......	1½	U; Eng. & Ger.
Brahms, Suabian folk-song [*Davison*]..	31; 8¢; EC	4-5	2	g'3	F# 3	1	U
——Suabian folk-song [*Gibb*].........	1664; 10¢; B	4	1	....		1½	U; Simplified arr.
Jüngst, Dearest, farewell............	4314; 10¢; GS	4	2	g'2		1½	U
Saar, Thy mouth, fair maid, is a rosebud red.................................	550; 16¢; EC	4-5	2	ab'6	......	1½	U; Eng. & Ger.
Schumann, G., The nightingale........	4968; 9¢; GS	4-6	3	bb'1	E 1	1½	U
G. W. W., Good night...............	901; 16¢; EC	4	2	ab'2	Eb 5	1½	Eng. & Ger.
IRISH							
Cain, Bendemeer's stream............	45; 15¢; Ho	4-5	2	g'1	F	2	U; Easy except 1st T.
Davison, The foggy dew............	83; 15¢; EC	4-5	2	bb'1	F	2	U; T. solo
——Has sorrow thy young days shaded.	23; 15¢; EC	4	2	a'4	E 2	2½	U; S. or T. solo
Fletcher, The Galway piper [*Manney*]..	302; 15¢; Wo	4	2	g'	F	2½	
Gartlan, The foggy dew (NOTE: *Not the same tune as above*)...............	6620; 12¢; GS	4	2	bb'2		3	U; Easy except 1st T.
——My thousand times beloved......	6619; 6¢; GS	4	2	g'	E 1	2	U
Mason, The Cruiskeen lawn..........	10866; 15¢; D	4	3	ab'	C 2	2	U; no P.R.
Silver, Love's benediction (Londonderry air)...............................	4264; 15¢; J	4-5	2	g'2	Eb	2½	U
Whiting, Lament for Owen Roe O'Neill.	7002; 16¢; GS	4	1			2½	Bar. solo; two-piano acc.
Wood, I've a secret to tell thee........	1163; 15¢; CC	4	1	f'6	F	1½	U
RUSSIAN							
Baldwin, From the lonely isle........	74; 15¢; AM	4-6	3	a'	D 2	2	U
——Marching in chains.............	79; 15¢; AM	4-6	3	bb'1	C 5	2½	U
——Sleep your last slumber.........	73; 15¢; AM	4-7	3	bb'5	Db	2½	U
Davison, (a) Fireflies [*G. W. W.*, arr.]	73; 25¢; EC	4	2	g#'6		1	
(b) Song of the life-boat men...	....	4	3	a'3	D 1	1½	Bar. solo
(c) At father's door...........		4	2	a'1		1	
Krone, Czecho-Slovakian dance song..	2652; 12¢; MW	4	1	g'2	F# 1	1	U; a "la, la" chorus
Mussorgsky, O, the joy of living, loving	632; 12¢; O	3	2			1	U; two T. solos to a'
Ornstein, Russian festival..........	63; 30¢; AM	4-6	2	ab'4	F	2½	U
Schindler, The prisoner in Caucasus...	6665; 15¢; GS	4-6	3	ab'5	Eb 2	1	U
Smith-Aschenbrenner, I won't kiss Katy	2203; 15¢; C	4-5	1	a'1	E	3½	U; lively

Composer; Title; Arranger (or, Arranger; Title)	Octavo No.; Price; Publisher	Number of Parts	Grade of Difficulty	Highest Tenor Note (Above e')	Number of Times	Lowest Bass Note (Below G)	Number of Times	Length in Minutes	General Remarks
FOLK-SONGS—(Continued)									
(**Note**—Some of the more attractive folk-song material will be found under "Encores, Humorous Songs, and Novelties")									
Arranger: SCANDINAVIAN									
Grieg, Fair Toro	1486; 8¢; GS	4	2	a'	4	F#	4	2	U; no P.R.; Bar. solo
Palmgren, Finnish lullaby	73; 12¢; HW	5	3	a'	3	F		2	U; Bass II F through entire piece
——I'm coming home	72; 15¢; HW	4-5	3	ab'	3	Db	1	½	U; humoresque
SCOTCH									
Andrews, The Campbells are comin'	—; 15¢; Ga	4	3	g'		E	2	1½	U
Buck, Annie Laurie	9064; 10¢; GS	4	1	g'	2	F	4	3	U; no P.R.
——Robin Adair	1016; 8¢; GS	4	2	a'	1	F	3	1½	U; no P.R.
Burleigh, Ho, ro! My nut-brown maiden	847; 15¢; R	4	2	a'	5	F	3	2½	U
Candlyn, Hush-a-by Bairnie	2172; 15¢; C	4	1					2½	U
——The wee cooper o' Fife	2175; 16¢; C	4	1					4	Humorous
Davison, Bonnie Dundee	909; 18¢; EC	4	2	ab'				2½	Four-hand piano
——Rantin', rovin', Robin	84; 20¢; EC	3-4	2	a'	1	E	1	3	Bar. solo
——Turn ye to me	908; 16¢; EC	4	3	bb'	1	Eb	1	3	T. solo
Malin, The Campbells are comin'	1057; 16¢; CC	3	1	f#				1½	(TTB arr.)
Murchinson, The hundred pipers	6952; 12¢; GS	4	3	a'	4	F		2½	U
Roberton, My faithful fond one	1022; 12¢; Pn	4	2	a'	2			1½	U
Vaughan Williams, Loch Lomond	79; 20¢; St	4-5	2	g'	5			3	U
WELSH									
Brewer, All through the night	1548; 12¢; GS	4	2	bb'	3	F		3½	U; Bar. solo
Davison, (a) The monks' march	943; 18¢; EC	4	2	a'	1	E	1	1½	
(b) Oh, why camest thou before me		4	3	bb'	2	Db	1	1½	U
(c) Men of Harlech		4	3	bb'	5			2	
Protheroe, The old minstrel	1822; 12¢; B	4	2	g'				1½	U
Wood, Hob a derry danno	1159; 15¢; CC	4	1	g'	2			2	U
CHANTEYS, SONGS OF THE SEA, SONGS OF THE HUNT									
CHANTEYS									
Armbruster, The high Barbaree [*Treharne*]	2048; 18¢; F	4	2	g'		F#	1	2	T. or Bar. solo
Bartholomew, As off to the south'ard we go	7216; 10¢; GS	4	1	g'	2			1	U
——Shenandoah	7211; 12¢; GS	4-6	2	g#'	1	E	3	2	U
——Three chanteys	7241; 25¢; GS	4	1						U
(1) Eight bells			1	g'	2	E	1	1½	
(2) Away to Rio			1			E	1	1	
(3) Old man Noah			1	g'	1			2½	
——Two Chanteys:									
(a) Mobile bay	7755; 12¢; GS	{4	1	f'	1	Eb	1	1½	U
(b) A-roving		.	1	g#'	1	E	1	1½	U
Hall, High Barbary	7577; 16¢; GS	4	1	g'	4			2	U
Treharne, Reuben Ranzo	490; 15¢; CC	4	1	g'	1			1½	T. solo
Winslow, Blow the man down	7874; 15¢; GS	4	1			F		1½	
SONGS OF THE SEA									
Andrews, Sea fever	6834; 15¢; GS	4	2	g'	4	D	1	2½	U
——Skye boat song	227; 12¢; HW	4-6	3	c''	1	Eb		2	
Bishop, An English sailor song	6109; 15¢; GS	4	3	a'		F	5	3½	U
Buck, On the sea	1022; 12¢; GS	4	3	a'	2	E#	1	2	U; no P. R.
Clark, The sea gypsy	82079; 15¢; F	4	1					2	
Cole, The fisherman	4008; 10¢; HF	4	1	g'	2			1	U; no P.R.
Faning, Song of the Vikings [*Dunhill*]	611; 30¢; N	4-5	2	a'	5	F#		5	Piano or orch. acc.
German, Rolling down to Rio	551; 25¢; N	4	2	a'	2			1½	

Composer; Title; Arranger (or, Arranger; Title)	Octavo No.; Price; Publisher	Number of Parts	Grade of Difficulty	Highest Tenor Note (Above e')	Number of Times	Lowest Bass Note (Below G)	Number of Times	Length in Minutes	General Remarks
CHANTEYS, SONGS OF THE SEA, SONGS OF THE HUNT—(*Continued*)									
Songs of the Sea—(*Continued*)									
High, Pirate's song	2059; 16¢; F	4	1	f#'2		F#		2½	
Holst, Swansea Town	8096; 15¢; GS	4	2	a'		E	1	2½	U; folk-song
Howard, The sea	7971; 12¢; GS	4	2	a'3		E		2½	U
Parry, The sailors' chorus	82019; 12¢; F	4	2	g'				2	U; no P.R.
Protheroe, The sea gulls	1475; 20¢; B	4	1	a'1		F	1	2	
——Song of the sea	651; 12¢; GH	3	1	f'5				2	Piano *ad lib.*
Robertson, The Jolly Roger [*Deis*]	7658; 16¢; GS	4	1	g'				1	
Rowley, Sacramento	644; 15¢; N	4	2	a'4				2	U; T. II tog#'
Stebbins, A song of the sea	12358; 12¢; D	4-6	3	bb'1		D	2	2½	T. II to ab'
Sullivan, We sail the ocean blue [*Riegger*]	82508; 12¢; F	3	1	f'1				1	(TTB arr.); from "Pinafore"
Vene, A sea dirge	913; 15¢; R	4-6	2	gb'1		Eb		2	U
Wagner, Sailors' choruses [*Page*]	212; 8¢; CC	4	1						From the "Flying Dutchman"
(a) Final chorus Act I			1	f#'5				1	
(b) Steersman, leave the watch			1	g'1				1½	
Warren, White horses of the sea	7678; 18¢; GS	4	1	g'2				2	Piano acc. difficult
Vaughan Williams, Ward, the pirate	50518; 15¢; JC	4	3	a'4				2	U
Songs of the Hunt									
Andrews, John Peel	427; 15¢; HW	3	2	a'1				2	U (TBB); old Eng.
Bailey, The forester's song	461; 15¢; HW	4	2	a'1		E	3	2	
Bantock, Hope the hornblower	50653; 15¢; JC	4	2	bb'1		F	2	1½	U
Bartholomew, Dawn through the wood is creeping	7231; 10¢; GS	4-7	2	a#'1		F#	3	1	U; old Ger.
Cox, Song of the hunt [*Saar*]	552; 16¢; EC	4	2	a'2				2	Old Warwickshire
DeKoven, Hunting song [*Baldwin*]	9082; 15¢; GS	4-5	2	ab'6				2½	From "Robin Hood"
Kun, Hunting song	11; 15¢; HW	4	2	a'2				1	U
Kuntz, A-hunting we will go	2361; 15¢; MW	4	1	f'4				1	Piano *ad lib.*
——The hunter's horn	2365; 15¢; MW	3	1	f'2				1½	With trumpet acc.
Ryder, John Peel	14071; 15¢; D	4-6	3	g'				2	U; Old Eng.; T. solo to bb'
Saar, 'Tween the mount and deep, deep vale	551; 16¢; EC	4	1	g'3		F	5	1½	U; Eng. & Ger.; Ger. folk-song
SPIRITUALS									
Arranger:									
Bantock, Deep river	639; 15¢; N	4	2	g#'4		F#	2	3	U; Bar. solo
——Peter, go, ring dem bells	637; 15¢; N	4	1	g'2				1½	U; Bar. solo
——Somebody's knockin'	634; 15¢; N	4	2	ab'2		F	2	2	U; Bar. solo
Bartholomew, Battle of Jericho	7390; 18¢; GS	4	1	g'				1½	U; lively
——De animals a-comin'	8046; 15¢; GS	4	1	bb'1				2	U; humorous
——De wind blow over my shoulder	8048; 12¢; GS	4	1			F#		2	U; T. solo
——Humble	8049; 15¢; GS	4	1	g'1				2	U; T. solo; humorous
——I got shoes	7144; 12¢; GS	4	1					1½	U
——Keep in the middle of the road	7391; 20¢; GS	4	2	g'				2½	U; lively
——Lawd, I cannot stay away	8047; 15¢; GS	4	2	g'		E	1	2	U; Bar. solo
——Standin' in de need o' prayer	8050; 12¢; GS	4	1	ab'1		F	1	1½	U
——Three spirituals	7757; 16¢; GS	4	1						U
(a) Ready when he comes			1	f#'1		F#		1½	U
(b) Roll, Jordon, roll			1					1½	U
(c) Bones come a-knittin'			1	g#'1				1½	U; humorous
Burleigh, Ezekiel saw de wheel	700; 15¢; R	4	2	ab'1		Eb	1	2	U; lively
Cain, Chillun' come on home	57; 15¢; Ho	4-7	3	a'		E	1	3	Acc. *ad lib.*; T. solo
Dawson, Jesus walked this lonesome valley	822; 15¢; GH	4	3	g'				2	Bar. solo
——King Jesus is a-listening	4025; 15¢; HF	4	2'	ab'2				1½	U
Dett, Listen to the lambs	7405; 15¢; GS	4	3	a'4		E	4	5	U; T. solo (In style of spiritual)

Composer; Title; Arranger (or, Arranger; Title)	Octavo No.; Price; Publisher	Number of Parts	Grade of Difficulty	Highest Tenor Note (Above e')	Number of Times	Lowest Bass Note (Below G)	Number of Times	Length in Minutes	General Remarks
SPIRITUALS—(*Continued*)									
Arranger:									
Enders, Wade in de water............	961; 15¢; R	4-8	2	ab'2		F		2½	U; no P.R.; Drum *ad lib.*
Guion, De ol' ark's a-moverin' [*Deis*]..	7110; 15¢; GS	4	2	a'2		F		2	Humorous
High, Little David play on your harp..	2015; 15¢; F	4	1	f'		......		1½	
Horton, There's a man goin' roun' takin' names................................	52; 15¢; Ho	4	2	g'		E	2	1½	U
Manney, He's the lily of the valley....	314; 15¢; Wo	4	2	ab'2		......		2½	U
Pitcher, I saw de light................	103; 10¢; CC	4	2	g'		......		1	U; Bar. solo
——Scandalize my name............	144; 8¢; CC	4	1	g'1		......		1½	U; Humorous
Reddick, Travlin' to de grave........	5317; 15¢; J	4	2	g'		......		1½	
Stoessel, Three traditional spirituals.. (Steal away; Religion is a fortune; and Swing low, sweet chariot)	327; 25¢; CC	4	2	a'2		F	1	4	Medley
MUSIC FOR SPECIAL OCCASIONS									
Arbor Day									
Rasbach, Trees [*Huhn*]..............	9073; 10¢; GS	4	2	a'2		F	4	1½	
Christmas									
Anonymous, Christmas carol of the Pifferari	1544; 9¢; GS	4-5	2	a'3		F	3	4	U; no P.R.; Neapolitan
Bach, Break forth, O beauteous, heav'nly light [*Davison*]....................	53; 15¢; EC	4	2	g'5		E	2	1	
——Good news from heaven [*G. W. W.*]	900; 16¢; EC	4	2	g'		F#	2	2	
Cornelius, Three Kings have journeyed [*Damrosch*]....	1470; 10¢; GS	4	2	g'3		D	1	2	U; Alto or Bar. solo
Darcieux, Christians, hark [*Davison*]...	89; 16¢; EC	1-4	2	ab'2		......		3½	Bressan carol
Davison, Angels, o'er the fields........	926; 25¢; EC	4	2	g#'4		F#	6	2	U; Fr. carol; Eng. & Fr.
——Bring a torch, Jeanette, Isabella...	97; 15¢; EC	4	1	f#'		F#		1½	U; Fr. carol; four verses
——In dulci jubilo................	25; 12¢; EC	4	2	g#'3		F#	3	2½	U
——The miracle of Saint Nicholas [*G. W. W.*]........................	81; 20¢; EC	2-4	1	ab'1		Eb	1	4	T. and Bar. solos; Fr. carol; piano & organ; Eng. & Fr.
——Ye watchers and ye holy ones.....	65; 16¢; EC	4	2	a'2		F#	1	2	Old Ger.; piano & organ acc.
Jüngst, Christmas hymn (While by my sheep).............................	1414; 8¢; GS	4	2	g'		F		3	U
Lefebvre, Catalonian Christmas carol..	1255; 15¢; HW	4	1	f'		F	4	1	U
——March of the Kings.............	816; 25¢; R	4	3	bb'1		......		4½	U; Old Fr. Noël; Eng. & Fr.
Malin, A Babe is born.............	3122; 12¢; GH	4-7	1	g'		......		2	U; S. solo
Millet, The song of the birds..........	7651; 10¢; GS	4	2	a'1		......		2	U; S. or T. solo; Catalan folk-song
Praetorius, Lo how a rose [*Davison*]....	24; 8¢; EC	4	1	f#'2		......		1½	U
Schwalm, Old Bohemian Christmas carol	1543; 8¢; GS	4	2	a'6		......		1½	U; no P.R.
Strangways, Babe divine.............	1133; 15¢; CC	4	2	f'		F		4	U
Willan, (a) The mummer's carol......	W. 2; 15¢; O	1-4	1	g'4		F	1	1½	U; no P.R.
(b) God rest you merry, gentlemen.	....	....	1	g'2		F	4	1½	U; no P.R.
New Year									
Fletcher, Ring out, wild bells..........	589; 15¢; N	4	2	ab'1		......		3	
Easter									
Beethoven, Hallelujah chorus [*Davison*].	56; 20¢; EC	4	3	a'5		......		10	From "Mount of Olives"
Handl, Alleluia! Today is Christ risen [*Davison*]........................	931; 16¢; EC	8	2	g#'		E	1	2	U
Handel, Your voices raise [*Davison*]....	86; 20¢; EC	4	2	g'4		......		2½	

Composer; Title; Arranger (or, Arranger; Title)	Octavo No.; Price; Publisher	Number of Parts	Grade of Difficulty	Highest Tenor Note (Above c') Number of Times		Lowest Bass Note (Below G) Number of Times		Length in Minutes	General Remarks
MUSIC FOR SPECIAL OCCASIONS—(*Continued*)									
MOTHER'S DAY									
Dvořák, Songs my mother taught me [*Baldwin*]	9066; 8¢; GS	4	2	a'1		. : .		1½	U
Kramer, Mother o' mine	2654; 15¢; MW	4	1	f♯'1		F	1	1½	
Roberton, The old woman	1568; 12¢; Pn	4	1			E♭	1	1½	U
Tchaikovsky, The song that you sang long ago [*Root*]	3037; 12¢; Su	4	2	a'2		E	1	3	T. and B. solos
SPRING FESTIVAL—MAY DAY									
Morley, Now is the month of Maying [*Davison*]	22; 12¢; EC	4	2	g'		F	2	1½	U; Madrigal
Schubert, May song	1413; 12¢; O	3	2	g'				2½	U; No P.R.
Taylor, May Day Carol	4832; 15¢; J	4	2	g'6		F	1	2½	Eng. folk-song
Treharne, Ye maids of Helston, gather dew	1843; 15¢; B	3	1	f'3				2½	U; (TTB); Eng. folk-song
PATRIOTIC (Armistice, Decoration Day, Thanksgiving)									
Adam, Comrades in arms	5305; 15¢; GS	4	2	g'		F		4	U
Bloch, America	807; 10¢; CC	4	1	g'2		F	4	1	U; from symphony "America"
Davison, Reapers' song	905; 16¢; EC	2-4	2	b♭'3				2	Thanksgiving; two-piano acc.
Demarest, America triumphant	392; 12¢; AP	4	1	g'1				3	
Holst, A dirge for two veterans	50542; 15¢; JC	4	3	b♭'1				5	Acc. of brass and drums
Kountz, The night march	1734; 20¢; B	4	2	b♭'1		F		3½	U
Kremser, Prayer of Thanksgiving	9057; 8¢; GS	4-6	1	a'1				3	Thanksgiving or festival; Dutch folk-song
Rachmaninoff, Triumph! Thanksgiving [*Manton*]	541; 15¢; EC	4	2	a'3		E	1	2	Organ acc.; Thanksgiving or festival
Schubert, He whose flag	1408; 12¢; O	3	1	g'4				1½	U; no P.R.; (TBB)
Scott, Sail on! O Ship of State	495; 12¢; AP	4	1	f'				2½	U
Sibelius, Dear land of home [*Manney*]	254; 15¢; Wo	4-5	1	g'5				3	U; from "Finlandia"
Ward-Stephens, The phantom legions	1041; 15¢; CH	4	2	a♭'2				2	
OPENING AND CLOSING CHORUSES; ENCORES; NOVELTIES; CONVIVIAL SONGS									
OPENING INVOCATIONS									
Bach, Now let every tongue adore Thee [*Davison*]	30; 15¢; EC	4	1	a♭'2		F	4	2	U
Beethoven, The heavens are declaring [*Holden*]	8425; 8¢; D	4	2	a'1				3	
Brewer, Hymn to music	6497; 25¢; GS	4-8	3	b♭'3		E♭	1	7	U
Cole, Wake up, sweet melody	4726; 12¢; GS	4	2	b♭'2		F		3	U; no P.R.
Franz, Dedication [*Enders*]	82065; 15¢; F	4	1	g'1		F		1½	U; Eng. & Ger.
Grieg, Brothers, sing on [*McKinney*]	6927; 15¢; J	4-6	2	a'1				1½	U
Saar, To music	4027; 15¢; HF	4	3	a'1		F♯		1½	U
Schott, Sing a merry song [*Rhys-Herbert*]	2833; 12¢; J	3	1	g'4				1½	U; (TTB)
Stevens, To the Spirit of Music	4353; 15¢; J	4	2	a'1				3	
Volkmann, Night shades are gently falling [*Luvaas*]	125; 11¢; CC	4	1	f'2				3	U
Wood, Invocation	732; 24¢; O	4	1	f'		F	3	4	U; (ATTB)
CLOSING CHORUSES									
Abt, Serenade	424; 12¢; B	4	2	a♭'3		E♭	2	2½	U; no P.R.
Dickinson, Music, when soft voices die	128; 10¢; HW	4	2	g♭'3				1	U
Macfarlane, Barter	7598; 16¢; GS	4	3	b♭'1		F♯	1	3½	U; optional b'

RECOMMENDED OCTAVO MUSIC FOR MEN'S VOICES

Composer; Title; Arranger (or, Arranger; Title)	Octavo No.; Price; Publisher	Number of Parts	Grade of Difficulty	Highest Tenor Note (Above e'); Number of Times		Lowest Bass Note (Below G); Number of Times		Length in Minutes	General Remarks
OPENING AND CLOSING CHORUSES; ENCORES; NOVELTIES; CONVIVIAL SONGS—(*Cont'd*)									
Closing Choruses—(Continued)									
Matthews, Music, when soft voices die.	7669; 12¢; GS	4	1	ab'3		F	1	1	U
Protheroe, A nocturne	4381; 12¢; GS	4-5	3	bb'2		F	6	2½	U; no P.R.
Johnson, How soft the shades of evening creep	863; 15¢; B	4	2	ab'3		F		1½	U
Saar, A note of golden song	4022; 15¢; HF	4-6	2	a'2		F	4	2½	U
Silcher, Fare ye well [*Luvaas*]	28; 12¢; CC	4	1	g'2		F	2	1	U
Young, Ships that pass in the night	50656; 10¢; JC	4	1	g'2				1½	U
Encores—Humorous Songs									
Adams, Sir Marmaduke	5510; 15¢; W	4	2	g'5		F	3	1½	Bar. solo
Serrano, Flowering cherry tree [*Baldwin*]	—; 15¢; R	4	2	g'6				1	
Bartholomew, Black eyed Susie	8045; 20¢; GS	4	1	g'3				3	North Carolina folksong; humorous
—Grandma grunts	7254; 10¢; GS	4	1	g'1		F		1	U; Optional solo; no P. R.; (N. C. Mt. song)
Bergen, The bow-leg boy	520; 15¢; GH	4	2	ab'1		Eb	2	1	Piano *ad lib.*
Bogart, Two little fleas	7270; 12¢; GS	4	1	a'1		F	2	1	Humorous
Brahms, Marching	1467; 9¢; GS	4	2	a'3		F	3	2½	U: no P.R.
Burleigh, A fatuous tragedy	714; 15¢; R	4	2	ab'2		Eb	6	1	U; humorous
Carse, Nursery rhymes	596; 15¢; N	4	2	a'4		F	5	2½	U
Charles, The green-eyed dragon	1457; 15¢; Bo	4	2	a'1		E	2	3	
Cross, The duel	2146; 15¢; C	4	2	a'1				2	
Dvořák, R., Sophomoric philosophy	1108; 12¢; GH	4	1	f'4				1	U; humorous
Edmonds, Triolet	57; 15¢; St	4	1	f#'1				1	U; no P.R.; humorous
Forsyth, Mr. Alphabet's holiday	4524; 15¢; J	4	2	a'2		E	2	1½	
Gibson, The elf-man	4225; 6¢; GS	4	2	a'4		E	2	1	U; no P.R.
Groton, When girls are sweet sixteen	82050; 12¢; F	4	2	ab'2		Eb	1	½	U; humorous
Halter, The deers	3070; 10¢; Su	4	2	ab'3				2	
Hawley, The cat tale	1872; 15¢; B	4	1	g'1				1	Humorous
Huntley, A protest	4014; 10¢; HF	4	2	a'2				1	U
—Nobody home	4016; 10¢; HF	4	2	a'4		F#	2	1	U; humorous
Ingle, Knocked 'em in the old Kent Road	82033; 16¢; F	4	1	g'		F		1½	Cockney dialect
Jacobsen, H., Tobacco is a dirty weed	7778; 16¢; GS	4	2	a'2		E		2	U; humorous
Jüngst, By the well	4246; 8¢; GS	4	2	bb'2				2	U; no P. R.
Kun, Weavily wheat	917; 15¢; R	4	2	a'6		F#	1	1	U; humorous
Newton, The frog	1650; 12¢; N	3	2	g'		F#	3	3	Piano *ad lib.*
O'Hara, The male chorus	883; 20¢; R	4	2	a'2				3½	Piano *ad lib.*
—Wing Tee Wee	2088; 15¢; C	4	2	g'4		F		1	Humorous
Othegraven, The maiden's answer	5453; 10¢; GS	4	1	g'				1	U; no P.R.; S. solo
Protheroe, The grouch	4024; 12¢; HF	4	1	f#'6				1	
Purcell, The three fairies	535; 16¢; EC	3	2	ab'4		F	3	4	U; (TTB); humorous
Saar, Rondeau	2063; 15¢; C	4	2	a'1		F	3	1	U; no P.R.
Sanderson, Captain Mac [*Samuelson*]	1473; 15¢; Bo	4-6	2	a'		E	2	3	
Shaffer, Turkey in the straw	2573; 20¢; MW	4	2	g'		F	6	2	U; choral paraphrase
Speaks, Charity [*Peery*]	7385; 10¢; GS	4	1	g'4				1½	Acc. *ad lib.*
Treharne, Singing a merry hi ho!	2171; 15¢; C	4	1	g'1				2½	U
Turges, From stormy windes	1435; 20¢; O	3	2	f#'5				5	U; (TBB); humorous
Vaughan Williams, Tobacco's but an Indian weed	638; 16¢; O	4	2	g'2		E	1	1½	U; humorous Eng. folk-song
—The world it went well with me then	637; 24¢; O	4	2	a'1				2½	U; humorous Eng. folk-song
Vene, Sigh no more	960; 15¢; R	4	2	ab'2		Eb	1	2	U; humorous
Whittaker, There was a maid went to the mill	612; 24¢; O	3	3	g'		F	2	2	U; (TBB); humorous; Eng. folk-song
Williams, G., Old Farmer Buck	50622; 24¢; JC	4	2	b'1				1½	U; humorous folk-song
Wolfe, Bone come a-knittin'	82064; 16¢; F	4	2	g'				2½	Piano *ad lib.*
—Short'nin' bread	82062; 16¢; F	4	2	g'4				3	

OPENING AND CLOSING CHORUSES; ENCORES; NOVELTIES; CONVIVIAL SONGS—(Cont'd)

Composer; Title; Arranger (or, Arranger; Title)	Octavo No.; Price; Publisher	Number of Parts	Grade of Difficulty	Highest Tenor Note (Above é)	Number of Times	Lowest Bass Note (Below G)	Number of Times	Length in Minutes	General Remarks
NOVELTIES									
Abt, Laughing song	1299; 8¢; GS	4	2	a'4				1½	U; no P.R.
Andrews, The clock (Humoresque)	7091; 12¢; GS	4	2	g' 3		E	2	1½	U
Bingham, Root hog or die	379; 12¢; HW	1-4	2	g'3		F	4	1½	Bar. solo; cowboy song
Bliss, African drums	5358; 15¢; W	4	1	f'1				3½	Bar. solo
—Mosquitoes	4010; 12¢; W	4	1	gb'2				2	U; humorous
Bornschein, The scissors-grinder	586; 20¢; CC	4	2	a'3				2	Humorous
Buck, The song of the drum	4224; 20¢; GS	4	2	ab'1		Fb	1	3	U; no P.R.
Clokey, The bee	3068; 8¢; Su	4	1	a'2				1½	U
Gaul, The song of the Jersey roadmaker [*Riegger*]	7654, 16¢; GS	4	1	ab'3				3	
—Sons of the Prophet, sons of the Bey	6502; 15¢; J	4	3	ab'6		D	1	3½	U
Gibson, The drum	4227; 16¢; GS	4	2	f'		F		2½	U; no P.R.
Grieg, A barn song	8051; 20¢; GS	4	1	g'				3½	U
Hadley, The musical trust	512; 15¢; GS	4	2	a'				2	U
Howe, Chain-gang song	7117; 25¢; GS	4	2	g'		E	2	10	Treble voices *ad lib.*
Hughes, Doctor Foster	1507; —; Bo	4	2	g'6				1½	
Jüngst, The scissors-grinder	4976; 15¢; GS	4	2	g'				1½	U; Flemish folk-song
Nagler, Serenade in the snow	7984; 12¢; GS	4	2	a'3		E		1½	U
Othegraven, The hand-organ man	4863; 12¢; GS	5	3	ab'		F		3½	U; no P.R.
Rimsky-Korsakoff, The flight of the bumble bee [*Enders*]	7733; 16¢; GS	4	3	a'2		E	1	1½	From "Tsar Saltan"; flute and piano acc.
Saar, The beetle's wedding (Folk-song)	549; 18¢; EC	4	1	f'3		F		1½	U; Eng. & Ger.; T. and Bar. solos
Sabin, Song of the tinker	6713; 20¢; GS	4	3	bb'1		Eb		2	U
Sumsion, Is my team plowing	50670; 10¢; JC	4	2	g'4		D	1	2	U; T. solo
Warren, Merry-go-round	449; 15¢; HW	4	2	a'1				2	
Wolfe, De glory road	7956; 25¢; GS	4	3	a'		E	3	4	Negro dialect ballad
CONVIVIAL SONGS—DRINKING SONGS									
Andrews, Rum puncheon	7879; 12¢; GS	4	2	ab'6		F#	2	1½	U
Bach, And now 'tis time to go	1564; 16¢; Pn	4	2	a'2		F	1	2½	
Brower, Plastered	2162; 15¢; C	4	2	a'3		F	6	1½	U; humorous
Grieg, When I meet a friend	487; 9¢; GS	4	2	a'2				3½	U; no P.R.; Bar. solo
Isaacs, Wine and water	7824; 12¢; GS	4	1	f'5		F	3	2	U
MacMillan, At the inn (Au cabaret)	1761; 20¢; B	4	3	g#'3		E	4	2	U; Eng. & Fr., Fr.-Canadian folk-song
Mendelssohn, Turkish drinking song	3; 12¢; C	1-4	1	g'				3	U; no P.R.; soli
Ryder, The flagon's chime (Carillon du verre)	440; 20¢; B	4	1	g'1		E	3	1½	Old Fr.; Eng. & Fr.
Schubert, Drinking song in winter	1415; 12¢; O	1-3	1	f#'4		F#	5	1½	
Schumann, Wanderer's song [*Vogrich*]	1095; 12¢; GS	4	2	a'1		F	5	2½	
Smith, Burns' grace	7; 12¢; Pn	4	2	a'2		F	3	1	U; for banquet; Bar. solo
Sullivan, Ho, jolly Jenkin [*Rhys-Herbert*]	4696; 12¢; J	4	1	a'1				3	U
Timmings, Gluggity Glug	7377; 20¢; GS	4	1	g'4		F#	6	2½	U; humorous
Vene, Bacchanalian song	915; 15¢; R	4	3	g#'4		Eb	5	1	U
Vogrich, Here's to the maiden of bashful fifteen	130; 10¢; GS	4	....	a'2		F	6	1½	U

Intercollegiate Prize-Songs Used in National Contests for College Clubs

1924. George Henschel, "Morning Hymn"
1925. John Dowland, "Come again, sweet love"
1926. Horatio Parker, "The Lamp in the West"
1927. Robert Schumann, "The Lotus Flower"
1928. Jan Sibelius, "The Broken Melody"
1929. Anton Dvořák, "Songs my mother taught me"
1930. Thomas Morley, "Hark, jolly shepherds"
1931. Edward Elgar, "Feasting, I watch"
1932. Friedrich Faltin, "Fight"
1933. Jacob Arcadelt, "Ave Maria"
1934. Robert Schumann, "The Dreaming Lake"
1935. Vaughan Williams, "Down Among the Dead Men"
After 1935, contest continued as regional festivals.

Inter-Preparatory (High School) Contest Prize-Songs

1925. Brahms-Davison, "Suabian Folk-Song"
1926. Dudley Buck, "On the Sea"
1927 Edward Elgar, "After Many a Dusty Mile"
1928. Mendelssohn, "Gipsy Song"
       Marshall Bartholomew, "Shenandoah"
1929. Robert Schumann, "Dreaming Lake"
       Mendelssohn, "Hunter's Farewell"
1930. Mark Andrews, "Now sleeps the crimson petal"
       George Henschel, "Morning Hymn"
       Granville Bantock, "Give a rouse"
       Cecil Forsythe, "Tell me not of a lovely lass"
1931. Seth Bingham, "Gently Johnny"
       Edward Elgar, "It's Oh! to be a wild wind"
       Hugo Jungst, "While by my Sheep"
       Vaughan Williams, "Down among the Dead Men"
1932. Arthur Hall, "High Barbary" (Chantey)
After 1932, the contest continued as a festival.

1925-26   Common Repertoire Lists of the Associated Glee Clubs of America

Baldwin, "Hymn Before Action", White-Smith Publishing Co.
Dvořák-Smith, "Songs my mother taught me", A. P. Schmidt Co.
Franck-Davison, "Chorus of Camel Drivers", E. C. Schirmer Music Co.
Barnaby-Dressler, "Sweet and Low", Oliver Ditson Co.
Foote, "Bedouin Song", Arthur P. Schmidt Co.
Sullivan, "The long day closes", H. W. Gray Co.
Whiting, "The Hundred Pipers", G. Schirmer, Inc.
Speaks-Gaines, "Sylvia", G. Schirmer, Inc.

1926-27

Schubert-Liszt, "The Omnipotence", G. Schirmer, Inc.
Buck, "On the Sea", G. Schirmer, Inc.

German, "Rolling Down to Rio", H. W. Gray Co.
MacDowell, "Dance of the Gnomes", Arthur P. Schmidt Co.
Burleigh, "Deep River" (Negro Spiritual), G. Ricordi & Co.
Forsythe, "The Bell Man", Oliver Ditson Co.
Huhn-Lynes, "Invictus", Arthur P. Schmidt Co.
Speaks-Baldwin, "Morning", G. Schirmer, Inc.

1927-28

Clarke-Lucas, "The Blind Ploughman", Chappell-Harms, Inc.
Beethoven-Sachs, "Creation Hymn", H. W. Gray Co.
Hawley, "Ashes of Roses", John Church Co.
Taylor, "Concordia Laetitia", J. Fischer & Bro.
MacDowell, "The Crusaders", Arthur P. Schmidt Co.
Storch, "Night Witchery", G. Schirmer, Inc.
Schumann, "Rose stood bathed in dew", Oliver Ditson Co.
Burleigh, "Mother o' Mine", G. Ricordi & Co.

1928-29

Protheroe, "Laudamus", Boston Music Co.
Dickinson, "Music, when soft voices die", H. W. Gray Co.
Davison, "Reapers' Song" (Bohemian Folk-Song), E. C. Schirmer Music Co.
Fletcher, "A Lullaby of Love", H. W. Gray Co.
Reddick, "Sweet Canaan" (Spiritual), Boston Music Co.
Mair, "Twilight", Oliver Ditson Co.
Bartholomew, "Shenandoah", G. Schirmer, Inc.
Andrews, "Sea Fever", G. Schirmer, Inc.

1929-30

Bach, "Stay thou with me", John Church Co.
Gaul, "Mirage", G. Schirmer, Inc.
Wagner-Andrews, Pilgrims' Chorus, from "Tannhauser", G. Ricordi & Co.
Brahms-Lefebvre, "The Little Sandman", G. Ricordi & Co.
Forsythe, "At the Play", H. W. Gray Co.
Clokey, "Arab Song", J. Fischer & Bro.
Parker, "My Love", G. Schirmer, Inc.
Kountz-Baldwin, "The Sleigh", G. Schirmer, Inc.

1930-31

Davies, "Hymn Before Action", H. W. Gray Co.
Woodworth, "Gute Nacht" (German Folk-Song), E. C. Schirmer Music Co.
Shaw, "Hey, Robin, Jolly Robin", G. Ricordi & Co.
Andrews, "Now sleeps the crimson petal", G. Schirmer, Inc.
Sullivan, Entrance of the Peers, from "Iolanthe", Oliver Ditson Co. or E. C.
    Schirmer Music Co.
Grieg-Matthews, "Ave Maris Stella", Oliver Ditson Co.
Bartholomew, "Jericho" (Spiritual), G. Schirmer, Inc.
Logan-Baldwin, "Lift thine eyes", G. Ricordi & Co.

1931-32

Kun, "Hunting Song", H. W. Gray Co.
Widor-Moore, "Contemplation", Galaxy Music Corp.
Branscombe, "At the Postern Gate", A. P. Schmidt Co.
Bach-Davison, "Now let every tongue adore Thee", E. C. Schirmer Music Co.
Stebbins, "A Song of the Sea", Oliver Ditson Co.
Bruch, "Media Vita", G. Schirmer, Inc.
Gibb, "Calm and Storm", Boosey & Co., Inc.
Wagner-Andrews, "Pilgrims' Chorus", G. Ricordi & Co.

1933-34

Willan, "Agincourt Song", Carl Fischer, Inc.
Burleigh, "Ezekiel saw de wheel", G. Ricordi & Co.
MacDowell, "From the Sea", A. P. Schmidt Co.
Palmgren, "I'm coming home", H. W. Gray Co.
McMillan, "Stenka Razin", G. Schirmer, Inc.
Palestrina-Davison, "Tenebrae Factae Sunt", E. C. Schirmer Music Co.
Roberton, "The Old Woman", Chas. W. Homeyer & Co.
Shvedof, "We praise Thee," Boston Music Co.

1934-35

Peri-Bimboni, "Invocation of Orpheus", M. Witmark & Sons
Sanderson-Samuelson, "Susan is her name", Boosey & Co.
Noll, "The Four Winds", G. Schirmer, Inc.
Sibelius-Manney, "Dear Land of Home", B. F. Wood Music Co.
Kernochan, "Smuggler's Song", Galaxy Music Corp.
Clokey, "The Musical Trust", C. C. Birchard & Co.
Purcell-Burleigh, "Passing By", G. Ricordi & Co.
Fletcher, "Ring out, wild bells", Novello & Co.

1935-36

Brahms-Andrews, "May Night", M. Witmark & Sons
Gaines, "Cornish Fiddler's Song", J. Fischer & Co.
Enders, "Wade in de water", G. Ricordi & Co.
Schumann-Scherer, "Wanderer's Song", H. W. Gray Co.
Fox-Andrews, "My heart is a silent violin", Carl Fischer, Inc.
Tchaikovsky-Riegger, "Pilgrim's Song", Harold Flammer, Inc.
Gaul, "Sonnet from the Portugese", G. Schirmer, Inc.
Cadman-Baldwin, "Glory", Galaxy Music Corp.

1936-37

Taylor, "Waters ripple and flow" (Bohemian Folk-Song), J. Fischer & Bro.
Faning-Ryder, "Song of the Vikings", Oliver Ditson Co.
Lully-Chambers, "Lonely Woods", H. W. Gray Co.
Brahms-Treharne, "Mount your horses", Boston Music Co.
Messager-Matthews, "Long Ago in Alcala", Theodore Presser Co.
Hadley, "It was not in the winter", G. Schirmer, Inc.
Gaul, "Ozymandias, King of Kings", Oliver Ditson Co.
Rheinberger, "Evening Hymn", White-Smith Co.

1937-38

Handel-Noble, "Sound an alarm", Carl Fischer, Inc.

Tchesnokov-Davison, "Salvation belongeth to our God", E. C. Schirmer Music Co.

Flagler, "Boots", Harold Flammer, Inc.

Sullivan-Davison, Finale from "The Gondoliers", E. C. Schirmer Music Co.

Mair, "Suomi's Song", G. Schirmer, Inc.

Foster-Baldwin, "De Camptown Races", J. Fischer & Bro.

Northcote, "All Through the Night" (Welsh Folk-Song), Curwen, Inc.

Converse, "Laudate Dominum", Boston Music Co.

1938-39

Richter, "The Creation", Harold Flammer, Inc.

Sjoberg-Balogh, "Visions", Galaxy Music Corp.

Thomas, "Meg, the Gypsy", Carl Fischer, Inc.

Burleigh, "Were you there?" (Negro Spiritual), G. Ricordi & Co.

Fox, "Rain and the River", C. C. Birchard

MacFarlane, "Open our eyes", G. Schirmer, Inc.

Foster-Soderstrom, "I dream of Jeanie", Fitzsimons Music Co.

Verdi, "The Bandit", H. W. Gray Co.

1939-40

Handel-Davidson, "Hallelujah Amen", E. C. Schirmer Music Co.

Bortniansky-Ham, "Cherubim Song (No. 7)", H. W. Gray Co.

Dürrner, "Kyrie at Sea", Boston Music Co.

Handel-Spross, "O, majestic trees", The John Church Co.

Haydn-Daltry, "Great and Glorious", B. F. Wood Music Co.

Merwin, "In Flanders Field", G. Ricordi & Co.

Levenson, "The Days of Sorrow" (Russian Folk-Song), Clayton Summy Co.

Gaines, "Immortalis", J. Fischer & Bros.

RECOMMENDED COLLECTIONS FOR MEN'S GLEE CLUBS

Note: The recommended books are listed in the order of the date of their publication. The majority of the following books include both accompanied and unaccompanied material.

1. "Young Men's Choral Assembly for Schools"; selected and edited by F. Melius Christiansen; published by G. Schirmer, Inc., 1936; price 75c., paperbound.

  25 four-part songs of an easy grade of difficulty and varied appeal: 17 unaccompanied and 8 accompanied; for high schools and groups with limited voice range.

2. "Over the Air"; G. Schirmer, Inc., 1923; selected and recommended for radio, concert, home, and business men's clubs by G. Schirmer, Inc.; price 75c., paper-bound; for mature voices.

  Contains 11 favorite four-part songs for quartet or chorus: five unaccompanied and six accompanied.

  Range from E♭ in Bass to b♭' in Tenor; majority of songs of medium difficulty.

3. "Twice 55 Part-Songs for High School Boys" (The Check Book); C. C. Birch-ard & Co., 1930; compiled and edited by Peter W. Dykema; price $1.25, cloth-bound.

Contains 106 songs: 11 two-part, 7 three-part, and 88 four-part; 26 ballads and songs of sentiment, 21 folk-songs, 13 humorous songs, 18 hymns and devotional songs, 4 spirituals, 3 patriotic, 6 rounds and canons, 12 songs for special occasions, 19 special program numbers, 13 songs for sport and out-door use; majority of songs unaccompanied and easy.

Range from G in Bass to f♯' in Tenor; majority of songs have still smaller range. Suited for use in high schools, and for other male groups with voices of limited range.

4. "Glee and Chorus Book for Male Voices"; Silver Burdett & Co., 1929; com-piled and edited by Earl Towner and Ernest Hesser; price $1.20, pasteboard-bound.

Contains 39 songs: 4 unison, 22 three-part, and 12 four-part; 9 folk-songs, 18 part-songs and choruses, 7 operatic choruses, 8 patriotic and devotional songs. Majority of songs with piano accompaniment, from easy to moder-ately difficult.

Range from G in Bass to g' in Tenor; majority of songs have still smaller range. Suited to high schools and to other male groups with voices of limited range.

5. "Twice 55 Community Songs for Male Voices" (The Blue Book); C. C. Birch-ard & Co., 1926; compiled and edited by Peter W. Dykema; price 50c., paper-bound.

Contains 110 four-part songs for male voices with a variety of interests and types of songs. Most of the songs intended for unaccompanied singing, easy to moderately difficult.

Range in most songs does not exceed G in Bass to g' in Tenor, or an even more limited range. Adapted to high school, college, or community groups.

6. "Mendelssohn Glee Club Favorites"; selected and edited by a special com-mittee; G. Schirmer, Inc., 1918; price $1.25, paper-bound.

Contains 36 songs of a varied character selected from the repertoire of the Mendelssohn Glee Club; 4-6 parts, unaccompanied, suitable only for mature voices.

Range from E♭ in Bass (some optional notes lower) to b♭' in Tenor; majority have smaller range.

7. Small, inexpensive collections published by Hall & McCreary Co.:
   (a) "Choruses for Male Voices"—24 unaccompanied choruses, majority easy; arranged or composed by Noble Cain, Walter Goodell, and Richard Grant, price 12c., paper-bound.
   (b) "Famous Spirituals"—42 spirituals arranged by Walter Goodell; major-ity unaccompanied, four-part, easy; price 20c., paper-bound.
   (c) "Sea Songs and Chanteys"—18 songs; majority unaccompanied, four-part, easy; price 12c., paper-bound.

8. "Hampton Series of Negro Folk-Songs", recorded and edited by Natalie Curtis-Burlin; Book I and Book II; price 50c., each, paper-cover; G. Schirmer, Inc.

Four easy unaccompanied spirituals in each book.

RECOMMENDED COLLECTIONS FOR BOYS' GLEE CLUBS

(Adapted to junior high school voices, ages 11 to 16—the period of voice change)

Note: The recommended books are listed in the order of the date of their publication.

1. "Close Harmony for Boys"; Boston Music Co., 1929; selected, edited, and harmonized by Earl L. Baker and Cyrus Daniel; price $1.25, cloth-bound.

   Contains 74 songs in four parts (except the rounds): 5 operatic songs, 8 folk-songs, 5 patriotic songs, 9 art-songs, 6 sentimental and home songs, 11 college and school songs, 10 humorous songs, 2 songs of the sea, 7 southern melodies and spirituals, 6 sacred songs, 5 rounds.

   Range from A in Bass to e″ in Boy Soprano; majority of songs in much more limited range, unaccompanied, easy to moderately difficult.

2. "Glenn Glee Club Book for Boys"; Oliver Ditson Co., 1928; edited by Maybelle Glenn and Virginia French; price $1.25, cloth-bound.

   Contains 50 songs in three and four parts: 21 folk-songs, 12 sacred songs, 17 ballads, art-songs, etc.

   Range from A in Bass to e″ in Boy Soprano; majority of songs have much smaller range, accompanied, easy to moderately difficult.

3. "Twice 55 Part-Songs for Boys" (The Orange Book), C. C. Birchard & Co., 1927; compiled and edited by Peter W. Dykema; price 50c., paper-bound.

   Contains 113 songs in three and four parts: 45 ballads and songs of sentiment, 36 folk-tunes, 10 songs for special occasions, 5 patriotic songs, 10 songs of nature, 8 songs of sport and out-of-doors, 15 humorous songs, 6 songs of greeting, 4 Negro spirituals, 12 religious and devotional songs.

   Range—majority of songs from B♭ in Bass to b♭″ in Boy Soprano; some have still smaller range; majority unaccompanied and easy.

4. "Second Chorus Book for Boys"; G. Schirmer, Inc., 1925; compiled, arranged, or composed by Ella M. Probst and J. Victor Berquist; price $1.00, cardboard-bound.

   Contains 53 four-part songs, of a varied character and appeal; majority unaccompanied and easy.

   Range from B♭ in Bass to d″ Boy Soprano; many have a smaller range.

5. "First Chorus Book for Boys"; G. Schirmer, Inc., 1922; compiled by Ella M. Probst and J. Victor Berquist; price $1.00, paper-bound.

   Contains 53 four-part songs of varied character and appeal; majority unaccompanied and easy.

   Range from B♭ in Bass to d″ in Boy Soprano; majority in still more limited range.

3. MUSIC FOR TREBLE VOICES

Remarks on the List of Recommended Octavo Music for Treble Voices

1. For the sake of brevity, music is listed under only the one heading under which it seems most appropriate. It may be necessary to look under a number of different headings in order to find all music of a certain school, or by a certain composer.

2. It must not be presumed that all music listed under such headings as "Humorous Encore" or "Novelty" is of a lower musical quality than that listed under other headings; most of the music listed under such headings is good enough to be regularly programmed.

3. This list features secular music; only those sacred compositions especially suitable for secular performance as well are included.

4. The music listed includes both accompanied and unaccompanied with piano reduction for rehearsal unless otherwise noted. Unaccompanied (*a cappella*) music is noted in the "General Remarks" column with the abbreviation "U".

5. Music is listed alphabetically under the different headings by composer (or arranger).

6. In case the same composition is published in arrangements of equal worth by two different firms, the lower-priced issue is listed; if the price is the same, both issues are listed.

7. A key to abbreviations of publishers will be found on p. 93; to grade-of-difficulty estimates, exact pitch indications, and other abbreviations, on p. 94.

8. When extremes of range are reached *over* six times, no numeral follows the letter.

9. The performance-time indicated is an estimate; it is not to be considered exact for purposes of radio or concert.

10. It is suggested that directors seeking suitable new music for their groups will save time and receive the greatest value from the music catalogued here by proceeding in general as follows:
    a. Find the sections which list the type of music in which you are most interested.
    b. Determine from the grade of difficulty, the composer-arranger, the title of the composition, and general remarks, which music seems most promising. In most cases, single copies may be secured on approval.
    c. Select by careful review from these "On Approval" copies the music which seems most suitable for your group.

11. Every effort has been directed by the compiler towards making all the information correct. However, prices change, grades of difficulty differ with each chorus, performance-time varies with the tempo chosen, *etc*. The reader should consider all the information given only as approximately exact.

RECOMMENDED OCTAVO MUSIC FOR TREBLE VOICES

Composer; Title; Arranger (or, Arranger; Title)	Octavo No.; Price; Publisher	Number of Parts	Grade of Difficulty	Highest Soprano Note (Above f'') Number of Times	Lowest Alto Note (Below a) Number of Times	Length in Minutes	General Remarks
One- and Two-Part Music with Descant (Suitable for any group of treble, male, or mixed voices)							
Dunhill, A-hunting we will go.........	D45; 12¢; C	1-2	2	g''1	f 2	2	Old Eng. Song
——Aye waukin' O!...................	D47; 12¢; C	1-2	1	......	......	1	Old Scottish
——Billy boy......................	39; 12¢; C	1-2	1	......	......	2	Old Eng. song
——David of the white rock........	D48; 12¢; C	1-2	2	......	......	2	Welsh traditional song
——God rest you merry, gentlemen....	32; 12¢; C	1-2	1	g''1	......	2	Eng. carol
——Golden slumbers kiss your eyes...	D2; 12¢; C	1-2	1	......	......	1½	Old Eng. song
——It came upon the midnight clear...	19, 16¢, O	1-2	1	......	......	3½	Old Christmas tune
——John Peel....................	16; 12¢; O	1-2	2	......	......	2½	Traditional Eng.
——Oh! Breathe not his name........	30; 12¢; C	1-2	2	......	......	1½	Irish folk-song
——Old King Cole.................	3; 16¢; C	1-2	1	......	......	1½	Traditional Eng.
——The Campbells are comin'.......	33; 12¢; C	1-2	2	......	......	2	Scottish song
——The holly and the ivy..........	18; 12¢; O	1-2	1	......	......	1½	Eng. carol
——The jolly miller...............	7; 12¢; C	1-2	1	......	......	1½	Old Eng. song
——The meeting of the waters.......	D38; 12¢; C	1-2	2	......	......	2	Old Irish song
——The mermaid.................	14, 16¢, C	1-2	1	......	......	3½	Old Eng. sea-song
——The moon shines bright..........	20; 12¢; O	1-2	1	......	......	3½	Lancashire carol
——The Morris dance..............	6; 12¢; O	1-2	1	......	......	1½	Old Eng. dance-song
——The oak and the ash..........	35; 12¢; C	1-2	1	......	......	3	Old Eng. song
——Ye banks and braes...........	9; 12¢; C	1-2	1	......	......	1½	Old Scottish song
Northcote, The lover's farewell........	157; 12¢; O	1-2	2	......	......	3	Somerset folk-song
Summervell, The Grasmere carol......	164; 16¢; C	1-2	2	g''3	......	2½	Christmas carol
Two-Part (Suitable also for men's or mixed voices)							
Acton, Song of a wood nymph........	6020; 12¢; GS	2	1	......	......	2	
Bach, Spring comes laughing..........	1544; 12¢; Pn	2	2	a''1	......	1	From "Peasant Cantata"
Brahms, Three love-songs:............	1055; 18¢; EC	2	1	......	......	....	Two pianos with violin obbl.; Eng. & Ger.
(1) Like the sunset's crimson splendor..	....			......	......	1	
(2) Bird in air will stray afar.....	....			ab''1	......	1	
(3) Seat thyself, my dearest heart.	....			......	......	1½	
Brambach, The coming of spring.......	14313; 15¢; D	2	2	f#''	......	2½	
Chaminade, Angelus..................	4843; 9¢; GS	2	1	......	......	3	
——Duet of the stars..............	4922; 12¢; GS	2	2	a''1	......	2½	
Cowen, Bridal chorus.................	483; 12¢; GH	2	2	g''	......	3½	
Davison, Christians, hark!...........	1027; 18¢; EC	2	1	gb''1	......	3	(Noel of the Bressan Waits)
Delibes, Flower song [*Lefebvre*]........	648; 20¢; Ga	2	2	ab''2	......	3½	From "Lakme"
Dobson, Sunrise....................	5989; 10¢; GS	2	1	......	......	2	Two-part canon for equal voices
——What the nightingale sang........	9162; 12¢; GS	2	1	......	......	2½	Two-part canon
Elgar, My love dwelt in a northern land	290; 15¢; N	2	1	g''2	......	2½	
——The woodland stream............	7721; 12¢; GS	2	1	......	......	1½	
Farjeon, Chimes...................	1; 15¢; JWm	2	2	......	......	1	
Fletcher, Madrigal of spring........	47; 12¢; N	2	2	......	......	1½	
Franck, Cradle song of the Virgin (La Vierge à la Crèche)................	5520; 10¢; GS	2	1	......	......	3	Eng. & Fr.
Gounod, Flower song [*O'Hare*]........	295; 10¢; JF	2	1	......	......	2	From "Faust"
Handel, Come and trip it............	1551; 12¢; C	2	2	a''1	......	2	From "L'Allegro"
Mendelssohn, Greeting.............	9030; 12¢; D	2	1	g''2	......	1½	
Molloy, The Kerry dance [*O'Hare*].....	318; 10¢, K	2	1	......	......	1½	
Morley, I go before, my charmer......	902; 15¢; EC	2	1	......	......	2	Canzonet
Moussorgsky, Youth at dance [*Silver*]..	4215; 12¢; J	2	1	g''2	......	1½	Russian dance tune
Pierne, All hail, bright spring.......	1092; 18¢; EC	2	1	a''1	......	3	Fr. & Eng.
Proctor, Drowsily come the sheep [*Brower*]...................	87003; 15¢; F	2	1	......	......	1½	
Rowley, Song of the pedlar............	178; 12¢; C	2	1	......	......	½	
Rubinstein, Wanderer's evening song...	9173; 8¢; GS	2	1	f#''3	......	1½	Eng. & Ger.

Composer; Title; Arranger (or, Arranger; Title)	Octavo No.; Price; Publisher	Number of Parts	Grade of Difficulty	Highest Soprano Note (Above f'') Number of Times	Lowest Alto Note (Below a) Number of Times	Length in Minutes	General Remarks
Two-Part—(Continued) (Suitable also for men's or mixed voices)							
Saint-Saëns, The swan [*Gaines*]	14076; 10¢; D	2	2	g''2	g 2	1½	
Schubert, Serenade [*Hoffman*]	6621; 12¢; D	2	2	g''3	......	3	
Thomas, Lords and ladies all are we [*Rix*]	9175; 9¢; GS	2	2	g''2	......	1½	Gavotte from "Mignon"
Vincent, Merry June	107; 10¢; Pr	2	1	g''1	......	2	Vocal polka
Von Suppe, Woodland night [*O'Hare*]	277; 10¢; K	2	1	g''1	......	1½	Two-part chorale

MUSIC OF THE SIXTEENTH, SEVENTEENTH, AND EIGHTEENTH CENTURIES
(Madrigals, Motets, Glees, Chansons, Canzonets, Chorales, etc.)

Composer; Title; Arranger (or, Arranger; Title)	Octavo No.; Price; Publisher	Number of Parts	Grade of Difficulty	Highest Soprano Note (Above f'') Number of Times	Lowest Alto Note (Below a) Number of Times	Length in Minutes	General Remarks
ENGLISH							
Arne, The lass with the delicate air [*Fox*]	9114; 12¢; GS	3	1	....	......	3	S. solo
——The lass with the delicate air [*Robinson*]	12656; 12¢; D	3	2	b''1	f# 3	3	
——Under the greenwood tree [*Shelley*]	9113; 10¢; GS	3	1	g''1	g 1	2	
——Where the bee sucks [*Barratt*]	46; 10¢; JF	3	1	g''2	g 1	2½	
Barratt, The willow song	41; 10¢; JF	3	1	g''2	g 2	3	
Byrd, Sacerdotes Domini [*G. W. W.*]	815; 15¢; EC	4	1	......	g 1	1½	U; Latin
Dowland, Come again! sweet love	507; 12¢; N	4	1	......	ab	3½	U
Este, How merrily we live	5359; 12¢; GS	3	1	f#''	......	1½	U
Gibbons, The silver swan [*Geer*]	1054; 15¢; EC	4	2	a''2	g 3	1	U
——The silver swan [*Manney*]	284; 12¢; Wo	3	1	g''2	......	1	U
Handel, The smiling dawn	150; 10¢; GS	3	1	g''2	......	3	From "Jephtha"
Lock, Ne'er trouble thyself	JP6; 16¢; O	3	1	g''3	......	1½	U
Morley, I go before, my charmer	824; 15¢; EC	2	1	......	......	2	U; Canzonet
Playford, (a) Comely swain	JP28; 20¢; O	3	1	......	......	1	U
(b) Where the bee sucks [*Wilson*]	....					1½	U
Purcell, In these delightful, pleasant groves	434; 12¢; EC	3	1	f#''2	......	1	U
——Nymphs and shepherds [*Harris*]	12840; 12¢; D	3	1	g''2	......	1	
——With drooping wings, ye cupids come [*Geer*]	1053; 15¢; EC	4	1	g''2	f# 2	1½	U; From "Dido and Aeneas"
Weelkes, Cease, sorrows, now [*G. W. W.*]	835; 15¢; EC	3	1	......	g 1	2½	U
——Four arms, two necks, one wreathing [*G. W. W.*]	834; 15¢; EC	3	1	......	ab6	1½	U
——The nightingale [*Leslie*]	1008; 15¢; EC	3	1	g''6	g 1	2	U
——On the plains, fairy trains [*G. W. W.*]	831; 16¢; EC	4	2	f#''	......	3	U
——Strike it up, Tabor [*G. W. W.*]	836; 15¢; EC	3	1	......	......	1	U
Wilbye, Adieu, sweet Amarillis [*Davis*]	1076; 16¢; EC	4	....	g''4	g 4	2½	U
——Come, shepherd swains	1; 15¢; St	3	2	a''2	f# 2	3	U
——Weep, O mine eyes [*G. W. W.*]	481; 16¢; EC	3	1	......	g 1	2	U
FLEMISH							
Waelrant, Winter song	489; 16¢; EC	3	1	f#''4	g 4	1½	
GERMAN							
Aichinger, Assumpta est Maria	6250; 8¢; GS	3	2	a''3	f 1	1	U; no P.R.; Latin
Bach, Bourrée [*Snodgrass*]	83094; 15¢; F	3	1	ab''3	......	2½	
——Let all the heavens adore Thee [*Hinkle*]	14573; 10¢; D	3	1	g''2	g 4	1½	From "Sleepers Awake"
——O Jesu sweet [*Geer*]	377; 12¢; C	4	1	gb''1	gb1	1	U; Eng. & Ger.
——Sleepers, wake! a voice is sounding	7428; 15¢; GS	3	1	g''4	g	3½	From "Church Cantata No. 140"
——Thus, then, the law of the spirit	7604; 6¢; GS	3	1	g''3	g 1	½	U
Bach, W. F., No blade of grass can flourish [*Frank*]	5676; 10¢; GS	4	1	g''6	g	2	Acc. *ad lib.*; Ger. & Eng.

Composer; Title; Arranger (or, Arranger; Title)	Octavo No.; Price; Publisher	Number of Parts	Grade of Difficulty	Highest Soprano Note (Above f'')	Number of Times	Lowest Alto Note (Below a)	Number of Times	Length in Minutes	General Remarks
MUSIC OF THE SIXTEENTH, SEVENTEENTH, AND EIGHTEENTH CENTURIES—*(Cont'd)* (Madrigals, Motets, Glees, Chansons, Canzonets, Chorales, etc.)									
ITALIAN									
Gagliano, O my soul [*Roper*]	185; 15¢; St	3	1	f#''3				1½	
Lotti, Vere languores nostros [*G. W. W.*]	822; 15¢; EC	3	1	g''1		g 2		2	U; Latin
Palestrina, Ave Maria	6251; 10¢; GS	4	1	f#''				4	U; Latin motet
Palestrina [*Rossini*]	6439; 15¢; J								
(a) Patres nostri peccaverunt		3	2	g''2		g 1		1½	U; Latin
(b) Adoramus te, Christe		3	1	g''2				1½	U; Latin
Perti, Adoramus te [*Saar*]	14397; 10¢; D	3	2	gb''2		gb 1		1	U; Eng. & Latin
Scarlatti, My heart is yearning [*Sammond*]	6191; 15¢; J	3	1			g 2		3½	Latin & Eng.; Organ acc.
——Where, my thoughts, where do you flutter? [*Roper*]	186; 16¢; St	3	2	g''1		g 1		1½	
NETHERLANDISH									
Gombert, Canon apertus	7135; 20¢; GS	6	1	g'' 1		ab 1		2	U; Eng. & Fr. (SSÁAAT)
Lasso, Adoramus te, Christe	5604; 8¢; GS	3	1					1	U; Latin
MUSIC OF THE NINETEENTH AND TWENTIETH CENTURIES									
AMERICAN									
Andrews, Gather ye rosebuds	34; 12¢; HW	3	1	g''2		ab 1		1	
——Pierrot	790; 15¢; R	3	1	g''1		g 1		1	Acc. difficult
Beach, Dusk in June	6695; 12¢; GS	4	2	a''1		gb 1		1½	U
——Prayer of a tired child	6534; 12¢; GS	4	2	g''3		g		1½	
Beatty, Snowflakes	7084; 15¢; GS	3	2	a''6		g 2		1½	
Berwald, The stars	7121; 12¢; GS	5	2	g''1		f# 3		1½	S. solo; acc. difficult
Boyd, Balloons in the snow	3025; 15¢; HF	3	2	g''				1½	
——In Italy	855; 15¢; GH	3	2	ab''1		ab 1		1	
Branscombe, A wind from the sea	881; 12¢; AP	3	3	b''1		g 1		3	
Cadman, Four American-Indian songs	7253; 25¢; WS								
(1) From the land of the sky-blue water		3or4	1					1	
(2) The white dawn is stealing		3or4	1			g 4		1½	
(3) Far off I hear a lover's flute		3or4	2	g''5		g 3		2	
(4) The moon drops low		3or4	2	g#''2				2	
——Indian mountain song	11987; 12¢; D	4	2	g#''1		g#		2½	
——Little papoose on the wind-swung bough	11782; 10¢; D	3	2	g''1		f 2		2	U; no P.R.
Cain, Nocturne	83085; 16¢; F	4	2	ab''4		ab		2½	
Carter, Vesper hymn	4041; 12¢; Su	3-4	2	gb''1		g 1		2½	
Chadwick, Thistledown	422; 12¢; GS	4	2	a''1		g 1		1½	
Clokey, A bird flew	5506; 15¢; J	3	1	a''1		ab 1		2	
——Flower of dreams	1004; 14¢; CC	3	2	a''1				2½	
——Kye song of St. Bride	818; 10¢; CC	3	1	g''4				1½	
——The last night	5507; 12¢; J	3	2	bb''1				3	
——Night song	1001; 8¢; CC	3	1	g''3				2	
——A snow legend	120; 14¢; CC	3	1	a''2		ab 1		3	
Curran, Dawn	9118; 12¢; GS	3	2	bb''1		ab 2		2	
——Rain	9119; 12¢; GS	3	1	g'' 3		ab 1		2	
Daniels, Eastern song	1; 16¢; AP	3	2	g#''1		g# 1		4	Piano and 2 Violins
——June rhapsody	593; 12¢; AP	3	1	g''3				2½	
——Song of the Persian captive	666; 12¢; AP	3	1	a''1		g 2		3½	
Del Riego, Homing [*Ferris*]	3013; 15¢; CH	3	2	ab''1		f# 1		3	
Ferrari, Moon madness	7046; 15¢; GS	4	2	ab''1		g 6		2	Modern idiom
Forsythe, To the wayfarer	14417; 12¢; D	3	2	g''5		g		4	
Foster, Beautiful dreamer [*Riegger*]	83090; 15¢; F	3	1					2	Violin *ad lib.*
Fox, My heart is a silent violin [*Andrews*]	5217; 15¢; C	3	1	g''2				2	
Friml, Allah's holiday	9142; 12¢; GS	4	1	g#''1		g# 1		1½	From "Katinka"

Composer; Title; Arranger (or, Arranger; Title)	Octavo No.; Price; Publisher	Number of Parts	Grade of Difficulty	Highest Soprano Note (Above f'')	Number of Times	Lowest Alto Note (Below a)	Number of Times	Length in Minutes	General Remarks
MUSIC OF THE NINETEENTH AND TWENTIETH CENTURIES—(*Continued*)									
AMERICAN—(*Continued*)									
Gaul, Dream rhapsody	6692; 20¢; J	4-6	3	a''1		f♯ 1		7	Viola and flute *ad lib.*; S. & A. solos
——List! The cherubic host	6007; 12¢; GS	4	1	a♭''2				5	Bar. & S. solos
——Soft, soft wind	4937; 12¢; GS	4	2	g♭''4		f 3		1½	
Gilchrist, The bells	5750; 20¢; GS.	4	2	g''3		f♯ 2		2	
Gordon, Hymn to the night	548; 20¢; CC	3	2	g♯''1		g♯ 5		3	Partially U
Goring-Thomas, Time's garden [*Harris*]	6159; 15¢; J	3	1	g♭''2				3	'Cello Acc.
Hadley, Bid me to live	83072; 15¢; R	3	2	a''2		a♭ 1		1	
Harris, Echo song	878; 12¢; AP	3	1					3	
Henschel, Morning hymn [*Clough-Leighter*]	478; 15¢; EC	4	2	g♯''1		f♯ 2		1	
Horsman, Sonnet (When to soft sleep)	6735; 15¢; GS	4	3	a''3		f 2		3	Requires good Alto II
Huhn, The unknown	1408; 20¢; B	3	2	a''1		g 1		4	Piano and organ acc.; Organ *ad lib.*
Kountz, The sleigh [*Baldwin*]	7399; 12¢; GS	3	2	g''		g 1		½	S. optional b♭''1*
Lang, The dream robber [*Chaffin*]	1183; 12¢; B	3	1	g'' 6		g 1		2½	Two violin acc. *ad lib.*
Lieurance, Moonlit lake of the isles	468; 8¢; CC	3	1					2½	Piano optional
——Pakoble (The rose)	10940; 8¢; Pr	3	2			e 1		1½	
——Where dawn and sunset meet	20521; 10¢; Pr	4	2	a''3				1	Violin obbl.
Loomis, Hurakan, the west wind	450; 8¢; CC	3	1	f♯''1				1	
MacDowell, Dance of gnomes [*Ambrose*]	671; 12¢; AP	4	2	g''3		g		1	U
——Menie [*Ambrose*]	990; 12¢; AP	3	1			g 2		1½	
——To a wild rose [*Ambrose*]	754; 12¢; AP	3	1			g 1		2	
——Through the meadow [*Page*]	——; 20¢; BH	3	1	a''1				1½	
MacFarren, Ye spotted snakes	389; 12¢; GS	4	2	a''2		g		3	
Maley, He came all so still [*Chaffin*]	503; 15¢; H	4	1	g''1		f 1		2	Semplice, legato
Matthews, Dusk	14547; 15¢; D	4	1	g♯''2		g 1		3½	
Michael, The snow	2558; 15¢; MW	3	1			g 2		1½	U; no P.R.
——Song of the rain	2557; 15¢; MW	3	2	a''1				2	U; no P.R.
Mueller, The blue swan	83072; 15¢; F	3	1	g''1				3½	Modern idiom
Park, The romaika [*Taylor*]	13445; 15¢; D	3	3	b♭''2				1½	
Proctor, Drowsily come the sheep [*Engel*]	83015; 15¢; F	3	1	g'' 1		g 4		2	
Repper, What is more gentle than a wind in summer	934; 15¢; CC	3	1	a''1				2½	
Richardson, Near an ancient hostelrie	11927; 15¢; D	3	1	g''1		a♭ 1		3	
Saar, The little gray dove	6086; 15¢; GS	3	2			g 2		2	S. solo to b♭''
——The nightingales	1056; 20¢; EC	3	2	f♯''1				3½	T. solo; oboe, flute, or violin obbl.
Smith, Why so pale and wan?	7402; 15¢; GS	3	2	a♭''3				3	U; modern madrigal
Spross, Come down, laughing streamlet	2384; 20¢; JCh	4	2	a''1		f♯ 1		1½	
——Will o' the wisp	2821; 12¢; JCh	3	1	g''3				1½	
Stickles, Shepherd, play a little air [*Treharne*]	83006; 12¢; F	4	2	g''5		g		1	
Treharne, Oh! snatched away in beauty's bloom	7169; 15¢; GS	3	1	g♯''1		g 4		3½	
——Patter of the shoon [*Engel*]	3016; 16¢; F	3	1	g''1				1	
Tyson, The lilacs are in bloom [*Treharne*]	7843; 12¢; GS	3	1	a'' 1				2	
Vene, Love is a sickness	7919; 12¢; GS	4	2	a''4		a♭ 2		2½	U; madrigal
——Love not me for comely grace	7924; 12¢; GS	4	2	g''1		g 2		2	U; madrigal
Ware, Dance the romaika [*Treharne*]	38002; 15¢; F	3	1	a''1				2	
Warren, Autumn sunset in the canyon	367; 12¢; HW	3	2	g''6				2½	S. optional b♭'' 1*
——Down in the glen	7474; 16¢; GS	3	1	a''1		g 2		2	
——Spring morning in the hills	365; 12¢; HW	3	2	a''1				1½	
——Summer noon on the desert	364; 12¢; HW	3	2	a♭''1		g♯ 1		3½	
——Winter night in the valley	368; 12¢; HW	3	2	a''2		a♭ 4		3	

* Such numerals indicate the number of times an extreme note occurs.

RECOMMENDED OCTAVO MUSIC FOR TREBLE VOICES

Composer; Title; Arranger (or, Arranger; Title)	Octavo No.; Price; Publisher	Number of Parts	Grade of Difficulty	Highest Soprano Note (Above f") Number of Times	Lowest Alto Note (Below a) Number of Times	Length in Minutes	General Remarks
MUSIC OF THE NINETEENTH AND TWENTIETH CENTURIES—(*Continued*)							
AMERICAN—(*Continued*)							
Wendt, Go down to Kew	7496; 16¢; GS	3	1	a″1	.....	3	
Wood, A brown bird singing	3003; 15¢; CH	3	2	ab″2	g 2	2	
Woodman, O happy sleep	6528; 15¢; GS	3-5	2	ab″1	g 2	5	
ENGLISH							
Bantock, Elfin music	——; 20¢; BH	3	1	g″2	g 2	3	
——On Himalay	129; 12¢; HW	3	1	a″1	ab 1	1½	
——Silent strings	1467; 15¢; Bo	3	1	g″ 1	ab 1	3	
——To the evening star	71365; 15¢; JC	4	2	g″2	g 5	3	U
——To the muses	71364; 15¢; JC	4	3	bb″1	g 1	2	U
Bingham, Rosalynd's madrigal	199; 15¢; HW	4	2	g#″2	.....	2	U
Callcott, How sweet the moonlight sleeps upon this bank	391; 8¢; GS	3	1	g″1	.....	3	
Elgar, As torrents in summer	8; 12¢; N	3	1	.....	g 5	1½	From "King Olaf"
——The snow	1603; 15¢; B or 274; 15¢; Wo	3	2	g″2	g 4	5	Two violins and piano acc.
Faning, The miller's wooing [*Spicker*]	4744; 15¢; GS	4	2	ab″1	ab 3	1½	
Fletcher, The cloud	8095; 15¢; GS	3	1	g″ 1	.....	3	
——The witches' carnival	71371; 30¢; JC	3-6	2	a″3	.....	12	
German, Beauteous morn	34; 15¢; N	3	2	.....	f# 1	3½	
Gibbs, The song of shadows	1508; 15¢; Bo	3	1	f#″1	ab 2	2	
Handel, Let us wander [*Diack*]	1571; 12¢; Pn	3	1	g″2	g 3	1	U; from "L'Allegro"
——Two choruses from "L'Allegro" [*G. W. W.*]	837; 30¢; EC	2-4	3	.....	.....		Two piano acc.
1. Or let the merry bells ring round	.....	.....		a″3	g 2	4	
2. These delights if thou canst give	.....	.....		a″2	.....	4	
Holst, Choral hymns from the Rig Veda							
3. Hymn to Vena	289; 12¢; HW	4	3	ab″1	g 1	5	Harp or piano acc.
4. Hymn of the travelers	290; 10¢; HW	2-4	3	a″1	f# 1	2½	Harp or piano acc.
——Pastoral	62; 15¢; St	3	1	.....	.....	2½	U
——Songs from "The Princess":							
2. The splendour falls	362; 15¢; N	4-8	2	f#″	g 4	2	U
3. Tears, idle tears	55; 12¢; N	4	2	f#″2	f# 1	2	U
4. O swallow, swallow	364; 12¢; N	3	1	g″2	.....	1½	U
——Two eastern pictures	52; 25¢; R	.....		.....	.....	3	
1. Spring	.....	3	2	.....	g 3		
2. Summer	.....	4	2	.....	g# 4		
——The swallow leaves her nest	71458; 10¢; JC	2-4	1	.....	.....	2	U
Hulbert, Orpheus with his lute	71772; 15¢; JC	3	2	ab″1	g 1	2½	Flute or violin obbl.
Humphries, Where, from the eye of day	12; 16¢; JWm	3	2	g″1	g 5	2	U
Jenkins, Night in the desert	71448; 15¢; JC	3	1	g#″1	.....	2	
Ketelbey, In a Persian market	27; 20¢; Bs	3	1	g″5	g	4	
Lee, The dream seller	71731; 15¢; JC	3	1	g″ 2	g 5	2½	U
Leoni, Tally-ho! [*Harris*]	9108; 12¢; GS	3	1	g″1	.....	1½	
Lloyd, Grey stones	1109; 15¢; CC	3	2	g″1	g 2	2	U
Odell, Supplication (Prayer of Mary, Queen of Scots)	1612; 16¢; Pn	3	1	g″2	g 2	3½	U
Roberton, Little Boy Blue	1569; 12¢; Pn	3	1	g″1	g 2	2½	U
——Hear the sledges with the bells	71536; 15¢; JC	3	1	ab″2	gb 2	1	U
——The shepherdess	71500; 10¢; JC	3	2	g″3	g 4	1½	U
Sullivan, Finale from "The Gondoliers" [*Clough-Leighter—G. W. W.*]	474; 25¢; EC	4	2	a″1	.....	3½	Two-piano acc.
Taylor, How sweet the moonlight sleeps	115; 25¢; St	3	2	ab″1	ab 6	2½	Orch. parts obtainable
Thompson, Charming Chloë	209; 16¢; Ar	1-3	1	g″5	.....	1½	
Vaughan Williams, Sound sleep	69; 25¢; HW	3	2	g″ 3	g 1	3½	
Williams, G., Ora pro nobis	71667; 15¢; JC	3	2	g″ 3	.....	2½	U
Wood, Cowslips for her covering	1178; 10¢; CC	4	1	.....	ab 2	1½	
——Echo	1186; 20¢; CC	3	1	f#″2	.....	3½	
——The starlings	201; 16¢; Ar	3	1	f#″6	.....	1½	U

Composer; Title; Arranger (or, Arranger; Title)	Octavo No.; Price; Publisher	Number of Parts	Grade of Difficulty	Highest Soprano Note (Above f'')	Number of Times	Lowest Alto Note (Below a)	Number of Times	Length in Minutes	General Remarks
MUSIC OF THE NINETEENTH AND TWENTIETH CENTURIES—(*Continued*)									
FRENCH									
Bizet, Fireflies [*Kountz*]	5010; 15¢; MW	3	1	g''1				1	From "Carmen"
Chaminade, Dance of the snowflakes [*Rix*]	6537; 12¢; GS	1-3	2	a''				1½	The "Scarf Dance"
——Evening prayer in Brittany	285; 15¢; GS	3	3	a''1				4	S. and A. solos
Delibes, Butterfly, butterfly [*Gaines*]	14064; 15¢; D	3	2	ab''5				2	Waltz from "Coppélia"
——Passepied [*Aslanoff*]	7536; 16¢; GS	3	2	c'''2		ab		1½	S. solo; easy except one Sop. c''' (an "ah" chorus)
——Pavane [*Aslanoff*]	7535; 15¢; GS	4	1	......		g		3	U; S. or A. solo
Dubois, Chorus of Seraphim [*Baldwin*]	9105; 12¢; GS	3	1	g#''5				4	From "Paradise Lost"
Fauré, Sancta Maria [*Shelley*]	9106; 15¢; GS	3	1	a''2				3½	Eng.
——Tantum ergo (Therefore we, before him bending)	861; 16¢; EC	3	2	g''1		g# 2		2	S. solo; organ acc.; Latin & Eng.
Gounod, Chorus of Bacchantes [*G.W.W.*]	820; 16¢; EC	3	1	g 2				1½	From "Philémon et Baucis"
——Flower song [*O'Hare*]	918; 12¢; K	3	1	......				2	From "Faust"
Lecocq, She is so innocent [*Pitcher*]	547; 8¢; CC	4	2			g 1		1½	U; *ad lib.*
Paladilhe, Psyche	2687; 15¢; MW	3	1	g''1				2	Optional violin obbl.
——The song of brother Jacques	5667; 15¢; GS	3-4	2	g''				4	U; Fr. & Eng.
Saint-Saëns, The swan [*Engel*]	934; 12¢; K	3	1	f#''5				2	
GERMAN									
Beethoven, Hymn to night [*Spicker*]	4370; 12¢; GS	4	2			gb		2½	
Brahms, Fidelin	1069; 15¢; EC	4	1	f#''2		g# 2		2½	Eng. & Ger.
——Four love-songs [*Clough-Leighter*]	810; 35¢; EC	4	2	ab''2		f#		5½	Eng. & Ger.
1. Was once a pretty, tiny birdie								2	Four-hand piano acc.
2. In wood embowered, 'neath azure skies								1½	
3. No, there is no bearing with these spiteful neighbors								1	
4. Secret nook in shady spot								1	
——Greetings	4302; 12¢; GS	3	2	ab''2				3	Two horns and piano acc.
——Gypsy songs [*Vene*]:									
No. 3	993; 15¢; R	3	1	g''2				1	Eng. & Ger.
No. 8	998; 15¢; R	3	1			g 2		1½	Eng. & Ger.
——I hear a harp	4300; 12¢; GS	3	2	g''4				3	Horn and Harp optional
——Love songs [*Spielter*]:									
Nos. 1, 2, and 3	83052; 16¢; F	3	2	g#''1				4	Eng. & Ger.
Nos. 4, 5, and 6	83053; 15¢; F	3	2	ab''1		g		2½	Eng. & Ger.
——Lullaby and good night [*Riegger*]	83075; 12¢; F	3	1	gb''2				1	
——Miller's daughter	1071; 16¢; EC	4	2	g''		f 4		1½	Eng. & Ger.
——Roses are blooming	1072; 16¢; EC	4	2	g#''6		f# 3		1½	Eng. & Ger.
——Serenade	345; 15¢; R	3-4	2	g#''2		g 1		1½	Eng. & Ger.
——Six love-songs [*Clough-Leighter*]:	811; 30¢; EC	4	2	a''5		f 4		5	Eng. & Ger.
1. A tremor's in the branches								½	Four-hand piano acc.
2. Nightingale, thy sweetest song								1½	Violin obbl. optional
3. Bird in air will stray afar								1	
4. From yon hills the torrent speaks								½	
5. Locksmith, ho! a hundred padlocks								½	
6. Now, ye muses, be hushed								1½	
——Song from Ossian's "Fingal"	4303; 15¢; GS	3-4	1	ab''5		g 3		4½	Two horn acc. optional
——Song from Shakespeare's "Twelfth Night"	4301; 10¢; GS	3	1	g''3				1½	Horns and harp acc. *ad lib.*
——The gypsies	4640; 15¢; GS	3	3	bb''1				3½	
——Voice of spring (The bridegroom)	1068; 18¢; EC	4	1	ab''2		ab 6		1½	Eng. & Ger.

Composer; Title; Arranger (or, Arranger; Title)	Octavo No.; Price; Publisher	Number of Parts	Grade of Difficulty	Highest Soprano Note (Above f'') Number of Times	Lowest Alto Note (Below a) Number of Times	Length in Minutes	General Remarks
MUSIC OF THE NINETEENTH AND TWENTIETH CENTURIES—(*Continued*)							
GERMAN—(*Continued*)							
Bruch, The dawn	49; 15¢; GS	3	2	a''1	g 1	5½	S. solo
——Frithjof at his father's tomb	344; 12¢; GS	3	2	f#''1	f# 2	10	Bar. solo difficult; Chorus parts easy
Humperdinck, Prayer from "Hansel and Gretel" [*Riegger*]	83087; 12¢; F	3	2	g''2	g 2	1½	
Liszt, Loreley [*Jones*]	——; 25¢; SP	3	3	b♭''1	f# 1	4	Eng. & Ger.
Mendelssohn, Hear my prayer, O Lord	56; 10¢; N	3	1	g''6	......	3	Latin & Eng.
——I would that my love [*Schmelz*]	182; 10¢; GS	4	2	a''3	g 5	2	U; no P.R.
——Lift thine eyes	26; 6¢; GS	3	1	g''3	......	1½	From "Elijah"
——On wings of song [*Riegger*]	83078; 15¢; F	3	1	g''3	......	2½	Eng. & Ger.
——The skylark's song	476; 15¢; EC	4	1	......	......	2½	U
——Ye sons of Israel	9109; 15¢; GS	......	......	......	......	6	Organ or piano acc.
No. 1. Chorus		3	1	g''6	......	4	Eng. & Latin
No. 2. Terzetto (Double chorus)		6	2	a♭''1	......	2	
Mozart, Behold the golden sun upsoaring	1043; 15¢; EC	3	1	g''1	......	2	From "The Magic Flute"
Rubinstein, The angel	269; 8¢; GS	3	1	f#''1	......	2½	
——The dew is soft	21120; 12¢; Pr	3	1	g♭''2	......	1½	
——Wanderer's evening song	266; 8¢; GS	3	1	f#''3	......	2	
Schubert, The Lord is my shepherd	5302; 12¢; GS	4	1	a♭''2	a♭ 2	4	
——To be sung on the water [*Brower*]	5099; 15¢; C	3	2	g♭''3	g 4	3½	Eng. & Ger.
——Whither	396; 12¢; GS	3	1	......	......	2	
Schumann, The dreaming lake [*Saar*]	5110; 10¢; C	4	1	......	g 2	1	U; no P.R.
——The gypsies	209; 12¢; GS	3	1	g''2	......	2½	Short S. and A. solos
——The return [*Harris*]	13538; 12¢; D	4	2	a''3	g 3	2	U; canon in the fifth
——The Spanish tambourine girl	309; 10¢; GS	4	1	a''1	......	½	Acc. *ad lib.*; Eng. & Ger.
——To earth May winds are bringing	312: 10¢; GS	2-3	2	a''1	......	2½	Eng. & Ger.
——The walnut tree [*Saar*]	5439; 15¢; GS	3	1	f#''3	......	3	Violin *ad lib.*
Strauss, J., By the beautiful blue Danube [*Spicker*]	4921; 20¢; GS	3	2	a''	......	7	
——Strauss waltz-song [*Harris*]	5268; 20¢; GS	3	2	a''5	g 5	4½	Eng. & Ger.
——Tales from the Vienna woods [*Riegger*]	83095; 18¢; F	3	1	a''1	......	4	
Strauss, R., Memory day (Allerseelen) [*Rix*]	6457; 10¢; GS	3	1	a♭''1	g 1	2	Eng. & Ger.
Wagner, Chorus of flower maidens [*Koppitz*]	1067; 20¢; EC	3-4	2	g''2	a♭ 2	3½	From "Parsifal"; S. solo; Eng. & Ger.
——Prayer to the Virgin	210; 9¢; GS	3	1	g''4	g 6	6	From "Tannhäuser"
——Whirl and twirl (Spinning chorus)	46; 12¢; GS	3-4	2	g#''2	......	2½	From "Flying Dutchman"; difficult piano acc.
Weil, In autumn [*York*]	6831; 12¢; GS	3	1	g''4	......	1	Violin obbl.; Eng. & Ger.
HUNGARIAN							
Kodaly, Dancing song	544; 20¢; O	1-4	2	a''1	g	2	U; no P.R.; modern idiom
——King Ladislaus' men (or, Magyars and Germans)	550; 20¢; O	2-4	2	a''1	g	1½	U; no P.R.; modern idiom; Eng. & Hungarian
——Whitsuntide	549; 32¢; O	4	3	a''1	f#	12	U; no P.R.; modern idiom; Eng. & Hungarian
ITALIAN							
Mascagni, Queen of the heavens [*Dunham*]	1906; 15¢; B	4	3	a♭''1	f 2	4	S. solo; from "Cavalleria Rusticana"
Pinsuti, Good night, good night, beloved	20957; 8¢; Pr	3	2	g''4	g♭ 1	3½	U *ad lib.*

Composer; Title; Arranger (or, Arranger; Title)	Octavo No.; Price; Publisher	Number of Parts	Grade of Difficulty	Highest Soprano Note (Above f'') Number of Times	Lowest Alto Note (Below a) Number of Times	Length in Minutes	General Remarks
MUSIC OF THE NINETEENTH AND TWENTIETH CENTURIES—*(Continued)*							
ITALIAN—*(Continued)*							
Respighi, Mists (Nebbie) [*Harris*]	419; 20¢; R	3	2	g''4	......	2	Eng. & Italian
Sadero, In mezzo al mar (Out seaward) [*Taylor*]	490; 20¢; R	3	1	a''1	ab 4	3	Alto solo; Eng. & Italian
RUSSIAN							
Gretchaninoff, Afar [*Kramer*]	427; 15¢; R	3	1	ab''1	......	1	
——On the steppe [*Stebbins*]	14188; 15¢; D	3	2	ab''1	ab 1	3	
Moszkowski, The dance [*Richards*]	83056; 16¢; F	3	2	a''1	......	4	Waltz melody
Paderewski, Minuet [*Rix*]	6540; 16¢; GS	3	1	g''4	......	3	
Rachmaninoff, The island [*Harris*]	8027; 12¢; GS	4	1	gb''4	f# 1	2	Piano *ad lib.*
Tchaikovsky, Come, ye maidens	6095; 12¢; GS	3	1	g'' 2	......	2½	From opera "Eugene Onégin"; Ger. & Eng.
——Dance of the reed flutes [*Bornschein*]	5951; 12¢; J	3	2	f#''	......	2	
——The nightingale [*Luvaas*]	592; 15¢; CC	4	1	......	......	3	U; S. solo
SCANDINAVIAN							
Grieg, At the cloister gate	19; 15¢; GS	4	1	......	g 1	6	S. & A. solos; Eng & Ger.
——Autumn storms [*Page*]	4255; 15¢; J	3	2	g'' 3	g 3	3	Eng. & Ger.
——Elfin dance [*Stickles*]	5018; 15¢; CH	4	1	......	g 3	2	
——In the boat [*Harris*]	9122; 12¢; GS	3	2	......	g 1	2	Eng. & Ger.

FOLK-SONGS

(Note—See also "Songs for Special Occasions", "Encores", "Novelties", etc.)

Composer; Title; Arranger (or, Arranger; Title)	Octavo No.; Price; Publisher	Number of Parts	Grade of Difficulty	Highest Soprano Note (Above f'') Number of Times	Lowest Alto Note (Below a) Number of Times	Length in Minutes	General Remarks
AMERICAN							
Arranger:							
Brockway, Frog went a-courting	140; 15¢; HW	3-4	1	......	g 2	3	Kentucky Mt.
——The nightingale	141; 15¢; HW	3-5	1	......	g 2	2½	Kentucky Mt.
Niles, Down in yon forest [*Brant*]	8025; 10¢; GS	3	1	g''	g	2	U
Treharne, Come all ye fair and tender ladies	5365; 15¢; W	3	1	g''1	......	3	Virginia
CZECHO-SLOVAKIAN							
Manney, Morning now beckons	356; 15¢; Wo	3-4	1	a''1	f# 2	1½	
Taylor, D., Waters ripple and flow	5065; 15¢; J	3	2	g''1	......	3½	S. and A. solos
ENGLISH							
Davis, The cobbler's jig	490; 16¢; EC	3	1	g''1	g# 2	2	
——The day of the fair	833; 16¢; EC	3	1	g''5	g 6	3	
——The old woman and the pedlar	1060; 20¢; EC	3	1	......	ab	3½	U
Grainger, P., There was a pig (or Christmas Day in the Morning)	6535; 20¢; GS	4	2	a''3	g 2	3½	U
Jacob, The oak and the ash	538; 20¢; O	3	2	g''3	g 6	2½	U
Taylor, D., May Day carol	4763; 12¢; J	4	1	......	gb 1	2½	
——My Johnny was a shoemaker	4760; 12¢; J	3	1	......	......	1½	
——The loyal lover	4761; 15¢; J	4	2	......	g 2	2½	
White, The bailiff's daughter of Islington	71814; 15¢; JC	3	2	g''	g	3½	
——Sing, all a green willow	71811; 15¢; JC	3	2	g''	g	3	
Williams, G., Sweet Kitty	511; 20¢; O	3	2	g''	g	3	U *ad lib.*
FRENCH AND FRENCH CANADIAN							
Hill, I am not so bad (Je ne suis pas si vilaine)	834; 10¢; CC	4	2	g'' 4	f# 2	1½	Eng. & Fr.
——While rolling my ball (En roulant ma boule)	835; 15¢; CC	4	2	f#''4	f# 2	4½	Eng. & Fr.
Saar, At the clear fountain (A la claire fontaine)	5039; 15¢; C	3	1	......	......	1½	Eng. & Fr.

Composer; Arranger; Title (or, Arranger; Title)	Octavo No.; Price; Publisher	Number of Parts	Grade of Difficulty	Highest Soprano Note (Above f'') Number of Times	Lowest Alto Note (Below a) Number of Times	Length in Minutes	General Remarks
FOLK-SONGS—(*Continued*)							
(**Note**—See also "Songs for Special Occasions," "Encores," "Novelties," etc.)							
FRENCH AND FRENCH CANADIAN—(*Cont'd*)							
Saar, Gay is the rose (Gai l'on la, gai le rosier)	5038; 15¢; C	3	1	......	......	2	Eng. & Fr.
——Tambourin	2569; 25¢; MW	3	1	......	......	2	Eng. & Fr.
Taylor, D., Le Sabotier (The sabotmaker)	4758; 15¢; J	3	1	......	......	1½	S. & A. solos; Eng. & Fr.
GERMAN							
Brahms, In Silent Night [*Riegger*]	83089; 15¢; F	3-4	1	......	a♭ 2	1½	U; Violin obbl.
Davis, Between the mount and deep, deep vale	1058; 16¢; EC	3	1	......	......	1	U; Eng. & Ger.
Luvaas, Kathryn's wedding day	1063; 15¢; CC	3	1	......	......	3½	Lively
HUNGARIAN							
Hering, Six Hungarian songs:	4743; 25¢; GS	3-4	1-2	......	......	12	
(1) Through the wild				g''4			
(2) The shepherd lad							
(3) Evening peace				g''3			
(4) At the spinning wheel				a♭''2	a♭		
(5) Recruiting Hussars				a''3			
(6) Kermess				g#''1	g# 6		
Kodaly, God's blacksmith	535; 12¢; O	2	3-4	......	g# 4	1½	U; children's "Counting-out song"
——The swallow's wooing	542; 16¢; O	2	2-4	......	g	1	U; children's song
IRISH							
Fletcher, Follow me down to Carlow	8102; 20¢; GS	3	1	g'' 1	......	1½	
——The Galway piper	299; 15¢; Wo	3	1	g'' 1	g	1½	
Molloy, The Kerry dance [*O'Hare*]	936; 12¢; K	3	2	......	......	3	Bagpipe imitation
Moore, Bendemeer's stream	1399; 10¢; Pa	3	1	......	g 3	1	
NORWEGIAN							
Hatch, To rest I call ye lambkins all	6830; 9¢; GS	4	3	a''3	f# 1	3	U
RUSSIAN							
Dargomyzhski, The Three Cavaliers [*Schindler*]	6693; 20¢; GS	4	1	g''4	......	2½	S. solo
Riegger, Dark eyes	83091; 15¢; F	3	1	......	......	1½	
Schindler, Vasilissa the fair	6692; 25¢; GS	4-7	3	b♭''2	......	5	Choral ballad; soprano solo
Whitehead, The eagle	5089; 15¢; C	3	1	g''1	g 2	2	U *ad lib.*
SCOTCH							
Buck, Robin Adair	64; 10¢; GS	4	2	a''1	f 3	2	U
Gibb, A wee bird came	1051; 12¢; CC	4	1	f#''5	g 1	2	U
Lawson, Turn ye to me	116018; 15¢; R	3	1	g''	......	2	
SICILIAN							
Sadero, Mary's litany (Litanie di Maria)	7450; 15¢; GS	4	2	......	f 2	2	Eng. & It.
SOUTH AFRICAN							
Wendt, Play the sweet mabile	7347; 10¢; GS	4	1	g''1	......	1	
SPANISH							
Schindler, The dove (La colomba)	5748; 10¢; GS	3	3	g''1	......	2	Eng., Spanish, & It.
SWEDISH							
Bartholomew, Spring breezes	7530; 12¢; GS	3	1	......	......	1½	
——The water sprite	7529; 12¢; GS	3	1	......	g 2	3	Mezzo-S. solo
Davis, O little star in the sky	1065; 16¢; EC	3	1	g''6	......	1½	
Gaines, The seasons	9121; 10¢; GS	3	1	g''5	g 6	2½	
Kramer, The maiden in the alderwood	298; 15¢; R	3-4	1	g'' 1	g 4	3	
WELSH							
Fletcher, The bells of Aberdovy	8111; 25¢; GS	3	1	g'' 1	g 3	3	U *ad lib.*

RECOMMENDED OCTAVO MUSIC FOR TREBLE VOICES

Composer; Arranger; Title (or, Arranger; Title)	Octavo No.; Price; Publisher	Number of Parts	Grade of Difficulty	Highest Soprano Note (Above f'') Number of Times	Lowest Alto Note (Below a) Number of Times	Length in Minutes	General Remarks
NEGRO SPIRITUALS							
Burleigh, De blin' man stood on de road	1013; 15¢; R	4-5	3	a''1	f 6	3	U
——De gospel train [*Taylor*]	169; 15¢; R	3-4	1	g''2	......	1½	
——Deep river [*Page*]	116382; 15¢; R	3-4	1	a''1	......	1½	
——Eziekel saw de wheel	699; 15¢; R	3-4	1	a''1	......	1	U
——O Peter go ring-a dem bells [*Harris*]	447; 15¢; R	3-4	2	ab''4	g 1	1½	
——Hard trials [*Taylor*]	108; 15¢; R	3-4	1	......	g 1	2	
——I don't feel noways tired [*Page*]	116561; 15¢; R	3-4	1	f#''	......	1½	
——Nobody knows de trouble I've seen	116452; 15¢; R	3	1	......	ab 1	3	
Dett, Done paid my vow to the Lord	2611; 15¢; JCh	3	1	g''1	g	3	Bar. or A. solo
——There's a meeting here tonight	35008; 15¢; Pr	3	2	g''1	g	2	
Holmes, Short'nin' bread	93; 15¢; Ho	3	1	......	g#	2	Negro folk-song
Huntley, Swing low, sweet chariot	7253; 12¢; GS	4	1	......	g 2	2	U
Johnson, Honor! honor!	5212; 15¢; C	3	1	a''2	......	2	
Luvaas, Let us cheer the weary traveler	88; 10¢; CC	4	1	a''2	......	1½	U
Robinson, Water boy [*MacArthur*]	1697; 20¢; B	4	1	g''1	f# 1	2	U; S. solo; humming cho.
LULLABIES							
Arensky, Cradle song [*Page*]	815; 8¢; CC	3	1	g'' 1	g 2	1½	
Bantock, O can ye sew cushions	9; 15¢; N	3	1	gb''5	......	2	U *ad lib.*
Beach, Drowsy dream-town	973; 15¢; AP	3	1	g''5	ab 4	1½	
Brahms, Little sandman [*Lefebvre*]	767; 15¢; R	3-4	1	f#''2	......	3	
——Lullaby [*Rieger*]	83075; 12¢; F	3	1	gb''2	ab 1	1½	
——Lullaby	83080; 15¢; F	4	1	g''2	ab	1½	
Byrd, Wm., Lullaby, my sweet little baby [*Fellowes*]	146; 10¢; St	3	2	g''2	f 1	½	U
Crist, Baby is sleeping	5025; 15¢; C	4	2	......	f 3	½	From the Chinese
Davies, Lullaby	545; 15¢; N	3	2	......	g# 2	2½	S. solo *ad lib.*
Davis, Basque lullaby	1500; 16¢; EC	3	1	a''1	......	2	U
Ferrari, Lullaby	114; 12¢; HW	4	2	a''2	f# 3	1½	U *ad lib.*; Eng. & Fr.
Gaines, Cossack cradle song	5947; 12¢; GS	4	2	g''4	g	2½	U
Gaul, Mammy's song	100; 12¢; GH	4	2	......	g 6	2	Southern dialect
Gibbs, Balow	71805; 15¢; JC	3	1	g''3	......	2½	
G o d a r d, Lullaby (from "Jocelyn") [*Simonton*]	12995; 15¢; D	3	2	g''4	......	4	Violin *ad lib.*
Gretchaninoff, Berceuse [*Barlow*]	273; 15¢; R	3	2	a''1	......	2	S. solo; Eng. & Fr.
James, Lullaby	5739; 12¢; GS	4	1	......	f 2	1½	
Lester, Cossack lullaby	3012; 12¢; HF	3	1	g''2	g 2	2	
Lieurance, Wi Um (A Pueblo lullaby)	20525; 8¢; Pr	3	1	......	......	2	
Mozart, Lullaby [*Spicker*]	5000; 10¢; GS	3	1	g'' 4	......	2	
Palmgren, Finnish lullaby	324; 15¢; N	4	1	g''1	ab 1	2	
Reynolds, Sleep gentle dove	5286; 15¢; J	3	1	g''2	......	2	Eng. & Fr.
Roberton, Celtic lullaby	8109; 10¢; GS	3	1	......	g 1	1	U
Sadero, Rock-a-bye-baby mine [*Taylor*]	489; 20¢; R	3	1	......	......	1½	Eng. & It.
——Hush-a-by [*Taylor*]	493; 20¢; R	3	1	......	......	2	Eng. & It.
Taylor, C., In the warm blue summer weather (from "Slumber songs of the Madonna")	419; 15¢; N	4	3	a''3	f# 2	2	U
Taylor, D., Dobru Noc (Good night)	5063; 15¢; J	3	1	......	g 1	2½	Eng. & Czech.
Tchaikovsky, Yolanda sleeps [*Kramer*]	651; 20¢; Ga	3	1	g''3	g 2	3	From "Yolanda"
Treharne, Cronan	1911; 15¢; B	6	2	a''1	g# 2	2½	U *ad lib.*; an old Lochaber lullaby
Wendt, Cradle song	5227; 10¢; C	3.	1	......	......	1½	
——Zulu slumber song	7349; 15¢; GS	4	2	g#''1	g 1	1½	S. and A. solos; South African tune
Whitehead, A Scottish croon	5092; 15¢; C	3	2	g#''3	g#	3	U; Scottish folk-song
Wood, Golden slumbers kiss your eyes	251; 16¢; Ar	4	1	......	......	1½	U

Composer; Arranger; Title (or, Arranger; Title)	Octavo No.; Price; Publisher	Number of Parts	Grade of Difficulty	Highest Soprano Note (Above f'') Number of Times	Lowest Alto Note (Below a) Number of Times	Length in, Minutes	General Remarks
SPECIAL OCCASIONS							
ARBOR DAY							
Cui, Tree-time (Nocturne) [*Harris*]....	7830; 12¢; GS	5	2.	ab''2	g 1	1½	U
Rasbach, Trees................	7844; 12¢; GS	4	1	g#''2	g# 2	1½	
Sister, M. B., Trees..............	20750; 10¢; Pr	3	2	g''2	g 1	1½	Violin *ad lib.*
CHILDREN'S DAY							
Rachmaninoff, To the children [*Kramer*]	2550; 15¢; MW	4	3	......	f 6	3	
CHRISTMAS							
Bach, O Jesu so sweet [*Davis*]........	1049; 16¢; EC	3	1	......	f 3	2½	U; Eng. & Ger.
——Good news from heaven (Chorale) [*G. W. W.*]..................	805; 16¢; EC	3	1	......	g 2	1	From "Christmas Oratorio"
Briel, Carillon...	3024; 15¢; HF	3	1	f#''1	......	1½	
Byrd, Rejoice! rejoice! [*Geer*]..........	855; 16¢; EC	4	2	g''	f 1	8	Long Alto solo; organ or string acc. *ad lib.*
Chaminade, The sailor's Christmas.....	400; 12¢; GS	1-4	2	a''3	......	3½	
Cornelius, Christmas song............	427; 10¢; GS	4	2	g''3	g	1½	U; Alto or Bar. solo
Daniels, The holy star.............	962; 20¢; AP	4	3	g''5	g 6	3½	
Davis, Pat-a-pan.............	1052; 16¢; EC	3	1	......	......		Old Fr. song; Eng. & Fr.
——In the bleak midwinter..........	1084; 18¢; EC	3	1	......	ab 6	2	U
Davison, Angels o'er the fields........	844; 18¢; EC	3	1	f#''4	g#	2	U; Eng. & Fr.
——Bring a torch, Jeanette, Isabella..	838; 12¢; EC	4	1	......	g#1	1½	U; old Fr. carol
——Christians, hark! [*H. W. K.*].....	1027; 16¢; EC	2	1	gb''1	......	3	Bressan carol
——Touro-louro-louro........	1502; 18¢; EC	3	1	......	g 2	1½	U; French carol; Eng. & Fr.
Dickinson, Bring a torch, Jeanette, Isabella..	182; 15¢; HW	3	1	......	g 2	1½	U *ad lib.*
Gevaert, The slumber of the infant Jesus [*Davis*]..................	1088; 16¢; EC	3	1	......	g 3	1½	U; Fr. & Eng.
——Slumber song of the infant Jesus [*Dickinson*]..................	29; 12¢; HW	3-4	1	......	g 3	1½	U; Eng. & Fr.
Geer, Five Polish Christmas carols:....	852; 20¢; EC	3-4	1-2	g''	f#	7	U
(1) When the Savior Christ is born .							
(2) Hark, in the darkness.........							
(3) Hark! Bethlehem...							
(4) Sleep thou my jewel..........							
(5) He is sleeping in a manger.....							
——Catalonian Christmas dance.......	424; 15¢; C	4-6	3	bb''1	g	1½	U; Catalonian folk-song
——Presents for the child Jesus.......	426; 12¢; C	6	3	......	g	1½	U; S. solo; Catalonian folk-song
Grainger, There was a pig went out to dig	6535; 20¢; GS	4	2	a''4	g 2	2½	U; Eng. folk-song
Ketelbey, A dream of Christmas......	37; 20¢; Bs	3	1	......	......	4	Yuletide fantasy to be used with pantomime
Kricka, Five Czech Christmas carols:..	854; 20¢; EC	2-5	1	f#''	g	5	U
(1) Now the rarest day..........							
(2) Hearken to me............							
(3) Sleep, baby, sleep........							
(4) Strangers say a King is born....							
(5) Gloria in Excelsis.........							
Luvaas, Hark, now, O shepherds......	170; 15¢; CC	3-4	1	......	g 1	2	Moravian melody
Manney, Three French Christmas carols:	345; 18¢; Wo	3	1				
(1) Angels o'er the fields.........	....					2	
(2) With a torch, Jeanette, Isabella						2½	
(3) Sleep, little dove..........						3	
Mirande, Alsatian Christmas song.....	6750; 8¢; GS	3	1	gb''2	......	1½	Eng. & Fr.
Praetorius, O all ye people, give ear....	410; 15¢; C	5	2	g''2	g 6	4	Partly Eng. & Latin
(a) Lo, how a rose e'er blooming..	497; 15¢; EC	3	1	......	......	1½	U
(b) While shepherds watched their flocks..................		3	1	f#''2	......	1½	U
——Lo, now a rose is blooming [*Riegger*]	83093; 15¢; F	3	1	g''2		1½	

Composer; Arranger; Title (or, Arranger; Title)	Octavo No.; Price; Publisher	Number of Parts	Grade of Difficulty	Highest Soprano Note (Above f'') Number of Times	Lowest Alto Note (Below a) Number of Times	Length in Minutes	General Remarks
SPECIAL OCCASIONS—(*Continued*)							
CHRISTMAS—(*Continued*)							
Saar, Joseph dearest, Joseph mild......	371; 16¢; C	4	1	......	ab	3½	S. or T. solo; violin obbl.; old Ger.
——Whence, O shepherd maiden	5040; 15¢; C	3	1			2½	Fr.-Canadian
Schindler, Adoration of the shepherds [*V. F.*].............	14677; 10¢; D	3	1	g''6	g 1	2	Catalonian folk-song
Schloss, Bells of Noel [*McKinney*].....	6058; 15¢; J	3	1	......		2½	Violin *ad lib.*
Thompson, Ballad of the stork.......	14640; 15¢; D	3	1	g''3	......	2	U; Alto solo
Treharne, Waiting for the kings.......	6333; 15¢; J	3-4	2	g''2		2½	
Whitehead, The croon carol (Joseph dearest, Joseph mild).............	417; 15¢; C	3	1	f#''	g# 3	3½	Old German carol
EASTER							
Liszt, Easter song of the angels [*Dickinson*].............	177; 20¢; HW	3-4	3	a''2	e ♭	6	Orch. parts available
Rubinstein, Seraphic song (Rêve angélique) [*Gaines*].............	13981; 25¢; D	4	3	b''2	f 2	7	Alto or Mezzo-S. solo and violin obbl.
Scheidt, Four Easter carols [*Geer*]:......	859; 20¢; EC	4	2				U
(1) Tell it out, the story....	....			g#''3	g# 6	2½	Belgian
(2) On Easter morn, ere break of day.............	....			g#''2	g# 4	1½	Scotch
(3) Christ the Lord hath risen....	....			f#''3	f# 2	2	12th Century
(4) The world itself keeps Easter day.............	....			f#''6	f# 4	3	From "Piae Cantiones"
MAY DAY—SPRING FESTIVAL							
Bainton, The Dancers.............	206; 24¢; Ar	3	1	g''6	......	2	
Berwald, Lawn dance.............	13505; 10¢; D	3	1	g''3	......	1½	
Davis, Come, lasses and lads.............	1098; 18¢; EC	3	1	......	gb 5	2	U; Eng. 17th Cent.
Fletcher, The Staines Morris.........	71358; 20¢; JC	3	1	a''1	g 4	3½	U *ad lib.*; English 16th Cent.
Ganne, Holiday [*Manney*].............	281; 15¢; Wo	3-4	1	a''1	......	3½	
Gounod, A May-time night [*Page*].....	290; 14¢; CC	3	2	ab''2	......	2½	From "Romeo & Juliet"
Grieg, To spring (An den Frühling) [*Spielter*].............	83022; 15¢; F	3	1	a''1	......	2	Eng. & Ger.
Mansfield, Let us all go maying.....	555; 24¢; O	3-5	2	ab''2	g2	2½	U *ad lib.*
Moffat, Sweet, how sweet the hawthorn blooming.............	560; 12¢; AP	3	1	g''4		2	Old Welsh
Morley, Now is the month of maying ...	430; 12¢; EC	3	1			2	U; madrigal
Scarmolin, Month of May.............	1006; 11¢; CC	4	2	g''	g 5	1	
Schumann, To earth May-winds are bringing.............	312; 9¢; GS	1-3	1	a''1		2	Eng. & Ger.
Taylor, D., May Day carol.............	4872; 15¢; J	3	1	......	ab	3	Eng. folk-song
——May Eve.............	12911; 16¢; D	4	2	g''4	g	3	
Treharne, Country gardens (Morris dance).............	1675; 15¢; B	3	1	g''1		2½	Eng. folk-song; U *ad lib.*
Vellucci, The hawthorn tree.............	910; 15¢; R	3-4	2	g''3	f# 1	2	U; no P.R.
MOTHER'S DAY							
Burleigh, Little mother of mine [*Page*]..	116476; 15¢; R	3	1	....		3	
Dvořák, Songs my mother taught me [*O'Hare*].............	931; 12¢; K	3	1	gb''4	......	1	
PATRIOTIC Armistice Day, Decoration Day, Thanksgiving							
Bloch, America.............	809; 12¢; CC	3-4	2	g''2	f 1	1	From symphony "America"
Davis, Morning comes early.............	1099; 16¢; EC	3	1	a''1	g 1	1½	Thanksgiving; Slovakian folk-song

RECOMMENDED OCTAVO MUSIC FOR TREBLE VOICES

Composer; Arranger; Title (or, Arranger; Title)	Octavo No.; Price; Publisher	Number of Parts	Grade of Difficulty	Highest Soprano Note (Above f'')	Number of Times	Lowest Alto Note (Below a)	Number of Times	Length in Minutes	General Remarks
SPECIAL OCCASIONS—*(Continued)*									
PATRIOTIC—*(Cont'd)* Armistice Day, Decoration Day, Thanksgiving									
Handel, O lovely peace [*Manney*]	351; 15¢; Wo	3	1					5	From "Judas Maccabaeus"
Sarson, Autumn song	186; 12¢; Ar	2	1	f#"2				1	Thanksgiving
Smith, The wind-swept wheat	4955; 25¢; GS	3	2	a"1		f# 1		7	S. solo
OPENING AND CLOSING CHORUSES									
OPENING INVOCATIONS									
Abt, O lovely night	246; 6¢; GS	3	1					3	
Braun, Ode to music	344; 20¢; R	3-4	3	bb"1		g 1		3½	Eng. & Ger.
Franz, Dedication [*Daggett*]	1934; 12¢; B	3	1			ab 4		1	U *ad lib.*
Roberton, Here a solemn fast we keep	71784; 10¢; JC	3	1			gb 2		½	U
Schubert, To music (An die Musik) [*Saar*]	5440; 9¢; GS	3	2			f 2		2	Bar. solo; string-orch. *ad lib.*; Eng. & Ger.
Stevens, To the spirit of music	4324; 15¢; J	4	2	a"1				3½	
Zollner, Ode to music (Die Musik)	363; 20¢; GS	4	3	g#"2				5	S. & A. solos; orch. *ad lib.*; Eng. & Ger.
CLOSING CHORUSES									
Dickinson, Music, when soft voices die	127; 10¢; HW	4	1			g 4		1	U *ad lib.*
Herts, Music, when soft voices die	1027; 12¢; GH	4	2	a"1		g 1		1	U
Roberton, Music, when soft voices die	1574; 12¢; Pn	4	1	gb"1		g 1		1	U
Rogers, At parting [*Baldwin*]	9171; 10¢; GS	2	1	f#"2				1½	
Saar, A note of golden song	3020; 15¢; HF	3	2	g"2				2	
Wood, Music, when soft voices die	1122; 15¢; CC	3	1	gb"2		ab 2		2	
Woodman, Dreams at twilight	6588; 10¢; GS	3-4	1	a"1				2	
ENCORES, NOVELTIES									
ENCORES									
Bartholomew, What I have promised	7531; 12¢; GS	3	1	f#"2				1	Swedish folk-song
Beach, The candy lion	6531; 12¢; GS	4	1	f#"1		g 4		2	
——A Thanksgiving fable	6532; 8¢; GS	4	1	g"2		g 1		2	
Berger, W., The two geese (Die beiden Gänse)	3; —; AM	3	1	f#"1				1½	Eng. & Ger.
Blandford, Cherry-stones	101; 12¢; St	3	2	a"1		g 6		2	U; no P.R.
Emmell, Philosophy [*Manney*]	273; 15¢; Wo	3	1					1½	
Forsyth, Says Jane	6801; 12¢; GS	4	1					2½	
Gibb, The quest	54; 10¢; CC	3	1					2½	Bohemian folk-song
Gilberte, La Phyllis [*Riegger*]	7533; 12¢; GS	3	2	g"4		g 2		2	
Grieg, My Johann [*Aslanoff*]	7682; 15¢; GS	3	2	a"1				1½	
Gregor, Coquetry	7362; 15¢; GS	3	1	g"4		g 2		2	
Hadley, The Catechist	5623; 12¢; GS	3	1	g"2		f# 1		1	U
Harwood, An old man came courting me	524; 16¢; O	1-4	1			g 1		2	S. solo; Eng. folk-song
Holst, Hares on the mountains [*Imogene*]	553; 12¢; N	3	1			g 4		1	U
Horton, March wind	186; 10¢; CC	3	1	g"1				1	
——Mother Goose suite	2616; 15¢; MW	3	1	a"1				3½	U
Keiserling, A birdland symphony	13523; 12¢; D	2-3	1	g"1				2½	
Lester, Maiden sweet, be more discreet	1105; 15¢; GH	3	1	g"2				1	U *ad lib.*; Provençal folk-tune
Protheroe, Strawberry fair	3009; 15¢; HF	3	1	g"5				1½	
Rasbach, Overtones [*Aslanoff*]	7558; 12¢; GS	3	1	g"3		g 1			
Rich, American lullaby	7770; 10¢; GS	3	1					1½	U
Schaffer, Pop! goes the weasel [*O'Shea*]	2584; 15¢; MW	3	1	g"				1½	

Composer; Arranger; Title (or, Arranger; Title)	Octavo No.; Price; Publisher	Number of Parts	Grade of Difficulty	Highest Soprano Note (Above f'') Number of Times	Lowest Alto Note (Below a) Number of Times	Length in Minutes	General Remarks
ENCORES, NOVELTIES—(*Continued*)							
ENCORES—(*Continued*)							
Skilton, Cat tails...................	5077; 12¢; C	3	1	g''1	......	½	
Spross, Minor and major............	2840; 12¢; JCh	3	2	a''2	......	1½	
Taylor, C., The desire..............	71525; 10¢; JC	3-4	2	f#''4	f# 4	1½	U
Taylor, D., Grizzly, grumpy granny (La Boiteuse).......................	4767; 15¢; J	3	1	......	......	2½	French folk-song; Eng. & Fr.
Treharne, Beside the winding river....	1931; 15¢; D	3	1	......	......	2½	Welsh folk-song
Weelkes, Come, Sirrah Jack ho [*G. W. W.*]..................................	840; 16¢; EC	3	3	g''6	f	2	U
NOVELTIES							
Bassett, The icicle [*Treharne*]........	83018; 16¢; F	3	1	......	......	1	
Brockway, Frog went a-courting.......	140; 15¢; HW	3-4	1	......	g 2	2	Kentucky folk ballad; humorous
Crist, What the old cow said.........	5026; 15¢; C	4	2	......	g# 4	1	From Chinese Mother-Goose Rhymes
Davies, The pedlar's song............	546; 15¢; N	3	1	g''5	......	1	
Davis, The beetle's wedding..........	1057; 18¢; EC	3	1	......	g	1½	U; Eng. & Ger.
Delibes, Passepied [*Aslanoff*].........	7536; 16¢; GS	3	2	c'''2	......	2½	After an old French melody
Donovan, Chanson of the bells of Osney	549; 20¢; R	3-4	3	a''1	g 6	3	
——Oranges and lemons..............	317; 10¢; HW	3	1	a''1	......	1	
Farley, The night-wind.............	7417; 15¢; GS	3	2	g''5	......	1	
Grant-Schaefer, The old family clock...	875; 12¢; AP	3	1	......	......	2	
Manna-Zucca, The big brown bear.....	9146; 10¢; GS	3	1	......	......	1	
Manning, K., Hop-Li, the rickshaw man	7710; 15¢; GS	4	2	f#''1	ab 4	1½	
Mozart, The alphabet [*Pax*]..........	260; 10¢; GS	3	1	g''6	......	½	U
Rogers, The two clocks..............	12073; 12¢; D	4	2	g''1	f 3	1½	U

RECOMMENDED COLLECTIONS FOR TREBLE VOICES*

Note: Texts are listed in the order of the date of their publication.

1. **Concord Song Book for Women's Voices;** E. C. Schirmer Music Co., 1935;

   compiled and edited by Archibald T. Davison and Thomas Whitney Surette; price, students' edition, $1.25; teachers' edition, $3.00, cloth-bound.
   Contains 100 songs; from easy to difficult; majority easy or moderately difficult, with piano accompaniment; 22 unison, 16 two-part, 20 three-part, 23 four-part, and 19 rounds, catches, canons, and patriotic songs; of a wide variety of appeal and usefulness; adapted to junior and senior high schools, colleges, assemblies, and community groups. The Complete Edition of this text includes at the end a short list of supplementary octavo music for treble voices recommended by the editors.

2. **Glenn Glee Club Book for Girls;** Oliver Ditson Co., 1929; edited by Maybelle Glenn and Virginia French; price $1.25, cloth-bound.
   Contains 42 three-part songs, easy to moderately difficult; 23 folk-songs, 15 sacred, and 19 art songs; adapted to junior and senior high schools and colleges; piano accompaniment included.

3. **Choral Repertoire for Young Ladies;** Boston Music Co., 1928; arranged, selected, and compiled by Laura Bryant and Paul Bliss; price $1.25, cloth-bound.
   Contains 21 songs: 1 unison, 2 two-part, 16 three-part, and 2 four-part with piano accompaniment; majority easy to moderately difficult; adapted to junior and senior high schools and colleges.

4. **The Choral Treasury for Young Ladies;** Boston Music Co., 1927; arranged, selected, and compiled by Laura Bryant and Paul Bliss; price $1.25, cloth-bound.
   Contains 22 choruses, easy to moderately difficult, with piano accompaniment: 6 two-part and 16 three-part; no extreme ranges; adapted to junior and senior high school and college groups.

5. **Twice 55 Community Songs for Treble Voices** (The Rose Book); C. C. Birchard & Co., 1927; compiled and edited by Peter W. Dykema; price 20c., paper-bound.
   Contains 110 unison, and two- and three-part songs of various types and appeals, the majority easy, with piano accompaniment; adapted to junior and senior high schools, colleges, assemblies, and community groups.

6. **Laurel Songs for Unchanged Voices;** C. C. Birchard & Co., 1914; edited by M. Teresa Armitage; price $1.25, cloth-bound.
   Contains 152 unison, two-, three-, and four-part songs, easy to moderately difficult: 25 unison, 12 rounds and canons, 18 two-part, 76 three-part, and 21 four-part songs of varied type and appeal; majority with piano accompaniment; adapted to junior and senior high schools, colleges, assemblies, and community groups.

*Recommended collections for boys' glee clubs are listed on page 130.

7. Small, inexpensive collections for treble voices published by Hall & McCreary Company:

   (a) **Choruses for Treble Voices**, No. 2; selected, arranged, or composed by Noble Cain and Walter Goodell; 9 choruses easy to moderately difficult, with piano accompaniment; 2 two-part and 6 three-part; price 12c., paper-bound.

   (b) **Two-Part Choruses for Girls Voices**, No. 11; selected and arranged by Noble Cain and Walter Goodell (one original composition by Charles Vincent); 9 easy choruses with piano accompaniment; price 12c., paper-bound.

   (c) **Three-Part Choruses for Girls Voices**, No. 12; selected and arranged by Noble Cain and Walter Goodell; 8 easy choruses: one *a cappella*, the remainder with piano accompaniment; price 12c., paper-bound.

Reference List for Further Reading
on the Subject of Program Building and Materials

Program Making:
  *Wodell, *Choir and Chorus Conducting*, Presser, Philadelphia.
  *Cain, *Choral Music and its Practice*, Witmark, New York City.
  Coward, *Choral Technique and Interpretation*, Gray, New York City.
  Greene, *Interpretation in Song*, Macmillan, New York City.
  Schoen, *Effects of Music*, Harcourt, London.

Recommended Materials:
  *Cain, *Choral Music and its Practice*, Witmark, New York City (lists Octavo music for *a cappella* mixed chorus).
  Davison and Surette, *Concord Song Book for Women's Voices*, E. C. Schirmer, Boston (at end of book gives short list of supplementary octavo music recommended for treble voices).
  *Locke, *Selected List of Choruses of Women's Voices*, Smith College, Northampton, Mass.

*Especially recommended as supplementary readings.

INDEX

Praise for BLIND SUBMISSION

"Welcome, Debra Ginsberg! Blind Submission is a debut novel that kept me turning the pages. Wicked fun and suspense from a talented new writer with an original, clever voice."

—Lisa Scottoline, author of *Dirty Blonde*

"[Ginsberg's] novel takes us into a little-known corner of the industry— the literary agency—in wonderfully entertaining ways."

—*Los Angeles Times*

"A good story that treads familiar territory yet introduces a fresh twist. With savvy plotting and writing . . . Blind Submission *delivers on its promise of a smart, fun ride through the publishing world."*

—*San Diego Union-Tribune*

*"*Blind Submission *makes for a delightful and humorous read with ample sarcasm and dry wit to entice even those who shun the* The Devil Wears Prada *genre— and enough mystery to keep a reader turning pages late into the night."*

—*Daily Camera* (Boulder)

"This debut novel's sharp writing and intriguing mystery elements turn what could be the same old story into something fresh and new. . . . The suspenseful 'who-wrote-it' sets the novel apart from other so-called 'assistant lit.'. . . Ginsberg clearly knows the ins and outs of the publishing world, and Blind Submission *offers an engaging look."*

—*BookPage*

"A page-turner."
—*People* Style Watch

BLIND
SUBMISSION

Nonfiction by Debra Ginsberg

About My Sisters

Raising Blaze:
Bringing Up an Extraordinary Son in an Ordinary World

Waiting:
The True Confessions of a Waitress

BLIND
SUBMISSION

A Novel

DEBRA GINSBERG

THREE RIVERS PRESS • NEW YORK

Copyright © 2006 by Debra Ginsberg

A Reader's Guide copyright © 2007 by Three Rivers Press, an imprint of the Crown Publishing Group, a division of Random House, Inc.

Excerpt from *The Grift* copyright © 2007 by Debra Ginsberg

Published in the United States by Three Rivers Press, an imprint of the Crown Publishing Group, a division of Random House, Inc., New York.
www.crownpublishing.com

THREE RIVERS PRESS and the Tugboat design are registered trademarks of Random House, Inc.

Novel Thoughts colophon is a trademark of Random House, Inc.

Originally published in a slightly different form in hardcover in the United States by Shaye Areheart Books, an imprint of the Crown Publishing Group, a division of Random House, Inc., in 2006.

This book contains an excerpt from the forthcoming book, *The Grift*, by Debra Ginsberg. This excerpt has been set for this edition only and may not reflect the final content of the forthcoming edition.

Library of Congress Cataloging-in-Publication Data

Blind submission : a novel/Debra Ginsberg.—1st ed.
    1. Literary agents—Fiction. I. Title.
PS3607.I4585B56   2006
813'.6—dc22   2006013198

ISBN 978-0-307-34638-4

Printed in the United States of America

Design by Mauna Eichner and Lee Fukui

10 9 8 7 6 5 4 3 2 1

First Paperback Edition

For all the writers who have yet to be published and for the book lovers who will one day read their work.

PROLOGUE

IT WAS THE FIRST MINUTE of my first day and my first impulse was to run. Just turn around and get the hell out of there as fast as I could. In that frozen moment between initial response and subsequent action, I stood mute, my vision tunneled to the desk in front of me. It was piled to toppling with files, pink message slips, newspaper clippings, and indeterminate scraps. A multi-line phone was half buried in the middle of this chaos, its angry flashing call buttons casting a blinking orange glow across the papers. What struck me with the greatest force, though, was the sheer number of words I saw in front of me. With the exception of the phone, every inch of the desk was layered in a dizzying collage of blue-black fonts and scribbles. And every word was screaming at me to pay attention and respond. This was my desk. This was my job.

I could feel the muscles in my legs twitching with the effort to keep still. I clutched the strap of my purse with one hand while the other gripped the to-go coffee cup I'd brought in with me. Fight or flight. Every cell in my body was held taut, waiting for the adrenaline rush. My mouth was dry and I knew I had bitten off more than I could chew. Inside my head, the voice of reason told me that this was only a job, not an invitation to walk off a cliff. But the much louder voice of instinct shouted that walking off a cliff was exactly what I was about to do. I was in the wrong place at the wrong time, it insisted, and I had to get out *now*. Before it was too late.

I *could* leave, I thought. I could back up and exit the way I came in and nobody would know I'd ever been there. The girl at the desk to my left hadn't even noticed my arrival. She was murmuring into her own phone, wrapped up in an intense conversation. There was nobody else in sight. Nobody to greet me or to welcome me to my first day on the job. Nobody to express alarm if I just bolted out of the office. It would be easy to simply disappear, go home, and reconsider the whole thing. And then, later, I could call and say that something unforeseen had come up, that I was terribly sorry, that I was unable to take the job, but thank you, thank you so much for your consideration. I could hear the conversation in my head—could hear myself murmuring the apology. In all likelihood, I thought, I wouldn't even have to talk to *her*.

I drew a deep breath and felt the muscles in my shoulders start to relax. Yes, escape was a possibility, and in it I found the comfort I needed to release the death grip on my purse strap and take a tentative step toward the mountain of words on my desk.

I knew then that I wouldn't leave, that I'd stay there come what may. I made an effort to push my misgivings to the farthest reaches of my consciousness and focus on why I was standing there in the first place. The truth of it was, despite my moment of panic, I wanted this job more than I could remember wanting anything. I wanted it with a single-minded desire I hadn't even known I possessed. I'd fought for it and I'd won it and nothing, especially not a few first-day butterflies, was going to stop me from taking it.

I took my second deep breath in the space of five seconds and felt my head start to spin with dizziness. I blinked a few times and swallowed hard. It wouldn't do, I thought, to start hyperventilating before I'd even had a chance to sit down. I took one more glance at what was now *my* overloaded desk, savoring my last few moments of stillness. And then, with one step forward, I moved into the fray.

ONE

IT WAS MALCOLM'S IDEA that I apply for the job at the Lucy Fiamma Literary Agency. Without his prompting, it never would have occurred to me. Which was peculiar, he pointed out, not only because I was about to become unemployed, but because of my almost fanatic love of books and anything to do with them. And it was true; I *was* a passionate reader, able to devour whole tomes in a single sitting. My unquenchable appetite for books was something I'd developed very early in my life. It seems a cliché now to say that books were a welcome escape from reality, but in my case this was the truth. It wasn't that I had a miserable or neglected childhood, but it *was* unstable. My single, hippie mother could never stay in one place ("place" being defined as various communelike encampments) for very long. She was on a relentless quest for enlightenment and never found it, unsurprisingly, outside of herself. Not that this stopped her from searching, or from dragging me with her. I had little in the way of continuity in my schooling and next to no contact with kids my own age. What friends I did make I soon had to abandon when my mother decided that a Buddhist retreat in Arizona was spiritually superior to an organic foods cooperative in Oregon, or that an artists' colony in California was morally preferable to a Wiccan enclave in New Mexico. My mother seldom had a man in her life to tie her down, and that included my father, whoever he was or might have become. My mother claimed she never even learned his name on the one night they spent together.

Books were the one constant in all this flux and I turned to reading whenever I wanted to be rooted and still. I loved my mother fiercely but never shared her enthusiasm for perpetual change. Nor did I fully trust the revolving groups of people (almost always women) she surrounded herself with. My mother chose to search for her truths in people and places, but I preferred to search for them in books.

But reading was only part of the thrill that a book represented. I got a dizzy pleasure from the weight and feel of a new book in my hand, a sensual delight from the smell and crispness of the pages. I loved the smoothness and bright colors of their jackets. For me, a stacked, unread pyramid of books was one of the sexiest architectural designs there was. Because what I loved most about books was their promise, the anticipation of what lay between the covers, waiting to be found.

Malcolm knew my passion very well. We met, after all, in the aisles of Blue Moon Books, the bookstore where I worked. I was immediately and embarrassingly attracted to him. He was extremely good looking—tall and tan with chiseled jaw and cheekbones—but there was something else about him that made me weak-kneed and fluttery and willing to drop all pretense of professionalism just to talk to him. He was a writer, I learned, which explained the depth of my instant crush on him. Malcolm was looking for a reference book that would help him get his novel published, so I pulled out several guides to literary agents and small publishers and went through every one of them with him, desperate to keep talking to him, about books, about his writing, and, not least, about whether or not he'd consider having coffee with me next door when I got my break.

"How is it you know so much about books?" Malcolm asked me when, to my trembling delight, he took me up on my offer. "Are you a writer?"

"Oh no," I told him, attempting to flip my hair in a sexy gesture without dragging it through my coffee. "That's not my thing at all."

"Really?" he said, nonplussed, raising one blond eyebrow. "Not even screenplays? Or poetry?"

"No, no," I said, giving him what I hoped was a beguiling half-smile, "I don't write at all. I *can* write, of course, if I have to. Like letters, and, um, I wrote papers in college, naturally, but, anything else, you know . . ."

It was a valid question. We were living near San Francisco, a city that seemed to contain, among many other things, a plethora of writers. To be more specific, I lived in Petaluma—the wrist-wrestling capital of the country—and Malcolm lived a little farther south, in Novato. For my mother, Petaluma had been at least three stops ago, but I'd come of age after we'd landed there and had just stayed. Despite the lack of panache our cities had, both Malcolm and I considered ourselves "Bay Area" denizens, although Petaluma, especially, was pretty far removed from the San Francisco Bay. Still, there were plenty of aspiring writers dotting my landscape. The ones I met came into Blue Moon, located in an otherwise bland strip mall in Corte Madera, searching for books on how to get into print and were usually doing something else to pay the rent. That "something" was often food service. Such was the case with Malcolm, as he went on to tell me, who waited tables in a high-end Marin County restaurant while he crafted his novel.

I was simply a book *lover,* I told Malcolm. I had no aspirations to write one myself. I was happy in my job as manager of Blue Moon Books, where I had unlimited access to the stuff of my addiction. I even liked Elise, the owner of the store, who paid me more than she could afford in order to keep me afloat and had always been more like a mentor and friend than a boss. Because I quickly developed a good sense of which books would sell well in the store, having read most of them, Elise had even put me in charge of buying for Blue Moon, a responsibility I truly enjoyed. I'd already been working at the bookstore for four years when I met Malcolm, but the job still felt as new and fresh as if I'd just started.

"It's like being a kid in a candy store," I told him.

Malcolm must have found this charming because, when we'd finished all the coffee we could hold and I reluctantly informed him that I'd have to get back to work, he asked if I'd like to continue our discussion over dinner. I couldn't believe my luck. The good-looking, confident guys never gravitated to me, especially not the guys who had Malcolm's level of sex appeal. It wasn't that I was unattractive myself. Although, like every woman, I found aspects of my face and body that are too long, short, wide, or narrow, I knew that I couldn't really complain. I'd even done some modeling, which had helped pay for college. So it wasn't my looks that turned off the self-assured, handsome men and drew in the socially insecure, less-than-anatomically-perfect, and vaguely desperate ones. There was something else about me, although I'd never been able to figure out what, that repelled men like Malcolm.

I'd complained about this to Elise on more than one occasion, most often after being hit on by dentally challenged musicians or would-be philosophers with marginal hygiene who'd wander into Blue Moon.

"You're easy to talk to, honey," Elise told me, after she finished laughing at my tales of woe. "And you don't have a bit of snobbishness about you."

"So that makes me a target?" I asked her.

"Not at all," Elise said. "These people—these guys—feel that they can trust you, open up to you. Hell, everyone opens up to you. That's how you can sell books that people didn't even know they wanted to read!"

"That's all well and good," I said, "but why can't a great-looking, successful guy open up to me, too?"

"Don't you worry, honey," Elise had assured me, "it will happen."

And, with Malcolm, it finally had.

It didn't take long for the two of us to become an item and for me to give Malcolm his own key to my apartment, which was where we ended up spending most of our time together. It was there, on the queen-size bed that took up the lion's share of my small studio, that we compared the notes of our days, where we shared our bodies and our dreams. Malcolm's dreams involved getting published and making it big as a novelist. My dreams mostly involved him. I wanted him to succeed as a writer as much as he did, and I was more than willing to support him in every way I could. If my social life was a bit limited (Malcolm made up most of it and Blue Moon accounted for the rest), I didn't mind. While I wasn't exactly a loner, I'd always been able to entertain myself. Reading a good book, after all, was still my idea of a great time. I suppose that somewhere in the depths of my consciousness I knew that I wasn't really making enough money at Blue Moon and that, much as I enjoyed working there, it wasn't turning into what one might consider a career. And I was going to need a career eventually. Although we didn't discuss it that often, Malcolm and I were planning to get married at some point in the future and one of us was going to need to make some decent money.

Otherwise, though, I was content with my life. There was no reason for me to change anything. That is, until Elise told me that she was closing Blue Moon and that I'd have to find another job.

I wanted to believe that Elise would find a way to keep the store open, and so, even as she began liquidating, I held on in a state of denial for several weeks. That denial might have carried me all the way to the unemployment line had Malcolm not come up with a plan.

I came home from work one evening, in what had become my usual dazed do-nothing state, and found a want ad circled in red and taped to the bathroom mirror. I went to brush my teeth and peeled it off, watching my own curious expression reflected behind it. There was barely any text to the ad.

"ADMIN ASST WANTED," the ad began, "FOR BUSY, SUCCESSFUL LITERARY AGENCY."

I didn't like the first line. The dreaded "administrative assistant" title was just a glorified term for slave. Still, the rest of the ad was very intriguing:

> CANDIDATE MUST BE SMART, DETAIL AND MULTI-TASK ORIENTED. PREVIOUS PUBLISHING EXPERI-ENCE VERY HELPFUL. LOVE OF BOOKS A MUST. FAX RÉSUMÉ ATTN: CRAIG AT LUCY FIAMMA LITERARY AGENCY.

Under the ad, Malcolm had scrawled, *A—This is the perfect job for you! xxx, M.*

Malcolm was right. I had all the bases covered on this one, I thought. By the time he arrived home from his dinner shift that night, I'd added Blue Moon to my old résumé and printed out a copy. I faxed my résumé from the bookstore the next day and, within a few hours, there was a message for me from someone named Anna requesting that I call to make an appointment for an interview.

"Lucy and Craig would like to meet you," the tired voice said. "Please give us a call so we can set up a time."

When I called back, Anna gave me complicated directions to the office in the same listless tone. In the background, I could hear what sounded like an entire bank of ringing phones.

Elise was encouraging, if not exactly enthusiastic, when I asked for a morning off to go to the interview.

"Well, well. Lucy Fiamma," she said. "That's the big time, isn't it? Of course, you know I'll help you in any way I can." A whisper of a frown crossed her features. "Just be careful, dear," she said, and walked away before I could ask her what she meant.

Malcolm, on the other hand, was thrilled to hear that I'd landed an interview. He was so excited that he took me to dinner at Postrio, a Wolfgang Puck restaurant in the city that was way out of our normal budget.

"You know I don't have the job yet," I said as we toasted with glasses of Chianti.

"Oh, you'll nail it, baby," Malcolm said. "I have no doubt."

PREPARING FOR MY INTERVIEW turned out to be a nightmare. It took a full hour in front of the mirror to come up with an outfit I didn't even like. I'd settled for a blue dress, the most conservative of the three in my closet, and the only one that covered the tattoo—the small but vivid angel wings on the top of my right breast. I'd gotten the tattoo when I was seventeen and angry at my mother, so after downing a few shots of vodka supplied by my bad-girl friends of the moment, I'd allowed myself to be talked into being poked by an inky needle. Getting that tattoo was the only overtly rebellious act I committed in my tame teenage years and I regretted it almost immediately. My mother couldn't have cared less, for one thing, which completely undermined my purpose in getting it in the first place. I hated the way it looked for another thing and always ended up trying to cover it. Every time I looked at those wings I couldn't believe I'd been stupid enough to brand my own flesh.

Malcolm, however, thought my tattoo was cute—"Angel's wings," he called it—and made a point of kissing it whenever possible. "It's so conveniently located," he always said with a smile. But because we were usually in a state of undress when he delivered these kisses, I was usually focused on things other than my ill-advised tattoo.

My hair was another problem. Up or down? Barrette or free-flowing? At the best of times, I didn't know what to do with my wild mass of curls. It was a difficult color—mostly red, but with enough gold to allow me to classify it as *titian* when I was being both generous and literary about my appearance—and it fell halfway down my back. In the end, I twisted it into a librarian-type bun at the back of my head and hoped it didn't make me look too severe.

Makeup was an issue as well. I didn't wear much to begin with since, unlike many redheads, I had a smooth, almost olive, complexion, with eyelashes and brows that were dark enough not to need mascara. I searched through my pitiful supply of shadows and decided that none of them really matched the hazel of my eyes, the red of my hair, *and* the blue of my dress. I'd have to go bare, I thought, but made a vow to go shopping for both cosmetics and clothes if I got the job.

I was none too pleased with my last glance in the mirror. My legs looked overlong and pale under the dress, and my shoes were undeniably shabby. I didn't dare put on panty hose. Nobody wore panty hose anymore unless they were the thigh-high, my-boyfriend's-coming-over-with-a-bottle-of-champagne variety. And the shoes were just further proof that I'd gotten way too comfortable in jeans and sweaters and had smothered any kind of fashion sense I might have had. Overall, though, I was annoyed with myself for fussing so much over my appearance and didn't want to admit that I felt anything but supremely confident. Finally, I just ran out the door before I could change my mind about my hair, my outfit, or going to the interview at all.

As I drove in search of the office, which was nestled in the heart of lush, leafy, and very tony San Rafael, I tried to take my mind off my inadequacy by reviewing everything I knew about Lucy Fiamma and her agency.

Although I'd never met her, I'd heard enough about Lucy to feel like I knew her. Of course, I wasn't the only one who felt this way. Anyone who worked in any corner of the book business, from booksellers to aspiring writers, "knew" Lucy Fiamma in some fashion. At the very least, they knew her story.

Lucy had been a literary agent for a few years when she got the mother of all big breaks: the publication of *Cold!*, a memoir written by her client Karanuk, an Alaskan Inuit writer. *Cold!* described life in the dark frigidity of the Alaskan wilderness and went into detail about tribal customs and rituals. The emotional impact of the writing was intense, and Karanuk's descriptions were strikingly vivid. It was all those adjectives that reviewers fling around when they love a book: evocative, brilliant, riveting, powerful. For me, though, it was simply a *great* read. You couldn't help but feel the frost creep into your bones as you read through to the dramatic, chilling end. It was one of very few books I wanted to read again as soon as I finished it.

Karanuk and *Cold!* came out of nowhere (literally, in this case) and were a huge hit. There was nothing else out there like it. People who had never bought a book in their lives purchased a copy of *Cold!* At Blue Moon, I'd sell it to customers who claimed they hated reading, but just *had to have* this one. In addition to stirring up huge interest in the Inuit, Karanuk's book was the front-runner in what soon became a memoir craze. So many great books out there never get the kind of attention that *Cold!* did, so its success said quite a bit about what could happen when talent combined with luck. *Cold!* hit at exactly the right place at exactly the right time. The hardcover was on the *New York Times* bestseller list for two full years until the paperback took its place in permanent residence.

Naturally, *Cold!* found its way to Hollywood as well. The movie version won several Academy Awards, including Best Picture. Inevitably, a whole line of *Cold!*-inspired merchandise found its way to various outlets. There were *Cold!* dolls, *Cold!* fur hats, and even a *Cold!* line of frozen dinners. My personal favorite was the series of cruises around the Alaskan coast that promised glimpses of the scenery immortalized by the book. *Cold!* also became a required text in many university cultural studies classes.

But what made this appealing book even tastier was that the author was totally reclusive. He rarely gave interviews, and when he did, it was always to small, obscure newspapers or magazines. He almost never appeared in public, and the majority of his readers, myself included, had no idea what he looked like. The jacket photo on the original edition showed only a frigid landscape of snow, broken by a single stunted, leafless tree. There were no photos at all on subsequent editions. There was a big brouhaha at one point when Oprah picked *Cold!* for her famous book club and Karanuk turned down the invitation to appear on her show. Of course, unlike the other authors Oprah had selected, Karanuk hardly needed the sales or the publicity. The fact that he *wouldn't* make an appearance only added to his mystique.

After the Oprah incident, the one thing everyone wanted to know was when Karanuk was going to write the *next* book. I answered the same question at least once a week at Blue Moon:

"Say, you know that Alaska guy, Canoe? Kanuk? The *Cold!* guy? When are you going to get his next book?"

"As soon as he writes it," I always answered.

Lucy Fiamma was the woman behind Karanuk and his book. In various interviews, Lucy spun the tale of how she'd tirelessly shopped a partial manuscript of *Cold!* to disinterested publishers, meeting with a wall of rejections. "But I believed in it," Lucy was often quoted as saying, "so I never gave up." She'd finally convinced an associate editor at a small house to purchase the manuscript for "a song" with the promise that the finished book would be exquisitely written. A big publishing company bought the small house soon after and the associate editor was now one of its executive editors.

Unlike her author, Lucy Fiamma had no qualms about appearing in public. She accepted the ever-reclusive Karanuk's literary awards (of which there were several) on his behalf, always telling the same story of how she discovered her "frozen diamond in the rough."

After the huge success of *Cold!*, the Lucy Fiamma Literary Agency became one of the hottest spots for literary representation in the country, New York be damned. Despite the fact that her agency was located on the West Coast and not even *in* San Francisco proper, and that it wasn't attached to a larger well-established agency, Lucy Fiamma represented big-name authors from around the globe. Karanuk enabled Lucy to pick her shots, and according to *Publishers Weekly,* her books usually sold with big price tags attached. None of her books matched the success of *Cold!* (how could they?), but there were several best-sellers in the bunch and most of them were very well written. Still, and I'd always found this a little odd, few of Lucy's authors seemed to write more than one or two books before they faded from the literary landscape.

I'd gathered much of what I knew about Lucy Fiamma from Elise and from the various interviews I'd read, but also in a more personal way from Malcolm, who had submitted his manuscript to her agency several months earlier and was, for lack of a better word, a Lucy Fiamma groupie. He'd come over one night after work in a state of total agitation. Could I *believe* who had come in for dinner and sat at *his* table? he wanted to know. None other than Lucy Fiamma herself! They'd discussed writing, of course, because, well, he *had* to tell her he was a writer, didn't he, and she seemed so *nice* anyway, he didn't think it was a terrible imposition. She *loved* the title of his book, Malcolm stressed, and, could I believe it, she asked him to *send it in.*

I wasn't as starry-eyed as Malcolm—I'm not a writer, after all—but his excitement was infectious. I helped him create the "perfect" cover letter for his submission, gather clips of all his previous publications in little literary magazines, and put them together for maximum effect. Then there were five empty weeks while we waited for a response. Although Malcolm was quiet about it, I knew he was spinning scenarios of literary glory. As the days crawled by, I watched, pained, as his excitement turned to something much bleaker. Finally, a form letter appeared in the mail, tucked into the self-addressed stamped envelope that Malcolm had provided.

Although your novel shows much creativity and hard work, the letter began, *we regret that it does not meet our needs at this time and we are unable to accept it for representation. . . .*

At the bottom of the letter, there was a quickly scrawled line in blue ink.

Malcolm, it said, *you have a wonderful feel for setting, but your characters are flat! Work on the first 50 pp., try to get your reader <u>hooked!</u> Then I'd consider taking a 2ⁿᵈ look! LF.*

Malcolm held the letter in his hand for a long time, staring off into space while clouds of disappointment darkened his face. He was silent for so long, I started to get nervous and blurted out the first thing that came to mind.

"She uses a hell of a lot of exclamation points, doesn't she?"

Malcolm looked at me, a shadow of condescension crossing his features as if I had clearly missed the point. "She's right," he said. "The characters *are* flat. Very flat. Flatter than flat. I don't know how I didn't see it before. I'm going to rework it." He folded the letter and placed it carefully in his pocket. "She read it *herself*," he said with more than a hint of awe in his voice.

Malcolm hadn't mentioned Lucy or her agency again until he cut out that want ad for me, but he'd been working on the manuscript like a demon. I knew none of its content aside from the title, *Bridge of Lies.* I was not allowed to read it until it was finished, Malcolm said, and I gladly went along because, although I hated to admit it, I was afraid. Afraid I would be disappointed. I'd read all of Malcolm's short stories and I liked them. But if I was totally honest with myself, I had to say that they were just okay. I'd started helping Malcolm with some of these stories, suggesting little revisions here and there, and he took well to my editorial comments. There was a lot of promise in Malcolm's writing and I could see that he was getting better. So I had every reason to believe that his novel represented a major breakthrough. I had every reason to believe it was *great.*

Thinking about Malcolm's novel gave me a twinge of doubt—the same twinge I'd felt when I'd first read the note he'd taped to the bathroom mirror. It didn't take a genius to figure out that Malcolm stood to gain by having me work for one of the best literary agents in the country.

He'd admitted as much, but he'd also pointed out that I hadn't given a whole lot of thought to developing a career, and that this job was an ideal place to start. He wasn't wrong about that—not by a long shot.

I forced my thoughts away from Malcolm and on to the road in front of me. I'd been driving for much longer than I should have been, considering the distance between my apartment and the office, and was starting to realize that Anna had given me plenty of unnecessary or incorrect information—the names of streets that were nowhere near where I needed to be, for example, and several left turns that should have been rights, or norths that should have been souths. If I had given myself only the half hour Anna told me it would take instead of the hour I'd neurotically opted for, I would definitely have been late. Finally, after doubling back at least twice, I found the famous Lucy Fiamma Literary Agency.

The office, as I'd been told, was an add-on to a spacious two-story home. About this, at least, Anna had been very clear. "Come around and park at the back entrance," she'd said. "The front door is to Lucy's house and you *cannot* go in there."

I felt a little like Alice in Wonderland, standing in front of the small white door, rubbing my sweaty palms on the sides of my dress, and waiting as one, two, three knocks went unanswered. I experienced a moment of total confusion before I turned the handle and just let myself in.

I was immediately surprised by the large size of the office. From the outside, it was impossible to gauge this breadth of space. Directly in front of me was a desk piled with papers of all kinds that looked to be the repository of all office items that didn't have a place. On my right, there were two more unattended desks in various states of disarray. One had the remnants of someone's lunch scattered across the surface and I could detect the smell of peanut butter. The other had several folders spread unevenly across the top. The fourth desk, to my left, which was the only tidy one in the room, was occupied by a dark-haired girl on the telephone, who jumped as I walked in and then motioned with her hand for me to stay where I was. From floor to ceiling, one entire wall of the office was taken up with books, all of which I assumed were titles sold by Lucy Fiamma. The whole room had a strange half-moon shape caused by the protrusion of a semicircular wall in the back. There was a closed door in the middle of this wall which, I assumed, led to Lucy's private office.

Frozen in place by the girl on the phone, I turned my attention to her end of the conversation.

"Yes, the first fifty pages," she was saying. "No, we don't need to see more than that." There was a long pause. "Well, five hundred pages is too much for us to read all at once. We'll be able to get an idea of the writing from the first fifty." Another pause. "No, she's not available at the moment, but I can tell you that she likes to have a look at the writing before she speaks to an author. No, we don't take e-mail submissions. Why don't you just send it in and— No, I'm sorry, she is *not* available." In the final pause that followed, her head sank lower and lower until it was almost resting on the desk. I could tell that she was being upbraided in a most pointed manner. The tirade on the other end continued for some time until, finally, she said, "Thank you, we'll look forward to reading it," and hung up.

She looked up at me then, an expression of abject despair on her face. The words *I hate my job* might as well have been printed on her forehead.

"Can I help you?" she said as she pulled herself out of her chair and walked over to me. She was painfully thin and the paleness of her skin made a stark contrast to the sheets of straight black hair that hung below her shoulders.

"I'm Angel Robinson. I'm here for an interview. I spoke to Anna on the phone. I'm sorry, are you Anna?"

"No," she said. Her wide gray eyes were too big for her face. Close up, they looked like windows onto a bleak, rainy day. I thought she might be older than I'd first guessed. Her skinny body was that of a little girl, but her face was lined and pinched.

"Anna's in the bathroom. She should be out in a minute. Do you want to sit down?"

I took a quick scan of the room and saw that there was no chair available that didn't belong to a desk. "I'm fine," I told her, wondering if she was going to offer her name. "Thank you, uh . . ."

"My name is Kel— I mean, Nora. My name is Nora."

"Okay," I said. "Thanks, Nora."

Kel-I-mean-Nora went back to her desk, where she busied herself pulling cards from three separate Rolodexes. I didn't know what to do with myself, so I stood there like a piece of driftwood for an uncomfortable minute or two until I heard a toilet flush somewhere out of sight and saw another young woman approach me.

"Hi, I'm Angel Robinson," I said, extending my hand. "Anna?"

"Yes, hi, nice to meet you," Anna said without taking my hand. Anna was the polar opposite of Nora. She was stocky and had bobbed blond hair tucked behind her ears and smallish, squinty blue eyes. Her cheeks seemed unnaturally flushed and she gasped a little, as if she were short of breath. She also had a rather unpleasant expression on her face that I put somewhere between petulance and condescension.

I noticed, with dismay, that both Anna and Nora were wearing jeans. Clearly, in spite of all that posturing in front of the mirror, I had over-dressed.

"Lucy's in a meeting with Craig at the moment," Anna said, gesturing to the closed door in the middle of the round wall, "but she should be with you shortly. Why don't you sit down?"

It felt more like an order than a suggestion, so I backed myself into the chair belonging to the desk piled with the stacks of manuscripts. Anna hoisted herself onto the desk in front of me, her ample backside irretrievably crumpling several sheets of paper beneath it. One wrong move, I thought, and the whole show would topple to the carpet.

"So how did you hear about us?" she asked me. Something subtly different crept into her voice as she spoke. It sounded nasal and squeezed at the same time, as if she were trying to speak while someone sat on her stomach. It was slightly disconcerting.

"I saw the ad in the paper," I said. "But of course I've heard about Lucy Fiamma before. Who hasn't, right?"

"So you have experience in publishing?" Now there was a note of officiousness in her tone. I didn't like Anna already and I'd only known her for five minutes. Not a good sign, I told myself. I wasn't in the mood for what was turning into a pre-interview, so I answered her question with one of my own.

"Have you been working here long?"

"Yes, I've been here awhile already. About four or five months."

An intercom buzzed loudly on the desk and Anna leaned her entire body over the stacks of files to answer it, promptly knocking several piles to the floor.

"Yup," she said into the phone.

"Anna, am I going to get that subsidiary rights list today? These magazines are closing for the summer, you know." The voice sounded extremely unhappy. Anna's cheeks flushed crimson.

"I've got calls in," she said, "and I'm waiting for the copies to come back from Kinko's on the George manuscript and—"

"I don't want to hear excuses, Anna. Do I have to tell you how important subsidiary rights are? There's a reason we keep serial and audio rights, Anna. Not to mention *film*. Will the list be done today or not?"

"I don't think that's possible, Lucy."

"Then bring me what you've got now." The intercom disconnected with a loud click. Anna slid off the desk and stared down at the mess on the floor. She looked so miserable I jumped out of my seat and started gathering papers in an attempt to help her clean up.

"You don't have to do that," she snapped. "That was Lucy. I'll go tell her you're here."

I looked over at Nora as Anna stalked into Lucy's office, but she was steadfast in avoiding eye contact with me. Okay, I thought, so it's not exactly the welcome wagon around here. But I wasn't about to let it get me ruffled. They were obviously very busy and I was clearly an outsider. I heard the rise and dip of muffled voices coming from Lucy's office and then, unexpectedly, the sound of giggling. Anna reappeared, smiling but still ruddy. "You can go in now," she said.

Lucy Fiamma's office was unlike any I'd seen before. The circular room looked as if it had been designed with a specific purpose in mind, but I couldn't tell exactly what that purpose was. It was pristine, especially compared to the disarray of the outer office, without so much as a paper clip out of place. Adding to the overall effect of cleanliness and light was the fact that the entire room was done up in white, glass, and chrome. There was no window, but a generous amount of light streamed down from a large dome-shaped skylight cut out of the ceiling. The almost blinding whiteness of the wall, couch, chairs, and carpeting reminded me of something, an image just out of reach that I couldn't quite put my finger on.

"Welcome, Angel Robinson." Lucy Fiamma strode toward me and extended her hand. I noticed that her immaculately manicured fingernails were long, pointed, and ended with half moons of white polish. Her hand was small, soft, and very cold as I shook it. The rest of Lucy Fiamma was much more imposing. She was very tall, for one thing. I was five-four at last measure and Lucy towered over me by at least six inches. I had to look up to meet her smile. Her white-blond hair floated in a cloud around her face. It had the appearance of hair on which much time has been spent to create the impression of windblown effortlessness. She was wearing a peculiar combination of clothing: white capri pants, a lime green cable-knit sweater, and a red leather belt. The whole outfit was finished off with black leather flats. All the separate pieces were of very good quality, yet they were just wrong together. It was difficult for me to gauge Lucy's age; she had smooth, unlined skin, but her face had a vaguely unhealthy pallor as if she had just recovered from a nasty bout with the flu. Her mouth was big—or generous, if one wanted to be flattering about it—and filled with teeth that were on the large side, but, like everything else in her office, spotlessly white. Her eyes were laser green, with glittering gold flecks. I had no doubt she could speak volumes with the hypnotic stare she was fixing on me. All put together, Lucy was a striking woman, but there was something both unconventional and overwhelming about her looks. Perhaps it was the palpable sense of power that emanated from her, washing over me so completely that for a moment, I felt as if I were drowning in her presence.

"I'm so pleased to meet you," I said. "I've heard so much about you."

"Well, it can't have been too bad," she said, laughing, "or you wouldn't be here, would you? This is Craig Johnson, my right-hand man and the voice of reason in this office."

I hadn't even been aware of Craig's presence until Lucy introduced him. He was fairly easy to miss, so fair and slight he practically faded into the wall behind him. Craig looked as if he hadn't had a decent meal or a good night's sleep for some time. His eyes were sad and brown and his clothes hung lifelessly from his bony frame. So I was shocked when he said, "Nice to meet you, Angel," in a rumbling baritone. Craig had a radio star voice trapped in a milquetoast body. Just one more in a growing list of peculiarities here, I thought.

"Well, why don't we sit down and get started?" Lucy said, gesturing for me to sit on the couch. Craig positioned himself on a chair next to me, holding a legal pad on his lap. Lucy sat down next to me, so close our knees were almost touching, holding a small pad of her own.

"Now, where's your résumé?" she said to nobody in particular. "Nora!" she yelled toward the door. "Can I have this woman's résumé please?"

Nora appeared at the door and said, "It's on your desk, Lucy."

"It most certainly is not."

Nora shuffled over to Lucy's oversize glass desk, removed a sheet of paper, which I immediately recognized as my résumé, and handed it to Lucy.

"Nora, it would help me a great deal if you didn't *hide* these things, don't you think?" Lucy said. Nora simply sighed and left the room.

"Okay," Lucy began, "Angel Robinson. What a name! Surely that's not your real name. You must have changed it, yes?"

"No, no, that's my real name. From birth."

"Then maybe you *ought* to change it. I mean, *Angel* of all things. Quite a title to live up to, I'd think."

"Well, my mother . . . She saw me as her little angel, she said, when I was born, and so she thought, I mean . . ." I trailed off into an awkward silence. The truth was, I'd always been embarrassed by my name. It didn't help that the mega-bestselling book *Freakonomics* listed Angel as the number one "white girl" name that best indicated parents who were uneducated. I hoped Lucy hadn't read *Freakonomics* and resisted the urge to wipe my hands on my dress. My palms were slick with sweat and I could feel the prickle of perspiration on my lower back.

"Names are very important," Craig said suddenly. Again, I was startled to hear such a deep, sensual voice coming out of such a mouse of a man. I didn't know if I'd be able to get used to it. "My wife decided to hyphenate our names so that she could keep her own identity," he added.

"Hyphens are even worse," Lucy said dismissively, and then stopped short as if something important had just occurred to her. "Do you have a *husband*?" she asked me, her tone making *husband* sound a lot like *herpes*.

"No, no. I mean, I have a boyfriend—fiancé, actually—and he . . ." He what? I cursed myself. Is writing a book? Would love to be represented by you? How was it possible that I had spoken no more than a handful of words and was already in such a deep hole? And why had I referred to Malcolm as my fiancé? The two of us hadn't even come close to making any official plans to wed.

"Are you planning to get married sometime soon, then?" Lucy asked. "I mean, I'd hate to offer you a position and then have you disappear on a honeymoon or something. Or get pregnant. You're not planning *babies*, are you? Little Angels, as it were? Because we can stop right here if you are and not waste any more time. Time is money here and I don't have nearly enough of it to squander."

"Actually, we haven't really set a date." I could hear my own voice getting smaller in my throat. "And I haven't even begun to think about children."

"Good," Lucy said, "because this is an extremely busy office, and while I don't expect my employees to work twenty-four hours a day, there will be plenty of reading to do outside of the office and occasions when you may have to come in early or stay late. And as my assistant—" Lucy stopped herself short, her eyes narrowing, a new question working its way to her lips. "You understand that this position is that of *my assistant*?"

"Yes, of course," I said, but I was confused by her emphasis.

"Because if you are thinking of being hired as an *agent,* we should probably terminate this interview immediately."

"Oh no," I rushed to assure her, "I understand the position. And I'm not interested in agenting." I gave Lucy a broad smile to underscore my words, but I questioned, if only for a fraction of a second, just how truthful they were. *Would* I be interested in being an agent myself? Who knew? I hadn't even seen it as a possibility until that moment. I was surprised, and maybe even a little intrigued, that Lucy had. But no, I thought again, I could never—

"Good," Lucy said, drilling me with her laser eyes.

Nora entered the room once more. "Lucy," she said, "Natalie Weinstein's on line two for you."

"I have to take this," Lucy said, leaping from the couch. "This is a *very* important editor. I've been waiting for this offer."

Craig rose from his seat in tandem. "I'm going to make a couple of calls while you get this," he said. "I'll be back in a few."

"Fine, go, go," Lucy said. "You can make yourself comfortable, Angel. Have a look at all of our books." She made a sweeping gesture at the room around us and then sat down at her desk to take the call.

"Natalie, my dear," she began, "are we in business on this delicious book? I'd love to tell the author that you have won the prize. . . ."

My head had started to buzz and I found myself unable to focus on Lucy's conversation. I felt my interview had started badly, but I couldn't explain why. I distracted myself by looking around the room. There was a display on my left, a virtual shrine to Karanuk that I hadn't noticed earlier. Nestled between various animal pelts and a costume I assumed was native Alaskan garb was every edition of *Cold!* in print. Beside all the English editions in hardcover and paperback there were two shelves of foreign editions. I studied the spines for title changes. *Fa Freddo!* screamed the Italian title in red. The French copy was much quieter. *Le Froid,* it said in beige lettering. There was no exclamation point.

"No, it's certainly not a bad offer," Lucy was saying, "but this payout schedule is simply not going to work. Frankly, the author's no spring chicken, if you know what I mean. Is she going to live long enough to get this money? I can't say." Lucy flashed me a toothy grin. I smiled back and turned my head, afraid to be caught eavesdropping, even though she was clearly speaking loud enough for me to hear every word. But some poor writer's fate was hanging on the outcome of this conversation and it just seemed wrong for me to know how it would all turn out before the writer did.

"No, I'm not implying that she's ill," Lucy went on. "What I'm saying is that we might *all* be dead by the time this advance is paid out."

I turned my attention to another shelf of books. A slim volume caught my eye. I recognized it immediately as *Long Shadows,* the one book I'd always said I'd want with me on a deserted island. It was a short but densely written novel about three generations of women who were all writers. Through the different voices of her characters, the author gave a layered, intricate account of women, history, and the writing process. I'd first read it in college and still kept my copy where I could reach it easily, just to thumb through it. It was the author's first and only book. I reached over, almost involuntarily, pulled the book from the shelf, and felt its compact weight in my hand. I let out a breath I didn't realize I'd been holding and got a little light-headed.

I knew then that Malcolm was absolutely right about this being the perfect job for me. The author's mind was certainly where the seeds for great books germinated, but this was the place where they began to bear fruit. Without this agency, who knew how many books would have remained out of sight forever. I replaced the book on the shelf and realized that I really wanted this job. I'd been detached, even equivocal, when I'd first walked in the door, but after being surrounded by this flurry of literary activity for only a few minutes, I couldn't stop the flush of excitement from overtaking me. I wanted this job so badly I could feel my fingertips tingling with desire for it. I wanted—no, I *needed* Lucy Fiamma to hire me, and I scrambled frantically to come up with ways I could convince her to do just that.

Lucy was off the phone. "I see you've been admiring some of our books," she said.

"Oh yes," I said. "*Long Shadows* is one of my all-time favorites. I *love* that book."

"Yes, that was a good one," Lucy said. "One of my first. It's a pity the author only had that one in her." She gave an exaggerated shrug. "And of course you've read *Cold!*?"

"Oh, of course. It's a brilliant book," I said. "But you must know that," I added.

"Hmm," Lucy said, and rose from her desk. "Let me tell you a little publishing story, Angel. Since we're discussing brilliance. Of course, *Cold!* is a phenomenal book, no question, and would have done well regardless. But do you know what really made that book work? In terms of *market*?"

Several possible answers raced through my brain, but I settled for silence.

"What did it, I mean *really* did it, was the exclamation point on the title," Lucy said triumphantly. "And *I* am the one who put that exclamation point there. Indeed." There was a new note in her voice, something like, if this were possible, flirtatiousness. I was dumbfounded as to how to respond, but had developed an instant understanding of her fondness for exclamation points. I smiled like an idiot.

"Right," she said briskly, as if snapping out of a trance, "let's get down to this. I'm really running short on time now." She sat down on the couch and patted the space beside her. "I've looked over your résumé and your experience looks pretty good, but my concern is that you haven't had any direct experience in publishing."

"Yes, but I—"

"Which could actually work in your favor," she interrupted. "It means you have no preconceived notions about how things should work. Am I correct?"

I nodded mutely.

"Of course, in terms of *salary,* I'd have to take your limited experience into consideration. I'm sure you can understand. But let's discuss salary later, shall we?"

I couldn't figure out if Lucy meant that to be a rhetorical question, so, again, I just kept my mouth shut.

"I should let you know that this will be a very different environment than Blue Moon. As you've seen, we are very busy here. So you think you'd be able to juggle several tasks at once? Are you prone to feeling overloaded?"

"Oh no, I—"

"Well, let me ask you this. Say you're sitting here, answering the phone, and you get two calls at once. One is an associate editor at a small publisher you've never heard of who just wants to touch base with me. The other is an author whose book I'm about to sell. Say it's *Karanuk,* for example. Who do you put through to me and what do you say to the other one?"

I hesitated, unable to solve this Sphinx-like riddle with any kind of ease.

"Hurry!" she said. "You're not going to have time to mull this decision with two lines blinking."

"I put Karanuk through to you and let you know that the editor is on the other line," I said quickly. "Then I tell the editor that you'll be with her—or him—shortly."

Lucy smiled again, showing all her gleaming teeth. I exhaled and felt my shoulders relax a little, confident that I'd given the right answer.

"Wrong!" she said. "*Always* put an editor through first, no matter how small. That's where the money is. Without publishers, we have no business. That small-time editor could be a big-time publisher tomorrow. It's happened before and it will happen again."

"Oh," was all I could think to say.

"But you're obviously an author advocate. That's very sweet."

Craig had come back into the room in the middle of this interchange and seated himself with his pad once again. The two of them proceeded to ask me a series of questions, all of which seemed more or less standard, considering the position. Which books were my favorites? Why? Which popular books hadn't I liked? Why? What had I learned about publishing trends from my work at Blue Moon? How fast and how accurately could I read?

I answered all their questions with responses I'd prepared ahead of time, but part of me was removed from the interview and watching in dismay. I was quite sure I'd blown my chances with my answer to Lucy's editor/author question.

"Now . . . *Angel*," Lucy said, my name seeming to stick in her throat before she forced it out, "I must, of course, ask you why you've decided to leave Blue Moon. Doesn't Elise treat you well?"

"Oh no, it's not that at all," I said quickly. "Elise is wonderful! But she's closing the store." I felt a pang of sadness just saying it out loud. "I guess you didn't know."

"What a shame," Lucy said, shaking her head. "Although I've often told her she needed to do more to keep up with the big boys. Too idealistic—that's Elise's problem. What a pity."

"Yes," I said, "it's a real—"

"We could talk all day, I'm sure," Lucy interrupted, rising to her feet, "but I've really got to get back on the phone, and I have several other candidates to interview today. Really, we've had an overwhelming response from that ad, haven't we, Craig?"

"Overwhelming," Craig rumbled.

"What I'd like to do is to get your take on a couple of manuscripts," Lucy said. "Why don't you have Nora give you some things from today's mail and also something that we're working on now? She can give you the George proposal. I think that one would be good. You can drop off your notes if you like or fax them in. We'll talk again after that. How does that sound?"

"Great," I said, and shook her hand once more. "Thank you so much."

"Just one more question," Lucy said. "You're not a *writer*, are you? There's no place for writers here."

My mind stumbled over the irony of that statement while my mouth started forming an answer, but Lucy interrupted me once more. "I *have* made the mistake of hiring writers before. It doesn't work." She shuddered, as if remembering a bad dream. "We represent writers here, we don't create them. Is that clear?"

I had no difficulty responding this time. Of all the questions Lucy had asked me, this one had the surest answer.

"I have no talent for writing," I told her. "Reading is my passion." I thought about Malcolm and felt strangely guilty, as if I was somehow betraying him and lying to Lucy at the same time.

"Good, good," Lucy said, ushering me to the door. "What do you think of my office, by the way? Do you think you could be comfortable working in such a beautiful environment?"

"It's fantastic," I said, and as soon as the words were out of my mouth, I realized what her office reminded me of, the image that had been nagging for definition at the back of my mind. Lucy Fiamma's office was very much like an igloo.

AT THE SOUND OF Lucy's door shutting against my sweat-damp back, Nora and Anna simultaneously swiveled their heads in my direction. Nora looked completely wretched. Anna simply looked annoyed. Both of them raised their eyebrows, forming two sets of inverted parentheses, as if to ask me what the hell I wanted *now*. Standing next to Anna was a tall blond woman wearing a tailored gray suit and clutching a briefcase in one hand. She was, I assumed, the next "candidate" scheduled to interview with Lucy. She gave me a quick, questioning look as if to ask me what to expect, but I looked right past her. I meant to get this job and I wasn't about to offer someone else any help to take it from me, even if that help came from a simple smile. I turned toward Nora.

"Um . . . I . . . Lucy . . ." I drew back some of the oxygen that seemed to have been sucked out of my lungs and started again. "Lucy asked if you could give me some manuscripts from today's mail and the . . . um . . . the George proposal?"

Nora slid out from behind her desk and began riffling through a mail tub full of manuscripts. Anna got up as well, only to sit down again on the edge of the same desk she'd wrecked before. Both of them seemed to be intent on completely ignoring the woman in the gray suit.

"Guess it went okay in there?" Anna inclined her head toward Lucy's office. I smiled at Anna as politely as I could and hoped that would suffice as a response to the nosy question I had no intention of answering.

"This'd be your desk, you know," Anna said, patting the papers underneath her rump. "It's the closest one to her."

"Right," I said. "That makes sense." I looked away from Anna for a moment, not wanting to brand the image of her backside spilling onto the desk. If I managed to get the job, it wasn't a vision I'd want every time I reached for a Post-it.

"Does she want you to write notes? On the manuscripts?" Anna asked.

"Yes, that's what she said. And I'll fax them in."

"Do you know how to do that?"

"How to fax?"

"No, how to write a report."

"Oh. Well, I—"

"Make sure you put your name on it and the author's name. And what the genre is. The genre's very important."

"Okay," I said. "Thanks."

Anna turned toward Nora. "Don't forget to give her the George proposal, Kelly," she said.

Kelly? Who was Kelly?

"I'm sorry," I said to Nora/Kelly, "did I get your name wrong? I thought it was Nora?"

Nora/Kelly sighed heavily.

"It's my mistake," Anna said, an air of smugness hanging around her like a low cloud. "Her real name's Kelly, but we call her Nora. Lucy feels that Nora is a better name for her. So she's Nora here. Sometimes I forget. Sorry." Although she clearly wasn't sorry at all.

"I understand," I said, although I didn't.

Nora/Kelly looked at me as if she'd like to vaporize me on the spot. "Here are a few random manuscripts from today," she said through gritted teeth, "and here's a copy of the George proposal." She shot a poisonous glance in Anna's direction. "You should keep them separate. You can give me a call before you fax them in. Or you can drop them off. But we'll need them back pretty soon." I could tell she'd delivered this drill before. The phones were ringing and Anna had managed, once again, to vanish.

"I have to get that," Nora/Kelly said. "Nice to meet you," she added, and turned her attention to the phone.

"Um, excuse me?" I heard the gray-suit-woman say. "I have an appointment?" As I walked past her to leave, I thought I could see desperation flicker across her face.

When I opened the door and let myself out, the glare of daylight hurt my eyes. I hadn't realized how muted the light had been inside the office, even with all that whiteness. I felt weak and a little dizzy. A headache was starting to throb at the back of my skull. I clutched the manuscripts under one arm and my purse under the other and headed for my car, stumbling in the brightness like a drunk.

Lucy Fiamma
Lucy Fiamma Literary Agency

Dear Lucy,

I don't know if you remember me, but I came to the seminar you gave ten years ago at the college in San Francisco. Anyway, I'm writing to you because I have written a memoir and I would like you to represent it.

The book is about me and my cat, Hairy, and the years we spent together, developing recipes. This may sound odd, but my cat spoke to me and told me what ingredients to use and then we made the dishes. Since he doesn't have hands, I do most of the cooking, but he stands right there on the counter as we work. Together we developed many amazing recipes and stories. So I guess this is sort of a memoir/cookbook.

I am enclosing one of the best recipes here for you to look at. The manuscript is completed (it is 527 pages long) and I can send it to you right away.

I look forward to hearing from you.

Sincerely,
Clara Reynolds

Hairy Mac and Cheese

½ cup macaroni (cooked)

3 cups heavy cream

1 can Tuna

1 cup buttermilk

1 cup 2% milk

4 tbsp. melted butter

Combine ingredients in large skillet.

Sautee at medium-high heat for 20 minutes.

Serve hot!

Lucy Fimma Agency
Att: Lucy Fimma

Dear Ms. Fimma,

I am writing as to inquiry on my fiction book manuscript entitled ONE DARK NIGHT. This is a mystery thriller set in modern times but has an antiquity feeling.

I am looking for an agent to sell this book to publishers and I have read in the guide to literary agents that you have sold books of this type.

I am enclosing the first fifty (50) pages of the book for you to read and a self-addressed-stamped-envelope.

I have also sent this letter and the manuscript to ten other agents.

Thank you,
Robert Brownering

ONE DARK NIGHT

Chapter 1

It was windy a dark night raining. The street was quite for now except for the cars that drove down it no one ever saw the body lying under the curb. He body was dressed ornately because in the subsequent years before this happened he had made a lot of money selling Memberships in a Secret Society sort of like Insurance Salesmen but with riddles. Now he was shot through the heart once there was a brown ring around the wound with silvery dust on the edges. The second clue was the stream of blue ink that was running from his pocket into the storm gutter. The ink forbore to slowly trickle with alacrity across the dry cobblestones.

Above the street where the dead man laid was a late nite restaurant that served all the usual victuals to those who crept through its walls in the deepening hours that raced by in the dead of night. Two people were seated at the counter in the yellow glow. They looked a lot like that famous Hooper print from the 1920s The one person was a Cop and the other was a hooker prostitute, "Why don't I give you a ride home?" the Cop asked the prostitute by the name of Sadie who told him "I don't need a ride of the kind your going to give me."

They walked slowly outside into the warm dry night. The Cop looked into Sadie's eyes were rich in opaqueness the color of coffee. He thought she was beautiful so he didn't notice that as they exited the restaurant he stepped right over an important Clue to what would become the greatest act of subversion and to-

TWO

Lucy Fiamma
Lucy Fiamma Literary Agency
RE: PARCO LAMBRO (book proposal)

Dear Ms. Fiamma,

I am a well known Italian pastry chef living in San Francisco. I have been in this country since the age of 22 and I have taught myself English from reading books. The best books I have read are represented by you, especially *Cold!* by Karanuk. That book made a very big impression on me and it also made me realize that one man's story can be understood and felt by many, even if the experience of the man is new to most people. I, too, have a story to tell and this is why I am writing to you. I was a heroin addict for many years before I left my country. Heroin was a very big problem for young people in Italy in the 1970s and it probably still is. I had a group of friends I spent time with during these years and we hung out together in a park called Parco Lambro in Milano. I was able to quit, but I had to leave my home to do so. My friends were not so lucky. Many bad things have happened to them since then. My story is about the years I spent in the Parco Lambro and about my friends. It is also about how I managed to give up the drug and become successful here in America. It is a memoir. I am enclosing some pages from the book for you to read. I have never written anything before, but this story is from my heart. I have come to you because I know what good work you do and because Fiamma is an Italian name. I know that you will understand what I am trying to say.

Sincerely,
Damiano Vero

PARCO LAMBRO

By Damiano Vero

Everywhere there are lemons. Yellow rinds of lemons, old and new, rotting and fresh. Yellow pulp of lemons shining brightly on the green grass of the park. We need this fruit to clean our stuff. We only use the juice. Sometimes tourists come here and walk around, lost. They come with cameras in their hands and new shoes on their feet, looking for a photograph. They are confused by all the half-lemons squeezed out and left in the sun. If they look closer, they see more. Drinking fountains stained red with blood and the crunch of needles under feet, poking through the grass like an apocalyptic crop. This is when they leave the park, and maybe Italy too.

"We had a terrible time in that city," they will say when they return home. "It was not at all like the travel brochures say. You can't imagine what we found in this park."

There are no strangers in the park today. We are here today as we are every day. We are sitting and standing and lying where we fall. Now we are gathered together in a loose knot, looking over the still body of a young man who has collapsed on the ground. We've dragged him to a shady place under a tree and he lies there, unconscious. His face is beginning to turn the blue color of death. He is Luigi, our friend. We whisper over him and sway a little. Our voices swim slowly through the air, coming up from the bottom of a narcotic lake. We are trying to decide if Luigi wants to be saved. Soon he will be dead.

Soon is a changing concept in the park. Time is stretched differently here. It is elastic and free with a carnival shape. I have to sit down. The wet summer air is heavy with the sharp smell of lemons and it washes me down to the ground. I see someone moving towards Luigi, giving him something. But my eyes are closing and everything is moving very slowly. I can't tell what is happening. The sun is red and yellow behind my lids. I am warm for the first time in days.

When I open my eyes again, Luigi is sitting up, awake and angry. He wants to know who has come to his rescue and why?

"You ruined my high," he says. "Do you know how expensive that stuff was?"

Nobody speaks. The colors around me get brighter and then fade away. Green grass, blue sky, yellow lemons. This is our postcard from Italy.

FAX: 1 of 2
TO: Lucy Fiamma
FROM: Angel Robinson
RE: Reader Reports

Dear Lucy:

I enjoyed meeting with you yesterday and very much appreciate the opportunity to interview for a position in your agency. I have prepared reader's reports for the manuscripts that Nora gave me and plan to drop those off at your office by the end of the day. However, I thought I would fax the following report to you now, as I think this particular manuscript has some spectacular writing and shows a tremendous amount of potential.

I look forward to speaking with you soon.

With best wishes,
Angel Robinson

Title: PARCO LAMBRO
Author: Damiano Vero
Genre: Memoir
Reader: Angel Robinson

Author is Italian, living in S.F., and works as a pastry chef. This is his first book and he has no previous publishing credits. The story is a memoir about the author's struggle with heroin addiction in Milan in the 1970s. He goes on to describe how he overcame this addiction when he moved to the U.S. I believe there's much to recommend here. The author has an interesting way with language, which probably comes from his own internal translation of English. The pages we have here are very moody. The book opens with a gripping scene from the park of the title and goes on to describe the daily "habits" of the author and his group of friends; how they managed to support their addictions by stealing, etc. There are some great descriptions of Milan, and the author's struggles are related in a very compelling way. It's a sad story in many ways and definitely not how we Americans think of Italians. However, the second half of the story (at least how the author has described it) is much more hopeful—his hard-won success in this country, his efforts to help the friends he left behind, and so on. I think the writing is just great (I was hooked from the first sentence and didn't want it to end) and I also think it would have excellent market appeal for all the reasons listed above. I'd give it a strong recommendation.

I BEGAN MY JOB as assistant to Lucy Fiamma on Monday morning, five days after my interview with her. I walked into the office that day armed with nothing thicker or more durable than a sense of trepidation and the small cappuccino I'd purchased at the Peet's conveniently located less than five minutes from Lucy's office. I must have looked anxious because the girl making my coffee asked me twice if I wanted decaf and seemed almost troubled when I told her I had to have regular.

As I clutched my extra-foam cappuccino and made my way to my desk for the first time, I realized I had no idea whether it had been my interview, my reader's reports, or sheer desperation on Lucy's part that had convinced her to hire me. Anna had been the one to call me to tell me I'd gotten the job and that I should plan to start immediately. I hadn't even spoken to Lucy herself since the interview. I hovered over my paper-strewn desk for a moment and decided that it didn't matter. The job was mine and it started now.

"Hi, Angel!"

I turned toward Nora/Kelly, who, after a full five minutes, had finally noticed my presence in the office.

"Good morning," I said, infusing my words with as much perkiness as possible.

"How are you?" Nora/Kelly sounded almost hysterically glad to see me. She also looked hungrier than the last time I'd seen her.

"Fine, thanks. I'm ready to go. Is Lucy here?"

"She's on the phone, but she left a note for you on your desk."

"Okaaaay," I said, wondering how in the hell I was going to find a note from Lucy in that disorganized horror. Nora/Kelly returned her gaze to her own meticulously neat desk once again and started fiddling with loose Rolodex cards. Our moment of girlfriend-bonding was clearly over. I touched the edges of the files stacked highest on my desk. I had absolutely no idea what I was supposed to do with them or where they were supposed to go. I needed help. "Say, Kel— Nora, could you help me sort this a little?"

"I'm really busy right now," she said. "Lucy left you a note. And Anna will train you when she gets here."

"Great, thanks."

"And can you please just call me Nora? I'm Nora here, okay?"

"Okay, Nora."

Lucy had, indeed, left me a note. It was lying on the seat of my chair for lack of available desk space. I almost sat on it.

> Welcome, Angel!!!! We're all so happy to have you on board! Your 1st task will be to sort through the papers on your desk and file them accordingly. Please try to have this done by noon. Anna is overloaded at the moment, but I've asked her to help you in this interim period. Try to use her as little as possible, though, and rely on your own smarts and organizational abilities to get started. I'd also like you to start making phone calls for me as soon as possible!!! Remember, NY is three hours ahead of us, so we need to make those calls by 2pm!! Anna can show you where my call list resides on the computer and I'll expect you to up-date it as per my notes. As everyone can tell you, the phone is the _lifeline_ of this office, so please keep your calls as brief as pos-sible and limit personal calls to _EMERGENCIES ONLY_!!! Your 3rd assignment is to sort through last week's rejections and get them sent back to the authors as quickly as possible. And at some point today, I'd like to discuss your notes on the Italian book. Again, WELCOME!!!   —L.

I made a place for myself on the chair and began sifting through the files. I stole a glance at Nora, who was busy trying to look as if she wasn't looking at me. The phone was ringing. It shrilled three times before Nora said, "You need to answer that. Lucy wants _you_ to answer the phones first. Just remember, don't put anyone through to her unless it's someone she wants to speak to."

And how, exactly, was I supposed to know who she wanted to speak to? I gave Nora a look that I hoped would wither her and picked up the phone.

"Good morning," I said, "Lucy Fiamma Lit—"

"Is she there?" a tired man's voice interrupted.

"Ms. Fiamma is on another line at the moment," I said. "May I ask who's calling, please?"

"Who is *this*?" Now he sounded irritated as well as tired.

"This is Angel Robinson. I'm Ms. Fiamma's new assistant."

"Another one," he muttered. "Help me . . . How long have you been there, five minutes?"

I looked at my watch. "That's about right," I chirped. "May I ask who's calling, please?"

"This," he said, "is Gordon Hart. Of HartHouse Publishers. I am assuming you've heard of us?"

"Oh shit," I said, before I could stop myself. My first call was the head of one of the most well-respected publishers in the country. I bit my lip hard, hoping he hadn't heard.

"I take it you have," he said, and there was a smile in his voice. Lucky for me. "If it's not too much trouble," he continued, "would you mind very much putting *Ms. Fiamma* on the phone? No, no, on second thought, don't bother. Just tell her I won't be able to give her a decision today. She'll know what I mean. Thank you, good-bye." He hung up loudly in my ear and I felt a little sick.

"Who was that?" Nora asked.

"Gordon Hart," I said miserably.

"Oh my God!" Nora squealed. "Why didn't you put him through?"

"He didn't want me to."

"No, no, you've got to put *him* through. Don't you know that? You've got to go tell her. Go now, quickly!" Nora waved her skinny arms around wildly. She looked like an infuriated mouse. I couldn't tell how much of her hostility was pure bitchery and how much was self-protection, but I made a mental note to sort it out as soon as possible.

I had fever sweats and a hammering heart as I knocked on the door to Lucy's office. Craig opened the door a crack and leaned his face out. He looked flushed and disheveled, as if he'd been wrestling with something. "Don't knock," he said. "Use the intercom in the future." There was that teen idol voice again. If you put a large bag over Craig's head, I thought, he'd be utterly irresistible.

"I have a message for Lucy," I said, and Craig ushered me in. Lucy was sitting behind her desk, talking on the phone, and gave me a broad smile as I walked in. She was dressed in a blood-colored pantsuit with shoes to match. Her wild hair was restrained in a small knot at the back of her head. A large pendant, which looked very much like an amulet with a crimson stone in its center, hung from her neck. She gestured for me to come sit in a chair opposite her.

"Yes, my dear," she was saying, "I understand how traumatic this surgery can be, but at least you'll have one kidney left, won't you? And think of it this way, for a couple of days you'll have no kids to distract you. And you can take your laptop with you—get a little writing done. You are due to deliver your first draft, you know. What do you think?" She paused for the response, her mouth turning down as she heard it. "But the anesthesia is a small part of the process," she went on. I could hear an indignant voice on the other end of the phone rise by several decibels and Lucy looked at me, rolling her eyes. She covered the mouthpiece with one hand and as the voice ranted on she said, "What is it, Angel? Why are you sitting here?"

"Gordon Hart called," I whispered. Lucy's expression changed abruptly to one of sharp concern.

"Why didn't you tell me?" she hissed, and uncovered the mouthpiece. "Listen, Lorraine, I have to go now. We'll speak later. No, Lorraine, I can't, I've got one of the most important men in publishing waiting to talk to me. Bye." She hung up and turned to me. "What line is he on?" she asked, scanning the lines, none of which were lit or blinking.

"He's not on the line. He left a message."

"You *let him off the phone*? Why? Do you know how important he is?" She stood up and held her considerable height over me. Flanked against all the white of her office, she looked like a large, open wound. She seemed so angry that for a paranoid second I thought she was going to slap me. "Get him on the phone. Now," she said through clenched teeth.

"He said that he won't be able to give you a decision today," I said breathlessly.

"Just get him on the phone," she repeated. "We'll talk about this later."

I felt myself skipping out of Lucy's office as if the soles of my feet were burning. On my way out, I caught a glimpse of Craig's expression. It was one of amused pity.

I walked-ran over to my desk and picked up the receiver on my phone, only to realize that I was completely clueless as to where to find Gordon Hart's phone number, or *any* phone number, for that matter. I searched my desk, looking for a Rolodex, and found nothing. I did, however, manage to sweep several piles of paper to the floor, spilling what I could only assume were vital documents. My intercom flashed and screamed.

"Angel. Get Gordon Hart. On the line. Now." Lucy's angry voice penetrated my marrow. The useless and unwelcome thought that I was going to have to buy a better deodorant skipped across my brain.

"Uh, yes, I . . . just one moment, please." I brushed some more papers out of my way. "Say, Nora, could you maybe help me find the phone number for—"

"I'm really busy," Nora said, sighing. "But you might want to try turning on your computer. All the phone numbers are listed in the database."

I gave her a look of disbelief. I hadn't even seen the computer behind the reams of paper. Surely she had the number in one of the Rolodexes she was so intent on searching. I couldn't imagine why she wouldn't give it to me.

"Angel!" Lucy's voice shouted through my intercom once more. "I can't talk to Gordon Hart now. If you've got him on the line, tell him I'll get back to him."

As she finished this pronouncement, the phone started ringing again.

"You should get that," Nora said. "Lucy wants *you* to answer the phone."

"I know," I snapped. "Thanks for your help."

"Huh!" Nora favored me with a look of pure indignation and reached below her desk for something unseen. For a moment, I was sure she was going to pull out some sort of weapon, but instead it was a box of Slender-Aid diet protein powder, which she opened and proceeded to eat dry, with a spoon. I picked up the phone.

"Good morning, Lucy Fiamma Literary Agency."

There was a long pause on the other end of the line, punctuated by what sounded like heavy breathing. I tried again. "Lucy Fiamma Literary Agency. Hello?"

"Yes," a man's voice (and a smoker by the sound of it) finally spoke. "Lucy Fiamma, please."

"I'm sorry, she's on another line at the moment, can I help you?"

"She's reviewing my work," he said, "and I'd like to know when we'll be able to discuss it."

"Certainly," I said. "May I have your name, please?"

"Peter Johnson," he said. Proudly, I thought.

"Please hold," I said, and put him in limbo. "Nora?" I couldn't help myself, I needed her. "Peter Johnson's on the line. Should I—"

"He calls every day," Nora said, sniffing over her protein powder. "We keep rejecting him but he never goes away. His manuscripts stink of cigarettes. Ugh. He should really quit." Two other lines began ringing simultaneously. "You'd better get those," Nora said. "Lucy wants you—"

I punched Line 2. "Lucy Fiamma Literary Ag—"

"This is Lorraine. I need to talk to her now, please. Don't tell me she's on another line." Lorraine sounded as if she were weeping.

"Okay, please hold, Lorraine."

I punched Line 3. "Lucy Fiamma Agency."

"Yes, this is Fabio and I'm calling to confirm Ms. Fiamma's dinner reservations for this evening at Baciare Ristorante?"

"Please hold."

I stared at the three blinking lines in total dismay. The obvious choice was to put Lorraine (whom I assumed was the same Lorraine Lucy had been instructing to write through anesthesia) through to Lucy, but I was rapidly learning that the obvious choice wasn't necessarily the right one in this office. Occam's razor was turned on its ear here. I took a chance anyway and buzzed Lucy.

"Yes?" she said.

"Hi, Lucy, I've got Lorraine on Line 2 and Fabio from Baciare on Line 3?"

"Fabio!" she exclaimed. "Put him through."

Right. Fabio went to Lucy and I punched Line 2, dreading the conversation I was about to have with the weepy Lorraine.

"Hi? Lorraine? This is Angel Robinson, Lucy's new assistant. I'm really sorry, but Lucy's on a ca— conference call at the moment and she really can't get off. But she asked me to tell you that she'll call you back the minute she finishes." I didn't know where I was coming up with this and was vaguely surprised that I was able to lie with such ease.

"Sure," Lorraine barked, and hung up in my ear.

Peter Johnson was still blinking on Line 1.

"Mr. Johnson? I'm afraid Ms. Fiamma's unavailable at the moment. Can I help you?"

"Have you read my book?" he asked, coughing into the phone.

"Actually, I'm new here, so I haven't had a chance to—"

"We can still talk about it," he said. "Let me tell you the plot, if you've got a minute. It's a winner, I'm telling you. A real winner."

"Why don't I take your number, Mr. Johnson, and I'll make sure to deliver the message."

He coughed again and rasped out his phone number, promising that it was no trouble at all for him to call again and that he'd be happy to call tomorrow, and oh yes, congratulations on my new job at one of the finest literary agencies on earth. I hung up and stole a glance at my watch, sure that hours had passed since I'd first walked in at eight o'clock. I'd been there for exactly twenty-three minutes.

THE NEXT TIME I CHECKED, it was after one. Pacific time, that is. There was one clock in the office and it was set to New York time. Anna had arrived at nine but was only marginally more helpful than Nora in showing me around the office. She was, however, intent on telling me every detail of her eating habits. Instead of learning where Lucy's call list was, I learned that Anna had consumed eggs and bacon for breakfast. Rather than explaining how the filing system worked, Anna chose to tell me that she was planning a Chinese chicken salad for dinner, and what did I think of honey mustard dressing? Every so often, she'd throw out a bit of useful information, like where the filing cabinets were located, for example, or where I could find the manuscripts that were slated for rejection and had to be sent back to their authors, but these were delivered almost as afterthoughts. At least, thankfully, when I managed to unearth my computer and turn it on, Anna was able to direct me to the various databases of names and phone numbers that I'd be needing.

Craig spent most of the morning wearing a path between his desk and Lucy's office. When he was seated behind his folders and files, he was all but invisible. Aside from the brief conversation I'd had with him in Lucy's office, he hadn't spoken to me at all.

Anna must not have heard that I was to be the first person answering the phone, because, unless she was on a call herself, she leaped at it every time it rang. Her conversations were loud and she giggled often. These were not personal calls, either, because she put several through to Lucy, but she spoke to everyone as if she were a long-lost chum. I answered a few calls of my own, more successfully than the first, but still felt uneasy about the Hart episode. Lucy had not emerged from her office, and I expected to be called onto the sparkling white carpet at any minute for screwing up. When my intercom buzzed at one-thirty, I actually jumped.

"Angel, can you come in here now, please." Despite the *please,* it was clearly a command and she sounded none too pleased. I considered the possibility of being fired on my first day.

"Come, come, Angel. Sit down." Lucy was perched on her white leather sofa, holding a manuscript. I recognized the mass of curling blue script on the first page. I sat down on the edge of her couch and she gave me a look I could only describe as a "once-over."

"What have you come as, my dear?" she asked, her tone much less gentle than her words.

"Excuse me? Wha—"

"I mean, what are you *wearing,* Angel?"

I looked down at myself, as if I needed to be reminded of what I'd put on earlier, and saw a beige button-down shirt, jeans, and black mules. It was a very similar outfit to the ones both Anna and Nora were wearing. Obviously this was some kind of trick question. I had no idea what the answer was supposed to be.

"Um . . ."

"Oh, for God's sake, I don't have time for this," Lucy said with exasperation. "I want to talk to you about this Italian book." She handed me Damiano Vero's manuscript. My notes were clipped to the top and I saw that Lucy had written all over them. "Now, I gather that you really liked this, yes?"

"Yes, I thought the writing was great." I scrambled to switch gears in an effort to keep up with Lucy's broad jumps in topic.

"Well, it *is* very good, you're right, but I have some questions. First of all, it's set in Italy."

"Some of it."

"Yes, it's set in Italy and Americans are very xenophobic. They may not want to read about Italy right now."

"But what about *Under the Tuscan Sun*? Italy's always been seen as so romantic," I said. "Besides, when he gets to this country, he really cleans up his act. It's kind of an immigrant success story in a way." I was beginning to warm to the discussion. I'd almost forgotten about the files, the phone calls, and Nora's glowering looks.

"That's another thing. I don't think this should be a memoir. Memoirs—*especially* addiction memoirs—have become the wicked stepchildren of publishing lately. We're going to have to call this something else."

I watched as Lucy furrowed her brow in concentration.

"Let's pitch it as autobiographical fiction," she said finally. "That should cover all the bases." She gave me a sharp glance. "You should be writing this down, Angel." I looked down at my empty hands, debating whether or not to make a run for my desk for pen and paper. "Next time," Lucy stated, "come in here prepared, please. Now, is he still addicted? That would make a great angle. We could get him into rehab, give him interviews from a hospital or something."

"Actually, I think his point was that he's clean now."

Lucy shot me a disapproving look. "Well, we'll see what we can do about that. Much better if he *hasn't* cleaned up. This book could *be* his salvation instead of the book being *about* his salvation. Yes, yes, that's *much* better. What does he do?"

"He's a pastry chef."

"No, that's no good. Too many chef tales out there already. We're on the fourteenth minute of that story and the clock's ticking." She paused for a moment, tapping her Waterman fountain pen against the pages on her lap. "We'll just say he's unemployed. Impoverished and addicted. That's much better. Heroin and pastry don't make a sexy combination. This stuff about the park is fabulous," she said, flipping through the bent sheets. "Is the manuscript finished?"

"I don't know."

She sighed. "These are the things you really need to be paying attention to, Angel. Well, it doesn't matter. I can sell it on a partial with the right pitch. I can sell it as . . . an Italian *Trainspotting*. Yes, that's it. Unless you think the heroin thing is played out at this point. What's your take on that, Angel? You're young, you should know."

"I don't think so," I said tentatively. "It never really seems to be, you know, *finished* really."

"Has he contacted any other agents?"

"I'm not sure."

"Haven't you spoken to him?" She seemed appalled.

"No, I—"

"I left a note on your desk about this. I mentioned, specifically, that you needed to call him as soon as possible."

"I'm sorry, I didn't see it."

She stared at me hard, as if weighing my answer for the truth in it. "Angel, attention to detail is *paramount* in this office." I was a very small mouse to her great big cat, and there was nowhere to run. But as soon as I began to formulate some sort of verbal escape, Lucy shifted her tone once more. "This is very *filmic*," she said. "Yes, I definitely think so. Get him on the phone, let's sign him up before he goes somewhere else." I started to rise, but she held up her hand, palm out. "No, wait," she said. "Let's just see something first." She walked around to her desk and punched her intercom button. "Anna!"

"Yup?"

"Get Natalie Weinstein on the phone."

"Okay, Lucy. Is there anything else you need right now? I could get you a—"

"Natalie. Weinstein. Anna. Now."

Lucy positioned herself at her desk and motioned for me to come closer. "I want you to hear this," she said. I noticed that her voice had dropped an octave or two and had what I could only call a seductive tone washing through it. As soon as she was connected with Natalie Weinstein, Lucy began rearranging the items on her desk with her free hand. This was a pattern I would soon become very familiar with. Whenever she was on the phone, and that was a good portion of every day, Lucy compulsively stacked the notepads, paper clips, pens, and anything else that was on her desk. She moved the largest items into the center first, progressively piling on items as they decreased in size, until there was a small tower in the middle of her desk. Then she took them down, item by item, and placed them in the corners of the desk. If she was still on the phone at that point, she'd begin the process again. She repeated these motions over and over as she talked to Natalie Weinstein, and I became hypnotized, watching her hands move back and forth as her voice filled the room.

"It's really hot," she was saying, "and I thought of *you* first. I've got a virgin author here, came in over the transom. Yes, we *do* read our unsolicited manuscripts over here. Anyway, he's a divine Italian man with a blockbuster novel idea. Yes, I have the novel right here."

I watched the notepads stack up and come down.

"Well, it turns out he's written the Italian *Trainspotting*. Actually, it's more like *Trainspotting* meets *Under the Tuscan Sun*. Exquisite writing."

Up, down, up, down.

"He's a heroin addict and he's written the most vivid account of— Yes, I agree, there certainly is a market. Listen, Nat, this is *very* hot. He's still addicted. What? No, did I say addicted? *Recovery*. He's still in recovery. But it's—well, you know what a slippery slope recovery can be."

I watched her hand pick up a pen and begin writing a note.

"Yes, he's Italian. From Milano. Drop-dead gorgeous. You know how Italian men are."

She held up the note for me to see. *Do we have author photo?* it asked. I shook my head in the negative. She continued to write. *He'd better be good looking!* she added to her note.

"He's already working on a sequel. Actually, he has two more books in the works. We could have an antihero series character here. He's calling it the . . . let me find it here . . . yes, *The Horse Triptych*. What? Well, that doesn't matter, he can always change the title."

She offered me a dramatic eye roll.

"Yes, I will, Nat. I can't guarantee— Well, I can offer you an exclusive if— Fine, I'll have it on your desk tomorrow. You understand, I have to move on this right away. But, of course, I thought of you first."

Lucy hung the phone up abruptly and, snapped out of my trance, my eyes shot to her face. I was impressed and also a little frightened. Lucy was assuming an awful lot without having spoken one word to Damiano Vero. I had no doubt, however, that she would get everything she was asking for.

"And *that* is how it is done, Angel," Lucy said. She was smiling broadly, her teeth glowing in preternatural whiteness. "All right, Angel, get the author—what's his name again? Anyway, get him on the phone and then put me on with him. He's not going to know what hit him. I'm going to make him a star. And make sure to take the manuscript home with you tonight. It needs some work. Go over it carefully, fix it up, and have him make the changes. We've got to get this out in as perfect shape as possible. These editors are busy. They don't have time for books that need a whole lot of work from the outset, believe me." She drew a breath. "Right, I want to have it out by the end of the week, the latest. We'll need at least five more editors. I'll generate the list."

"But aren't you just sending it to Natalie Weinstein?"

Lucy looked at me with an expression of disbelief. "That would be a very big mistake," she said. "Now, go, go, we've got work to do." As I walked out of her office, Lucy added, "And find out about the other two books he's working on."

I paused at the door for only a millisecond. That was how long it took me to decide not to tell Lucy that the two books were figments of her imagination and not the author's. What did it matter? If she wanted two more books, he'd have to write them.

Damiano Vero had listed three phone numbers on his cover letter. The first gave me a busy signal and the second rang with no answer. I finally tracked him down on the third.

"*Ècco, sì!*" he exclaimed when I announced myself. "But I just sent it. So fast you are."

I smiled into the phone, thinking that this was the first happy phone conversation I'd had all day. "Lucy would like to talk to you," I said. "Can you hold a moment while I put you through?"

"Of course," he said.

"Lucy, I've got Damiano Vero on Line 1 for you."

"*Who?*"

"Damiano Ve— The Italian book?"

"Oh, him. Well, put him *through,* Angel. You're wasting time."

I sighed to myself as I punched the necessary buttons. At least, I thought, she didn't seem to have very good short-term memory when it came to my first-day screwups. My stomach growled and twisted, having had nothing to digest since the banana I put in it six hours before. After she'd polished off her entire box of protein powder, Nora left the office briefly to go collect the mail. Nobody else had made any kind of movement to take lunch outside the office, although Anna had pulled out a messy, smelly meat-laden sandwich and was eating it noisily at her desk. She felt my eyes on her and looked up at me.

"We don't take a lunch break here," she said. "I hope you brought something with you."

"I didn't know that," I said. "So, no, I didn't."

Anna shrugged and took a large bite out of her sandwich. Something that looked like mayonnaise oozed from the bread. She was still chewing when her intercom buzzed.

"Yeth, Luthy?"

"Anna, is your mouth full or do you have a cold? If you are ill, make sure you wipe down the phone after you use it. I shouldn't have to tell you. I need an agency contract for Damiano Vero now, please. And tell Angel to pick up Line 1 and talk to him."

"Angel," Anna said, nearly choking as she swallowed, "you need to—"

"Thanks, I've got it." I picked up my phone. "Hi, Mr. Vero. This is Angel."

"Please call me Dami," he said. "It's more easy."

"Okay. It's great to meet you. I really like *Parco Lambro*. I don't know if Lucy told you. It's very exciting."

"Oh yes," he said. "Very exciting. I had a good feeling about Luciana. I knew she would be the best person for this book. And she tells me that we will be working together, you and I. You are going to make some changes for me?"

"Yes, we talked about that. Of course, I'll just make suggestions and then whatever seems right to you . . ."

"*Bène*. Luciana gave me your phone number at home, but I think maybe we could meet at some point?"

Luciana? My home phone number? "Sure, that would be great. I can call you. . . ."

"*Bène*. I look forward to it. *Mille grazie*, Angel. Good-bye for now."

Before I could replace the phone in its cradle, my computer chirped with the sound of an instant message. I looked over at the rectangle of blue text and saw that the initials of the sender were AA. Anna.

Did she tell you about St. Lucy? the message read.

Did who tell me? I wrote back. I looked over at Anna. She was bent over her desk, looking very busy, clacking away at her keyboard. My computer sounded off again with another message:

LF. She likes to tell the new staff how St. Lucy is one of the patron saints of writers. They tried to burn St. Lucy but she was flame-proof. They had to stab her in the throat to kill her. She was Italian.

No, she didn't tell me, I wrote back.

I just thought it might help you with that Italian author, Anna responded.

I briefly entertained the notion that Anna might be insane and was debating a possible response to her last message ("thank you" just didn't seem appropriate) when Nora approached me with a large plastic tub full to the top with manuscripts and query letters.

"Lucy wants you to sort this," she said. "It's usually my job, but she wants you to get familiar with the submissions."

"These are just today's submissions?"

"It's not bad, really," Nora sniffed. "There are only about fifty today. Sometimes we get close to a hundred." She smiled. It was an expression that looked both awkward and foreign on her face. "Have fun," she said.

ANNA DROPPED A MANUSCRIPT on my desk, where it landed with a plop and a rush of air. "This is my reading for last night. It's a reject, but you should look it over. Lucy likes to get second opinions. I'm outta here, so I guess your training's done for the day. You can probably go now, too." I looked down at the manuscript and then up at the clock, subtracting three hours. It was six o'clock and my eyes were stinging. A hunger headache throbbed at the back of my head. Nora was gone. I could hear Craig's voice sounding from behind Lucy's door.

"Yes," I said, and gathered my purse, *Parco Lambro* notes, and several manuscripts to review, including the one that Anna had just dropped on me. "I have to eat something. I think I'm going to pass out." But I was talking to an empty room. Anna was out the door before I could finish my sentence. She had also left me without explaining what, if anything, I was supposed to do to close up or finish out the day. With a sudden rush of resentment, I realized that everything I had learned over the course of my extraordinarily long first day, I'd figured out for myself—in spite of, not because of, Anna's so-called "training." I tried to formulate a plan for how I would approach Anna, Nora, and even Craig in the coming days to elicit a little more help, but my brain was too hungry and tired to give shape to a single thought.

I stood up to leave, but a low-blood-sugar head rush kept me from moving until I could steady myself. The phone rang, loud in the now-silent office, cutting through my dizziness. *Answer it. Don't answer it.* If only I'd left a half minute earlier.

"Hello, Lucy Fiamma Agency."

There was static coming through the receiver and then a small voice speaking, it sounded like, from far away. "Ah, ook."

"Hello? Can I help you? Hello?"

"Ka." Crackle, hiss. "Oo."

"I'm sorry, I can't hear you. Hello?" There was more crackling and an extended hiss on the line. I was about to hang up when I heard it, faint but clear.

"Karanuk."

"*Karanuk?* Yes, please, yes, one moment please, just one moment."

I didn't bother trying to buzz Lucy with the intercom, opting, instead, to run to her office, knock rapidly on the closed door, and open it without waiting for a response. Lucy was seated at her desk, looking as fresh as if she'd just started her day. Craig was kneeling next to her (yes, *kneeling*), holding out papers for her to look at.

"Angel?"

"Karanuk," I blurted. "Karanuk's on Line 1 for you." Lucy lifted one of her boomerang-shaped eyebrows and stared at me, puzzled. "It's not a very good connection," I ran on. "He must be calling from Alaska. He's holding."

"Angel," Lucy said, "Karanuk lives in Los Angeles."

"Oh, okay. Um, he's on Line 1. And I'm going to go home now. Thank you."

Lucy shook her head, as if she couldn't quite believe what she was hearing, and picked up the phone.

"Thank you, Angel," Craig boomed, rising from his position on the floor. "We'll see you in the morning."

I backed out the door, gathered my manuscripts, and ran from the office as if my hair were on fire. *Stupid,* I cursed myself as I got into my car and drove home. *Stupid, stupid, stupid,* I thought as I unlocked my door and sat down on my bed. *Idiot,* I added, as I spread the manuscripts out in front of me and prepared to go through them. Although I'd relived the last five minutes of my day at least twenty times on my way home, I still couldn't believe that I'd been stupid enough to barge into Lucy's office, stammering like a fool. There was a dull but insistent ringing in my head.

On balance, I thought, I hadn't given a particularly stellar performance for my first day. I wondered, not for the first time, if I would even last the week. The ringing in my head persisted. I looked up. It was my phone.

"Hello, Lu— Um, hello?"

"Angel!" Lucy's voice slammed through the phone, hitting my brain like a mallet.

"Lucy?"

"Listen, dear, we hardly had a chance to chat and get acquainted to-day. You ran out of here so quickly." She gave a short, coughlike laugh.

"I know, I'm—"

"Anyway, dear, I wanted to welcome you and tell you that I think you have tremendous potential as a team player in our agency. Really, *tremendous*. I'm very pleased with your work on the Italian book and I think this is only the beginning. You've got a good eye and this is something we've been sorely lacking."

"Thank you," I said, exhaling the breath I'd been holding.

"And because there's been a lack in that area," she went on, "I want you to review *all* the submissions very carefully. You know, Anna's very sweet and she means well, but she clearly doesn't have your eye. I worry about what we're missing with her. Do you understand?"

"Um . . ." I glanced down at the rejected manuscript Anna had given me. Her reader's report was clipped to the top and started with, *This is a stupid idea. And boring.*

"So just *entre nous,* Angel, keep a close watch on what she's doing, all right?"

"Sure."

"Perhaps you can come in a little earlier tomorrow morning and we can have a quick meeting before the rest of the staff arrives. Because, frankly, Angel, I really can't spend this much time on the phone with you. I have dinner reservations."

"Sure, Lucy. No problem."

"You've brought the Italian book home with you?"

"Oh yes, I've got it—"

"Fabulous. I'm so excited about this book, Angel. See if you can make some inroads on it tonight. We'll discuss it in the morning."

"Okay."

"Again, I'm so pleased that you're joining us, Angel. I knew you were sharp the moment I laid eyes on you."

"Thank—"

"Just one more thing, Angel, and then I really must go. I realize that today was your first day and all, but I must insist that you dress a little more professionally. There's no need for a business suit or anything that formal, but I believe that jeans are too casual and send the wrong message. So no more jeans, all right, Angel?"

"No more jeans," I repeated thickly.

"Fabulous. I'll see you in the morning. Early. Good-bye, dear."

I replaced my phone in its cradle, tenderly, as if it were a newborn. The last thing I wanted was for it to wake up and start ringing again. I picked up the manuscript that Anna had so summarily rejected and stared at it, the words blurring in front of my tired eyes. For the first time that I could remember, I had a fully formed desire for an alcoholic beverage. But I had no time to think about when or where I might get one because, to my horror, the handle to my front door was turning, opening, and someone was walking in.

A handsome blond man stood in front of me, holding a bottle of wine in one hand and what looked like a very large manuscript in the other.

"Baby!" he said. "How was your first day?"

Malcolm. For a second, I hadn't even recognized him.

THREE

Lucy Fiamma
Lucy Fiamma Literary Agency

Dear Ms. Fiamma,

I am a writer seeking representation for my first novel, titled ELVIS WILL DANCE AT YOUR WEDDING. As per your recommendation in the guide to literary agents, I am enclosing the first fifty pages of the novel, a synopsis, and a self-addressed stamped envelope for your response. The entire novel is available if you'd like me to send it.

Although this is my first novel, I have published several short stories in literary journals over the last few years. Most recently, my stories have appeared in *Elephant Cage Quarterly* and *Flabbergasted*. I would be happy to furnish you with copies at your request. I am a graduate of the MFA writing program at California University. ELVIS WILL DANCE AT YOUR WEDDING was originally written as my master's thesis, but I have since revised it substantially.

The novel is about a road trip that takes place over a

twenty-four-hour period of time. The two main characters, Michael and Jennifer, drive from Los Angeles to Las Vegas, get married, and drive home again. They are a young couple and know very little about each other as they begin their journey into matrimony. Over the course of the novel, several secrets are revealed and they learn a great deal about themselves and about each other.

I understand that your time is valuable, so I'll keep my letter brief and hope that the writing will speak for itself. I look forward to hearing from you.

Sincerely,
Shelly Franklin

ELVIS WILL DANCE AT YOUR WEDDING

By Shelly Franklin

Chapter 1

Michael's eyes are the color of phosphorescent algae. They are so bright and so green that as Jennifer opens the back door and walks in, she speculates for a moment that the color is chemically induced. But love, Jennifer thinks, can do this too. Her thought is a bright spark in the darkened room. So, this glow is from love. This is what Jennifer chooses to believe as she approaches the man who will soon be her husband.

He is sitting in near dark and the TV is on without sound. He's left the windows open and the September air is warm and moist coming through the screen. Jennifer doesn't wonder why he has turned out all the lights. She knows he uses the TV like some people use food. For him, it's a nurturing lifeline. She glances quickly at the TV and recognizes a home shopping channel. An under-fed woman in red is selling golden angels on a chain for under twenty dollars.

"I'm sorry I'm late," Jennifer says, kissing Michael on the cheek.

"It's all right, Jen," Michael says, his voice a pan of melted butter. "We've got plenty of time. Las Vegas never sleeps."

Jennifer puts her arms around Michael's neck. His ocean eyes shine up at her and his mouth curves up into a smile. "Nervous?" she asks. She keeps her tone light because she can smell the fear on him, subtle but biting.

"Yeah," he says. His hands find a place in the small of her back and press in. "Aren't you?"

No, Jennifer thinks. She's not nervous. She's never been more sure of anything in her life. She says, "Do you have the rings?"

"I've got the rings, Jennifer. And, more importantly, I've got the car. Did you see the car?" He presses his lips on the side of her neck. He smells of the cigarettes he supposedly quit smoking three weeks ago and the mints he's chewed to disguise them. She can also detect the faint but unmistakable odor of alcohol.

"The car?" she asks.

"Go look outside," he says.

Jennifer breaks his grip, walks slowly over to the window. There is a candy-apple red Corvette sitting in the driveway. Even in the dark, it glows like a Pacific sunset.

"What's all this, Michael?"

"You like it?" He is smiling wide enough to swallow a small lake. "I rented it. For tonight."

"Why?" Jennifer asks him.

"Isn't it beautiful? I figure if we're going to do this, we're going to do it right. A classic car for a classic American experience. A wedding in Las Vegas. What do you say?"

Jennifer wants to be as enthusiastic as he is over this car, but she can't quite catch the same thrill.

Still she says, "It's great, Michael. When does it have to be back?"

"Tomorrow."

Jennifer raises her eyebrows in surprise. "Well then, cow-boy," she says. "We'd better get going."

Title: ELVIS WILL DANCE AT YOUR WEDDING
Author: Shelly Franklin
Genre: Fiction
Reader: Anna

This is a stupid idea. And boring. The title is awful. The author has an MFA and she has had some things published in literary magazines, but otherwise no credits. This is a first novel. It's about a couple who drive to Las Vegas to get married. I don't think anything else happens. It's very slow and it's a dumb premise. The writing is dry and not evocative. I don't know where this is going. I don't know why Elvis is in the title. She doesn't say if she's sent it to any other agents, but I don't think it matters. This isn't our kind of thing. My recommendation is to reject.

Title: ELVIS WILL DANCE AT YOUR WEDDING
Author: Shelly Franklin
Genre: Fiction
Reader: Angel

Author is a graduate of the California University writing program, which has been producing many bestselling writers over the last few years, so I gave this (originally her thesis) a close read. I actually like the title. I know it's a bit wacky, but the novel is about getting married in Las Vegas. Who better than Elvis in the title? I also like the writing here. The author sets up a certain tension right away so we know, as readers, that there are already problems between these two people and that getting married might be a mistake. I didn't find the writing dry—quite the opposite. I read the synopsis and it's clear that the author knows where she's going with this material. She has a definite plot and structure, both of which will work, in my opinion.

The only possible problem I see is that the novel is written largely in the present tense. Although this works in terms of keeping us in the moment (and the novel does take place over the course of one day), it's also a bit confining and could become a little claustrophobic. However, I think this is easy enough to remedy if the author is willing to rewrite. I think there is potential here for a good book about contemporary relationships—always a topic of interest. I'd recommend contacting her right away to make sure she hasn't gone anywhere else with this and asking to see the complete manuscript.

MY FIRST DAY *at* work quickly turned into my first night *of* work. I read through my stack of manuscripts first, placing Shelly Franklin's novel at the top of the pile so as to rescue it from Anna's ham-fisted rejection, and then I turned my attention to editing *Parco Lambro*. I was surprised by how easily the work came to me. It was as if I knew, instinctively, which words to move around and shave off to uncover the picture Damiano wanted to create. I could hear his voice in my head as I read and sensed the story he meant to tell. I responded with marks from my red pen. I'd never really done anything like this before, unless you counted the minor editing I'd done on Malcolm's stories, but it felt entirely natural to me—unlike the other first-day tasks I'd fumbled through. The biggest bonus, though, was that I was truly enjoying myself.

Malcolm hovered around me as I worked, careful not to interrupt me at first, but growing increasingly impatient as the hours stretched on. It was clear he wanted a full report of everything I'd experienced at my new job, but I explained to him that he'd have to wait for the blow-by-blow account.

"She has to have this *tomorrow*," I told him, pointing to Damiano's manuscript.

Malcolm came up behind me and put his hands in my hair, stroking my neck. "Are you sure?" he asked, his voice heavy with seduction. "You've been at it so long, baby."

"Malcolm, please . . ."

"Fine," he said, dropping his hands and his attempt to sway me. "Then I guess I'll make you some coffee."

"That would be great," I said.

The next time I looked up it was close to dawn and Malcolm had passed out, fully clothed, on my bed.

———

I WAS ON MY WAY TO the office a few short hours later, and by the time I made it in, still long before nine o'clock, Lucy and Craig had already generated a list of ten top editors for *Parco Lambro*. In the meantime, Lucy had sent a copy of the unedited manuscript overnight to Natalie Weinstein, to whom she'd promised an exclusive. Natalie Weinstein would have it exclusively for exactly two days, but according to Lucy, that was long enough. "She knows this business," Lucy told me. "She knows that I can't let a hot manuscript languish on her desk."

While I walked Damiano through my revisions on the phone ("We need this yesterday, Angel," Lucy told me. "Make sure he gets it to you by tomorrow or type it up yourself. On your own time."), Lucy pitched his book to her ten editors. Because she wanted me to hear her make these pitches ("You need to learn how this is done, Angel."), I put Damiano on hold several times to run to her office, paper and pen in hand, and listened to her conversations in progress:

"Well, I can't give you an exclusive, you understand, Charles. However, I *can* guarantee that you will be the first to receive it. If you'll give my assistant your home address, I can overnight it to you there."

"I'm telling you, Katherine, I've really never read a manuscript with so much raw power. Of course, this is why I thought of you first. I know your talent for keeping such emotion fresh on the page."

"Yes, Julia, he's extremely marketable. Think dark and sexy."

"I thought of you immediately, Frank. This is bigger than genre—it's a sweeping social comment. What? Yes, I agree, we certainly do need one."

Periodically, during the course of these conversations, Lucy would hold up notes for me to read.

Where is author photo?!!! one said. *Need it NOW!!!*

Are edits finished? asked another.

And then there was, *Start pitch letter*.

I nodded and mouthed "Okay" after the last note, but I had absolutely no idea what she wanted. As I sat down at my desk, I gave a look around the office at my coworkers and debated who might be able to help me. My prospects weren't so hot.

"Damiano," I said into his perpetually holding line, "Lucy's really got a *lot* of interest and she wants to go out with this as soon as she can. Do you think you can get this done by, um, tomorrow?"

"Bella," he said after a pause. "Okay. I can call you later? How do I send it? And please call me Dami."

The sound of my intercom cut off my answer before it left my mouth. "Angel, have you begun that pitch letter? I'd like to see it, please."

"Listen, Damian—*Dami*," I whispered into the phone, "why don't you call me after you've made some more of these changes? And then you can just, um, e-mail it to me at home. I'll—I'll just print it out."

"Grazie," he said.

"And a photo," I added hurriedly. "Do you have a photo you can e-mail? Of yourself?"

"Not really, but—" he began, but my intercom buzzed again and I rushed him off the phone. After assuring Lucy that I'd have a pitch letter for her momentarily, I took a chance on the possible kindness of strangers and approached Craig.

"How are you doing, Angel?" he asked. Craig looked particularly scrawny in a blue polo shirt that was a size too big and brown pants that had seen better days. As he pushed his spectacles back on his nose, I was reminded of Woody Allen minus the irony. But that voice! It resonated in the center of my body and made my heart skip. Craig's wife, I thought, was obviously a lights-off kind of gal.

"I—I'm okay," I said. "But I wonder if you could give me a hand with something. Lucy wants me to—"

"Draft a pitch letter for the Italian book?" Craig asked.

"Right," I said. "And I don't . . ." I trailed off, not wanting to admit to Craig that I didn't have the vaguest idea how to start such a thing.

"There's a template on the computer," Craig said. "But if you want an example to follow, I've got one here somewhere." He slid open a meticulously neat file cabinet beneath his desk and pulled out a sheet of paper. "Here you go," he said. "But I'll need that back when you're finished with it."

"Sure," I said, but hesitated.

"You're going to have to jump right in, Angel," he said, and the sound of my name in his mouth made my throat constrict. "It's the best piece of advice I can give you. Don't be afraid to get wet."

This was, oddly, the warmest, most encouraging thing anyone had said to me since I'd started, and it immediately endeared me to Craig, who was, nevertheless, frowning as he uttered it.

"Okay," I said, giving him a high-wattage smile. "Right you are."

I returned to my desk and scratched out a one-page letter that included a brief description of *Parco Lambro,* heavy on superlatives, and a short paragraph stating why "Dear—(Ed.)" absolutely had to have it. I copied the sign-off on Craig's sample letter, which was "As always, Lucy Fiamma." And I supposed she was. Always Lucy, that is.

It took Lucy less than ten seconds to decimate my letter with razor-like flourishes of her fountain pen. *Redo as per my notes,* she wrote on top. *This reads as if a (small) child wrote it.*

I felt a flush spread up my neck as I read her comments and my ears began to burn with humiliation. I realized that I hadn't really been stung by Lucy until that moment and I found it particularly painful. The escape fantasy I'd envisioned for myself during my first five minutes on the job flared in my head. Craig must have sensed this somehow, because just as I was contemplating how long it would take me to gather my purse and exit, an instant message from him appeared on my screen.

Don't take it personally.

I sat down at my desk and typed one back. *I'll try not to,* I wrote. *Thanks.* I looked over at Craig, hoping for some kind of visual affirmation, but he was already on the phone, murmuring something about overdue royalties into his headset.

I rewrote the pitch letter five times. Each draft came back to me (via Anna, Nora, or myself as we took our turns through Lucy's office) with more strike-throughs and margin notes than the last. Lucy made corrections on her own corrections. Finally, I received a copy that stated, *Enough already—we're out of time. Let's get this done!* I looked at the changes and realized that the final copy was almost identical to the original I'd given her.

I returned Craig's sample pitch letter to him and hovered at his desk until he looked up at me and asked, "Is there something else I can help you with, Angel?"

"Well, actually, um . . ."

"The letter's fine. Is that it?"

"No. I . . ."

"We're kind of busy here, Angel."

I realized that I was sweating profusely and had no idea why I was finding it so difficult to broach a subject that should have been discussed and put to rest after my initial interview.

"I don't, uh, ha-ha, know exactly what my, um, salary is here, Craig." I gave him a big smile, hoping it would cover my conversational flailing. "I was sort of wondering if you could fill me in. You being the money guy and all."

Craig leaned back in his chair and, for a moment, a strange look passed across his washed-out features. If I hadn't known better, I could have sworn it was a kind of indictment—as in, why would I be so presumptuous as to assume I was actually going to get *paid* for this opportunity? The look passed quickly, before I could positively identify it, and Craig gave me a weak smile in return. He leaned over his desk, grabbed a scrap of paper, wrote *25K* on it, and handed it to me.

"And this is . . . ?" I searched his eyes for an answer.

"Yearly." He'd lowered his voice to a kind of Shakespearean actor's whisper.

"Okay," I said, staring at the paper, dividing it by twelve, subtracting taxes in my head, and coming up with much smaller figures.

"Most people who start in publishing make much less," Craig said. "This is a very generous starting salary. She has a lot of faith in you."

"Right. Of course. Thanks," I said, and went back to my desk. I'd barely seated myself when my intercom screeched once more.

"Angel!"

"Lucy?"

"My office!"

Before I could get more than one foot in her office, Lucy barked, "Copy and circulate," and thrust a memo at me.

We are not running Gap ads in this office!!!! it screamed. *Professionalism is paramount to the success of this operation! I must insist that, from now on, there will be NO JEANS worn to work! Please adjust your wardrobes accordingly! LF.*

I had, of course, already adjusted my "wardrobe" and was wearing a pair of khaki pants I'd pulled from the depths of my closet earlier that morning. Anna and Nora, however, were still clad in denim. Nora's reaction to the new "no jeans" directive was to fold and refold the memo until it was an extremely small square. When Anna read her own copy, she shot a pointed glance in my direction and turned to her computer. Two minutes later, I received an instant message from her:

LF has requested that we dress more professionally. No more jeans. Just so you know.

I held up my copy of the memo, but Anna's eyes were fixed on her computer screen.

Okay, I typed back. *Thanks for letting me know.*

Any idea why we can't wear jeans anymore? Anna sent back. *I'm just wondering because jeans were fine until today. Just thought you might know.*

My guess is as good as yours, I typed. I hoped that would be the end of it, but I suspected that Anna was just getting started. The phone started ringing again and she leaned back in her chair, sulkily refusing to answer it.

"Lucy Fiamma Agency."

"Listen to *you,* all professional!"

Malcolm. Damn it. "Hello there," I said, lowering my voice by several octaves.

"'Hello there'? You know who this is, right? Your boyfriend? The man you left lonely and unfulfilled in bed this morning?"

"Yes, Mal—of course I know who it is." I was whispering, which had drawn Anna's attention. I swiveled my chair away from her so that she couldn't see my face, but that put me squarely in Nora's sights. I was learning that privacy was at a real premium in this office. "I can't talk now," I breathed into the phone. "I'm not really supposed to get personal calls here, anyway."

"Well, you're not answering your cell phone."

"Of course I'm not answering my cell phone. I'm *working*."

"Angel, why do you sound like someone's standing on your hair?"

"I have to go," I told him.

"Wait, I'm calling to see if you want to go out to lunch. I can come get you—"

"No, no, I can't. I have to get off now—"

"Why *not*?"

I was desperate to get Malcolm off the phone, and although I was staring down at the note-covered surface of my desk, I could feel the heat of Anna's stare on me. "It's really busy here," I told Malcolm, trying to sound calm. "We're trying to get that book ready. You know, the Italian guy—the one I was working on last night."

"Who *is* this guy?" Malcolm asked. "Is he somebody famous or something? Why so much attention?"

"He's got a good book," I muttered.

"Has to be more than that," Malcolm huffed. "He must be some kind of stud or something. Is he? Angel?"

"I don't know, Malcolm!" I lowered my voice again. "I really have to go now." Two more lines were ringing and Anna refused to touch them.

"What about dinner, then? I'll cook."

"Great, great," I said. "I'll see you then. Good-b—"

"Angel, wait."

"*What?!*"

"Your mother called."

A long second passed, suspended and fraught. "Couldn't you have mentioned that first?" I whispered finally.

"Well, excuse *me*."

"I have to go," I said, and hung up on Malcolm, jamming my finger on the next call line button.

"Lucy Fia—"

"Angel, *bella!*"

"Hi, Dami, can you—" I thought about putting him on hold to answer the other calls and, in an instant, decided against it. As far as I could see, Damiano Vero was now my top priority. Nora would have to get her face out of her protein powder and pick up the phone. "Never mind," I said. "How are you?"

"Bene," he said. "But Angel, a couple of things. I don't have a photo. Is it so important?"

"Well, Lucy thinks . . ." I trailed off. How to tell him that she'd already pitched him as some kind of Johnny Depp–meets–Benicio Del Toro? To be honest, her ongoing descriptions of dark, brooding Italian sexiness had become my own mental picture of Damiano. Not that the dark look meant anything to me, particularly. For a moment, I debated asking Damiano to describe himself, until I realized how absurd that would sound.

"Lucy thinks it helps," I finished. I thought about Karanuk and wondered what the real reason was that nobody knew what he looked like. Was it possible he was so unattractive that Lucy had actually kept him hidden on purpose? Perhaps this was why she was so obsessed with seeing Damiano's photo.

"And if I don't have one?" he asked. He sounded amused.

"Well," I repeated, "Lucy thinks it helps."

"Okay," he said. "The other thing . . . *Penso che* . . . uh, sorry . . . I think I need some help tonight, Angel. With the book."

"Sure," I said. "How about if I call you when I get home? It'll be quieter there and then we can go over it. Does that sound okay?"

"Bellissima," he said. "That's wonderful. *Mille grazie,* eh? You are very kind, Angel."

"You're most welcome," I told him, and hung up smiling. It was only later, after dozens more calls and a sheath of memos from Lucy, that I remembered I'd told Malcolm we'd have dinner together and that the editorial session I'd promised Damiano was probably going to ruin those plans.

At five o'clock, with a good hour of office work yet to go, I sneaked into the "employee bathroom" (a guest bathroom tacked onto the office, which Nora had informed me it was *her* duty to keep clean, as if that were some kind of prize) and called Malcolm on my cell phone.

"Hey," I whispered when he picked up, "it's me. Listen, I'm sorry about before. I just can't . . . I mean, it's really crazy here."

"Must be," he said.

"What did my mother say?" I asked. "Did you talk to her?"

"A little," he said. "I'll tell you about it at dinner."

"Right. About dinner, Malcolm. I'm going to have to take a rain check."

"Why?" he asked. "Does the Italian guy need his shoes shined?"

"Don't be like that," I said. "Do I need to remind you that *you* were the one who advised I apply for this job?" I ran the water in the sink to drown out the sound of my voice.

"I'm sorry," Malcolm said. "I didn't mean— Angel, what's that noise? Are you hiding in the bathroom?"

"Shhh," I breathed into the phone. "She'll hear."

Malcolm gave a perfunctory sigh and said, "Okay, I get it. No dinner. But I'm coming over anyway, okay? Later."

"Okay," I said. "I'd better go."

"Angel?"

"Yes?"

"Love me?"

"Of course," I said. I waited for him to tell me he loved me, too, but I lost the connection before he got a chance.

As I closed the bathroom door and made my way back to my section of the office, I saw that Anna and Nora were in a huddle at Nora's desk. Before I could sit down, both of them looked up at me, wearing identical bemused expressions.

"What?" I said.

"Check this out," Anna said, gesturing to a letter in Nora's hand. I approached Nora with caution and read over her shoulder. Anna stood behind me, too close, as if she were guarding me. The single line of type on the paper was streaked as if someone had spilled water on it.

I am your next star author. The manuscript is on its way. Get ready.

"Hmm," I said.

"Kind of weird, don't you think?" Anna asked.

"Certainly a *novel* approach," I said, trying for levity.

Nora held the page away from her, between her thumb and forefinger, as if it smelled bad. "What am I supposed to do with this?" she asked. "There's no return address or anything."

"Then don't do anything!" Anna said cheerfully.

"Whatever," Nora said, and tossed the page into her reject pile.

Anna shrugged and I headed back to my desk, where there were several more demanding tasks screaming for my attention.

WHEN I GOT HOME, there were two notes and the still-unopened pinot noir from the night before sitting next to my telephone. The first one, slid under the bottle, said, *Drink me, I deserve it.* The second was scrawled with my mother's name, Hillary, and a phone number. I didn't recognize the area code, but I picked up my phone and dialed it, anyway. It rang five times before my mother picked it up and breathed, "Greetings," into the receiver. I could barely hear her. It sounded as if a hurricane were blowing across the line.

"Hillary!" I shouted. "Where are you?" One of the very first things my mother had taught me was to call her by her name and not by any modification of the word *mother*. I'd never even thought of her as *Mom*.

"Is that my Angel?" she sang into the phone. "Hello, darling."

"Where are you?" I repeated.

"I'm in the most beautiful place, Angel. You really have to come here. You must come. It's gorgeous. Trees and fresh air and—"

"But *where*?" I persisted.

"Near . . . it's near Seattle, Angel. Is that so important?"

"Well, it certainly would be if you wanted me to come visit," I said. "Everything okay? I haven't heard from you for a while, Hillary, I was starting to worry." This wasn't nearly the first time I had taken the mother role on the phone with mine. Nor, I suspected, would it be the last.

"Darling, don't you know by now that I will always be fine? Have a little faith, daughter. How are you?"

"I'm fine. Actually, I'm good. I just got a great job, Hillary. I'm working with Lucy Fiamma—she's a literary agent. I'm sure I must have mentioned. . . . Do you remember *Cold!*?"

"What? No, it's not at all cold here, Angel. Look, honey, I have to tell you something. I've found the most wonderful group of women. They are descended from actual *Amazons,* can you believe it? Anyway, we're planning a ritual cleansing, sort of a female sweat-lodge type of thing, and I would really like you to join us, Angel. You need to get in touch with your inner Amazon."

The only Amazon I was likely to get in touch with was the dot-com version, but there was no way of telling my mother this without sounding sarcastic and faithless. Sooner or later she always found the Wiccans, eco-feminists, or sculptors disappointing and moved on, but while she was in the throes of community ecstasy, there was nothing I or anyone else could say to dim her enthusiasm.

"Hillary, did you hear what I said about my new job?"

"What new job, sweetie?"

"I'm working for a literary agent," I almost yelled into the phone.

"Terrific!" A rush of static filled the phone and her next words were partially drowned out. All I heard was, ". . . to take care of yourself."

"What? I can't hear you, Hillary."

"Listen, honey, I have to go to a goddess meeting now. I'm running out as we speak. But I really want you to come up here, Angel. It's important. I'll call you later, okay? We can talk more then."

"Hillary—" I began, but she was already gone. I tried to imagine what a goddess meeting might entail, but stopped myself when I started envisioning a grotesque ceremony involving menstrual blood. Well, she was okay. That was good at least.

I looked at the bottle of wine, fighting an urge to open it and drink it down. I wished Malcolm were beside me and took immediate comfort in the knowledge that he'd be showing up soon. The last two days had worn me down and talking to my mother had just polished me off. Malcolm, I thought, would make a perfect balm. I'd be ready for him when he arrived, I thought. But first there was *Parco Lambro*. I picked up the phone and dialed Damiano's number, which, by now, I knew by heart.

WITH MY HELP, Damiano managed to finish his revisions by the end of the following day, and by the end of that week, all the editors on Lucy's list had received a copy of the manuscript. Despite the fact that Damiano had not managed to come up with a single photograph of himself, a point Lucy bemoaned constantly ("We're screwed if this author isn't mediagenic, Angel!"), every one of them wanted to buy his book.

Natalie Weinstein, who I could actually hear yelling through Lucy's telephone receiver, came in first, with an offer of one hundred thousand dollars, hoping vainly to preempt the others. Lucy then used Natalie Weinstein's offer as the "floor" with which to start an auction. Natalie was representing Weinstein Books, her own small imprint at Gabriel Press, which was, in turn, part of the behemoth Triad Publishing Group. *Parco Lambro*, like all of the books she acquired, would be a direct reflection of her taste and style; her name would be embossed on the spine of the book along with the author's. And she wanted this one badly.

I was amazed by how quickly the level of excitement escalated. Although the editors had enough time to do a surface read, how could each and every one of them have had the time to really feel the writing—enough to be so captured by it that they just *had to have it*? The answer, I believed, was Lucy herself. There was something about the way she spun that book, some mojo she managed to send through the phone that snared them completely.

"It's all about *buzz*, Angel," she told me. "You have to create it. You have to make it happen."

This, I was learning, was Lucy's particular genius, if it could be called that. There was something hypnotic or bewitching about the way she worked. I felt a little like the sorceress's apprentice as I traipsed back and forth from her office, watching her cast the spell.

Lucy gave the ten editors less than a week to prepare for the auction ("Have to keep it fresh," she said, "so that they stay ravenous"), during which time she debated endlessly whether or not to throw a few more into the mix. "I'm just wondering if Susie Parker might not just love this book," she'd say. And, "You know, we haven't yet tried Nadia Fiori. She *is* Italian." Ultimately, she hooked three additional editors, with more frantic overnight deliveries, to make a baker's dozen. I was sure that had she wanted to, Lucy could have involved half the editors in New York, along with many heads of houses. Gordon Hart was among those heads, and he called a few times during the course of that next week, never once actually speaking to Lucy on the phone, but managing to communicate with her through me.

"Are you still working there?" he asked every time I answered his call. "This has got to be a new record for her." That was another thing about Gordon Hart: He never referred to her as *Lucy*; it was always *she* or *her*. His tone was always extremely dry and crisp. It was difficult to tell on the phone, of course, but although he was clearly authoritative, Gordon Hart sounded like a relatively young man. Because he never seemed to be available when I called HartHouse for Lucy, I ended up logging quite a bit of phone time with his various assistants, most often Jessie Hill, who had recently been promoted to associate editor. It was Jessie who told me that Gordon Hart sounded young because he was only in his forties; he was the grandson of HartHouse's founder. It was also Jessie who told me that Gordon and Lucy went "way back," but she didn't explain in what way.

The day before the auction, Lucy circulated a memo through the office:

As you are all aware, we will be auctioning the Italian book tomorrow morning. Therefore, I would like to ask that you arrive to work a little earlier than usual—

> *Angel and Anna—6 am*
> *Nora—7 am*
> *Craig—8 am*

It is very important that you remain sharp, so get plenty of sleep tonight! If all goes well, we will have cause to celebrate!!! and you may go home early, at about 4 or 5. —L.

It occurred to me that Lucy might be one of those people who didn't need to sleep. I'd read about this syndrome somewhere. It went beyond garden-variety insomnia. There was a certain chemical in the brains of these individuals that kept them up and functioning on a fraction of the sleep that the average person needed, and when they did fall asleep, it was into the deepest sleep state. They had far fewer dreams than normal and never remembered the ones they did have. I made a mental note to research this further.

Anna, who had said not a word about the early-morning summons, beat me to the office the following morning. When I arrived, at six exactly, shivering, miserable, and clutching the strongest coffee I could find, she was already at her desk, computer fired up, a cherry-and-cheese Danish combination laid out on her desk. I stood still and stared at it for a moment, paralyzed with cold and exhaustion. Anna's face flushed carmine.

"It's for Lucy," she said, pointing at the pastry. "In case she needs something to keep her going."

"I don't suppose there's an extra one?" I asked, hoping I sounded sly and conspiratorial instead of tired and desperate.

Anna furrowed her sandy eyebrows into a misshapen **V**. "No," she said, "but you can have this." She thrust a fax at me and turned her attention back to her artful arrangement of Danish.

"What's this?" I asked her, but I was already reading it.

Your next bestseller is on the way. I hope you are ready. I am your next star author.

"Isn't this the same one who sent Nora that weird letter? When did this come in?" I asked, searching the fax for information and finding none.

"It was here when I got here," Anna said.

"Makes you wonder, doesn't it? I mean, if the manuscript is that good, why don't we have it already?"

But before Anna could answer me, Lucy's voice, shouting "My office, please!" came flooding through our intercoms.

I came in behind Anna, who had shoved her way in ahead of me, which was a good thing because the sight that greeted me temporarily stole my breath.

Lucy was standing in the middle of her office, arms and hands raised in a steeple above her head, exhaling expansively. She was dressed, head to toe, in blinding white. Her ensemble started with a white cashmere turtleneck, included a long string of pearls, an ankle-length white wool skirt, and white suede spike-heeled boots, and finished with a white Pashmina, which she'd draped insouciantly over one shoulder. Her hair, already a whiter shade of pale, floated loose around her face and seemed, like the rest of her, to be electrified. The brilliant green of her eyes and the scarlet cut of her mouth provided the only color in the entire office. For a brief, overtired moment, I thought I'd entered Narnia and was face-to-face with the White Witch.

"Yoga!" she barked, releasing her arms. "You should try it."

"I'm not as flexible as you are, Lucy," Anna gargled, sounding as if a small animal had lodged itself in her throat.

"Flexibility is a state of mind," Lucy said, and gave me a long, sweeping gaze. "What about you, Angel? Surely you could maneuver those long legs of yours into a few yoga postures?"

"Uh . . . yoga . . ." I managed, still entranced by the scene before me.

"All right, enough small talk!" Lucy snapped, moving toward her desk. "Are we ready?"

"All set for round one," Anna answered. I could hear her trademark smugness edging into her tone. "Would you like me to be first on the calls?"

"Don't be ridiculous," Lucy said. "I'm going to need both of you on the phones and then Nora when she gets here."

"Okay," Anna said. "And I've brought a pastry for you, Lucy." A weird, almost-smile appeared on Anna's face.

"What makes you think it would be appropriate to *eat* during an auction, Anna?"

"Well, I wasn't . . . I mean, you could . . ." Anna's face looked like a puzzle on the verge of coming apart. I felt an unwanted stab of sympathy for her. A short, bright silence filled the room for an instant and then the phone rang.

"Got it!" Anna squealed, and ran from the room. Lucy gave me a Cheshire grin. "You may leave my office now, Angel," she said. And then: "The Italian book. It begins."

When I returned to my desk, there was an instant message from Anna waiting on my computer:

Feel free to take the Danish.

Thanks, I wrote back, *I might.* Although we both knew that I wouldn't.

"Doesn't she look great?" Anna asked out loud.

"Who?"

"Lucy! Her outfit. She always wears white to her auctions. She says it brings her luck. I think she looks smashing."

"Right," I said. "Smashing."

"And just a tip," Anna sniffed. "Don't go into her office unless she calls you. Usually, she likes to be alone in there until the auction's over. Also for good luck."

"Okay, got it," I said, and picked up a ringing line.

"Good morning, Lucy Fiamma Literary Agency!" I realized, after the words were already out of my mouth, that I sounded almost hysterical. There was a distinctive coughing on the other end of the phone. Peter Johnson again. His timing was impeccable.

"Good morning. Ms. Robinson?"

"Mr. Johnson?"

"Yes!" he splutter-coughed into the phone. "You recognize my voice!" I stopped myself from telling him that of course I did. He called every day and I had somehow been assigned, after dispatching him on my first day, to be his personal rejection slip. If I hadn't answered his call, it would have been put through to me, anyway. Nora also slid his manuscripts over to me as soon as they arrived in the office, glad to rid herself of the task of sending them right back. Part of the problem with Peter Johnson was that he never failed to include a self-addressed stamped envelope with his submissions. He had to be answered. He also had to be rejected. His novels, or what we saw of them, ranged from bad to worse. They were tedious thrillers with rehashed plots and purple prose, and he seemed to have an endless supply of them for our review. The next one, he kept insisting, was the winner. But I didn't have time to hear about another one; I had to get him off the phone.

"Mr. Johnson, I'm going to have to call you back if that's okay. It's very busy here this morning."

"I just need a minute of your time, Ms. Robinson. I've got something here I think is—"

"Great, we'll be happy to look at it when you send it in."

"I don't think you understand." He was breathing very heavily and I hoped he wasn't working himself into some kind of fit. "I have a book that Ms. Fiamma is *definitely* going to want."

"That's great, Mr. Johnson. We look forward to reading!"

"Let me tell you—"

"Thanks so much! Have a great day."

The moment I hung up on Peter Johnson, every phone in the office seemed to explode with sound, and they just kept ringing. I didn't even notice Nora slink in at seven, and at some point, Craig just seemed to materialize at his desk. As Anna had predicted, Lucy remained sequestered in her office, communicating with us via intercom or e-mails. She never sent instant messages and I began to think that either her computer hadn't been set up for them or she simply didn't know how. There was one tense five-minute period during the third round of bids when, with every line blinking, Lucy seemed to vanish from her office and none of us could get her on the line. Anna stated that Lucy was probably inside her house "centering herself."

I placed several calls to Damiano as the day wore on and Lucy gave him updates on how high the bids were getting. I heard none of these conversations, of course, I merely placed the calls, but every time I got Damiano on the phone, he got more excited, awed, and, finally, disbelieving.

At about three o'clock, Lucy emerged from her office and stood, taller than usual it seemed to me, in the middle of ours.

"The deal is done," she said. "That Italian pastry chef is now a very wealthy man." Lucy had sold Damiano's book plus a sequel (she'd decided against the idea of a trilogy) for half a million dollars. The sheer magnitude of what she'd accomplished gave me gooseflesh.

Lucy clapped her hands briefly and then put them on her hips. "Congratulations, everyone. Well done." She looked over at me. "Let's just hope he can deliver," she said. "His new editor's about twelve years old. And she's no hand-holder."

FOUR

Lucy Fiamma
Lucy Fiamma Literary Agency

Dear Ms. Fiamma,

It is here.

Although I am sure that you receive many such claims, I am writing to tell you that I am your next star author and am ready to take my place in your literary heaven. I do realize that this is a rather grandiose statement, but I have the goods to back it up.

Rather than wasting any more of your time with this letter, I am enclosing a few pages from my novel, BLIND SUBMISSION. I am convinced that once you read them, you will agree with me that this novel has the potential to be a huge bestseller. It's a real winner.

Should you wish to see more (and I know you will), please contact me at ganovelist@heya.com

Happy reading!

BLIND SUBMISSION

Chapter 1

Alice wrapped her scarf around her neck to stave off the chill of the late winter morning. The pale sun looked like cold butter in a hazy sky as she raced down Fifth Avenue to get to the office by nine o'clock. Alice thought about stopping for a coffee to warm herself and decided that there wasn't time. She had only been working for Carol Moore, New York's most successful literary agent, for a few weeks and it was important that she stay in her boss's good graces. It wouldn't do to rock the boat at this stage of the game. Later, when Alice made herself indispensable, there would be time for maneuvering.

As she rode the elevator to the fifteenth floor, Alice thought about how easy it had been to land this job. Before she'd been hired, Alice's only publishing experience had been serving lunch to editors in the Manhattan restaurants where she worked as a waitress. She had learned plenty by listening to their conversations as she leaned over them with plates and glasses, but none of that could be put on a résumé. So Alice had fabricated jobs on her application and had bluffed her way through her interview. Carol Moore was both tough and smart and Alice had been sure that her made-up jobs wouldn't pass muster. However, if there was one thing Alice had learned in her twenty-seven years on earth, it was how to lie well. She kept her secrets closely guarded under the blonde halo of her hair. Her fake experience passed under the agent's radar and she convinced Carol Moore to hire her. Of course, the part that was true, the part that had probably tipped Carol Moore over the edge, was that Alice was driven and ambitious and that she desperately wanted the job. What Carol Moore didn't know was *why* and, if Alice had anything to do with it, she never would.

When Alice arrived at the Agency, the office was already a hive of activity. The phones and faxes were humming as Carol

Moore's well trained staff took their places at their desks. Alice observed her co-workers as she greeted them. There was Jewel, a tall, stunning natural blonde who could easily have made a career in modeling if she wanted to. According to Carol Moore, Jewel's good looks had always been more of a hindrance to her than anything else. Jewel was simply too smart for a career on the runway, Carol said. As a woman with secrets of her own, Alice found this difficult to believe and thought that Jewel probably had some sort of hidden disfigurement or weakness. Every woman had something in her past she was ashamed of. Alice planned to find out what this was and use it to her advantage.

There was Ricardo, Carol Moore's office manager. Ricardo was an extremely well-dressed and very handsome man who was, according to Carol Moore, as smart as Jewel. Ricardo kept the office lively with jokes and imitations of movie stars and was always very polite. Ricardo had a photograph of a wife and daughter on his desk, but Alice had looked at the photo and decided that it had come with the frame because the only woman Ricardo ever spoke about lovingly was Carol Moore herself. Yes, Alice thought, Ricardo too had something to hide. Everyone, Alice knew, had something to hide.

And then there was Carol Moore herself. Like Jewel, Carol Moore was very beautiful. Alice thought she had the look of an older Grace Kelly. Alice had researched Carol Moore before she applied for the job, so she knew that Carol had been a force in the literary world for almost thirty years, but she was carrying those years very well. Alice also knew that Carol Moore had grown up practically destitute and had worked very hard to obtain her position of power. And Carol Moore *was* a powerful woman. She represented famous writers from all over the world, some of them Nobel Laureates. When Carol Moore called, publishers listened. Alice was counting on that.

In their meager beginnings, Alice and Carol were similar. During her interview, Alice had implied, without ever seeming to, that she and Carol Moore shared a certain struggle. Alice was counting on Carol to feel drawn to her as a protégé and as someone Carol wanted to make in her own image. That would suit Alice very well indeed. Alice had cut off relations with her own mother long ago in an act of cruel finality and had never known much about what it meant to be a good daughter. But she was a quick study and planned to play on every maternal instinct Carol Moore possessed.

For now, Alice had positioned herself as close to Carol as she could. She hadn't minded at all that her title was that of assistant. For Alice's needs, her position was, at the moment, perfect. She was close to Carol, close to the files, and, most importantly, the receiver of all the mail that came into the office. On all three fronts, Alice had made excellent progress. Besides, Alice didn't plan to remain Carol's assistant for very much longer. She had started laying plenty of groundwork. Everybody Alice had ever known, both biblically and in less physical ways, who counted in any way or who could be useful in any way now knew where Alice was employed.

There was much excitement in the office when Alice took her place at her desk and began to prepare a list of the day's appointments. Carol Moore had just agreed to represent Vaughn Blue, an internationally known rock star. Vaughn was writing a memoir of his life in the business, much of which involved the sex and drugs that the music industry was known for. Although the book would tell all and name names, Carol Moore was most excited by the fact that Vaughn Blue was a brilliant writer. Vaughn Blue was something of a genius. He held a PhD, which he had completed before he broke onto the music scene, and his book would appeal both to celebrity hounds and book critics. The fact that he was one of America's sexiest men didn't hurt either.

Alice finished preparing her list and took it to Carol Moore who was on the phone and swaddled in Versace couture. Carol smiled at Alice and beckoned for her to sit on the chair opposite Carol's desk.

"I have a special assignment for you today," Carol Moore told Alice.

"Terrific," Alice said. "What is it?"

"Vaughn Blue is coming by the office to sign his contract at around noon," Carol said, "and I'd like you to take him to lunch. My treat, of course. I'd love to go myself, but I already have lunch scheduled with a publisher who will probably want to buy Vaughn's book! So what do you say? How does lunch with a rock star sound?"

"Fabulous!" Alice panted. "I'm so excited!"

Alice hoped she wasn't laying it on too thick in an effort to conceal her distaste. Dining with one of America's sexiest men would have held much more appeal if that man wasn't also a writer because, in her deepest heart, Alice hated writers. This was one of her secrets.

That she was a writer herself was another.

I rubbed my eyes, taking them off the pages in front of me. The words had been slipping and blurring and I struggled to retain focus. It was very early and I was very tired, but I had to keep reading. This, after all, was "the bestseller" that had been promised by letter, by fax, and now by submission from our "next star author."

After the author's admitted "grandiose" claims, I'd fully expected the manuscript to be awful. Because I thought I'd be able to reject it quickly, I hadn't even bothered to read it the night before, electing instead to get some much-needed sleep. But I was surprised to find that it wasn't awful at all. Strange, yes, and maybe even a little unsettling, but definitely not out-and-out bad. I read the cover letter again. There was no return address, no phone number, and no name. Was the anonymous-author conceit supposed to tie in to the novel itself? Or was it just to keep us interested enough to ask for more? I leaned over, stretching and touching my toes in an effort to get more blood flowing to my brain so that I could think a little more clearly.

It had been six weeks since I'd started working for Lucy. Every day of those six weeks had felt like an eternity in itself, but all put together they seemed to have raced by, giving me a strange split perception of the passage of time—a perception only reinforced by Lucy.

It had only been a few weeks since the sale of *Parco Lambro,* for example, yet she acted as if the auction were a distant memory. Although she'd sold two more projects since then, neither was auctioned or came close to generating either the excitement or the cash of Damiano's. Still, the first of those two, a comic novel about a vampire-hunting dog ("*The Dogs of Babel* meets *The Historian,*" as Lucy had pitched it), had sold for a respectable seventy-five thousand dollars and the second, a cultural history of lawn ornaments, had gone for fifty thousand. I'd brought both projects to Lucy's attention. The first had come directly from my reading pile and I'd rescued the second from a stack of rejections that were due to be returned when the cute photo of a garden gnome on the cover letter caught my eye.

But Lucy didn't seem to take much satisfaction from either of those sales and was getting edgy, asking every day if I'd found something that could compare to *Parco Lambro.* "It has to have power," she told me. "Self-help is bread and butter and nonfiction's hit or miss. I need something that will make them cry. When they cry, you know it's going to be expensive." I wanted to deliver for her. I, too, wanted to make them cry.

I passed my eyes over the manuscript in front of me again. It wasn't going to bring anyone to tears, I thought, and it needed some serious work, but it *was* different from anything else I'd seen lately. Despite its clumsy prose, there was something captivating and even subtly dark about it. And then there was the fact that it was set in a literary agency, something that added a whole other level of weirdness to it. The author's anonymity *had* achieved its desired purpose, I decided; it had gotten my—our—attention. The author had obviously submitted before, probably even to us, and had figured out how to keep from getting rejected instantly. And now I'd read the manuscript. And it wasn't bad. It had potential, I decided, and so I'd pass it on to Lucy.

While I booted up my computer to write the report, I gave a backward glance at my bed, where Malcolm was sleeping soundly. And why shouldn't he, I thought. Everyone but doughnut-makers and hospital workers were sleeping at this hour of the morning. My eyes itched with fatigue as I stared longingly in the direction of my pillow. Malcolm's body was a long shape deep under the covers. I could see only a bit of gold hair and the sloping edge of one cheekbone over the top of the fabric. It took a tremendous amount of will not to abandon my post and crawl in next to him. I didn't sleep until sunrise anymore, or even close to it. These predawn hours had emerged as the only time I had to get caught up on the avalanche of work that fell on me every day.

A big part of that catching up had to do with Anna. Her reading had become my reading and her reports were starting to become a big problem for me. I'd already rescued two good novels from the reject pile that she thought were "stupid" and "boring," two of her favorite adjectives. She was, rightly, convinced that I was undercutting her opinion by championing her rejects. Anna felt that once she'd put the kibosh on a manuscript, my function as a second reader should only be to support her. Of course, Lucy had made me the second reader on Anna's manuscripts for the exact opposite reason. All this had served to deepen Anna's hostility toward me. When I wrote my own reports on her rejects, I had to get very creative, writing in a fashion that would seem to support Anna's statements without pointing out what she'd missed, while implying that she was completely wrong in her assessments without appearing to do so at all. It was starting to become an exhausting process. It occurred to me once again that Lucy should just take Anna off the reading list altogether. But it seemed to me that Lucy got some sort of weird pleasure out of the growing conflict between Anna and me over the reading pile. During my first few days at the office, when Anna had still been chatty with me, she'd told me that Lucy was "grooming" her to become another agent in the office. Considering the fact that Lucy seemed to find the very thought of another agent in the office repugnant, I suspected Anna was not only an inadequate reader but delusional as well. Besides, if Lucy wanted to groom anyone to be an agent, she'd look to *me*.

I put Anna out of my mind, rubbed the cold out of my fingers, and started hitting the keyboard.

Title: BLIND SUBMISSION
Author: ?
Genre: Fiction
Reader: Angel

This is an interesting piece. It came in unsolicited through the mail, but the author, who is anonymous at this point, lists no phone number or address and only has an e-mail address as a contact. I suppose this adds some intrigue, since the novel is set in a literary agency (!!!), but it also means we know nothing about previous publishing credits, etc. My guess, judging from the writing, is that there aren't any. The author didn't provide us with a synopsis, either.

What this novel seems to be is something of a reverse "insider revenge" novel or, as the *New York Times* calls it, "bite-the-boss fiction." Here, instead of having a bitch-from-hell boss and a long-suffering assistant, we've got a manipulative assistant with a hidden agenda—something like *The Nanny Diaries* or *The Devil Wears Prada* but darker and told from the other side. I think the idea has potential, but I've got a couple of concerns. One is the setting. While I like the idea of setting a novel in a literary agency (the fact that it's close to home notwithstanding), the conventional wisdom is that books set in the publishing world don't sell. My other concern is the writing, which just seems a little stiff. And, although it feels as if the author also wants to come out right away with mystery and intrigue, the pacing is slow and the characters don't really stand out, especially the main character, Alice, who is supposedly "a woman with secrets." The writing is not particularly descriptive and, when it is, the descriptions are awkward. "The sun looked like cold butter," for example. The dialogue, too, seems a bit forced.

However, while these aren't minor details, they are workable. I think we should ask to read more (the author says there *is* more) to see if the pace picks up and if the writing gets stronger. If the author is willing (and able) to revise, this novel could be quite promising.

By the time I printed out the report, the small clock on my desk read 6:30 A.M. Lucy had succeeded in training me to function on New York time, and I couldn't help thinking that people in that city were already at their desks and working. Time was getting short. I had to be at the office at eight and I had a half-hour drive ahead of me. The last manuscript in my pile, a memoir from an Alaskan hairstylist titled *Perm-or-Frost,* was going to have to wait. I didn't have high hopes for it, anyway.

As usual, the sound of my morning shower and hair dryer did nothing to interrupt Malcolm's slumber. Watching him sleep had become something of a pattern for me. Before I started working for Lucy, he'd spent an average of four nights a week at my apartment, but since my first day, he'd come over every night, whether he was working late shifts at the restaurant or not. Not that this meant we were actually spending more time together. It was more like we were spending more time *next to* each other. My nights were consumed with reading. Malcolm watched TV. Or slept. Or pointedly reread his own manuscript.

Malcolm's novel; another thing I was going to have to deal with soon, I thought. Despite his protests that I was the major beneficiary of my new job, Malcolm had wasted no time in bringing his hefty manuscript over to my place. Of course, he hadn't demanded, or even suggested, that I take it to Lucy, oh no, he'd just sort of placed it on the floor beside the bed, so that I could "look it over, you know, to give it the final polish."

Right around the time of the *Parco Lambro* auction, Malcolm casually mentioned, "You know, whenever you want to take a look at my manuscript, Angel, please feel free. You've clearly got the magic touch."

"Let's wait a bit," I told him at the time. "It's too early for me to—"

"I'm just *saying,* Angel, if you want to look at it—"

"Right, of course."

"And I've started working on something else, by the way." He gave me a canary-eating cat smile and dropped his voice to a seductive whisper. "I'm really excited about this new one."

"Really? That's great."

"You're an inspiration to me, Angel. Since you've become the Mistress of Literature, I've been very productive. And notice, I'm not asking you to look at this new one."

"I know, Malcolm. I'll look at *Bridge of Lies*. I promise."

But I hadn't looked at it and wasn't sure I wanted to. Malcolm had stopped mentioning his book over the last week or two, but his silence felt heavier and more demanding than his "suggestion" that I read it. I knew I'd have to give it to Lucy at some point, but what would she think if this novel turned out to be less than stellar? And what if she gave it to Anna to read? I shuddered at the thought. There wasn't going to be an easy way out of this one. I felt a tiny flicker of resentment flare in the back of my brain. I couldn't help wishing that Malcolm hadn't put me in this position so soon, despite the guilt that wish brought in its wake. After all, if it hadn't been for Malcolm, I wouldn't even have this job. And, despite its challenges, I really did love my job. I'd never worked as hard in my life, but I'd also never experienced the kind of anticipatory rush I felt every time I sat down at my desk. Working for Lucy was . . . *extreme* seemed a fitting word. And with extremes, you had to expect both big highs and low lows.

I searched my closet for something presentable to wear and, as I did every morning, cursed Lucy's no-jeans policy. My new schedule didn't allow much time for things like laundry, so my wardrobe offered little in the way of acceptable items. I grabbed my last pair of borderline-clean pants and threw them on. I had no time or inclination to give myself a final inspection in the mirror and told myself that it didn't matter. In all the time I'd been working there, there had not been a single visitor to the office.

I heard Malcolm stir and sigh as I gathered my purse, manuscripts, and keys. I bent down into an awkward kneel by the bed so that my face was level with his.

"Hey," I whispered. "I'm on my way out. See you later?"

Malcolm smiled, his eyes half-closed, and reached out his arm to cover my shoulders. I could feel the enticing warmth of his skin through my shirt. He brushed the tips of his fingers across my cheek.

"Mmm, you smell so good," he said, deepening the corners of his smile. He pulled a strand of my hair free and rubbed it between his thumb and forefinger. A lewd gleam crept into his eyes. "Got a minute before you leave?"

"I really, really don't," I told him, and hoped that the regret in my voice sounded genuine.

"You sure, Angel?" he said, pulling me gently toward him. Our lips met for one moment before I lost my balance and slipped off the edge of the bed, dropping my purse and keys and kicking paper as I tried to find purchase on the floor.

"Baby, are you okay?" Malcolm looked down at me, laughter dying in his throat as we both saw that I'd fallen on his manuscript, tearing a couple of pages and flipping the rest across the floor.

"I'm so sorry," I said, quickly shoveling it back into place. "I just—"

"It's okay," he said. "Leave it." His smile had vanished and his voice had gone cold. I could hear everything he wasn't saying as clearly as if he'd been yelling it at me. *Go ahead, step on my work. That's what it means to you. That's what I mean to you.*

"Malcolm, I'm sorry. I didn't mean to—"

"Better go," he interrupted. "You'll be late." He turned away from me and burrowed under the covers.

"Malcolm—"

"Don't let it worry you, *Angel*." His voice, muffled by sheets, was almost a growl. "You've got more important things to do."

I allowed myself only a second to debate whether or not I should attempt to make things right by falling onto the bed next to Malcolm and burying my face in his neck. But I *was* going to be late and my desire not to be overwhelmed my desire for him. I'd have to make time later, I told myself, and gathered my things once more. And then, fighting with myself all the way, I collected Malcolm's pages from the floor and put them in with my pile. At the very least, I owed him enough to take the manuscript with me, even if I wasn't ready to give it to Lucy yet. If he heard me rustling, Malcolm gave no indication, and then I was out the door. It wasn't until I was already on the road that I realized I'd forgotten to say good-bye to him.

UNLIKE ALMOST EVERYONE I KNEW, I loved my morning commute. I felt as if the time I spent in my car was the only real time I had to myself—the only time when I didn't have to answer phones, respond to memos, or talk to anyone else. For a half hour in the morning and a half hour in the evening, I allowed myself just to think—to sort through the minutiae of my days and organize it all appropriately. It usually went all to hell once I set foot in the office, but that wasn't really the point. What was important was that I got a few uninterrupted minutes to just let my mind trip and wander wherever it wanted.

It helped, of course, that I had attractive surroundings to look at while I drove. As soon as I crossed the line out of Sonoma County into Marin, the dry, rural feel of Petaluma gave way to lusher scenery on either side of the road. The closer I got to San Rafael, the greener and better tended the streets became. San Francisco's famous fog was romantic and all, but I didn't mind trading it for the warmth and sunlight on the other side of the Golden Gate Bridge.

As I wound my way through the exclusive real estate that was San Rafael and my guilt over Malcolm's manuscript started to fade, my mind latched once more on to the anonymous novel, which was sitting next to me on the passenger seat, its presence as large as that of any person. It occurred to me that the author might have sent the manuscript out to several literary agents. If it *had* gone out wide and I hadn't chased it quickly enough, I'd risk some pointed wrath from Lucy. Nothing got Lucy more excited or more irritated than when a potentially hot author had his or her manuscript circulating among several agents. Of course, the fact that an author *had* interest from other agents went a long way to making that author hot, regardless of the potential book's content.

And hot was what Lucy wanted—what Lucy craved. Immediately after the sale of *Parco Lambro,* she'd circulated a memo (which I'd drafted ten times before she approved it) that said, *While our recent auction was a success, we cannot afford to sit back and take a break. We need to redouble our efforts to bring in more of the same. This office cannot support all of you without a healthy flow of cash. Remember time is $$$!!!! I expect you all to use yours wisely.*

Of course, I suspected that none of us was making the kind of money that would drain Lucy's coffers. My own probationary salary was barely a living wage after taxes. I'd done a little research and discovered that even starting salaries at New York publishers were a little higher. Elise had been paying me a little more, but I'd expected to take a dip in salary when I started working with Lucy. I just hadn't realized how lean things would become. Lucy had, however, called me into a meeting with Craig in her office after *Parco Lambro* and, with a great flourish, presented me with a bonus.

"I believe in incentives," Lucy said. "And although some might say that this is a foolish move, I believe you've earned this. And *I trust you,* Angel. Craig? Will you do the honors?"

Grimacing as if he'd eaten something rotten, Craig handed me a check for one thousand dollars. "Congratulations, Angel," he said. "And just so you know, there are no taxes deducted from this check. This is not part of your salary. You'll have to pay taxes on it separately."

"I—I don't know what to say," I said.

"'Thank you' is always appropriate," Lucy offered. "There's more where that came from, Angel, if you know how to get it." She took a dramatic pause. "And I think you do."

Of course I did. Like Skinner and Pavlov before her, Lucy was conditioning me. Every time I pressed the right bar, I'd get a fat check. Find another Damiano Vero. That was the message, but it wasn't one that Lucy needed to send. The desire was already alive in me. There was something surprisingly seductive about the rush of excitement *Parco Lambro* had created in me, and it wasn't about the money. It was very much like a drug, I thought. The intensity faded soon after the event, but enough of the memory remained to make me want more. I supposed it had to be the same for Lucy and was at least part of what gave her that insatiable drive.

—

I FOUND THE OFFICE EMPTY when I let myself in and realized that, despite the fact that I'd stopped for a cappuccino on the way over, I'd arrived ten minutes earlier than usual. I settled myself at my desk and flipped on my computer. There were multiple notes from Lucy in my in-box. At the top of the pile was her daily memo itemizing the tasks that were most important the moment she'd thought of them the previous evening, but that would probably change as the day went on.

> *Angel—*
>
> *Today's Top Priorities:*
>
> 1. *Report on reader's reports.*
>
> 2. *Chase Elvis!!!!*
>
> 3. *Find salon (as in SF Chron) and make appt. (Where is my blue pen?)*
>
> 4. *I need complete list of all projects in development/in submission/due for delivery/pubbing in the next two months.*
>
> 5. *Calls!!!*

It was a list of labors worthy of Hercules. The only items that were missing were "Kill Hydra" and "Clean Augean stables." Which actually wasn't a bad idea for a business book for one of our authors, I thought. I made a mental note to run it past Lucy; something like *Twelve Tasks for Better Business* or *Twelve Rules for Commercial Success*.

I wondered once more how Lucy was able to do it. How was it possible that she'd accumulated so much for me to do before the day even began? Not to mention the fact that I needed to crack the Da Vinci Code to figure out what each item on the list actually meant. I'd worked out that #3 was a request to make her a hair appointment at a salon that the *San Francisco Chronicle* had just named the hottest spot in town, but I couldn't quite grasp how she wanted me to chase Elvis. And, of course, the phone was already ringing.

"Good morning, Lucy Fiamma Agency." My voice sounded gravelly and tired. I cleared my throat and heard his trademark coughing on the other end of the phone. Peter Johnson.

"Hello, Angel. How are you?"

I wondered when I'd become Angel to him. He'd always been meticulous about calling me Ms. Robinson before.

"I'm fine, Mr. Johnson, how are you?"

"Please call me Peter," he wheezed. "I think we know each other well enough at this point." He lapsed into another coughing fit. He had a point, I supposed, although it had been a few days since I'd spoken to him last. I couldn't remember exactly when I'd sent his most recent rejection or if there was one just about to go out.

"Okay, Peter. You must be calling about your manuscript. I wrote you a note and sent it—"

"No, no," he rasped. "I got that. And thank you, Angel, for your kind words. But that's not why I'm calling." He took a breath and choked on it, hacking once more into the phone. I bit my lip with impatience and a little remorse. My "words" on his last rejection letter had been anything but kind. I'd tried my best to imply, without being nasty, that Lucy would never accept his work for representation. Apparently, he hadn't quite gotten the message.

"I'm calling because I'd like to give you one more chance. I need to tell you something. I've—" He interrupted himself with more hacking.

I couldn't stop myself from sighing into the phone. He wanted to give *us* one more chance? What was he talking about? How many different ways could I tell him no?

"You know, Mr. Johnson, I really don't think—"

"Please hear me out," he gasped, but I couldn't. I didn't know whether it was fatigue, impatience, or just irritation that got me, but I decided that it was time to put Peter Johnson out of his—and my—misery for good.

"Mr. Johnson, I think it's only fair I tell you that Lucy Fiamma has seen your work and it's just not right for her. She's not the agent for you. I'm sorry."

"You don't understand," he said. "You're not listening."

"Please," I begged him. "Do yourself a favor, don't send us anything else." There was a quiet pause. For a second I thought he'd stopped breathing altogether.

"You're making a mistake," he said. "And you are *not* Lucy Fiamma."

"I'm sorry if you—" I began, but Peter Johnson hung up on me. I stared at the receiver for a moment, stunned. He'd always been unfailingly polite. But so had I until this moment. I felt a twinge of discomfort. But really, what could he expect? I debated looking up his phone number and calling him back, but the phone shrilled again and I picked it up, assuming he'd beaten me to it.

"Fiamma Agency." I waited for the sound of labored breathing.

"Angel? Is that you?"

I was momentarily thrown by a woman's voice on the other end of the phone. "Uh . . . This is Angel Robinson. May I help you?"

"Angel, it's Elise."

"Elise!" At that moment, I realized how much I'd missed her. Our daily confabs, swapping customer stories and discussing books, came rushing back to me on a wave of instant nostalgia. And it wasn't just the easy camaraderie I had with Elise that I missed, it was her good nature, her lack of hard edges, and her centeredness. I missed the quiet enjoyment of working for her. It had been less than two months since I'd last sat with her at Blue Moon sharing quips and coffee, but it felt like the farthest reaches of the past.

"How are you, Angel? I haven't heard from you since you left. I thought I'd catch you at home this morning, but Malcolm said you were already at work." I'd forgotten that she knew Malcolm. I met him in her store, after all. She'd always been very protective of me when it came to him, telling me to watch my heart, not to give away too much of myself— even if he *was* one of the best-looking men she'd ever met. I'd almost forgotten all of that.

"I'm so sorry, Elise. I keep meaning to call you, but by the time I finish work, it's so late and then I don't remember . . . I'm sorry."

"You don't have to be sorry, Angel, I just wanted to see how you were doing. How's the job? Tell me honestly. She treating you okay?"

"Great!" I said too perkily. "Busy, you know. We just sold an amazing book by a new author. You'd love it, Elise." I wondered at my sudden desire to hold back the less pleasant details of my job to present the best possible face. Oddly, I felt as if Elise, who'd been both friend and mentor, had become an outsider.

"Really? That's wonderful, Angel. If I know you, you're doing an amazing job. I suppose you don't have very much free time, though, do you? I was hoping maybe we could get together for lunch or coffee. I've got something to show you—well, give you, actually. I found it when I was clearing out the store. I think you'll find it very interesting."

It was a nice idea, but I'd never be able to find the time to have lunch with her unless I took a vacation day, and Lucy had made it clear that I didn't have any of those coming to me for at least a year. Even the weekends were booked solid with reading.

"Maybe I could call you when I get home? We can set something up then." I was eager to get her off the phone before Lucy caught wind that I was on a personal call. "I'm so glad you called, though. It's great to hear from you."

"Are you sure you're okay, Angel?"

"I'm fine, great. I'll speak to you later. Bye, Elise." I hung up the phone and exhaled so hard, spots started dancing in front of my eyes. Elise was the second person I'd hung up on in the space of ten minutes. I sensed that this was to be a day of extremes.

"Angel!"

I startled and jumped at the sound of my name. I turned my head in the direction of her voice and had to stifle a gasp. Lucy was standing in the doorway of her office, clad only in a large, fluffy white towel.

"Glad you're finally here," she said. "It's going to be a very busy day today. I need you to start making calls now."

I couldn't answer, paralyzed by the sight in front of me.

"Is there a problem, Angel?" she asked.

"Um . . ."

Lucy shifted her position and the unthinkable happened: The towel sprang loose and fell to the floor before she could catch it. I lowered my eyes instinctively but not before the vision of her nakedness seared my retinas.

"Goddamn it!" I heard her curse. And then, "My calls, Angel! Now!"

FIVE

I SAT AT MY DESK, head down, eyes glued to my keyboard, for several minutes after I heard the click of Lucy's office door shutting. That was as long as it took for me to try, and fail, to erase the image of a naked Lucy from my brain. I wasn't exactly shocked at her lack of modesty. Like many memsahibs before her, Lucy didn't think much about revealing herself to her servants, and I'd often arrived at the office early enough to see her in various states of undress. This was the first time that I'd actually seen her unclothed, though, and it was a little much to take on an empty stomach. Perhaps I was just exhausted, I thought, working so many concentrated hours on so little sleep that I'd started hallucinating. Yes, that was it—I'd imagined the whole thing. But why, then, were the details so remarkably clear? It appeared that my vision had breast implants, for example, and I couldn't understand why my brain would choose to hallucinate those. The back of my throat was dry and scratched as if there were something small and sharp poking into it. I felt a little dizzy and slightly nauseated. I needed to drink something. As I bent toward my purse for my water bottle, my intercom buzzed, shrill in the empty office.

"Angel!"

"Yes, Lucy?"

"Why am I not yet on the phone? Is nobody working in Manhattan today? Some sort of holiday I'm unaware of?"

"No, Lucy. I mean, yes, I'm—"

"Did I not ask you to begin calling several minutes ago?"

So I hadn't imagined it. I waited a second, almost hearing the impatient thrum of passing time.

"Angel, is there something wrong with you today?"

"No, Lucy."

"Then why the *fuck* am I not on the phone at this moment, Angel?"

There was something about the way Lucy cursed, some sort of stiff nuance she placed on the word *fuck*, that took all the teeth out of it. It wasn't as if Lucy couldn't sound nasty, far from it. She could make almost any word sound like the vilest epithet when she placed the right venomous emphasis on the syllables. But she shaped those words like daggers herself, they didn't start that way. Words like *shit, fuck*, and *bullshit*, which she used with intermittent frequency, were already loaded, but I never recoiled when she cursed—unlike the times when she hurled my own name at me like a weapon.

"I'm sorry, Lucy, I'm calling right now." I moved to pick up the receiver on my phone.

"Too late! Put the phone down and come in here now, please, Angel. There's something else I need to discuss with you immediately."

"Okay."

"And bring your reading."

I realized I'd started perspiring. I could feel beads of moisture on my upper lip and the soles of my feet were tingling. It took me a second to identify the combination as my body's own response to fear.

I gathered up the *Blind Submission* manuscript and a pad of paper to take notes. Malcolm's novel stared up at me from its position in my bag. In a fit of guilty impulsivity, I grabbed it and added it to my stack. My morning at the office was already so strange and unsettling that trying to push my boyfriend's book hardly seemed uncomfortable. I knocked on Lucy's door, standing outside for as long as possible before she shouted, "Come *in*, Angel!" and I had to enter.

"I'm quite serious when I ask if you need medical attention today, Angel. First you walk in on me when I'm practically naked—please try not to do that again, by the way—and now you are just standing there. What is wrong with you?"

I took a deep breath and looked over at her. She was fully dressed, wearing a brown leather vest with a matching skirt, a chunky turquoise necklace, and a bright yellow turtleneck. The outfit did nothing for her complexion, but it was so much better than what I'd seen underneath. I could feel relief flooding my body like warm water. I was so relieved, in fact, that I decided to let her maintain the illusion that *I'd* walked in on *her*. It appeared she was capable of embarrassment after all.

"I'm so sorry, Lucy," I said. "I guess I'm a little tired today. I haven't been getting much sleep lately."

Lucy scrutinized me for a moment, one eyebrow arching, as if she was trying to decide between two responses.

"What you do in your *private* life is entirely up to you, Angel," she said, and again I noticed her particular talent for making the mundane obscene. "But I must insist that it not infringe on your job," she continued. "I'm sure you can understand my feelings about this. Perhaps you should save your late nights for the weekends, hmm?" Malcolm could certainly attest that my late nights had nothing to do with anything private and everything to do with the office, but it didn't seem wise to mention that with Lucy's eyebrow still arrowed in my direction.

"Right," I said.

"*Although,*" she said, stretching out the syllables, "I suppose you're young, aren't you? And there's a boyfriend, isn't there? A fiancé, no?"

"Yes, but—"

"No need to be prudish, Angel. Not for my benefit. Just the two of us girls here now." She grinned. "Angel, you're blushing! Well, isn't that sweet?" That seductive tone had worked its way into her voice again. Was she flirting with me? I had no idea how to respond. I was sure that the burn on my cheeks was deepening to a nice shade of scarlet. "You must be an angel after all," Lucy was saying. It sounded like a quote, but I had no idea from where. "All right, sit down," she said abruptly. "Let's get to it."

I sat-fell into Lucy's white couch and she left her desk to come sit beside me, turning so that her softly booted knees were just touching mine. I made a show of reassembling the manuscripts on my lap so that I could shift away.

"Not yet," she said, watching me shuffle the papers. "We have another matter to go over first."

"Okay," I said, pulling my notepad closer.

"No," she said. "No notes for this conversation. In fact, Angel, I'm going to have to ask you to keep this in strict confidence. This is a very sensitive issue and I wouldn't be discussing it with you at all if I didn't feel I could trust your judgment completely." She grinned at me again, showing all her white teeth. They seemed shinier than usual.

"Of course," I said. "I mean, of course I won't say anything."

"It's about Anna," she said, and stopped, waiting for my response.

"Okay," I said.

"I'm wondering," Lucy continued, leaning in closer, "if I should let her go."

"Oh," was the only response I could muster.

"The thing about Anna is that, although I believe her heart's in the right place, she's just not that sharp. Do you know what I mean, Angel?" Her tone implied that I should not only know what she meant, but that I should agree. I wasn't happy about the position that put me in.

"Um," I said, stretching for time.

"Don't be coy, Angel. I know for a fact that you've noticed what she misses with the reading."

"Well, I—"

"And, frankly, I'm not confident that she's detail-oriented enough for her other work, either. Although that could be fixed. The reading is the lifeblood of this office, Angel, I'm sure I don't need to tell you that. You can't train someone to have an eye. And that's what you have, Angel, it's why I hired you despite your naïveté and obvious lack of experience."

"Oh, yes. Thank you." Had I just thanked her for insulting me or had I agreed with her about Anna? The conversation was fast getting away from me.

"Now, Angel, even though I rely on your judgment, you cannot be the only person in this office with an eye for what will sell. I need every member of my staff to be as sharp."

"Right."

"Craig has plenty of responsibility outside of the reading, so I can't expect the same kind of volume from him. And Nora, well, that's another topic altogether, isn't it? I'll have to address that later. But Anna is clearly falling down in this area. So, my question to you is: Do I let her go? Do you feel the quality of her reading is getting better or worse?"

"Oh, Lucy, I'm not sure I'd be the best person to help you decide. . . . I mean, I . . ." I trailed off and looked down at my hands, as if what I should say next might be written there. It occurred to me that Lucy might be fashioning another one of her tests, along the lines of the "Do you put the author or editor through to me first?" question from my interview. Perhaps this was her way of separating the girls from the women? Some sort of office *Survivor,* perhaps? If that were the case, it was a particularly distasteful test. Lucy was waiting for an answer and I opened my mouth to speak. What came out of it next was a complete surprise to me.

"I don't think her reads are getting any better," I said. "I was just thinking this morning how she seems to be rejecting most of her manuscripts without really reading them carefully."

"Yes," Lucy said, and leaned back into the couch, an unpleasant grin spreading across her face. "I thought as much. So your recommendation would be to let her go, then?"

"No, I didn't—"

"You're pretty confident, aren't you, Angel? Only here a few weeks, and already you're suggesting I fire one of your superiors."

Up to that moment, I could safely say that I'd never felt my jaw drop. But it fell open then, independent of any will on my part, while the words that came to my mind—*What are you talking about?*—remained tangled and unspoken in the back of my throat.

"Oh, don't look at me that way, Angel," Lucy said, waving her hand. "You've got the killer instinct. That is not a disadvantage in this business. However, you'll have to put a leash on your ambition for a bit longer. I'd like to give Anna a chance to redeem herself. In fact, I'd like *you* to give her a chance. I want you to work with her, Angel. Let her know what she should be looking for and what she's missing. I've invested quite a bit of time and money in that girl, and I'm not willing to throw it all away just yet. Do you understand?"

"Yes," I said, although I didn't.

"Of course, I'll have to let her know that she's in a probationary period as far as the reading goes. We'll have a staff meeting when everyone gets here—draft a memo about that, please—and then perhaps I can see you and Anna together in my office." It wasn't a question.

"What time would you like to have the staff meeting?" I asked. Lucy looked over at me as if I'd lost my mind.

"The usual time, of course, Angel."

This meant that I'd have to make one up. We hadn't really had an organized staff meeting since I'd started the job.

"Now," she said briskly, "this brings me to my next point, and I have to say I'm somewhat disappointed in you, Angel." She reached down and plucked a manuscript from a pile on the floor. I recognized it as Shelly Franklin's novel, *Elvis Will Dance at Your Wedding*. So that's what "Chase Elvis" meant, I thought, and was seized with a quick panic. I'd given Lucy the manuscript weeks ago, but in the heat of Damiano's auction and everything else that had happened since I'd read it, I'd forgotten to ask her about it. I'd forgotten to anticipate, remind, and otherwise order Lucy's thoughts—a failing she was sure to pounce on.

"This," she said, waving *Elvis* in front of me, "is one of the very manuscripts you feel is better than Anna has given it credit for. Why, then, has it taken *so long* to get to me?"

"But—" I began, and stopped myself before I could say something stupid. I *had* given it to her right away, I just hadn't remembered to remind her of that fact. I couldn't figure out if I was guilty or innocent. "I did pass that on to you a while ago," I finished weakly.

"But I'm only seeing it now!" she exclaimed. "How do you account for that?"

Several insubordinate responses flashed through my brain, but I opted for the safest path, which was just to say, "I'm sorry, Lucy, I thought you'd read it already."

Lucy stared at me for a second, her gimlet eyes flashing, and then moved quickly to another thought. "Fine," she said, "I'll let it go this time, but really, Angel, you need to be more careful. I don't have to tell you. Anyway, let's just discuss this piece—and give me the short version, Angel, we're running out of time here."

"Um, well, it's . . . uh . . ." I remembered the manuscript well, but it was a struggle to pull the words out of the thickness in my brain. For one flashing second, I was sure I was going to pass out.

"The *short* version, Angel." Lucy leaned toward me so close that for the first time I could see that she had tiny lines around her mouth into which her brick-colored lipstick was bleeding. I was starting to feel that Lucy was about to eat me like a predator with its fallen prey and I forced myself out of my haze.

"Right, right. I think this one is really good. *Elvis Will Dance at Your Wedding*," I said. Lucy wrinkled her nose. "I know, I thought the title was too long when I first saw it, but it really does conjure the perfect image of what she's trying to get across here."

"Which is? Fiction or non?"

So she *still* hadn't read it, I thought.

"Fiction. Road-trip novel about a couple who drives to Las Vegas to marry. Good writing, very evocative. Voyage of discovery about themselves, their relationship. It's literary, but not too. Still has mass-market appeal. It comments on the state of modern love—no, actually, it's *post*modern love and marriage in the new millennium. *Wild at Heart* meets *Leaving Las Vegas*. But more upbeat." I'd come back to myself, finding all the right words, throwing them out in a rush and creating the kind of hot energy I loved. I could see that Lucy was warming to it as well. We were on a roll.

"Credits?" she asked.

"A few little lit mags. She's got a master's from California University, though."

"*Pretty Feet*," Lucy mused, referring to the last bestseller written by a California University MFA graduate. A quirky little novel about a young woman with enormous misshapen feet and her quest for love, *Pretty Feet* had been a solid fixture on the *New York Times* bestseller list for almost a year.

"Exactly," I said.

"Intriguing," Lucy said. "Has she contacted other agents?"

I bit the inside of my cheek and lied through my teeth. "No, we're it. Would you like me to call her? To get the rest of it, I mean."

Lucy gave an exasperated sigh. "You haven't done that yet? Come on, Angel, you have to take some initiative. You don't need my permission to call an author to request more material if you like something. That should just be a matter of course at this point, no?"

"No. I mean yes. Yes, of course."

"And you really like it?" she asked.

"Very much."

"As much as the Italian book?"

"Yes, but in a different way."

"Good! What else do you have?"

"This," I said, and thrust *Blind Submission* at her.

"Can you be more specific?" Lucy said, a cold edge of condescension creeping into her voice.

"Sorry. It's a novel set in a literary agency. Anonymous author." I smiled for effect. "Kind of fun."

"Really?" Lucy asked, taking it from me. "And how long have I been waiting for this one?"

I was sweating again. "Just came in," I said.

"Hmm," Lucy mused. "And you like it?"

"I think it needs some work, but it's got potential," I said.

"And have you written notes to that effect?"

"Yes," I said. "Of course."

"Fine, I'll read it right away," she said. "Is that it? Are we finished?"

"Yes, that's it," I said, standing up. I felt as if I'd been sitting on that couch for days. Time got completely distorted in Lucy's office. It really *was* similar to Narnia in its way.

"What's that?" Lucy asked, pointing at Malcolm's manuscript, still in my arms, which I'd just decided I shouldn't show her. But there was no escaping it now. Lucy's eyes missed nothing.

"It's . . ." I filled my lungs with air. What the hell. "My fiancé is a writer? And a big fan of yours?" Now I was forming my sentences as questions, the first sign of the conversationally weak and lame. Lucy was not going to help me at all with this one, I could see. She looked bemused. "Anyway," I went on, "he's written this novel. . . ."

"Have you read it?" Lucy asked me.

"No, I haven't."

"Then why in God's name should I waste *my* time reading it, Angel?"

"I've read his other work and I think it's good. I thought it might be hard for me to be objective about the novel, though, if I read it before, you know, I gave it to you. But I totally understand if you're too busy. I mean, he could have sent it in—he did, actually, send this to you once a long time ago, and you encouraged him to rewrite, but if he sent it now, I'd be the one seeing it first anyway probably and then—"

"Just give it to me," she snapped, and so I did. "This is a big favor I'm doing for you, I hope you realize," she said. "I hope *he* realizes." She glanced at the title page. "*Bridge of Lies,* is it? Interesting. Why are these pages torn like this? Looks like the dog ate it." She looked up at me, irritation creasing her features. "You're still standing there, Angel."

"Yes, okay, your calls. Thank you, Lucy."

"Get me Nadia Fiori first, please. We still have to settle the schedule on the Italian book." She was already at her desk, positioning her notepads and pens for their inevitable stacking and unstacking, as I left her office.

———

I DECIDED THAT THE "usual" time for a staff meeting should be at nine A.M.—lunchtime in New York—and placed a copy of the memo on everyone's desk. It would have been much simpler, of course, to just tell Anna, Craig, and Nora that there was a meeting, but Lucy insisted we have memos for every activity.

"What's this about?" Anna asked me, holding up her copy of the memo. For a paranoid moment, I was sure she'd somehow heard my earlier discussion with Lucy. She looked uncharacteristically pale and worn out. She'd gained some weight in the last couple of weeks and it wasn't sitting well on her. There was a gauze bandage on her left hand and wrist.

"I'm not sure," I told her. "What happened to your hand?"

"Cut myself making chicken," she said. "Spent all night in the emergency room."

"Why didn't you call in?" Nora said, materializing as if from nowhere. Nora's long hair was pulled back, accentuating the sharp line of her jawbone. She'd lost the weight Anna had gained recently, and its absence looked even worse on her. The half-circles under her large eyes looked as if they'd been drawn in charcoal. I wondered if I looked as unhealthy as my coworkers. It wasn't a pleasant thought.

"Can't call in," Anna said. "It's just a few stitches. Only twenty. I missed the vein, anyway."

"Well, at least it wasn't a paper cut from all the reading you've been doing," Craig said as he made his way to Lucy's office. "I'd hate to think you got a work injury at home." Anna, Nora, and I gave him matching perplexed stares.

"It was a *joke*, ladies," he said, his rich voice covering us like honey. "You know, ha-ha? Never mind, then. Join me for the staff meeting, won't you?"

There was a fair bit of shuffling around before the four of us found comfortable places to sit in Lucy's inner sanctum. Her office wasn't particularly well designed for meetings since the couch provided most of the seating and actual chairs were in short supply. Craig took his position on the one large chair in the office, while Anna, Nora, and I settled into the couch, all of us trying to keep our arms and elbows as close to our bodies as possible so as to avoid touching our neighbor. Lucy was seated at her desk, surveying the scene, and when we'd finally assembled and were sitting still, she said, "This is lovely and you all look very cozy, but there's one problem here." Nobody ventured to ask her what that might be. "Who is going to answer the phones?" she said.

Anna sprung up like a jack-in-the-box. "I will, Lucy!" she gulped.

"Anna, what *is* that on your arm?"

"I had a little accident last night. It's nothing, really, just a few stitches."

"Did you bandage that yourself or did you see a doctor about it?" Lucy asked.

Anna gave Lucy a puppyish smile and said, "No, I went to the emergency room. Thanks, I'm fine, really."

"Do you realize how much bacteria there is at a hospital?" Lucy said. "I hope you aren't carrying in some kind of staph infection. These are close quarters, you know. You might have thought of that before coming in to work today."

Anna sank back into the couch, her color rising to a bright red hue. Embarrassment was written all over her face, but I could see the hard, angry edge underneath it. I read her thoughts as one word: *bitch*.

"Nora, it will have to be you, then. No, don't leave. Come and take my place over here. You can answer the phone at my desk." Nora looked stricken. "And Craig, I'll take your place and you can sit next to the patient over there on the couch. I can't afford to take the chance." Craig moved without a word, his face expressionless, and Nora, moving with all the speed of someone approaching the guillotine, seated herself at Lucy's desk. The phone rang immediately, as if sensing her presence there.

"Lucy Fiamma Literary Agency, may I help you? Yes? Hi. Can you hold, please?" Nora pushed the hold button on Lucy's phone and looked up. "Lucy? It's Susie Parker for you?"

"Nora, we're in the middle of a staff meeting here."

"So shall I—"

"Yes, Nora, and do it now." Lucy sighed heavily and muttered, "No sense, that girl." She adjusted a notepad on her lap while Nora dispatched Susie Parker. "I don't know why these staff meetings take so long to get going," she said. "Really, it ought to be a simple thing. We're going to have to learn to be more efficient here, people, if we're going to keep the coffers full. I realize that we've made some impressive sales in the last few weeks, but we cannot stop, slow down, or look back. I shouldn't have to spend time getting a meeting like this started. You all should be ready to go the minute you arrive. Angel, I'd like you to draft a plan for how we can improve the efficiency of these meetings. Please have it to me for review before the end of the day so that I can go over it."

Staff meetings more efficient, I wrote.

"Now," Lucy said, "our first order of business is the reading." She took in a deep breath. "As you are all aware, the reading is key to the success of this business. . . ." Despite myself, I began to glaze over. I'd heard Lucy say the same thing so many times, I'd reached a saturation point. My brain could hold no more. I was heading into a full-scale drift until the sound of my own name reeled me back in.

". . . and Angel informs me that you are not keeping up your end of the reading, Anna. Apparently, you've rejected several projects that were worth keeping or at least worth passing along to me. Now, I don't know if this is because you feel you're overloaded with work and don't have time to do your reading carefully or if your judgment is impaired. Which is it, Anna?"

I felt as if I'd been slapped. Although I was sure she knew what she was doing, I couldn't imagine what good Lucy thought would come of pitting me against Anna in front of the entire staff. It was becoming more and more difficult to figure out what constituted a good work performance in this office.

"I wasn't aware that my reading was so bad," Anna said, shrinking into herself as she cradled her bandaged arm. "Angel never mentioned it to me or I would have done something about it." Anna gave me a look of undisguised hatred. There was nothing I could say and no denials I could offer that would mitigate the damage, so I opted to remain silent.

"Is that true?" Lucy asked me. "You haven't kept Anna in the loop on this?"

"No. I mean yes. I've just taken . . . I didn't think—"

"So the answer is no," Lucy said. "In all fairness to Anna, then, perhaps we should start over here." Lucy graced Anna with a smile.

"Perhaps the problem here is that Angel is unaware that she should be sharing information," Craig said. "We're a team here, after all." With that, Craig managed to make *me* the problem, and as I glanced around the room, I could see that everyone was giving me similarly poisonous looks. So Craig was no friend of mine. That much was clear.

"We are indeed a team," Lucy said, "and we need to start working as one. To that end, I'd like you to work with Anna on the reading, Angel. Perhaps you can share some of that insight you've got with her. I'll let the two of you decide how best you can accomplish this, but I'd suggest you get together at some point after work and create a plan. Maybe you can have dinner together? I understand that Anna's quite an accomplished cook."

Sure, I thought, right after hell froze over.

"Good, that's decided," Lucy said, without waiting for a response. "Now we can move on to my second order of business, which is *money*. If I am going to continue to pay all of your salaries, we need more of it. Angel has just been discussing a manuscript that looks as if it might be promising. Another *Pretty Feet,* or so you said, correct, Angel?"

"The Elv— Yes, right," I said.

"Good, so let's hope your instincts are as sharp as they were on the Italian book. But regardless of whether or not that one turns out to be something, we need to start getting more creative about increasing revenue. In our search for the next hot book, we seem to be neglecting a very important source of possible sales. Can anyone tell me what that is?"

"Subsidiary rights?" Anna asked, hope threading its way into her voice.

"That's not what I'm talking about, but yes, that is another front we've been neglecting. Which you should know, Anna, since you've been in charge of sub rights for the last two months. But what I'm referring to now is *our authors.* The ones we already have."

"Option books," Craig said.

"Exactly," Lucy said. "We have a number of authors out there who are not producing second or third books. They need to be contacted and, if necessary, they need to be given some direction on what to do next."

"I could compile that list for you, Lucy," said Anna. As sorry as I was for my part in Anna's earlier embarrassment, her sycophant approach to Lucy was starting to nauseate me.

"No, your plate's full of sub rights to attend to, Anna. And by the way, I'd like to see an updated list of what you're working on right now, please. Angel will generate the list of authors and possible projects. In the meantime, I have two authors in mind who can be contacted immediately." Lucy took a dramatic pause. I noticed that Craig was smiling as he jotted notes on his legal pad. I wondered if there was something I was missing because I couldn't understand what he might be finding so amusing.

"Karanuk!" There was a collective intake of air at Lucy's pronouncement. "Yes, that's right, Karanuk has begun work on a new book. I've spoken with him recently and he's ready to move forward. However, he needs a little . . . *encouragement,* shall we say." She cleared her throat and plucked some nonexistent lint from her skirt. "Angel, I would like you to call him and offer him whatever he needs to get going."

"You want me to call Karanuk?" I asked her. My heart had started thumping so hard that I coughed over the last syllable of his name.

"Yes, call him. You know how to operate a telephone, do you not? Why do you look so frightened, Angel? He's just a *writer,* you know. After all."

"Does he have pages you want him to send?" I managed to ask.

"He has a title," Lucy said. "He's calling the next one *Warmer.* At least that's what he's calling it now. What do we think of that title?"

"Sounds great!" Anna gushed. "A perfect follow-up."

"I like it," said Nora. "Sounds, you know, *warm.*"

"Maybe *Warm* would be better. Without the *er,*" Craig offered.

"Yes, with ellipses," said Anna. "Instead of, you know, the exclamation point."

I watched Lucy's face as they spoke. By the time it came around to me, I knew exactly what she was thinking and exactly how to respond.

"I guess it would depend on what kind of book he's planning to write," I said. "You wouldn't want him to spoof himself."

"No, you wouldn't," Lucy said. "Good, then. You'll call him. Now, the second author I have in mind is Stephanie Spark."

"*Eat, Treat, Defeat!*" Anna practically shouted.

"Exactly," Lucy said. "As I'm sure you all know, that was a fabulous book. The meditations were excellent, but the diet was what really sold it. People lost thousands of pounds on that diet."

"I was one of them," Anna said. "Of course, I put some back on, but that wasn't the fault of the book or the diet. I should go back on it again."

"Yes," Lucy said. "Anyway, one of the reasons the book did so well was because the author took her own diet very seriously. Too seriously, in fact. She now suffers from anorexia. I think there's a story to be told here about the so-called success of dieting and where it can lead from the standpoint of a bestselling diet book."

"Good idea," Craig said.

"I could call her," Anna said. "As someone who's tried her diet—"

"No, I want Nora to handle this one," Lucy said.

"Why? Why me?" Nora squeaked, shocked out of her customary silence.

"Well, isn't it obvious?" Lucy asked, scanning Nora with her eyes. "You're anorexic yourself, aren't you? You must understand the mind-set, surely."

"What? What? I am not! Why would you say that?" Nora flailed her arms as if someone were trying to pin them down. She started shaking her head back and forth, on the verge of hysteria.

"There's nothing to be *ashamed* of, Nora," Lucy said, her tone clearly indicating that there was. "There are treatments for this kind of thing, you know."

"I can't, I can't, I can't," Nora said, and started to cry. I felt as if I were watching a train wreck. I was horrified, but I couldn't look away. Neither, it appeared, could Anna or Craig.

"Nora," Lucy said, her voice slow and measured, "if you are unable to participate in this meeting, perhaps you should take a break. I'm trying to run a business here."

Still sobbing, Nora bolted from Lucy's chair and disappeared into the main office. After a minute of uneasy silence, punctuated by the sound of the bathroom door slamming shut, Lucy stood and reclaimed her own seat.

"Totally unprofessional," she said. "This is the problem with these *girls,* Craig." Craig shrugged and raised his palms as if to deny culpability. "I ask you, was that performance really necessary?" I almost expected Anna to answer because she seemed to love skewering herself on rhetorical questions, but this time she wisely left it alone. Lucy sighed heavily. "Well, I suppose you'd better go see to her," she told Craig. "More time wasted. And I suppose we'll have to adjourn this meeting until later. Angel, you've got work to do. Anna, you stay here, I need to talk to you."

"Okay," Anna said. "I'll get the door." The look of self-satisfaction on her face annoyed me more than I wanted to admit.

There was a small tempest hovering over Nora's desk when I walked back into the office. Stacks of manuscripts sat on her chair, on the floor, and in the middle of her desk. Spilled Rolodex cards lay scattered on her computer keyboard and an assortment of rubber bands, paper clips, and pens decorated the remaining space. Nora was bent over the mess, emptying the contents of her top drawer into a large canvas bag. I watched as she threw in a jar of mustard, a container of protein powder, a hairbrush, a spoon, and a small notepad decorated with iridescent hearts. Craig sat in pacific calm at his own desk, attending to a file. Not only was he not "seeing to her," as Lucy suggested, he wasn't even looking at her. I felt a jolt of panic followed by a stab of guilt. Panic because she was obviously quitting and her workload would no doubt fall to me. Guilt because my panic wasn't even slightly tempered by any sympathy for Nora. I wondered if I should talk to her, offer some words of encouragement, or try to convince her to stay. But I'd already decided that it wasn't really my place. I wasn't Nora's buddy and I wasn't her boss. And it wasn't like anyone would do the same for me. It was clear that we were all on our own here, despite Lucy's constant assertions that we were a team. I was the only one watching *my* back in this office. Besides, judging by the speed with which Nora was moving, it didn't seem as if any kind of supportive gesture would make the least bit of difference. The phone rang and I leaped to answer it, glad for the excuse to shift my attention.

"Lucy Fiamma Agency."

"Yes," a small voice said, "this is . . . my name is Shelly Franklin? I sent you a manuscript a while ago? I don't know if you've seen it?"

"Hi, Shelly!" I said, sounding ridiculously upbeat to my own ears. "This is Angel Robinson, Lucy's assistant. I was just about to call you!"

"Oh. You were?" Her voice became more timid and I could barely hear her.

"Yes, I really like your novel. Lucy's reviewing it right now."

"Oh." She sounded almost disappointed. Not a good sign.

"We were wondering if you've sent this novel to other agents? You didn't mention that in your letter."

"Oh, I didn't? I was calling because I was wondering if I enclosed a self-addressed stamped envelope? If I forgot, I can send one in?" she whispered.

What was it about these authors? Every one of them seemed loony in his or her own way. "You did send one in as I recall," I said, my voice rising as hers dipped, "but we really don't need it right now because we'd like to see the rest of the novel."

"The rest?"

"You have the entire novel written, don't you? You did say that in your letter."

"Yes, I've written it."

"Can you send it to us?" I asked her. I realized I was almost shouting into the phone. There was obviously something wrong with this woman and I scrambled to try to figure out what it was.

"Okay," she said. "I'll send that out today. Thanks."

"Can I just ask you, have you sent this novel to any other agents?" I asked before I lost her.

"No?" she said, and hung up. I stared at the phone, as perplexed as I'd ever been. I'd have to call her back and I didn't relish the prospect. I looked up and saw Nora standing over me with a pile of manuscripts. She was dry-eyed, but tear-tracks stained both sides of her face.

"This is my reading," she said. "Now it's your reading. You'll have to go get today's mail."

"Okay," I said. "I'm really sorry."

Nora leaned in so that her face was close to mine. "She's cruel," she whispered. "It's one thing to be tough, but she's *cruel.*" She straightened up and turned to walk out. Craig's voice caught her before she could reach the door.

"Nora, if you leave now, I'll assume you're quitting. And if you're quitting, I'll need you to sit down for an exit interview," he said.

Nora shot him a look potent with hatred and misery. When she spoke, her voice trembled under the weight of unshed tears. "My name is Kelly," she said. "Kelly. *Kelly.*" She walked out, closing the door behind her, and Craig didn't try to stop her.

As if on cue, Anna emerged from Lucy's office before the dust from Nora's—*Kelly's*—exit could settle and walked over to my desk.

"Lucy wants me to ask you if you've called Karanuk yet," she said. "And we're supposed to have a meeting about my reading. But she wants me to read this first." She held up a manuscript for me to see. I recognized it immediately. Malcolm's novel.

"Hey," Anna said, noticing the unoccupied and disheveled desk for the first time. "Where's Nora?"

SIX

THE PHONES WERE RELENTLESS, ringing and flashing in an unremitting assault to my senses. If I hadn't known better, I would have sworn that Nora contacted every unpublished author who'd ever sent us a manuscript and instructed them to call right after she made her exit. Even Craig, who almost never picked up the phone, was forced to put on a headset and catch the calls that Anna and I couldn't get to. Lucy had voice mail on her phone system but hated the idea that any caller would ever hear a recording. It was unprofessional, she said, and gave the idea that we were a small, struggling agency. She wanted a live human to answer every call, even if that human had to spend the next ten minutes getting the caller off the line. Which is what Anna, Craig, and I did for the better part of two hours after Nora left.

"Just the first fifty pages and a self-addressed stamped envelope," I could hear Anna saying over and over again. Lucy hadn't emerged from her office since the staff meeting, and I wondered if she even knew that Nora had left. Surely, if she did, she would have called another meeting to discuss it.

I'd taken one break, if it could be called that, to retrieve the day's mail from the nearby postal store where Lucy had the agency's account.

Again, as if N— Kelly had planned it this way, there was an unusually heavy load. I dragged three full mail tubs to my desk and was frantically trying to separate the submissions from the catalogs, letters from editors, bills, and the usual choice items. Prospective authors sent in an astonishing array of ridiculous gifts in an effort to catch Lucy's attention. Most sent chocolates (Ghirardelli, Godiva) or money (cash stapled to cover letters), but others got more creative. Since I'd started working at the agency, we'd received a variety of animal pelts from writers trying to copy Karanuk's work, hand-painted mugs (stating *World's Best Agent* in gold glaze), theater tickets, gift certificates, and lavender-scented soap. All of these items had to be returned immediately, of course, along with their accompanying manuscripts. Nothing got a project rejected faster than when it had an attempt at bribery attached to it. Wading through all of this had been N— Kelly's job, and now it was mine. Whatever sympathy I'd had for her was fast dissipating as I struggled under the weight of my additional workload. Could she not have waited until the end of the day? As if she'd heard my thoughts and sent the gods to punish me, I caught my finger in an unusually stubborn clip and tore enough of the skin that I started to bleed on a manuscript.

"Damn, damn, damn," I whispered, smearing the cover letter in an effort to save it.

"Angel!" Anna's voice, high pitched and frantic, sliced through my consciousness. I dropped the manuscript into my own take-home pile and turned to Anna, trying to hide my bleeding finger, but she had already seen. "What are you doing?" she hissed.

"I cut—"

"Never mind! I need you to get the phone." I didn't ask her why she couldn't get the screaming thing, just turned and punched the line.

"Lucy Fiamma Agency," I said.

"Angel, is that you? It's Dami."

"Dami! Hi!" I was absurdly happy to hear from him and I was sure he could tell from my voice, which had turned high and squeaky. Anna must have heard it, too, because I could see her glowering at me from the corner of my eye.

"How are you?" he asked.

"I'm fine," I said. "How are *you*? You must be so thrilled about your book."

"It's amazing," he said. "I can't believe it."

"Well, believe it," I told him. "It's really going to happen. Do you need to speak to Lucy? If you hold on a minute, I can put you through. We've been really busy here today."

"I love to speak to Luciana, but I called now to talk to you," he said.

"Oh. Is there something you need help with? I can—"

"No, no, Angel. I want to come to the office today to thank you in person. I have something for you and Luciana. We have to celebrate."

"Oh." For a moment, I had no response to give him. I'd never seen a visitor of any kind in the office, let alone an author. Lucy had some local authors on her list, but most of her clients lived far away. I should probably ask her first before I extended an invitation to Damiano, I thought. On the other hand, I was almost positive that she'd nix the idea immediately. Lucy couldn't tolerate any kind of interruption of the workday unless she created it herself. And although I seemed on my way to becoming a liaison between her and her authors, I sensed that the last thing she wanted was for me to have any kind of personal relationship with them. Still, I was eager to meet Damiano. After spending so much time with him on the phone, and working through so much of his writing, I felt as if I already knew him. To hell with it, I thought. If Lucy complained, I could always plead ignorance. After all, I'd never received an *explicit* instruction not to allow an author into the office without permission.

"Well, it would be great to meet you," I said at last. "When were you thinking of coming by?"

"I'm coming from the city," he said, "so it takes me a while to get to you. The traffic, the bridge, you never know. So I'll be there sometime this afternoon."

"Okay, I'll let Lucy know," I said, although I had no intention of doing so. I didn't want Anna to hear, either, and had lowered my voice to a near-whisper. "Do you need directions?"

"Not to worry, Angel," he said. "I know where you are. *Ciao, bella.*"

"Who was *that*?" Anna asked as soon as I'd hung up, but I pretended not to hear her and picked up the phone again. My intercom line was flashing. Lucy had been silent long enough.

"Hi, Lucy."

"Angel, have you spoken to Karanuk yet? I'd like a status report on that."

"Not yet, Lucy. The phones have been crazy today."

"*Prioritize*, Angel," she barked, and hung up.

I hated to admit it to myself, but I was scared to call Karanuk. Despite what Lucy had said about him being "only a writer," I was intimidated by the very thought of him. What could I possibly say that would be helpful to someone of his literary stature? I had no idea what approach I was supposed to take with him. I could try fawning and cajoling, which would be preferable to a tongue-tied stammer, I supposed, but that didn't seem to be what Lucy had in mind. At any other time, the opportunity to speak to Karanuk would have seemed to me like a great honor. At this point, however, it was another fumble in a dark room.

As I dialed, I clung to the hope that I'd get voice mail or even an assistant, but no. Karanuk answered his own phone on the first ring with a simple but firm, "Karanuk."

"Hi, Karanuk?" (*Mr.* Karanuk? I had no idea.) "This is Angel Robinson? I'm Lucy Fiamma's new assistant? Lucy asked me to call you?"

"Yes," he said.

Yes . . . what? I thought, but forged ahead, anyway. "Lucy's very excited about your new book and she wanted me to ask you how—I mean when—she'll be able to take a look at the manuscript?"

"I don't have anything to show her," he said abruptly. I was sure he was going to hang up on me.

"Okay, do you know when you might have something? I think what she meant was just an outline or proposal, not the whole thing, of course."

Karanuk laughed, the first display of any kind of emotion since we'd begun talking. For a laugh, however, it didn't have much mirth. Like his voice, it was deep and strong, but devoid of accent or inflection. For someone who wrote as eloquently as he did, that absence of feeling seemed very odd. Which reminded me that I'd said nothing to him about his work.

"I'm a huge fan of *Cold!*, by the way," I said hurriedly. "It's one of the best books I've ever read."

There was a brief silence and then he said, "I live in Los Angeles. I'm not very cold anymore. Things are much warmer here and much different. My shape has shifted. I'm suffering the fate of a Klondike bar in the Sahara. There has been a melting process. Additives . . . plastic components . . . One does not know which way to proceed."

So he was off his head like almost every other author, I thought. But he'd given me an opening and I felt the jolt of an idea zip through my head.

"Oh, is that the theme of the new book?" I asked. "It's terrific. Displacement. Loss of self. Man out of his element. Disconnection from culture and reality under the hot sun of . . . of . . ."

"Celebrity," he said, and paused for a beat or two. "What did you say your name was?"

"Angel."

"Angel," he repeated. "You are her assistant? She has had many assistants. She needs much assistance."

"Yes, I've been here about . . ." I couldn't remember how long I'd been working for Lucy. Five minutes? Forever? They were the same thing here. "I've been here awhile."

"And you are a writer yourself?" he asked.

"Oh no, no. *No.* I don't write at all."

"But you know how a writer thinks," he said.

"Well . . ."

"I will send you pages. You can tell her that."

"That's great! If I can be of any help at all, please let me know."

"You have been of help already. That's why I am sending the pages to you."

"Great! And the working title is *Warmer,* is that right?"

Karanuk let out another mirthless laugh. "No," he said. "This book does not have a title. That's her title. If I wanted, I could compile an entire book with her proposed titles."

"Oh, okay. Well, it sounds fantastic. We can't wait to see it." As I hung up, I realized that, like Gordon Hart, Karanuk had not once re-

ferred to Lucy by name. Their relationship was obviously a very complicated one, and I didn't want to spend time trying to figure it out. Instead,
I allowed myself a minute to revel in the pure excitement of the fact that
I'd soon be reading a new work by Karanuk before anyone else. There
was a new title forming in my mind already. *Thaw.* I hoped he'd like it.

"Angel!" My intercom shrieked, punching a hole in the first moment
of silence we'd had all day. "My office. Now." I stood up too fast and
knocked into my desk, bumping my forgotten cup of coffee and spilling
it all over my pants.

"Shit," I hissed. Anna and Craig swiveled their heads simultaneously
to look at me. I caught the shadow of a smile forming on Anna's lips.
Craig raised his eyebrows in surprise. As if cursing were a novelty around
here, I thought.

"Angel!" she shouted again, and I ran to her office, the scent of old
cappuccino rising off me in waves.

"I asked you about Karanuk," she barked before I could get all the
way through the door. "What is the status, Angel?"

"I just spoke to him," I said.

"And?" She sat at her desk, imperiously straight, tapping her Waterman pen against a stack of notepads.

"He's sending pages."

"He's *what*?" Lucy got up and walked around to where I was standing, not stopping until she came within inches of my face. Her closeness
was unnerving. I felt cold and naked in her gaze of lusty anticipation.

"He's sending us pages for the new book. He didn't say how much,
but he asked me to tell you that he's sending it in soon."

"Really, did he," she said, but it was not a question. "And did he happen to tell you what his idea for this book is?"

"Um, yes, he's writing about his experiences since leaving Alaska
and how that has changed his life."

"How did you manage that, Angel?" Lucy's voice had dropped considerably and was softer than I'd ever heard it. I watched myriad expressions dance across her face like shifting clouds. In her eyes, which
were boring into me with laserlike precision, there was surprise, something that looked like pleasure, a hint of annoyance, and self-satisfaction

all at once. It was as if she couldn't decide to be angry or pleased that I'd done exactly what she'd asked me to do. Before I could answer her, though, she seemed to catch herself and draw all the emotion out of her features. "Good," she said. "I'll expect it shortly, then." She inhaled and wrinkled her nose. "What is that awful smell?"

I looked down at my wet-stained pants. "I had an accident with my coffee," I said, attempting a smile.

"That's disgusting," she said, backing away from me and heading back to her desk. "Children have accidents, Angel. Have Nora get you some soda water or something when she goes out for the mail."

If only she hadn't mentioned it. Now I was stuck having to be the messenger. "About Nora," I said. "She's gone."

"Well, send her out again when she gets back. What's the problem?"

"No, she's gone for the day. I mean, she's gone for good. I think she quit. She took all her things. . . ." I was frozen in place by Lucy's stare of unvarnished bitterness.

"These *girls*," she spat. "And after all I've done for her. You have no idea what I go through here. I need some *men*. Get me Craig. And bring Anna in here, too. What are you waiting for, Angel? Go!"

BY THE TIME he showed up at close to five, I'd completely forgotten that Damiano had said he was coming to the office. I was as surprised as Anna and Craig when a knock came on the door, which rarely opened during the course of the day. It was Anna who finally registered the sound and sauntered over to let him in. Damiano stood at the door, his face obscured by a giant basket filled with pastries and cakes and elaborately tied with gold and silver ribbon.

"Are you FedEx?" Anna asked, puzzled.

He lowered the basket and gave Anna an equally perplexed stare. "Angel?" he asked, disbelief in his voice. It was only then that I realized who he was.

"I'm Anna," she said, making no move to let him in.

"I'm so sorry," he said, grinning broadly. "Good to meet you. I'm Damiano."

"Ohhh," Anna crowed after one beat too long. "The Italian book. Well, come in." She turned around to me and waved her hand in my direction. "That's Angel," she said. "We didn't know you were coming. Lucy didn't say—"

"I'm sorry," he repeated. "This is a surprise visit. I wanted to come to thank you all in person for my great good fortune." He held the basket out to her. "These are for you all," he said. "I make them all myself. Something for everyone."

"Wow," Anna said, wrapping her arms around the basket and giving the pastries a look that could only be described as loving. Craig got up from his desk and came around to shake hands with Damiano.

"Very nice to meet you," he said. "I'm Craig. We've talked on the phone."

"Yes, yes. Luciana calls you 'the man with the money.' It's nice to meet you." He turned to me then and walked the short distance to my desk, where I sat, paralyzed, trying to figure out if I could smooth my hair without being noticed and wishing desperately that I didn't reek of spilled coffee. At least my finger had stopped bleeding.

"Angel," he said. *"Finalmente."* He leaned toward me but didn't extend his hand for shaking. I stood, awkwardly, unsure whether to offer my own hand. Somehow that gesture seemed too formal. He was shorter than I'd imagined—we stood almost eye to eye—but he held himself in a way that made him appear taller. He was olive-skinned and slender and his eyes were the color of dark red wine. His hair, thick and black with strokes of gray at the temples, was cut short but not buzzed. He had a decent five o'clock shadow darkening his jaw and it suited him well. He was a good-looking man, no question, but in a way that was not at all obvious.

"You have red hair," he said to me. "I'm surprised!"

"Well, I don't really sound like a redhead on the phone," I said idiotically, and made a move to shake his hand. He grabbed it instead and kissed me on both cheeks. He smelled delicious, like marzipan, chocolate, and citrus.

"*È vero,*" he said. "I saw a blond angel when I talked to you." I could feel the prickly heat of a blush spreading across my cheeks and could do nothing to stop it. A sidelong glance at Anna showed me that her color had risen, too, and that she looked extremely put out. Damiano's visit was already feeling like a runaway train and I had to do something to redirect its course.

"You know, we should probably tell Lucy that you're here," Anna said in a very loud voice. "Don't you think, *Angel*?"

"Of course," I said, and turned away from Damiano's amused gaze. "Lucy?" I said into my intercom. "Damiano Vero's here to see you." There was a second or two delay before my intercom flashed back. She wanted me to pick up the phone and I realized I would have to listen to a tirade with Damiano standing right in front of me, no doubt hearing every word of it.

"Lucy?"

"He is *here*? In the *office*?"

"Yes, Lucy."

"*Why*? And why was I not informed?"

"Nobody knew he—" I looked up at Damiano. One corner of his mouth was turned up in an ironic smile.

"DAMN IT!" she screamed.

"Should I tell him—" There was a loud click in my ear and she slammed her receiver down. Anna was smirking. Damiano looked bemused. I had no idea what to tell him.

"Any trouble finding us?" I asked him, stalling.

"No, not at all," he said.

"How . . . how did you know where we were?" I was seized with a sudden fear that I'd inadvertently given him our physical address during one of our conversations.

"Luciana told me where you are when I spoke to her. Is it okay?"

At that moment, Lucy sailed out of her office and with a toothy grin presented her hand to Damiano as if she were accepting a dance in a Victorian ballroom.

"*Buon giorno,* Damiano Vero!" she said. Her voice was high and fluty, a tone I'd never heard from her before. "In the flesh," she added.

"Luciana, *piacere*," he said, and moved to kiss her cheeks. There was an awkward moment when it became apparent that he wouldn't be able to reach her face gracefully, but he made a quick recovery by taking her hand and kissing that instead.

"Well!" she exclaimed. Her flustered schoolgirl tone was becoming a little grotesque. "You *are* a handsome man, after all. You should have sent a photo, Damiano, I could have gotten you even more money! Yes, indeed." She raked him with her eyes. "You're the best-looking heroin addict I've ever seen!"

To his credit, Damiano didn't flinch, nor did his expression change. I, on the other hand, was in a sweat of reddened embarrassment for him.

"I assume you've met my staff," Lucy continued, waving her hand in our direction. "And to what do we owe the honor of your presence today?"

"I bring a gift." He gestured to the basket that Anna was still holding. "I made some sweets."

"Charming," Lucy said, and took the basket from Anna. "Very sweet of you."

"I am so grateful to you all," he said, but looked directly at me. Lucy, missing nothing, followed his gaze and raised her eyebrows.

"Delicious, isn't he, Angel? Pity you're already spoken for." I felt my stomach clench and had to lower my eyes. The heat on my face had reached fever temperature. "I'll put this lovely basket in my office," Lucy was saying. "Why don't you come with me, Damiano? Since you're here, there are a few things we should discuss."

"*Bene,*" Damiano said, and started to follow her. "I almost forgot," he said, and walked back to my desk. "I have this for you," he said quietly, and pulled a CD jewel case out of his jacket pocket. He laid it on my desk and turned quickly to go after Lucy. I looked up, sure I would find a disapproving scowl from Anna, but she'd missed the whole interchange and was staring, bereft, as Damiano's basket disappeared into Lucy's office. I grabbed the CD before she could see it and tossed it into my purse. For all I knew, it was merely a copy of his manuscript on disk, but something told me that it wasn't for public consumption. My computer chirped with the sound of an instant message. Anna.

Well, I guess that's the last we'll see of those cakes.

I'm sure she'll share, I wrote back.

She won't. Nothing ever comes out of there once it goes in.

Just as well, they don't look too slimming, I wrote, and immediately regretted it. Now she'd think I was implying she was fat. I looked at the clock. It was just past eight in New York. It was to be a day without end, as the persistent twitter of Anna's instant messages reminded me.

Guess I'm reading your boyfriend's ms tonight, she wrote. *I'll try to be gentle.*

Just be honest, I typed, striking my keyboard with more force than was necessary. And skip the lame attempts at humor, I thought to myself.

Will do, she sent back. *Anything special I should know before I start reading?* She wasn't letting it go. I looked at the clock again and over at Lucy's closed door. Through it, I could hear the rise and dip of her voice mingling with Damiano's. I was suddenly and unbearably tired.

Yes, I replied to Anna, *I'm exhausted. I have one more thing to do and then I'm heading home.*

Before she had a chance to respond, I covered my last base of the day and sent an e-mail to the anonymous author of *Blind Submission.* I wasn't about to risk letting that one get away from me like I had with Shelly Franklin.

To: ganovelist@heya.com
From: angel.robinson@fiammalit.com
Subject: BLIND SUBMISSION

Dear "g,"

Thank you very much for sending the opening pages of BLIND SUB-MISSION to us. We have now had a chance to review your work and, on behalf of Lucy Fiamma, I'm happy to say that we are sufficiently intrigued by your pages and we would love to see more! In fact, if the entire manuscript is finished, please send it along as soon as possible. If you could let us know whether or not this novel has been submitted to other agents, that would be great. Could you please give us a call at 510-555-7666? We'll look forward to reading!

Many thanks,
Angel Robinson
Lucy Fiamma Literary Agency

I hit the SEND button on my computer, turned it off, and started gathering my substantial pile of take-home reading. But before I could get out the door, the phone started ringing in one final cruel burst of sound. Anna, head bent over some imaginary work at her desk, pointedly refused to answer it and so, with a loud sigh, I lifted the receiver.

"Good *evening*, Lucy Fiamma Agency."

There was laughing on the other end. "Still there, are you?" Ah, Gordon Hart.

"Hello, Mr. Hart." I looked at the clock. It was closing in on nine in New York. "We could say the same for you! It's very late there, isn't it?"

"No rest for the *wicked*," he offered. "I'm sure you're familiar. I'll assume she's still there as well, then?"

"Well, actually, she's . . ." I looked over at Lucy's closed door. Once again, I was faced with what I'd secretly dubbed the Lucy Challenge. Did I put the very important (and consistently elusive) Gordon Hart through to Lucy and, in the process, interrupt her conversation with her newest, brightest author, or did I take a message and risk her possible fire-breathing wrath? And then I realized that Lucy would like nothing better than to look as important and powerful as possible in front of Damiano by cutting him off to take a call from one of "the country's most important publishers." As soon as this thought occurred to me, I decided that I simply didn't want to give her the pleasure. It was a small thing, possibly even petty, but it gave me a substantial feeling of satisfaction.

"She's actually not here at the moment," I said. "But I can—"

"Really?" he said, and laughed again. "How *unusual*. But not to worry, I don't really need to *speak* to her. I was calling to leave a message. I'll be out of town next week and I wanted to make sure she knew that. I will call her back when I return. Let her know, will you, Ms. Robinson?"

"I will," I said.

"Good," he answered, and hung up.

Gordon Hart wasn't the only one who didn't want to talk to Lucy. Before she could emerge again with enough new work to keep me at my desk indefinitely, I grabbed my things and hightailed it out the door.

I LAY IN MY BED, awake and unmoving, Malcolm's warm body wrapped around me in the wordless intimacy of flesh against flesh. I could feel his slow, even breaths in my ear and his lips against my cheek. I reached my hand out in the dark to stroke his arm, my fingers tracing the swell of his shoulder, and he stirred, pulling me closer to him.

"Can't sleep?" he whispered into my hair.

"I guess not." I sighed. "Didn't mean to wake you, though."

"I wasn't sleeping," he said. He lay silent for a while and I was sure that he'd drifted off. I closed my eyes, hoping for the sleep that wouldn't come. "Do you want to talk?" Malcolm asked. "You've been so quiet." It was true; this was the longest conversation we'd had since he'd arrived hours earlier.

I'd found my kitchen nearly empty when I got home from work and realized that I couldn't remember the last time I'd gone shopping for food. Too tired to go out again but too hungry not to eat, I found myself staring into my refrigerator at an old carton of eggs that had expired the week before, wondering if they were still safe. I considered what would happen if they weren't. Perhaps they'd make me sick, I thought; maybe even sick enough to be hospitalized. And hospitalization was a perfectly legitimate reason to take a day off. I figured I couldn't lose. I had the eggs in my hand, ready to scramble, when I realized the horrible nature of my logic. Clearly, hunger and exhaustion were making me crazy. Because only a crazy person would consider making herself dangerously ill in order to miss work. In a fit of self-preservation, I turned instead to a stale box of crackers and polished them off while I unpacked manuscripts and laid them out for reading. But the thought of doing more work was so overwhelming, I found myself close to tears. I cued Damiano's CD in my stereo and was contemplating a hot bath when Malcolm knocked on my door.

I didn't ask him why he hadn't let himself in with his key because I didn't care. I was just so glad to see him. No, glad wasn't it, exactly . . . I was *hungry.* For him. He walked in and I grabbed him and pressed my face into his chest.

"Hey," he said as I clutched at him. "I'm sorry about this morning."

"Forget it," I said, and lifted my face for his kiss. Neither one of us had spoken another word until now.

"Want to talk about it?" Malcolm repeated. "Might help."

"My job . . ." I started. I closed my hand around his wrist as if to anchor myself. "I don't know if I'm going to make it."

Malcolm shifted beside me, separating his limbs from mine. "What do you mean?" he asked. "I thought you were doing so well there."

"I am," I said. "I mean, I think I am. You never know with her."

"You're not getting along with her?"

"That's not it, exactly," I said, and struggled to pull the right words out. I wished I could transfer my thoughts to him without having to verbalize them. "There's just so much pressure. And it's getting really weird in the office. One of the girls I work with quit today. She just walked out."

"But people quit all the time," he said. "What's so weird about that?"

"You don't understand. . . ." I sighed. I didn't know how to explain how casually cruel Lucy had been to Nora—*Kelly*—and how I'd just accepted it, even going so far as to blame N— Kelly herself.

Malcolm propped himself up on his elbow. I could feel his body tensing next to me. "Make me understand," he said. "I'm asking because I want to know. I care about what's going on with you."

He *did* want to know, I thought. He was concerned. He loved me. I should be able to tell him everything, otherwise what kind of relationship did we have?

"I saw her *naked* this morning," I told him. "I got to the office and she came out in a towel and told me to start making her calls. And then the towel fell off. Ugh."

"Are you talking about Lucy?" he said.

"Yes, Lucy. Totally naked. I nearly had a heart attack."

"What, she bent over to pick up the soap or something?"

"I wasn't in her *bathroom,* Malcolm. She came out into the office in a towel and it fell off. And then *she* accused *me* of walking in on *her.*"

"Oh, come on," Malcolm said, and laughed. "You're exaggerating, right?"

"Not in the slightest."

"Well, maybe she was embarrassed, A. Did you think of that? And did everyone else see this, too? Because that would have been even more embarrassing."

"No, nobody else saw it. She went back into her office, and when I went in there again, she was dressed."

"I think you're making a big deal out of nothing, Angel. The poor woman—"

"Poor woman? Are you kidding? There's nothing poor about Lucy Fiamma! Poor *me* is more like it."

"Okay, okay," he said. He waited a moment and then laughed. "So," he said, "is she hot or what?"

"Very funny," I answered.

"Okay, no jokes about naked bosses. What else is bothering you?"

"It's just . . . difficult," I said. "And it doesn't seem to be getting any easier." I'd lost my desire to share the particulars with him. Laid bare in my own bed, I felt overexposed.

"You're not thinking of quitting, are you?" he asked, his voice soft and serious.

"And if I was?" It came out sounding testy.

"Well, you haven't exactly given it much of a chance. And I know you love it. I've seen how involved you are. You're into it, admit it."

"I do love the work. Some of it, anyway. Just not all of it. And not all the damn time." I thought about telling him about the expired eggs and decided against it. He clearly wasn't in an empathetic mood.

He reached over me and fumbled around my bedside table until he found the stereo remote. "Let's have a little music, shall we?" he said, and clicked it on. I felt my whole body stiffen when the strains of the first song, "Angel" by Jimi Hendrix, washed over us in the dark. Damiano's CD. In my haste to drag Malcolm off to bed, I'd forgotten to take it out.

"What's this?" Malcolm asked.

"A new . . . a new CD I got."

"Hmm," he said, and curled around me once more. "You're not still mad about my novel, are you? You should just forget about it, okay, Angel? It's important to me, but not more important than us."

"I'm not mad at you, Malcolm." I hesitated before I went on, measuring my words. "I gave her your novel today," I said at last. "She's going to read it." *After Anna got to it,* I added silently, but I sure as hell wasn't going to mention that to him. There was a long pause. Because he was lying so close to me, I could tell that Malcolm actually stopped breathing for a few seconds.

"Really?" he asked finally.

"Yes, but Malcolm, I don't know if she's going to want to take it. You understand that, right?"

"Of course I understand it," he said, "but . . ." He hesitated. Jimi Hendrix gave way to the next song, Tom Petty singing "Angel Dream (No. 4)."

"But what?"

"Haven't you told me how much she respects your opinion? If you tell her it's great, don't you think that makes a difference? Seems like it's made a big difference for a few writers already."

"But I haven't read it, Malcolm. She'd know I was biased. This way I'm being fair."

"What do you mean? You told her it was your *boyfriend's* book?"

"Of course."

"Why 'of course'? What the hell, Angel? She didn't have to know the connection. Wouldn't it have made more sense just to give it to her without telling her who I was? It's not like you haven't been doing that with all the other assholes who send their crap in. Now she'll think I'm just trying to get a free ride off my girlfriend. She won't even *read* the thing."

"Hey," I said sharply, disentangling myself from him and sitting up. "You're *welcome*." There was a pointed silence and then Malcolm sighed, reached up and gently pulled me back down next to him. And that was when it occurred to me that he had a point. I could feel my face get hot with guilt and I was glad Malcolm couldn't see me in the dark. I sighed, hearing the sound of my breath between us.

"I'm sorry," Malcolm said quietly. "I didn't mean . . . I just thought you'd want to read it yourself. You know, before . . ." We lay still for a moment and then Malcolm folded his arms around me and put his hands in my hair, tickling the back of my neck with his fingers. He brushed his lips across my mouth and throat, moving downward, covering the angel wings on my breast with a long, exquisitely sweet kiss. For that moment at least, all was once again right with the world.

"Thank you," he whispered. "I mean that."

I put my arms around him and sighed again, this time with pleasure.

"Want to talk about anything else?" he asked.

"Mmm," I sighed. "No, no more talking. Just keep . . ." I put his hands back in my hair. "Keep doing what you're doing."

Malcolm did that and more, moving his hands across my back and his lips along my neck. He covered me with his body and I could feel the heat of him all the way to my bones. All the while, Damiano's CD continued to play in the background. "She Talks to Angels," "Maybe Angels," "Angel of Harlem," and more angels after that.

Malcolm stopped kissing me midway through "Angel of Mercy" and looked at me. I could just make out the glimmer of his eyes in the dimness.

"Where did you say you got this CD?" he asked. "They're all angel songs."

I supposed there was nothing quite like stating the obvious.

"Um, well, an author sent it to me. A wannabe."

"Really?" he asked. "That's a little overboard, isn't it?"

"You'd be surprised," I said. "Some authors will do anything to get published."

And then he covered my mouth with his own.

SEVEN

To: angel.robinson@fiammalit.com
From: ganovelist@heya.com
Subject: Re: BLIND SUBMISSION

Dear Ms. Robinson,

Thank you for your kind reply. Although this may sound a little "over the top," I am not surprised that Ms. Fiamma has taken an interest in my work. I believe, as you do, that this novel has the potential to be a blockbuster. A real winner, as it were. To answer your question, I have not submitted this manuscript elsewhere. Ms. Fiamma's agency is known to be among the very best in the country and that is why I selected her. I do not plan to submit elsewhere.

Having said that, I prefer to remain "anonymous" at this point for reasons I cannot disclose at the moment. Please assure Ms. Fiamma that, when the time comes, there will be no problem concerning my identity.

In the interest of retaining this anonymity, I will send the manuscript to you via e-mail. To that end, I've attached another chapter. Enjoy!

With best wishes,
G.

BLIND SUBMISSION

Chapter 2

Carol Moore was throwing a party at the office to celebrate the entry of yet another book onto the *New York Times* bestseller list. This one was a first novel by Svetlana Vladic, a book the *New York Times* called "a modern *Anna Karenina*."

Alice settled the bottles of Dom Pérignon in their ice buckets and suppressed the rage that had been building in her all day, all week, for her entire life. Svetlana Vladic was nobody—a pale, washed-out, passionless holograph of a woman. She'd lucked into this success and it tore a hole in Alice's heart. Alice had to admit that the book was good. No, the book was great, but the author wasn't. It was insanely unfair for someone as uncharismatic as Svetlana Vladic to have achieved this kind of glory.

Alice ground her teeth. The mask she wore in the office— that of model employee who wanted nothing more than to please her boss and her boss's clients—was slipping. What was under the mask was considerably uglier and Alice couldn't afford to show it. Yet.

Alice thought about the rejection letter she'd received from Carol Moore only days ago. Of course, Carol hadn't known that Alice was the author she was rejecting. Alice had submitted her own novel under a false name and had given it to Carol, telling the agent that it was some of the best fiction she'd ever read. Carol was inclined to believe Alice because Alice had proven herself to have an excellent eye.

"If you recommend it," Carol told Alice, "I'm sure it must be wonderful."

The ax fell soon after. Carol had called Alice into a private meeting and told her that she was sorry, but the novel was just not good enough for her to sell. "I understand that you were very fond of this one," Carol told Alice, and regarded her with a questioning look, as if she couldn't really comprehend why Alice had liked the novel so much, "so I read it very carefully. But it's just not for me. Perhaps you'd like to work with this author? You could make some suggestions and then we could take another look at it?"

Alice had to take a minute to gather herself after that. Her disappointment and anger flooded her like a tidal wave and she wasn't sure she could keep her face from showing it. Passing her own work on to Carol anonymously had been a calculated risk. Had Alice told Carol that she was the author, Carol would not have been able to read the pages objectively and might even have started looking into Alice's background. Alice couldn't afford that. Had Carol liked what she'd read, none of that would have mattered.

Damn her, Alice thought bitterly. Carol's rejection, however innocent, wounded Alice to her core. Carol had no understanding of what Alice felt. She could never understand what it meant to want something so badly and for so long that every day without fulfillment killed you a little more. And then to know that what you wanted would never happen the way you wanted it . . . To know that really, underneath it all, you weren't any good . . . Alice was again filled with red anger.

Finally, when she was able to contain herself, she told Carol, "I don't think so. If it isn't good enough for you, I don't think we should waste our time on it."

"Were you wanting to represent it yourself?" Carol asked. "Did I misunderstand? Because it's a little early for you to be taking on projects of your own. You understand, don't you, Alice? But we should talk about that if it's something that concerns you. I am certainly willing to work with you. In time, you could be a fine agent."

Alice tried to twist her bitterness into a smile. "You are very kind, Carol," she said. "I really appreciate it."

"Listen, I know how tough it is when you're just starting out," Carol said. "Especially if you're a woman. It's supposed to be easier now, for women, but it isn't. As I'm sure your mother told you—"

"I don't have a mother," Alice said, her words bitten off and strangled.

Carol's eyes widened. "Everyone has a mother, dear."

"Well, not me," Alice said. She could feel her hands turning into fists. She didn't think she could stand it if Carol kept this up.

"I'm sorry," Carol said, "I didn't mean to—"

"It's okay," Alice interrupted, "it's just . . . It's okay. Of course somebody gave birth to me. But I've been on my own forever. I've never had a woman I could look up to. Not until now, anyway." Alice's fists were so tight she could feel her manicured fingernails beginning to break the skin of her palms.

"That's very nice of you to say," Carol said. There was a pause between the two of them. Carol looked down at the letter opener on her desk and then back at Alice. "Listen, Alice, I tell you what I'll do—I'll write your author a long letter and make some suggestions." A tiny flicker of hope danced through Alice's head. Carol managed to extinguish it with her next words. "Perhaps that way it won't seem as harsh. And then there's always the option of trying again after a rewrite. Although, frankly, I'm not sure it would help too much."

"Great," Alice said, her rage threatening to explode in her brain.

Later, Alice had been forced to mail herself Carol's rejection letter. That letter was the point of a knife in Alice's heart. Now the success of yet another undeserving author had driven the knife clean through.

It was time for a new plan. As Alice picked up the phone to call Vaughn Blue's personal number, she knew exactly where she was going to start.

The arrival of *Blind Submission*'s second chapter couldn't have come at a worse time. The theme of ego-crushing literary rejection it illustrated so well wasn't so strange in and of itself, but the fact that the very same theme was playing out in my own life (and at my own agency) made it uncomfortable—even disturbing—to read. Of course, it wasn't my own work that had gotten rejected; it was Malcolm's.

Deep down, although I didn't like to admit it, I never truly believed that Lucy would agree to represent Malcolm. I had no concrete reason for my doubt, but I didn't need one. I was starting to develop an instinct about how Lucy would react—almost as if part of my unconscious was wired into hers—and it told me that Malcolm would never find his way into her pantheon of published authors. I'd certainly been no help at all. He would have been better off just sending it in himself.

The first sign that I was right came when Anna, perpetually behind in her reading, finished Malcolm's book in record time. Naturally, she didn't share her opinion of it with me. I assumed she'd disliked it (if she'd actually read it), or at least said she did, because that was the way things went in this office. Allying herself with me would do nothing to promote Anna's cause. Of course, Anna's reaction, whatever it was, was immaterial. The manuscript went to Lucy next and then, a day or two later, Lucy called me into her office.

She was sitting at her desk, wearing a lavender dress, gloves, and a hat to match. I'd quickly gotten used to Lucy's bizarre outfits, but this one, which was some sort of post–Henry Higgins' Eliza Doolittle, was stunning on many different levels.

"Do I strike you as someone who has a lot of spare time on her hands, Angel?"

The hat actually had a veil.

"I'm sorry, I don't understand what you mean, Lucy."

"I mean, do you, Angel Robinson, feel that I, Lucy Fiamma, have the time to *fuck* around with *bullshit,* or do you think that my time is possibly more valuable than that?"

"Of course your time is valuable, Lucy."

She was wearing white stockings. Not panty hose. Stockings.

"Well, then, Angel, why have you taken up my time with this?" She tossed Malcolm's book onto the carpet at her feet and waved her hand at it in disgust. I bent, almost involuntarily, and picked it up. I realized what a mistake I had made and cursed myself for being so stupid. Although it hardly mattered, I had to know—had to ask the question.

"Was it the writing?" I asked in a small voice.

"His writing is *okay*," Lucy sniffed. "But there's no plot! It's some sort of literary exercise, destined, at best, for midlist. You know what midlist is, don't you, Angel?"

"Yes, Lucy, I—"

"Let me put it this way," she continued. "If this book were a film, it would be going straight to video. Do you understand me?"

"Lucy, I—"

"What I don't understand is why you would risk your career over a man. Can you enlighten me, Angel? You're so smart in other ways."

"I don't know what you mean, Lucy." My voice was cold, if not loud, and I could feel ice spreading across my middle. I was angry, but I was also afraid. Afraid of Lucy and afraid that she was right. She so often was.

"He must be something," she went on, lowering her voice. "Is that it, Angel? Is he some kind of divine lover?" A green gleam entered her eyes. I debated making some kind of comment about the inappropriateness of her remark, but she started speaking again before I had the chance. "You're young, Angel, but you have to understand it's imperative that a girl—no, a *woman*—with intelligence like yours not give up yourself for a man. Or for anyone. We've been so conditioned to believe that we are nothing without men that we forget our own power. I would hate to see that happen to you, Angel. It would be a terrible, terrible waste."

She was completely sincere. Her ability to couch cold barbs in warm truth was another one of Lucy's singular talents. She'd tear you down in a heartbeat, but, at the same time, she'd be laying the foundation to rebuild you. What always got me was her accuracy. She could find the sore spot and press in relentlessly, but she was also able to find the unshakable strengths and tease them out. I knew that she was right about Malcolm. I *did* define myself through him. Until I started working for Lucy, my plans for my own future were dependent on Malcolm's plans for his. I'd merely been trying to fit myself into his vision. Of course, this wasn't his fault at all—it was mine. I found myself confused into silence as I stood in front of Lucy. She kept talking, her voice becoming soft and lugubrious as she went on.

"Now, I realize that you've put yourself in rather a tight spot with this man and his novel by giving it to me, so I've done you a favor." She removed her hat and placed it, with great care, on the edge of her desk. "I've called the boyfriend," she said. It took me a moment to realize that she was talking about Malcolm. "And I have given him some very good advice as to how he can improve his chances of becoming published. I know you understand how valuable such a discussion can be and I know that you are aware that this is something I *never* do. The authors I represent don't need the kind of advice I've given him free of charge and those who do need it I wouldn't represent in the first place."

Lucy pursed her lips and waited for my reaction, which was awhile in coming because I had to spend a few moments trying to figure out when she'd made the phone call and why Malcolm hadn't mentioned it to me.

"That was very kind of you, Lucy," I said at last. "I'm sure he really appreciated it. I know I do."

"Yes," Lucy said, and smiled broadly. The softness, however, was gone from her voice. "I'm sure I've spared you quite a bit of discomfort."

"Thank you, Lucy. I owe you." As soon as the words left my lips, I regretted them. Yes, I owed her for hiring me in the first place, but I'd more than proved my worth. If it hadn't been for me, she'd never have seen *Parco Lambro;* Anna certainly wouldn't have pulled it out of the pile for a second look. No, Anna's specialty was finding cute books about kitties and puppies and the occasional travel guide, nothing that required any actual *reading* or thought. Still, I should have read Malcolm's manuscript before I'd given it to her. That was my mistake. One I wouldn't make again.

Lucy had me fixed in that stare of hers again. "Yes," she said. "You owe me, Angel. You certainly do." She seemed to mull this for a moment and then snapped back into the mode I knew so well. "Now, let's get on with it. I don't even want to think about how much time we've wasted on this."

My heart sank at hearing Malcolm reduced to "wasted time."

"What we need to talk about," Lucy went on, rising from her desk and striding over to her couch, "are *these*." She picked up two manuscripts from the pile on her coffee table and held them out. One was *Blind Submission* and the other was *Elvis Will Dance at Your Wedding*. "Now, *this* is how you should be using your talents, Angel. Come on, sit down."

I settled myself on the couch, trying not to sit so close that we were touching. "My first question," she said, pointing to Shelly Franklin's novel, "is can you make this one work? Because if you can, it could be one of those literary darlings. Well, *I* can make it one of those literary darlings, at any rate."

"That was my thinking, too," I told her. "The author's willing to work, definitely, so I think—"

"Good! Make sure she has an agency contract by the end of the day." She tossed the manuscript at me and I caught it before it could slide off my knees to the floor. "Now, this . . ." She trailed off as she glanced over my original notes for *Blind Submission*. ". . . is very interesting." I was surprised to see actual excitement on her face.

"You like this one, Lucy?"

"Is there a reason I shouldn't?"

"Well, the writing's a little weak . . . I thought . . ."

Lucy raised her eyebrows in an exaggerated expression of surprise. "The writing is not overly literary, if that's what you mean. But I think the style suits the concept here, Angel. And I believe this has the potential to be an extremely commercial novel if it's presented correctly. Didn't you mention *The Nanny Diaries* in your notes? In any event, it would be nothing for you to retool the writing, would it, Angel?"

"Well, no, I suppose I could—"

"Of course you could." She leaned in close to me, her green eyes probing mine. "But yes, I like it and I find it most amusing that it's set in a literary agency. Don't you, Angel?"

She was leading me somewhere, but I couldn't tell where. My growing sense of discomfort told me that it wasn't a place I wanted to go.

"It's interesting," I said. "But what about the fact that books about publishing don't usually do well?"

"Nothing sells until it does, Angel. That's the rule of this business. Who cared about the Inuit before Karanuk? Did anyone, aside from myself, believe that *Cold!* was hot? You have to make it happen, Angel."

"Well, that's certainly true," I said. "But how do you feel about this anonymous thing? It's a little cloak-and-dagger, don't you think?"

Lucy's smile looked like an incision in her face. "I'm willing to play along," she said. "It might even add some glamour . . . some danger . . . to the package. The anonymous author worked for *Primary Colors,* didn't it?"

"Yes, but his *agent* knew who he was, right?"

She sat up straight and her demeanor changed again. She'd run out of patience. "Why am *I* trying to convince *you?*" she barked. "Didn't you give me this novel in the first place?"

"Yes, but—"

"Has the author contacted other agents, then? Have we lost it already?"

"No, in fact—"

"Well, then, get on it, Angel."

I tried to stand, but Lucy reached out and grabbed the fabric of my sleeve as if to pull me back down. The movement took both of us by surprise and she let go as quickly as she'd reached for me. "Is there anything else you want to tell me about this novel, Angel?"

"I don't think so," I told her. I still didn't know what she was driving at, and it was starting to make me very anxious.

"Are you sure? Nothing to tell me about the protagonist? The assistant who is also a *writer* and who sends in her own work *anonymously?*"

I stared at her for a moment, my mind a complete blank, but then it finally hit me—hard. "You don't think *I* wrote this, do you?"

"You needn't sound so shocked, Angel. Isn't that what you'd think if you were in my position? And it's not as if something like this has never happened before. I can't tell you how many aspiring writers I've had to wade through in this office. I didn't think you were one of them. But if it is you, I'd advise you to tell me now. Because I'll find out, Angel. You know I will."

"Lucy, I have no aspirations to write, none at all." I was almost laughing at the absurdity of it. "I can't write, anyway! I'm hopeless at it."

"Well, I don't believe *that*," Lucy countered. "Nobody who understands writers the way you do would be a hopeless writer herself."

I shrugged and offered her a limp smile. "What can I say?" I offered. "I love books. I'm a reader. I can't write, Lucy, that's the truth. And I certainly didn't write this." I waved the manuscript in front of me. Lucy tilted her head to one side, studying me, the movement giving her the look of a large bird. She removed one glove and then the other, placing them carefully on the coffee table in front of her.

"I hope you're not upset about your boyfriend's novel, Angel. Are you?"

Lucy's look had changed to one of concern and I wondered whether or not it was genuine. I decided that it was.

"I'm disappointed," I told her, "but not upset."

"I may have been a little harsh earlier," she responded, "but, Angel, you realize now how very difficult it is to sell even excellent projects. There's just no room for those that don't have at least the potential to be great. I hope you know that had I seen any possibility in that novel I would have considered taking it on."

"I do," I said.

"I see so much potential in *you*, Angel. I hate to see you squandering your talent. I'm looking out for *you*, dear. I believe you have an extremely bright future ahead of you."

Dear? Since when had I become a "dear"? But I believed her. Her tone was suddenly so soft, soothing, and laden with feeling that I wouldn't have been surprised if she went on to tell me she loved me.

"Thank you, Lucy." My voice cracked over the last syllable of her name. Her unexpected burst of sentiment had actually choked me up.

"I am investing in *your* future, Angel. I do hope you realize that. You have a wonderful opportunity here—so much room to grow."

I wondered again if she truly meant what she was saying, but there was nothing in her tone to suggest otherwise. "Thank you," I repeated because I'd lost track of what she'd said and this seemed like the only appropriate way to respond.

"Well, all right then," she said. "You'd better go back to work."

I left her office thinking I'd be able to do just that, focus on my work and shrug off my guilt about Malcolm's rejection, but I was mistaken. When I got back to my desk, the second chapter of *Blind Submission* was waiting for me in my e-mail in-box.

I WAS WIDE AWAKE, editing Shelly Franklin's novel, when Malcolm let himself into my apartment after his shift that night.

"I need to talk to you," I said.

"Mind if I take a shower first?" he answered. "It was a very long night and"—he sniffed the sleeve of his white shirt—"I think I've got at least seven different wines on my shirt. I stink."

I didn't want to wait. I had to talk to him about Lucy before it could fester in my brain any longer. "It's about your novel, Malcolm."

Malcolm sat down on one of the two chairs in my apartment, not on the bed next to me. I could see resignation lining his features but also, under that, a small glow of hope. I hated that I had to extinguish it and hated that he'd put me in the position of having to do it.

"What about it?" he asked.

"Lucy gave it back to me today. She's not going to represent it."

"I know," he said. "I thought maybe you were going to tell me she changed her mind."

It took me a second to realize why he knew and then it came back to me. Lucy had said she'd called him. Like a good author, he'd put his phone number and address on the cover page of his novel.

"Why didn't you tell me she called you, Malcolm?"

"Haven't exactly had the chance, have I?" A twisted, mirthless grin spread its way across his mouth. "You're not what I'd call available these days, Angel."

"What's that supposed to mean?" I put down Shelly Franklin's manuscript and capped the red pen I held in my hand. I needed to get up, but I was too tired to move. I was feeling very defensive and didn't think my bed was the right arena in which to deflect an attack. Malcolm was leaning back in the chair, his legs spread out in front of him. He looked worn out and exhausted but stubborn and ready to fight.

"You're a little caught up in work, aren't you?" he said. "Always so damn busy, so very, very important. Anyway, Angel, it doesn't seem as if you're particularly interested in what happens to me and my career. I think being rejected by your boss makes that pretty clear. If you'd taken just a little time out of your fascinatingly busy schedule to give your *fiancé* a little help—to *read* his damn book—like you give to every other nobody-writer who sends in a manuscript, perhaps it wouldn't have been rejected in the first place. Did that ever occur to you?"

"Fiancé?" I asked. "When did you become my fiancé?"

"Is that a joke, Angel?"

"No, it's not. When it suits you, obviously, we're engaged. But I don't remember having a discussion about this recently. When is the last time we talked about our future, anyway?"

Malcolm sat up in the chair, his face darkening with anger. "That's not really the point, is it, Angel? I think you're only bringing this up now to get out of taking responsibility for what you've done. You shafted me and you don't want to admit it."

"What are you talking about? The only reason I applied for this job in the first place was because of you."

"You might want to rethink that," he said softly. "It seems to me you've got a whole other agenda working here. I don't—" He stopped and looked down at his hands, flexing them. He cleared his throat. "I don't know what's happened to you, Angel. Since you started working at that place, you've become a different person. I mean, even *Lucy* cares more about me than you do. At least she took the time to call me."

"Don't read too much into that!" I snapped at him. "She did that for me."

"See what I mean?" he said. "You're becoming a real bitch."

We were both stunned silent after that one. Malcolm and I had disagreed from time to time, but we'd never had a fight like this. And we had never even come close to name-calling. He might as well have slapped me. I felt tears, hot with anger, welling in my eyes. If he was affected by them, Malcolm gave no indication. He stood up and headed over to the door. "I can't deal with this," he barked, and stalked out, slamming the door behind him.

FOR A LONG TIME after Malcolm left, I lay staring at the door as if I could erase the last hour by sheer force of will. My eyes filled, emptied, and filled again. The Malcolm I knew was sweet and loving and, for the past two years, had been my best friend. I didn't recognize the angry, bitter person who had just left my apartment.

The phone rang and I leaped up, convinced it was Malcolm calling to apologize, or to tell me that he loved me, or that it had all been a huge misunderstanding.

"Hi," I breathed into the phone, breathless enough to sound like a 900-number phone-sex operator.

"Angel?"

I was so shocked that the voice I heard belonged not to Malcolm but to Damiano that for a moment I just said nothing.

"I'm sorry," he said into my silence, "I must have the wrong number."

"No!" I said, much sharper than I'd intended. "This is Angel."

"I'm very sorry, Angel. It's so late. I woke you?"

"No," I said, pushing the hair off my forehead and trying to get my bearings. I was sliding between my office persona and that of weeping girlfriend and couldn't find any kind of conversational purchase. "I'm— I mean, it's okay. I'm not sleeping."

"I shouldn't have called," he said. "But I thought . . ."

"You thought what?"

"I didn't really see you before. When I came in to the office."

I had become very familiar with Damiano's broken English, and because I'd spent so much time with his words and thoughts through *Parco Lambro,* I was usually able to understand what he wanted to say before he finished speaking.

"It's okay," I told him. "You didn't have to . . . You came to talk to Lucy, anyway, right?"

"*Sì,* but . . . Angel," he said, "I don't know how to say it." There was a long pause while he formulated the correct words. "I have to thank you in some way. I know how much you have done for me."

"You don't. I mean, you have, Damia— Dami. You have thanked me."

"I just thought to call you and tell you, but . . ." He sighed into the phone and muttered something in Italian under his breath I couldn't catch. "Now it is so late and I have disturbed you. *Mi dispiace*. I'm sorry, Angel."

"Dami, it's really fine. It's okay. Thank you."

"I should find a better way than to call so late at night. I've made you sad."

"What?"

"You sound sad. That's the right word, no?"

For a heartbeat I considered what it would be like to tell him he was right, I was sad, but not at all for the reasons he thought. I had the sudden, strong feeling that he would understand, that he'd be able to read me as I'd been able to read him. It was tempting, but then, in an instant and for so many reasons, completely impossible.

"Yes, it's the right word. But I'm not sad, just . . . tired."

"I know, I am so sorry to call. I will find a better way to thank you. Good night."

"Good night, Dami."

"Sleep well, Angel."

I PREPARED FOR BED and lay down in it, but sleep was far from coming. There was no comfortable spot in my bed, no fold or corner that didn't continuously remind me of Malcolm's absence. When I couldn't stand it any longer, I reached for the phone, preparing to call Malcolm and act like the helpless, dependent woman I'd always hoped I'd never become. I couldn't tell if it was a last vestige of female pride or the fact that I saw her phone number tucked under the phone, but at the last minute, I decided to dial not Malcolm but my mother.

The phone rang so many times I was almost hypnotized by its steady sound. There was no answering machine, of course, and so I just held on, waiting and hoping. I was about to give up when she finally picked up and I heard her voice.

"Hello?"

"Hillary?"

"Angel? What's wrong?" There were some things, despite the distance and the differences in our worldviews, that my mother just didn't have to be told. "Are you in trouble?"

I couldn't imagine what my mother's definition of trouble might be, so I didn't try. "No, Hillary, I just wanted to talk to you—see if you were okay."

"I'm fine, love, never better. I'm glad you called. I was going to call you, honey. I was going to tell you that I'm moving and I don't know if I'll have access to a phone where I'm going."

"Didn't you just get there, wherever you are?"

"Well, I've been here long enough, that's certain. I'll have to tell you about it another time. Anyway, I've met these two amazing Inuit women and I'm going with them to Alaska."

"Alaska!" The first thing that came to my mind was the cover of *Cold!*

"It's still the United States, Angel. Don't sound so alarmed. But we can talk about that later. I want to know what's wrong with you. You haven't told me. Is it Malcolm?"

I wasn't surprised that she knew, but I wasn't glad, either. I knew what was coming.

"You're losing your center, Angel, I can feel it. Men will do that, especially this one."

"I don't know why you don't like him, Hillary."

"Why don't you ask yourself why you think I don't like him, Angel? I guarantee you'll find the answer if you look for it. What's he done to you? And why have you let him?"

"Nothing. Look, it's fine, okay? Never mind. I just wanted to talk to you, that's all. I'll call you— When are you leaving the Amazons?"

"I'll be here until the next new moon, so I have about three weeks yet."

"All right, I'll call you before the next new moon, then, Hillary."

"Angel, you know what will make you feel better?"

"What?"

"Read a good book, my love. From the time you were a tiny little thing, a good book worked better for you than antibiotics."

I started laughing because there was nothing else to do at that point. Maybe she was right. Maybe it had been too long since I'd read a *good* book.

I picked up Shelly Franklin's manuscript again and got back to work.

It was well past two when I stopped and finally turned off the light. Some time after that, I heard Malcolm's key turning in the door. He came inside very quietly and sat down next to me on the bed. He smelled like shampoo and soap and he'd changed into soft, fleecy clothes. As he bent over me his hair brushed my cheek. It was still wet.

"I'm sorry," he whispered.

"So am I," I said, reaching up and pulling him close to me.

Malcolm took off his clothes and slid into bed next to me. We turned to face each other and touched each other carefully, hesitantly, as if either one of us could shatter the other with the wrong move. We fell asleep like that, skin to skin, no space between our bodies. But the emotional distance between us was wide and full of everything we'd left unsaid.

EIGHT

‒‒‒

MEMO

To: Angel
From: LF
Re: BLIND SUBMISSION

Let's discuss.

Jackson Stark, Lucy's new hire and replacement for Nora/Kelly,
edged toward me and gingerly placed Lucy's glaring memo on my desk.

"Uh . . ." he began.

"Thanks, Jackson," I said.

"Um, yes. Sure. You're welcome."

"Okay," I said, knowing that there was more. I looked up at him,
waiting. The scent of his cologne (lush, expensive, but way too liberally
applied) engulfed me. He was twenty years old, a fact Lucy had shared
with all of us, and didn't have enough facial hair to justify the razor burn
on his smooth cheeks. He was wearing a silk shirt festooned with paisley
patterns and black, tight-fitting designer jeans. He'd been working with
us for three weeks and had worn jeans every day. There had not been a

single mention or memo from Lucy regarding his attire in all that time. I wondered if it was because he was male or, likelier, she was waiting for someone else (me? Anna?) to blow the whistle on him. It was Craig who had dug Jackson's résumé up from one of his mysterious files and called him in for an interview. Perhaps he'd been hired simply because he was male. On one of Lucy's memos to Craig during the interview process, she had written simply, *No more girls!!!!*

"I think she wants to talk to you about this," Jackson said, pointing at the manuscript.

"Okay, great. Thanks, Jackson."

He sighed and glided back to his desk. He rearranged his already ordered stacks of paper for a moment and looked over at me once more, concern darkening his eyes.

"I think she wants to talk to you about it, like, now."

"Got it. Thanks, Jackson."

"You're welcome."

Hearing this interchange, Anna looked up from the peanut butter sandwich she was eating and raised an eyebrow in my direction. "Whathat?" She pointed to the memo. I wished she wouldn't speak with her mouth full. It was really starting to annoy me.

"Memo from Lucy," I said.

"Whabout?" Anna asked.

I shot a disgusted look in her direction. At least swallow, I thought. "I don't know," I snapped, but of course I did. I hadn't given Lucy a progress report on *Blind Submission* for a few days and I knew she was expecting a revised, edited manuscript *yesterday*. It had been some time since anything even worth a second look had come in, and Lucy was starting to make plenty of noise about the "dry spell." It didn't seem to matter to her that Karanuk had sent the first couple of chapters of what was sure to be a gigantic sale (not that I'd had a chance to read it—Lucy had snatched it off the pile the moment it arrived in the office) or that, after I finished the Damiano Vero–style edit I was doing on Shelly Franklin's novel, she'd be able to sell *Elvis* for plenty of money. In fact, an auction seemed likely for that one. But Lucy still seemed hungry— ravenous, even—for more. It wasn't about the money. She had an insatiable, constant need for the next big thing. And *I* was the one who was supposed to deliver that to her. I'd become the miller's daughter of my favorite fairy tale, spinning a roomful of straw into gold overnight. Unlike the miller's daughter, however, I didn't have Rumpelstiltskin showing up to help me.

"Um . . . Angel?" Jackson and his cologne were at my desk again.

"Jackson?"

He pointed at Lucy's note. "I think, um, I mean, she, um, like, asked that you see her about that."

"I got it the first time, Jackson," I snapped. From the corner of my eye, I could see Anna's brow furrow with surprise and I felt Craig's disapproving glance from his corner of the office. I couldn't find it in myself to care. For his part, Jackson didn't seem to mind my tone at all. He nodded affably and made his way back to his desk.

"Angel!" Lucy shrieked into my intercom.

"On my way," I answered. I detected a whiff of satisfaction coming from Anna's desk as I jumped up from my chair.

Lucy was sitting on her couch, tapping her Waterman pen impatiently against her corduroy-clad knees, when I entered her office. "Finally!" she said. She didn't wait for me for me to sit down before she started. "What's going on with that novel about the literary agency?"

"I—"

"Have you spoken to the author? Do we have the complete manuscript? Do we have revisions?"

"No," I said. "And no."

"Why not, Angel?"

"The author wants to remain anonymous. I don't have a phone number. And I've been working on the *Elvis*—"

"Still?"

"Yes. But I don't have much to work with on the other one. And are you sure you want me to put so much time into it before we get an agency contract?"

"We don't *have* an agency contract yet?"

"No, but—"

"You'd better get one, Angel."

"Okay, I'm on it."

I got as far as her door before Lucy stopped me again with a question. "How are you and the boyfriend doing?" she asked. "Everything all right there?"

Why she'd ask, I couldn't tell and didn't want to know. The truth was things were not really all right with Malcolm, even if they weren't exactly all wrong. We were spending fewer nights together for one thing. We were getting along fine, but since our argument over his novel, there was a kind of emptiness between the two of us that neither he nor I seemed to be able to fill. This was most evident when we were physically close. It was then, when we were actually touching each other, that I noticed the space between us, as if there was a charged layer of air, a force field, keeping our bodies from joining the way they had before. I wanted to get back whatever we were missing, but I didn't know how. My growing fear, too, was that it had never been there in the first place. None of this was anything I wanted to share with Lucy. Despite the fact that she suddenly sounded all warm and girlfriend-y, the last thing I wanted was to get into a discussion about my love life with her. "Everything's fine," I said.

"Is it? Well, I'm happy to hear it."

"Thanks, Lucy." I thought she was finished then, and I was half out the door before she called me back yet again.

"Angel?"

"Yes, Lucy?"

"I'd like you and the boyfriend to join me for dinner." Although her words indicated an invitation, I knew Lucy well enough to realize that she was issuing a command. I didn't relish the thought of spending more personal time with her than I already did, but turning down dinner was no more an option than refusing to answer the phones. Why she'd want "the boyfriend" there was a mystery, but I was sure I'd find out soon enough. In the meantime, I'd have to make a show of being excited at the prospect.

"That would be great, Lucy."

"Good. Saturday at seven."

"Okay. Great. Um, which restaurant?"

Lucy looked at me with an expression of supreme exasperation. "At my *home,* of course, Angel." She tapped her pen again. I'd come to hate that sound. "You're still in my office, Angel. Is there something else? If not, I believe you've got a writer to chase."

"Okay," I said, and finally, I managed to escape.

To: ganovelist@heya.com
From: angel.robinson@fiammalit.com
Subject: BLIND SUBMISSION

Dear G,

Thanks so much for sending the new material. You haven't mentioned whether or not you have a completed manuscript. In any
event, Ms. Fiamma would like to discuss representing you! Could you
please give us a call at 510-555-7666 as soon as possible?

Many thanks,
Angel

I hit the SEND icon on my computer and let out a sigh. The anony-mous bit had gone on long enough and was starting to wear very thin. We were *interested;* wasn't that what the author wanted? What was the point of carrying on this way? I hoped the next e-mail from our mystery author would have more information and I'd be able to stop playing this guessing game. If not, I'd have to start pressing the author harder, and I wasn't sure I knew how to do that. That hard-bitten agent approach was really much more Lucy's style than mine.

"Go ahead and send the whole thing in, then."

I swiveled my head in the direction of Jackson's voice. I wasn't the only one—Anna was also staring at him, her mouth open in amazement.

"Yeah, it sounds really good," Jackson went on. "Okay, thanks. Bye now."

"Who was that?" I asked Jackson as he hung up the phone.

"Um, just a writer who wants to send something to us." He sounded defensive, but also slightly indignant.

"And you decided to tell him to send the *whole manuscript*?" I thought about checking my tone, which had suddenly become very sharp, but decided against it. It wasn't as if Jackson hadn't been trained—I'd seen to that myself after witnessing Anna's methods first-hand. Why he'd suddenly decided to tell an author to send in hundreds of pages was beyond me.

"But it sounded really good," Jackson said.

"If it's good, we'll ask to see more," I told him. "You never tell them to send the whole thing in first. Haven't we been over this?"

"But—" Jackson began, and found himself cut off by Craig.

"Angel, can I see you for a moment, please?"

I thought about how much I'd like to tell Craig that he could see me quite plainly from where he sat, but instead I got up and walked the short distance to his desk. Craig pulled out several drawers of the tall filing cabinet next to his desk so that we'd be partially obscured from view. This was what constituted privacy in this office. Of course, anyone within earshot (Anna, Jackson) could *hear* everything that was being said. Which, I suppose, was Craig's point.

"Don't you think you're being a little harsh with him?" Craig said, lowering his voice to a movie-star whisper.

"It seems pretty basic," I answered in a whisper of my own. "Telling callers to send in the first fifty is sort of the rule of thumb here, isn't it? I know *I've* told him."

"You're getting a little ahead of yourself, don't you think, Angel?"

Craig's eyes, normally washed out and vague, were alive with brown sparks I'd never seen there before. He was actually angry, and I sensed it didn't have as much to do with me as it seemed.

"What do you mean?" I asked him.

"There's only one boss here," he hissed. "And you're not her."

That set me back—literally. I moved away from Craig as if I'd been pushed. "I'm sorry," I said. "I thought when you asked me to train—"

"Exactly," Craig snapped. "I asked you to *train* him, not pass judgments on his character."

"I never—"

"Do you really think you are so far above the *little people* already, Angel Robinson? Have you forgotten where you came from only a few months ago?" Something caught Craig's eye then and he lowered his gaze to the vicinity of my chest. "Or where you've been?" he added ominously.

I raised my hand to my chest instinctively while looking down to see what Craig was staring at, and discovered that I'd managed to pop one of the buttons on my shirt, exposing a generous bit of bra and breast. And that damn tattoo. I clutched my lapels together, blushing furiously and trying desperately to regain some sense of dignity.

"Excuse me, Craig?" was the best I could come up with.

"Jackson's a good kid," Craig rasped. "You can go back to your desk." He slammed his filing cabinet drawers shut and bent over his desk, leaving me to plod the awkward steps back to my own. I avoided looking at Jackson at all but couldn't help seeing Anna's face. She was wearing a twin version of my embarrassed blush, and for a moment I was completely confused. Was it possible that she felt bad for me?

As if to answer that question, Anna sent me an instant message as soon as I sat down.

It's not your fault. I've told him the same thing. C doesn't like having his territory invaded.

I felt like a kid passing notes in high school. *I'm not invading anyone's territory,* I wrote back, deleting as I went.

He's pretty protective of Lucy.

I deleted the message and looked over at Anna, eyebrows raised. The red color in her face was fading, leaving pinkish splotches on her cheeks. She nodded meaningfully.

"Do you have a safety pin?" I asked her.

"Sure!" She began rummaging through her desk drawer. "What do you need it for?"

Why did she have to know everything? "Just got a problem with my shirt," I stage-whispered.

"Hmm," Anna mumbled. "Thought I had one in here . . ."

"Never mind," I said, watching her unwrap an ancient Tootsie Roll she'd found in the detritus of her desk drawer. "I'll just use a stapler." I reached for the heavy stapler on my desk and angled it to try to bind my gaping buttonhole.

"Angel!" Although I'd heard it countless times, Lucy's voice in my intercom always made me jump, and I just missed stapling my shirt to my exposed flesh.

"Yes, Lucy?"

"My office, please!"

She was holding out a pink memo when I walked in. "Give this to Craig, please," she said. "And Angel?"

"Yes, Lucy?"

"Have you contacted that author yet?"

"I sent an e-mail, yes."

"Why didn't you call, Angel? You know we don't take e-mail submissions here."

"There's no phone number, Lucy. Remember I told you? It's all anonymous?"

She sighed in exasperation. "Well, then, I hoped you asked for one. Now deliver that to Craig, please."

"Okay." I glanced at the memo. *C—my office. —L.*

"Angel?"

"Yes, Lucy?"

"How's the new one doing? Jackson?"

I could feel the flush spread across my face. Lucy couldn't have heard my conversation with Craig unless she'd bugged the outer office (not such a far-fetched prospect, really), but it was far likelier that this was just another instance of her psychic melding. Sort of the mental equivalent of the synchronized menstrual cycles that women get when they live or work in close quarters.

"He's fine."

"You seem unsure of that, Angel."

"No, he's doing fine."

"Because if he isn't doing a good job, it's on your shoulders. You trained him, yes?"

"Yes."

"Good."

I left her office and handed the memo to Craig, who glared at me, grabbed a folder from his desk, and stalked off to see Lucy. I could feel the throb of a headache starting at the base of my skull. It was going to be a bad one, I could tell. I leaned over to get the one-hundred-count bottle of aspirin I had started carrying in my purse and almost tripped over a large FedEx box sitting on the floor next to my desk.

"What's this?" I asked Jackson, who was looking over at me.

"Just came for you while you were in with her," he said. He waited a moment before hopping over to my desk like an eager kid on Christmas morning. "Open it!" he said. "Aren't you going to open it?"

I had to smile in spite of myself. It was almost quaint that he found an unopened box so exciting. Although I hated to admit it, Craig was right—I *had* been too harsh with Jackson. After all, unlike Nora/Kelly, Jackson was actually trying to work with me instead of against me. "Okay," I said. "But you realize it could just be some really big hate mail from a disgruntled author we've rejected."

"No, it can't be," he said. "Those people don't know this address."

He was right. I made another mental note: *Jackson. Smarter than he looks.* Not to be left out, Anna had also made her way over to my desk, and I opened the box with both of them staring at me in anticipation and pulled out its items one by one. Everything was packed with great care, which was a good thing because the first item was a small glass fishbowl. Inside it was a frantic fish swimming in a sealed bag of water. There were two other items in the box, a large package of fresh angel-hair pasta and a bottle of Angelica liqueur. There was a postcard taped to the bottle.

> Angel—
> *Something for your desk, something for your appetite, something for your dreams.*
> *Tuo Damiano*

I turned the postcard over. It was a photo of Angel Island, the park in the middle of the San Francisco Bay.

"Wow," Jackson said. "What kind of fish is that?"

"It's an angelfish," I said.

"How do you know?" Jackson asked.

"There are a lot of angel-themed things out there," I told him. "When you grow up with a name like Angel, you get to know them pretty quickly."

"Huh," Anna said. "Guess you've got a real admirer there." She looked as if she'd swallowed something extremely bitter. "Nice work, *Angel.*"

"You have to hand it to him," I said, more to myself than to anyone else. "He's incredibly creative." It was the most thoughtful gift I'd ever received from anyone, and I was so moved by it that I couldn't even concern myself with Anna's venomous glare. "Guess I'll put my fish in some water."

I filled the fishbowl with water from the bathroom sink, flipped the fish into it, and took my seat at my desk. An unsettling silence descended on the room after Jackson left to pick up the mail. There was no sound at all coming from Lucy's office and the phones were uncharacteristically quiet. Anna shifted in her chair, her cheeks slightly puffed out, as if she was getting ready to expel air. After a second or two, she started pecking halfheartedly at her keyboard and humming. There was something vaguely familiar about the tune, but I didn't recognize it until she started adding lyrics, one painful off-key word at a time.

"'Just call me . . . angel . . . of the . . . mor-ning, ba-by . . . hmm, mmm . . .'"

Trust Anna, I thought, to know a Juice Newton song. "Angel of the Morning" was probably the only angel song Damiano *hadn't* included on the CD he'd made for me. The only reason I recognized it at all was because my mother used to sing it to me. I felt an unfamiliar pang of sentimentality as I remembered how my mother used to brush my hair, always long and forever tangled, when I was little. It was always a lengthy procedure since there was always so much of it to get through, and my mother liked to style it, braiding it and curling it as she sang that song, imbuing the corny lyrics with special emphasis. But hearing the song in Anna's throat was torture, a perversion of a very sweet memory, and I didn't know how much longer I could take it.

Mercifully, after one more chorus the phone rang and I lunged to answer it.

"Lucy Fiamma Agency."

"Angel?"

"Malcolm . . ." He never called me at the office and I was first surprised, then dismayed (*no personal phone calls*), and finally, guilty (he couldn't possibly have known about Damiano's gift, could he?), all in the space of the two seconds it took to say his name. "What is it? What's wrong?"

"Nothing's wrong, Angel, I just wanted to speak to you. I just wanted to talk."

Just wanted to talk? Was he crazy? "Malcolm, you know I can't talk." I lowered my voice to a whisper, knowing that Anna could probably hear every word, anyway. "I'm not supposed to take personal phone calls here. You know that. I thought something terrible happened."

"Something terrible *has* happened. I haven't seen you for a couple of days. That's terrible. Why are you still whispering? Even people in the CIA make personal phone calls from time to time, Angel."

"I can't talk now."

"Of course not. All right, just thought I'd try—so kill me for that. I'll talk to you later."

"Malcolm, wait."

"What?"

The phone rang and Anna picked up the line. Even so, I lowered my voice until I could barely hear myself.

"Are you working Saturday night?"

"I work every Saturday night, Angel. Why?"

"Lucy's invited us to dinner."

"What? I can't hear you."

"Dinner with Lucy. She wants you to come."

"Angel, can you please speak just a little louder? I can't hear a word you're saying."

"Lucy has invited us for dinner," I said, raising my voice more than I meant to, the words coming out just as Anna put down her phone. So much for keeping that a secret.

"Really?" Malcolm said. "Okay, I'll get the night off. What time? What do you think I should wear?"

I sighed into the phone. "I'll call you later, okay? I really can't talk now. All right?"

"Okay, great! Call me. I'll see you later anyway, right?"

"Okay." Malcolm sounded disproportionately happy about this dinner invitation, and I found his happiness depressing. It was all backward and upside down. We were supposed to be on the same page, but it seemed as if Malcolm and I were reading from entirely different books. I wondered when that had happened. My computer trilled with the sound of an instant message from Anna.

Damiano Vero holding for you on Line 1.

I glanced over at her as I picked up the phone, but she was keeping her head down, buried once again in the chaos that was her desk drawer.

"Hi, Dami!" I said too brightly into the phone. "Thank you *so* much for your package. It's so . . . I don't know what to say. It's really beautiful."

"I'm so glad," he said. "I didn't know what to do else."

"I have my little fish right here," I said, watching it flick its tail back and forth in tiny flashes of color.

"Bene," he said. "I'm so glad."

"Thank you," I said. "Again." I waited for him to say something else, having run out of words myself, but he didn't, and after a moment, the pause between us stretched into weighted silence.

"I was working on my book," he said finally.

"Do you have— I mean, is there something I can help you with?"

"It's stupid," he said, and laughed mirthlessly. "I was just— It was a part of my life that was so difficult. I thought to call you. I don't know why."

I wanted to tell him that he didn't have to have an excuse to call me, that I enjoyed talking to him, that although I hadn't experienced a fraction of what he had in his life, I still felt as if I understood what he'd been through. But it wasn't exactly true; Damiano was a client of Lucy's and I was on her clock. The phone was ringing again and Anna was pointedly not answering it.

"Damiano, I'm so sorry, I have to—"

"I know, I can hear it, the phone. Go, go. *Ci vediamo,* Angel," he said hurriedly, and hung up. I punched Line 2.

"Lucy Fia—"

"Angel, hi. Listen, is this dinner formal or what? I want to make sure that—"

"I *don't know.*" My voice came out sounding high and shrill. I brought it down to a stage whisper. "I *can't talk,* Malcolm."

"Fine," he said, and hung up. I'd barely had time to draw my next breath before I heard the sound of Anna's next message on my computer.

You don't have to whisper about dinner with Lucy. I know she likes you better than me.

I felt a nauseating mix of revulsion, pity, and guilt churning in my stomach. I started to type a reply to Anna's message but stopped myself. This was the height of ridiculousness. We were separated by a few feet and there was nobody else in the office.

"Anna, I really don't think it's about who she likes better. I don't know why . . . I mean, I'm sure it—dinner—is work-related."

"Well, whatever," Anna said, her face flooding pink. "I'm just saying you don't have to feel bad. Or hide it from me. I should probably try to learn from you, in fact." She gave a small, uncomfortable chuckle. "Dinner with the boss. Good way to get ahead, isn't it?"

"Anna, I didn't ask—"

"It's *okay.* Come on, we're on the same team here." The phrase "honor among thieves" danced through my head. I shrugged in a palms-up gesture of surrender, as if to say I couldn't argue her point. "You know what would be really great, Angel?"

"What's that, Anna?"

"I'd love it if . . . I mean, if you would . . ." She stopped, flustered, her color rising dramatically. If the concept hadn't been so absurd, I'd have sworn she was getting ready to ask me on a date. "It would be great if you'd let me make dinner for you sometime." So it *was* a date she was angling for. My headache had come on full force despite the aspirin. "Oh, jeez, I'm sorry, Angel, that didn't sound right at all!" I could almost feel the heat of her red face at my desk. "I just mean it would be great to get together outside of work, you know. And I *am* a pretty good cook, so . . . Anyway, I feel like we kind of got off to a little bit of a bad start, maybe, and I'd like to sort of change that." She took a deep breath and exhaled noisily. "What do you think?"

I thought that I wouldn't be able to get through a meal with Anna unless I had several alcoholic beverages. What did we have in common aside from the job? I also sensed there was something other than a desire to be buddies that was festering behind Anna's invitation. Of course, I couldn't tell her any of that, nor, for the second time in one day, could I refuse. She and I both knew that if I turned her down after that pathetic plea, I'd be the world's biggest bitch.

"Sure," I said. "That would be great. Maybe when things quiet down a bit around here."

"Well, we can't wait for that, can we?" Anna said. "Hopefully, that will never happen! But yeah, okay. Thanks, Angel."

She was really laying it on thick. I repressed the urge to throw my stapler at her. "No problem. Sounds like fun."

"We're the only girls in the office now," she said, and gave me an exaggerated wink. "We have to stick together." Female anatomy, I thought. I stood corrected—she'd found something else we had in common. "And I *know* some things, Angel. Things you don't know. I could share them with you."

"What?"

"Shhh!" she said, shutting me up just as Craig exited Lucy's office. She put her head down and started typing. After a few seconds I got an instant message from her saying, *I'll tell you later.*

"Where's Jackson?" Craig barked from his desk.

"It's okay." Anna laughed. "He's only gone to get the mail. He hasn't quit."

Actual humor. Score one for Anna, I thought.

If he heard, Craig gave no indication. "Angel, can I see you for a moment, please?" His tone was now much more solicitous. I prepared myself for another bait-and-switch. This was turning out to be the day for them. Craig didn't bother pulling out the filing cabinets as I approached. "You can sit, Angel," he said, and as I positioned myself across from him, Jackson reappeared at the door, staggering under the weight of a full mail tub.

Craig looked over at Jackson for a second and then back to face me. "I've got some good news for you, Angel."

I gave Craig a big, if forced, smile. He seemed strung tight enough to be on the verge of a breakdown. I decided it would be wise to be as careful as possible with him. "Good news is always good," I said, wondering if Anna was listening.

As if on cue, the phones began ringing. Jackson and Anna went for separate lines and began talking. The office had come alive again.

"Your official probation period isn't up yet," Craig began, "but Lucy's decided to jump the gun a bit here and give you a raise." He looked up at me, waiting for a response. My intuition told me that it had better be an effusive one.

"Really? That's great!"

"Yes, well, you don't even know how great yet." Craig cleared his throat. "Lucy's been very impressed with how quickly you've assimilated in the office and with your reading. Guess that bookstore experience really paid off for you. Anyway, as you know, Lucy believes in rewarding good work, so she's made the decision to substantially increase your salary." He scribbled a figure on a piece of paper and slid it over to me. I stared at the numbers, utterly confused.

"But Craig, that's what I'm making now, isn't it?"

"No, Angel, that's not your new salary. That's the amount of your raise."

I could feel my eyes widen. The room seemed very bright. Craig was looking at me impassively, a slight twist in the corner of his mouth. This clearly hadn't been his idea, and I was sure that he had even lobbied against it.

"But . . . but that's double what I'm making now. Is that right?"

"Yes," Craig said. "I take it you're pleased?" I could only nod. My throat was dry and I didn't trust myself to speak. I could move into a place with an actual bedroom. Hell, I could probably even move out of Petaluma and closer to the city—maybe Berkeley. I could buy shoes and still have enough left over for dinner. And I could actually start making some inroads on my student-loan debt. That bill had been hanging over my head like the sword of Damocles since the day I'd graduated. I'd never allowed myself to get so excited about money. I was like a kid who'd just been told she could eat the cake, the ice cream, *and* the candy bar. It was a little overwhelming.

"There's one condition, though," Craig said.

Of course there was. This was Lucy Fiamma country, after all. "Oh?"

"Like any intelligent businesswoman, Lucy would like to protect her investment. And this is a rather large investment, I think you'd agree." I nodded again. "So, bearing that in mind, the condition is that you commit to your employment here for a period of two years from this date. Should you leave *voluntarily* at any point before that time, Lucy would expect you to return the difference in salary that she is offering you today."

It was as if she were offering me a book contract, I thought. If the book wasn't written and delivered within two years, she'd expect the advance to be returned. Only, in this case, I was the book. I didn't know if it was legal, but it was certainly interesting, and all that money was almost irresistible.

"Wow," I said after my heart rate slowed. "That's really amazing."

"I'll have the contract written up by the end of the day," Craig said. "You can sign and Lucy can countersign. I'm also a notary public—I don't know if I mentioned that before—so we won't have to take it out anywhere. You'll get a copy, of course, for your records. I take it you accept the terms?"

I stared into Craig's eyes, searching for a glimmer of the fire I'd seen there earlier, but there was nothing but the bleached effect of driftwood. "Can I sleep on it tonight? Just because, you know, it's a good idea to think things through."

"Lucy will need an answer today," Craig said. "Really, Angel, what's to think about? She's being absurdly generous here. And it's almost like a guarantee of employment. You know what the job market is like these days. *Especially* in publishing."

I closed my eyes for a moment, wanting to let Craig's rumbling Barry White voice wash over me. Looking at him simply ruined the effect.

"Okay," I said. "You're right, of course. I'm . . . I couldn't be happier."

"Good. And there's just one more thing."

"Yes?" I said. Craig leaned forward, grimacing, and for a moment I thought he was going to tell me that the whole thing was a joke, ha-ha.

"Lucy would like to give you the first year's raise in a lump sum."

"So—"

"Yes, all at once. Also, although this is a raise, Lucy will pay it to you as if it were a bonus, so we won't be taking any taxes out of it. Again, you'll be responsible for those. I can have a check ready for you by the end of the week. And, of course, the same terms apply. Should you leave before—"

"I think I understand, Craig. I'd owe it all back. Got it." I was actually counting it in my head, visualizing piles and piles of green dollars laid out on my bed.

"I'll write it up, then?" Craig said.

"Yes, thank you. Thanks so much."

"Don't thank me," he said. "It's all her."

There was an instant message and an e-mail waiting for me when I returned to my desk. The instant message, from Anna, read: *Congratulations.*

I didn't stop to think about her bionic hearing or what were the implications of her knowing about my huge pay increase, because the e-mail message demanded my immediate attention.

To: angel.robinson@fiammalit.com
From: ganovelist@heya.com
Subject: Re: BLIND SUBMISSION

Dear Ms. Robinson,

I am indeed pleased that Ms. Fiamma would like to offer me representation. I assure you that when the time is right, I will happily sign on with her. Rest assured that I will not be submitting elsewhere. You have my word. I thank you for getting in touch and look forward to our correspondence.

I will be sending you more text shortly. I am, just now, putting a few finishing touches on a key scene.

With best wishes,
G.

The e-mail struck me as both pompous and cheesy, a dreadful combination. I found I was really beginning to dislike this author, which didn't bode well for the manuscript. I mean, really, "ganovelist"? **Great American Novelist**? There was also something about the language of the e-mail that struck me as very familiar, but I couldn't place it. The whole thing—the manuscript, the e-mails, and the secret identity—was really starting to grate on me. It occurred to me that I should have rejected the manuscript when I'd had the chance, before Lucy even saw it. But then I had the unnerving thought that even if I *had* rejected it, the author would have found a way to get back in. It had become very clear that this particular author knew a little too much about the way things worked at our agency.

"Peeuwww!" Jackson was going through the day's mail. He held an envelope away from his face with one hand and made fanning motions with the other. "This one stinks!"

"What is it?" Anna asked.

"This manuscript smells terrible," Jackson said. "It reeks."

"Smokers," Anna said, and I nodded in agreement. "Their work smells so bad you don't even want to open it, let alone read it. You'd think they'd know that and open a window or something before they print it out."

"Yes, but if they knew . . ." It was right there, edging into my mental field of vision. I reached for it—

"Knew what?" Jackson asked.

—and grabbed it. "Peter Johnson!" I exclaimed out loud.

"Smokers knew Peter Johnson?" Anna asked. "What are you talking about?"

"When's the last time we heard from him?" I asked Anna.

"Who's Peter Johnson?" Jackson asked.

"Yeah, it's been awhile, huh?" Anna said. "He used to call every day, didn't he? Did you finally chase him off, Angel? I haven't seen one of his manuscripts for a long time. What was the last one? Wait, I remember, it was that awful one about the Russian spy who . . ."

I tuned her out as she went on. I knew exactly the last time we'd heard from Peter Johnson—it was the morning I'd given Lucy Malcolm's novel and started that whole mess in motion. He'd hung up on me, but not before giving me his usual speech, which sounded exactly like the words I'd just read in that e-mail. The mystery author had Peter Johnson's literary DNA all over him. And hadn't he said, in that last conversation I'd had with him, that he was giving *us* another chance? It had to be him.

"Hey, Jackson, can you do me a favor?" I said when Anna's breath ran out.

"Sure, what do you need?"

"Can you see if you can find an address or phone number for Peter Johnson in the submissions log? He's submitted so many times, we must have a record of it somewhere. He practically has a log all to himself."

"Why do you want to contact Peter Johnson?" Anna asked. But before I could answer her, my intercom vibrated with the sound of Lucy's voice.

"Angel? Can we talk?" She sounded like a bad imitation of Joan Rivers. She knew Craig had talked to me about her "absurdly generous" raise and she was waiting for a response. I knew what she wanted. I punched the button on my intercom.

"On my way," I said, and prepared to go fawn and grovel.

To: angel.robinson@fiammalit.com
From: ganovelist@heya.com
Subject: Re: Edit notes

Dear Ms. Robinson,

Thank you for your speedy response to my work. I have already made some of the corrections you suggested in the opening chapters. Let me also say that I am pleased to be working with you, but I'd just like to make sure that Ms. Fiamma is, in fact, the person who will be representing this novel? Before I send you the next installment, I'd like to go over some of your notes for my own clarification. To wit, you say that there should be "more intrigue right up front." Is it not intriguing enough to place a frustrated writer in a literary agency where she can only hope to usher in the works of other writers? Perhaps not. Perhaps you are suggesting that there needs to be a dead body? I need to kill someone off, as it were? If so, I can arrange that, but I may need a few more chapters to do it. Is this the direction you'd see as best for this novel?

You also say Alice needs more dimension and asked me to define what it is that Alice wants. The answer is: everything. At this point, her goal is to attain as much power as possible and she will be ruthless about obtaining it. She's also a frustrated writer in search of the perfect novel. She wants a bestseller and she doesn't care what she has to do to get one. Perhaps that aspect is not coming across as clearly as it should. (By the way, I appreciate your compliment about how I've gotten the details right where it comes to describing a literary agency. My research has paid off!)

As far as the Carol Moore character, I will try to "flesh her out," as you say. She is a very powerful character. Indeed, she holds the power that Alice is looking for, and that should come across for the reader. In your notes, you didn't mention whether or not you felt that Carol Moore was sympathetic or not. You did mention that it's important to have the protagonist be somewhat likable, which takes care of Alice (I assume she's not likable enough?), but I'm curious as to your take on Carol, the agent, since she's a very important character as well.

I will look forward to your reply, Ms. Robinson. You can expect my next installment shortly, along with corrections on what I've already sent.

With best wishes,
G.

Blind Submission, p. 68

Carol Moore held a staff meeting every morning. In addition to conducting the business of the day, she also liked to get caught up on the manuscripts that her staff was reading and allowed everyone the time to discuss whatever they thought was important. "Fresh ideas are crucial," Carol said. "And I have hired all of you because you all have excellent ideas on how we can better serve our clients." To make everyone feel comfortable and to encourage casual dialogue, Carol ordered muffins and coffee for every staff meeting. Alice noticed that Jewel ate at least three muffins every morning. It was starting to show, Alice thought. Those thighs of Jewel's weren't getting any slimmer.

Carol seemed especially excited for today's staff meeting. "It's easy to keep believing that this is just a business like any other," Carol was saying, "but the truth is that this is art. What our authors do is incredibly important and influential. It means something and their books make a difference in the world. It's so important for us to get them out there—to do what they can't do themselves."

Alice found herself drifting off as Carol spoke. Carol was right, of course, books were important, but it was too painful for Alice to listen to Carol's adulation of other authors.

"Can you stay here for a moment please, Alice?"

Alice came to attention in time to notice that the meeting was breaking up.

"Of course, Carol," Alice said, shutting the door behind Jewel and Ricardo.

"Vaughn Blue is very happy with the work you've been doing for him," Carol said once Alice was sitting down again. Alice's heart started beating a little faster and she searched Carol's face for an indication that Carol might know the real nature of Alice's "work" with Vaughn Blue. But Carol looked very happy and there was no sign that anything was amiss.

"For that matter," Carol went on, "I'm very happy with the work you've been doing. You are a real asset to this agency, Alice."

But not a good enough writer to be represented by you, Alice thought bitterly. What she said was, "Thank you, I appreciate that, Carol."

"I'm giving you a raise," Carol said, "and your own office. It's the small one next to mine, but it will be your own office. I think you've earned it."

"I don't know what to say," Alice said. "You're too good to me, Carol."

"Just carry on," Carol said. "You're doing a marvelous job."

Alice left Carol's office and prepared to move into her own. Yes, she was grateful to Carol, but not in the way Carol thought. And she would carry on, but not in the way Carol planned. She would carry on skimming the cream off the top of incoming proposals and manuscripts. She would carry on raping Carol's files and slowly undermining the efforts of her staff. She would carry on sucking ideas from out of Carol's clients' heads and then convincing them that those very ideas were completely unmarketable. She would carry on playing Vaughn Blue as expertly as he played his own instrument. And she would carry on letting Carol think that her greatest ambition was to become just like Carol herself. Very soon, Alice's careful planning would bear fruit. And Carol had just made it easier for Alice to do what she needed to do.

NINE

To: angel.robinson@fiammalit.com
From: ganovelist@heya.com
Subject: Quick question

Dear Ms. Robinson,

I hate to bother you on the weekend, but I am wrestling with what may be an important decision, and since you have been so very helpful already, I was hoping you could help me resolve it.

It occurs to me that my novel might be—or become—a little claustrophobic. What I mean is that the setting rarely strays from the inside of Carol Moore's agency. Do you think that this gets too confining? I was thinking that perhaps Alice could attend some kind of literary event outside the agency? Perhaps a book signing, for example. Or perhaps even a cocktail party honoring one of Carol's authors? That would add a little color and then the reader would also get a chance to see what Alice is like outside the agency.

What do you think?

With best wishes,
G.

I tapped my fingernail on the edge of my computer keyboard, debating whether or not to return G's message. I didn't want this author to think I was available 24/7 for editorial advice. Clearly, G didn't mind bothering me on the weekend—the e-mail was proof of that. On the other hand, G had known, somehow, that I'd check my e-mail on the weekend, so what was the point of pretending I hadn't? Once again, mystery G had managed to unsettle and irritate me at the same time. I wondered if I had developed some kind of literary stalker. Or was I just being overly paranoid? No, this was an author who knew just a little too much—who'd submitted manuscripts one too many times. I was almost positive now that it was Peter Johnson, only I hadn't yet been able to get in touch with him to confirm my hunch. The only twinge of doubt I had about my theory was that Peter Johnson wasn't really a good enough writer to have produced *Blind Submission*. But who knew—maybe all those rejections had actually sparked some kind of latent talent. Whether it was Johnson or not, though, it would have to wait. I turned off my computer and snapped it shut. I had a dinner to prepare for.

—

I DECIDED TO LET MALCOLM DRIVE us to Lucy's house for dinner. I didn't know if Lucy was planning to serve anything alcoholic, but if she did, I knew I'd be partaking. I'd never been much of a drinker—anything harder than the occasional glass of wine in a restaurant tended to make me ill—but if ever there was an occasion that called for an altered state of consciousness, dinner at Lucy's house was it. Malcolm was happy to be the designated driver for this soiree, and he laughed when I told him why.

"I don't think I've ever seen you drunk, Angel," he said, and winked at me. "Might be fun."

"I didn't say I was planning to get drunk," I told him, although I realized that I probably was.

Once we were in the car, I allowed myself a closer look at the clothes Malcolm had come up with for dinner. I'd never seen him dressed quite like it and didn't even know he owned such attire. Given his heroine worship of Lucy, though, it was entirely possible that he'd sneaked off and bought something just for this evening. His outfit looked like a cross between something you'd see in the pages of *Esquire* and *Cat Burglar Quarterly.* He was wearing a tight-fitting black silk T-shirt tucked into equally form-fitting black pants, which were neither jeans nor slacks but a happy blend of the two. All this was finished with sleek black loafers and *The Matrix*–inspired sunglasses. Altogether, his garb was slightly ridiculous, but it worked in a big way. The long-sleeved T-shirt outlined and clung to every line of muscle of his arms and chest, and the pants were not tight enough to be vulgar, but not loose enough to disguise what was underneath them. His thick blond hair and naturally tan skin nicely set off all the black he was wearing, and the perfect amount of stubble decorated his jaw. He was hot—no question about it.

After discarding several outfits as unworthy (and flashing back to my first interview with Lucy), I'd finally settled on the only black dress I owned. It was on the short side, the hem coming to mid-thigh, and cut so low in front that the angel-wing tattoo on my breast was plain to see and impossible to cover. But it was an excellent combination of casual and elegant and the best I could hope for, so I threw a gauzy scarf around my neck, draped it over my décolletage, and called it even. I hadn't gotten a haircut since I'd started working for Lucy, and had taken to wearing my hair in a sloppy twist in the office. It had gotten quite long and very curly, so rather than torturing it into some kind of fancy do, I just let it fall loose down the back of my dress.

Malcolm had purchased a big bouquet of red, yellow, and orange roses for us to give to Lucy and I held them on my lap as we drove into San Rafael. He was good with flowers and I couldn't argue with his statement "You can't show up empty-handed when someone invites you to dinner, can you?" but I felt somewhat put out, anyway. I should have remembered to get something, I thought, not to mention the fact that I was a more worthy recipient of those roses than Lucy.

"It's like taking coals to Newcastle," I told him as I buried my nose in the blooms. They were exceptionally fragrant. "People send her flowers all the time."

"Common courtesy," Malcolm said. "And you're welcome, by the way."

"So what do you think she'll serve?" I asked in a weak attempt to change the subject. I pulled down the passenger-side visor and checked out my reflection in the mirror. It was time to apply more lipstick.

"Who knows?" Malcolm said. "I'm sure it'll be good, though."

"Why are you so sure? God, I hope it's not some Alaskan thing, like roasted caribou or whale ice cream."

"Come on, you know she doesn't eat that stuff in real life," Malcolm said.

"What do you mean, 'real life'? She's all over the *Cold!* food. She tried to get Karanuk to write a cookbook once, did I tell you that?"

"Yes, you mentioned it," he said. I couldn't see his eyes behind his super-cool shades and that bothered me.

"I told you about his new book, right?"

"Yep."

"Did I tell you that he's going to call it *Thaw*? Like I suggested?"

"Really? That's great, baby."

"Lucy says she's trying to talk him into coming up here for an appearance. Top secret. Like only half a million people will know about it. Can you imagine how many books that would sell? So far he's not biting."

"Maybe *you* could talk him into it," Malcolm said. "He seems to really like you from what you've said. That would be some coup, huh?"

"Hmm." I pondered the scenario for a moment. Karanuk showing his face for even the briefest of appearances would be a bigger media event than J. D. Salinger showing up on David Letterman. I hadn't even thought of it as a possibility until Malcolm mentioned it, but planted now, the idea started to grow on me. It had weight, dimension, and infinite potential. At the very least, I could feel Karanuk out, see if he'd be amenable to the suggestion. It was worth a shot. I let myself drift into the daydream of a huge Karanuk book party. We could have ice sculptures that melted down during the event, signifying the "thaw" and the return to the unmolded shape of nature. . . . I bolted upright in my seat. I was thinking *exactly like Lucy*. It was as if she'd beamed the thoughts straight into my brain. I shook myself, literally, and looked ahead.

We were close to Lucy's house and I could feel the adrenaline surging as it did every time I approached the office. And then I realized that I wasn't driving. My stomach gave a sick little flip. I hadn't given Malcolm directions. How had he found his way here without them?

"Malcolm?"

"Baby?"

"How the hell did you get here?"

"I drove, love. You know, foot, gas, all that."

"No, Malcolm, I mean, how did you find it? I didn't give you directions. And you've never been here before. Have you?"

"Shit," Malcolm said softly.

"What? Tell me now."

"Look, I'm sorry, Angel, I didn't want you to know. . . . I'm so stupid."

"Malcolm, what the hell are you TALKING ABOUT?" I was yelling almost out of control, and I didn't even know why.

"I followed you, okay?"

"What?"

"A couple of times . . . When you first started working and you seemed so stressed out and I was just worried about you, okay? You were so tired—you're still tired all the time—and I just wanted to make sure you got there safely, okay? And it was always so off-limits, I wasn't allowed to call, to come take you to lunch, you know? Like it was some kind of white slavery ring or something." He let out a nervous giggle, incongruous next to his outfit.

"But how did you follow me without my seeing you?"

"Angel . . ." He took a long and very dramatic pause. "You don't see anything except what's right in front of you or inside your head anymore. You're so focused, a herd of elephants could sneak up on you. Of course you didn't see me. I don't think you saw anything."

He wasn't wrong. There had been many times I'd arrived at the office without remembering how I'd gotten there. But his following me—sneaking behind me—gave me a cold, nervous feeling in the pit of my stomach, and I couldn't shake it.

"You know, Malcolm, I don't know whether to think this is sweet or just totally creepy."

"Just trying to look out for you, Angel." He let out a long sigh and pushed his shades back on his nose.

"Look out for me or spy on me?"

"Why would I need to spy on you? How does *that* make sense?"

"I don't know!" I said, my tension and frustration coming through my voice. "It's weird, okay? It's just a weird thing to do."

"I'm sorry I didn't tell you earlier, I should have," he said. "I guess it *is* a little weird." He giggled again and I realized I really didn't like the sound of it.

"Yes, it is. Listen, Malcolm, next time just— Damn, we're here already." Malcolm pulled into Lucy's long, gravel driveway. I realized I'd never even looked at the front of the house before because I always entered through the back entrance. There was one other car in the driveway, a tired-looking Honda Civic. I happened to know that Lucy owned a silver Jaguar (I'd placed several calls to her mechanic, auto detailer, etc.), even though I'd never actually seen her drive anywhere, so I knew the car wasn't hers. It didn't belong to any staffers, either. Fabulous, I thought, a mystery guest. "I guess it's too late to back out now," I told Malcolm as we got out of the car.

"Come on, A, this'll be fun," he said, but he wasn't looking at me anymore. He'd fixed his gaze on Lucy's mansion and was striding toward it.

"Hey, want to wait for me?"

Malcolm turned slightly and hesitated. He looked annoyed. "I guess you want to give her the flowers?" he said.

"No, Malcolm, why don't you?" I said, shoving them into his hand. A couple of crimson and yellow petals dislodged and fluttered to the ground. Malcolm's eyes narrowed to gold slits. "What's wrong with you?" he hissed.

I chose to ignore him and stared at the front door, which was white, thick, and decorated with a giant silver knocker fashioned in the shape of Alaska, complete with Aleutian islands. I picked it up with some difficulty as it was incredibly heavy and let it fall against the door. There was no sound from inside. I tried again, still to no avail. I looked at Malcolm, telegraphing my instant panic with wild eyes. I could feel perspiration begin to seep through the thin fabric of my dress.

"You might want to try this," Malcolm said, pointing to a doorbell on the jamb. "Clearly, the knocker is just for show."

"Clearly," I said, and jammed my finger into the bell. There followed a resounding ring from inside the house. "That must be our Angel," I heard echoing toward me, and the sweat froze under my arms.

The door swung open and Lucy appeared inside it, her lightning-colored hair fanned out around her face, her arms spread wide as if to hug us both. She was wearing a black dress that was frighteningly similar to mine, although hers was no doubt a Donna Karan or Dolce & Gabbana or something like that (I'd made a few pricey boutique phone calls for her, too) and mine was a designer-less fourteen-hour special from Robinson's (which was about as fancy as I got). Lucy was taller than I was and therefore her dress was even shorter on her, showing a truly horrifying amount of pale, albeit firm, naked thigh. I hoped she wasn't planning to bend over at any point in the evening because I didn't think I'd be able to stomach a glimpse of whatever she'd thrown on for underwear. The scoop of her neck was slightly lower than mine as well, exposing the tops of those full-moon breasts I'd had the displeasure of glimpsing that morning in the office. Her shoes were just as startling—high satin heels ending with straps that laced all the way up her calves. She'd finished the ensemble off with a few pieces of silver jewelry similar to ones I had in my own jewelry box. It was disconcerting to see them on Lucy because—and I felt terribly ageist even thinking this way—they just looked too young for her. So, despite the fine quality of her jewelry and clothing, and despite the intensity of her looks, her getup had a mutton-dressed-as-lamb feel to it, as if she were intentionally dressing up as a much younger woman.

"Welcome!" she exclaimed, and to my horror, smothered me in a Chanel-soaked embrace. "And this must be the boyfriend! Malcolm, is it?" Lucy released me and turned her attention to Malcolm, whose face had turned the deep reddish-brown color of barbecued meat.

"It's wonderful to meet you. In person," he said, and thrust the roses out in front of him. "Thanks so much for inviting me tonight. It's really a pleasure. We brought— These are for you. For your house."

I'd never seen or heard Malcolm be so awkward. Lucy fixed him with an expressionless gaze, as if waiting to see just how deep a hole he could dig himself into. I would have felt sorry for him had I not been so irritated by his transformation into a stuttering marionette.

"Lovely," Lucy said as Malcolm trailed off. "Let's see if Anna can find some water for them. Follow me, will you?"

Anna? So she'd been invited after all. I wondered why I hadn't seen her car in the driveway and then realized that she must have parked in the back. Which still left the presence of the Honda unexplained.

"Angel, I don't believe you've seen my house before, have you?"

As Malcolm and I fell into step behind Lucy, I tried to catch his eye without being obvious about it, but he was marching ahead, a glazed look on his face. Lucy's house was huge, even more spacious than it appeared from the outside, and looked very much like an extension of her office space. We went from the foyer to the living room, which had light wood floors covered with an assortment of white rugs, and was furnished with chrome-and-glass tables and a blizzard of white furniture. In all this whiteness, there was not a single visible book.

"I don't think we need to go up there, do we?" Lucy said, waving her hand when we reached the free-standing spiral staircase in the center of the house.

"It's a beautiful staircase," Malcolm said reverently.

"I like to think of it as inspirational," Lucy said. "Shall we move on?" As she turned to continue her brisk tour, I was reminded of *Charlie and the Chocolate Factory*. I half-expected a team of Oompa-Loompas to march in and start singing a ditty about her inspirational staircase.

She took a left turn through an arched doorway and led us into a vast open kitchen, beyond which was a simple, sunlit dining area. Anna was standing in the kitchen, bent over a platter of what looked like cold cuts. A few feet past her, rising from a white-upholstered dining-room chair, was Damiano Vero.

"Damiano!" Lucy said brightly. "Your Angel has arrived!"

As my eyes scanned the varying levels of discomfort on every face but Lucy's, I knew one thing was certain: From this point until the day I died, I'd remember this as my life's most uncomfortable moment.

Lucy broke the silence, but not the tension, with her next gambit.

"Anna," she said, "can you relieve Angel's man here of his roses and put them in some water please?" It was then I realized that Anna was not at Lucy's house in the capacity of guest. I saw now that she was wearing a white shirt, black pants, and an apron tied around her waist. As unfathomable as I found it, she was to be our server.

"Sure," Anna said, her voice a small, strangled thing in her throat. "Hi, Angel."

"Hi, Anna."

"I'm Malcolm," he said, handing her the roses.

"So you are," Lucy chimed in. "Damiano, meet Angel's *fiancé*." Damiano looked both shocked and stricken at Lucy's announcement. I watched with helpless dismay as he struggled to regain his composure while Lucy forged ahead. "Malcolm, this is Damiano Vero, author of what is going to be a *major* book. But I'm sure Angel's told you all about him, hasn't she? They've spent so much time working together."

"Not really," Malcolm said, finally finding his voice. He shook Damiano's hand with quite a bit of force. "Angel keeps her work pretty well under wraps, actually. But congratulations, you must be very excited. I'm also a writer." He stole a nervous glance at Lucy. "It can be a rough road to travel."

"*Piacere*," Dami said. "I only just started with the writing. I owe Angel so much. She saw something in those pages to give to Luciana. They made a miracle together."

I could feel the heat of Malcolm's stare at my back as I leaned in to receive Dami's double-cheek kisses. "It is so nice to see you again, Angel," he said softly. He was the only person in the room who wasn't dressed in black. He'd opted instead for a light blue linen shirt over khaki pants. Rather than looking too casual, his quietly understated clothes made the rest of us look wildly overdressed. As his lips brushed my face, I could smell the same intoxicating citrus-sweet scent he'd worn when he came to the office. He backed away, fixing me with those purple-brown eyes of his. It was only the second time I'd seen him in person, but the visceral connection between the two of us was strong. All the time I'd spent talking to him on the phone and reading him, absorbing his words, his feelings, his thoughts, and his experiences made me feel as if I'd fallen right into his head. It was a strange familiarity—like déjà vu.

"Hardly a miracle," Lucy was saying. "It practically sold itself, didn't it, Angel?"

Lucy was on a fishing trip and she'd trained me very well. I bit down on the lure. "Oh no, that was all you, Lucy. That auction was brilliant," I said.

"I'll bet," Malcolm said. "Maybe one day I'll be as fortunate."

"Maybe you will, indeed," Lucy said, raking Malcolm with her eyes. She put her hands on her hips and assessed him as if he were livestock, one corner of her mouth turning up in a half-smile. For a moment she looked . . . *carnivorous* was the only word to describe it.

"Would anyone care for a drink?" Anna had appeared in the midst of our throng, holding a tray of cocktails no less.

"I thought martinis would be in order for this evening," Lucy said. "Please, help yourselves."

"Thanks," I said, and grabbed one from Anna's tray. As I did, I raised my eyebrows as if to ask her what the hell she was doing, but I got only a flat stare in response. I took a long sip from my martini and nearly choked on it. It was too strong and I hated gin, but I held my breath and swallowed more.

"I'll have one," Malcolm said, and took a glass from Anna's tray. I shot him a meaningful look, but he ignored me. Anna moved on to Dami, who said, "No, *grazie*. If you have a little mineral water?"

"Well, of course," Lucy said. "I forgot that you're in recovery. Although it's not like martinis and heroin really have much in common, do they, Damiano? Surely you can allow yourself a little now and then?" She plucked the olive out of her own glass and deposited it in her mouth. "Really, it's practically food."

"*È vero,*" Dami said, laughing. I marveled at his graciousness and his ability to retain his sense of humor around Lucy. It was truly a talent. "That's not the reason," he went on. "I don't like the juniper taste of the gin. The other . . . It has been a very long time. It's all in the past now."

"Hmm," Lucy mused. "Well, that's not particularly sexy, is it, Damiano? When this book hits, and it will hit big, I assure you, you may have to sex up that whole heroin thing." She turned away from Dami and focused her laser stare on Malcolm. "There are so many facets to an author's work," she said. "Don't you agree?"

"I'm sure," Malcolm said. "I'm looking forward to experiencing some of those." He gave her a dazzling smile. I hadn't seen such a big smile from him in quite some time, which explained why I hadn't noticed until now that he'd recently whitened his teeth.

"Yes," Lucy said. "You've got some looks, Mal. It's a pity you're only a waiter. If we could find you some kind of platform . . . take advantage of that face . . ."

"Thank you," Malcolm said. "I really appreciate that."

Appreciated *what*? Why was he thanking her? For that matter, why was he still staring at her with that shit-eating grin on his face? I finished my drink in one long swallow and reached for another. The alcohol was having no effect that I could sense and my nerves were winding tighter and tighter. I caught Dami's eyes over the rim of my glass. He gave me a knowing look full of humor and empathy, as if we were coconspirators—the only people in the room who got the joke.

"We should eat," Lucy announced. She gestured to Anna, who was standing behind a long marble island in the kitchen. "Anna will man—or should I say *woman*"—she laughed at her own joke—"the buffet table. Help yourselves, everyone. Malcolm, I see that your glass is empty. How are you on bartending?"

Lucy led Malcolm back into the living room, which was apparently where the bar was located, and I made my way over to Anna's buffet station, Dami following close behind me. Laid out for us, on a variety of white platters, was every kind of meat I'd ever seen and some I hadn't. Folds of ham, turkey, roast beef, and pastrami sat alongside a plate of veal cutlets and chicken wings. There was a ring of crackers decorating a mound of pâté, but no bread and not a vegetable in sight, unless you counted the parsley garnishes. It was either some kind of crazed Atkins fantasy or the embodiment of a vegetarian's worst nightmare.

"Would you like some meat?" Anna asked me.

"Anna, what are you doing here?" I whispered.

"You think you're the only one who can come to her house?" Anna whispered back, piling flesh onto my plate. "There's not as big a differ-ence between me and you as you think, you know. We're both working."

"What do you mean?" I stole a glance at Dami, who stood a polite distance away, allowing me to have a semi-private conversation with Anna.

"At least I'm getting *paid* to do this," Anna huffed.

"What do you mean?"

"You know," she hissed, "you ought to be a little nicer to her. You've got some attitude going."

"Anna, wha—"

"Here you go. I made the chicken, by the way. You should try it."

"I'll have some chicken," Dami said, appearing beside me. I watched as Anna fumbled a few wings onto his plate. "This is a very interesting dinner," he said, and looked at me, barely contained laughter straining at the corners of his mouth. I stared at him and found myself having one of those out-of-body experiences. For one moment, everything around me seemed like an elaborate fiction. Lucy, Anna, Malcolm, this ridiculous festival of meats—all of it became somebody else's work, the play of an insane writer. I felt as if I'd been following along, but my script pages had suddenly run out and I could no longer find my place. In that elon-gated disconnected second, I looked at Damiano and felt anchored. Somehow he knew, could sense what I was feeling, and his eyes told me he was right there with me. I wanted to stay inside that moment of clar-ity forever, but, too soon, I felt myself back inside my own skin, blink-ing my staring eyes, my heart beating double. It was the booze, I told myself. But I wasn't drunk. Not even close. What had he said about din-ner? How was I supposed to respond?

"Yes," I said, hoping that would cover it.

"Is she always like this?"

"She?"

"Luciana."

I took another swig of my martini, finishing it. That made two full drinks. When the gin finally caught up with me, it wasn't going to be pretty. Damiano was waiting for an answer and I didn't know which one to give him. I teetered on the brink of an honest response but held myself back. He had just substantially increased his net worth thanks to Lucy. If I were in his shoes, I'd be focused on the positive with her. He was an author, a *client,* after all. I felt I couldn't yet trust him with the contents of my head, even as his wine-dark eyes were telling me I could.

"She has a beautiful house, don't you think?" It was a lame deflection and Damiano saw right through it. He shrugged and moved toward the dining-room table. "*Sì, sì,*" he said. "Spectacular." He gestured toward a set of glass doors, through which I could see a large, completely empty deck. "It's too bad there are no chairs outside," Damiano said. "Outside would be nice."

The two of us sat down at Lucy's vast dining-room table. Damiano positioned himself opposite me so that I could either look down at my plate or at him. Those were my only options. I heard Lucy's laughter, high and girlish, coming from the living room.

"I didn't know you were . . . *agganciata,*" Damiano said. I looked at him, uncomprehending. He pointed to his left fourth finger. "To be married," he said.

"Engaged?" I said. "I'm not."

"But Luciana—"

"She's mistaken," I said.

"Do you listen to the CD?" Damiano asked after a minute, his voice lower than it needed to be.

"I do," I told him. "I like it very much." It was true. In the last few weeks, with more and more nights alone, I found myself playing Damiano's angel-themed CD late at night, using it to usher myself into sleep.

"And how's your *pesce?*" His smile was so bright it lit my face.

"You mean the fish?"

"*Sì,* the fish."

"He's very pretty, Dami. I leave him at the office, since I see more of him there." This was true, but the main reason I left the fish at the office was to avoid having to explain it to Malcolm. "It was such a sweet thing for you to do," I added.

"It was nothing," he said.

"How's the writing coming?" I asked him. "When you called the other day, you wanted to tell me something, didn't you? I feel like it's been awhile since we talked about your book. I . . . miss it."

Damiano smiled. "I don't think anybody understands it like you do," he said. "Would it be okay for you to look . . . ? I know how busy you are. You have been . . . I don't know the word. *Ispirazione.*"

"Inspiration," I said softly. "It's the same in English. I'd really love to read it, Dami."

"Bravo," he said. He smiled again. "I should do something for you. You have done so much for me."

I thought that the right thing to say was that I was just doing my job and that there was no need for him to repay me in any kind. But when I tried for those words, they became a dry wedge stuck in my throat.

"I would love that, too," I said, and felt a solar blush spread across my entire body. I ran one hand nervously through my hair as if that could dissipate the heat. Damiano watched me with the same knowing look he'd been wearing all evening.

"Your hair," he said.

"I know," I said, trying to laugh. "It's a mess. I couldn't figure out—"

"No," he said. "It's like a fire. Like the tail of a comet running down your back."

I looked up sharply as he finished the sentence. Lucy and Malcolm had suddenly materialized at the table, as if they'd been beamed in. I hadn't seen them coming at all. Malcolm held a fresh drink in his hand. His face looked dark and I couldn't read the expression in his eyes.

"Good!" Lucy proclaimed, apropos of nothing. "Let's sit. I have an announcement to make." She seated herself next to me and pulled her chair in close to mine. Malcolm took my other side, across from Damiano, and gulped his drink. So much for my designated driver. It was time for me to stop my own drinking for the night.

"A toast!" Lucy said, raising her glass. "Damiano, pick up a glass at least, will you?" Damiano obliged, lifting his mineral water. "Now, to books and all things literary." She drank greedily and we followed suit. "Angel!" Lucy exclaimed.

"Lucy?" I felt as if I were back in the office. My hand twitched at my side, ready to pick up a pen and write a memo on the spot.

"As you know, I travel to New York at least once a year." She swept her gaze over Malcolm and Damiano. "The heart of publishing is still in New York and it's important to have face time with these editors."

"But you're so successful in California," Malcolm said. I thought I detected the hint of a slur in his words. "And with the Internet and everything, is it still so important to be in New York? I mean, you're so well known. Seems to me they should come to *you*."

I was so embarrassed at Malcolm's unadulterated idolatry, I could only look down. My plate of meats glistened up at me.

"Well, that's terribly kind of you, Malcolm, and all ego aside, it's probably true. However, to answer your question, I do indeed have to go. But I find New York exhilarating and there's always something to learn, isn't there? None of us can say we're ever at the end of our learning curves, can we?"

There was a murmur of assent at the table, although I suspected that, like me, Malcolm and Damiano had no idea what she was going on about.

"*At any rate,*" Lucy went on impatiently, "the point of my mentioning this is not to give any of you a lesson in publishing. What I wanted to say was this: I have decided to take you, Angel."

"Take me?"

"Yes, on my upcoming trip to New York. You will accompany me to the Big Apple. Gotham. The City That Doesn't Sleep. I know you've never been there, but surely you've heard of it, yes?" She gave a tinkling little laugh into her glass, as if I should find that very funny. "Anyway, Angel, I'm taking you to New York with me. That's what I wanted to say. You've earned it."

"Wow, Lucy, I don't know what to say." I'd found that saying I didn't know what to say was an excellent time-filler, and I lingered over the words, playing for as many seconds as I could until I could figure out the response she wanted and align it with the one that came from my gut.

"What an honor for you, Angel," Malcolm said. "That's so very generous of you, Lucy."

Lucy nodded and tipped her head to one side. She was fixing Malcolm with a very peculiar look, as if she'd stepped in a pile of dog crap and then decided to flirt it off her shoe. I turned my head slightly to gauge Anna's reaction to all of this, but she'd vanished. Damiano's head was bent down toward his plate, but I could see his lips pursed tightly against a grin he was barely holding at bay.

"I'm very excited, Lucy. Thanks so much."

"Honestly, Angel, you don't sound very excited. You should know that I've never taken *anyone* to New York with me, let alone my assistant."

Malcolm was glaring at me. Damiano raised his eyes to meet mine.

"I'm just overwhelmed, Lucy. It's so . . . such a great opportunity for me."

"Exactly," Lucy said.

"Luciana, what is it you do there in New York? I'm so new to all of this, I don't know." Damiano shifted his entire body toward Lucy, his considerable charisma ratcheted up to full power, as though she were the most fascinating creature in the world. And he did it for me because he could see how I was struggling. It was an absolutely heroic save. Because he was focused on Lucy he couldn't see my eyes, but I sent my gratitude through them anyway as Lucy launched into a discussion of how she met with editors and publishers and pitched new projects. She talked about how exhausting the meetings were, scheduled back-to-back because every editor in New York wanted to see her. And then there were the parties, of course. There was always some kind of book "happening" in New York. She had several New York–based authors, she said, who had opted to go with *her* instead of the many well-known New York literary agents, and she always made time to see them. She was a native Californian, Lucy said, but she felt as if she had a New York sensibility. And at least she didn't hail from Southern California—she'd never be able to overcome *that* prejudice. At least those in the north had a little more credibility. Did Damiano find that as well, coming from Italy? Wasn't there a north/south split there as well? Which was somewhat surprising, considering that Italy was so much smaller than California. Her people, she said, hailed from northern Italy originally. . . .

As she went on, Damiano occasionally interjecting an Italian phrase or exclamation, I stole a glance at Malcolm. His face was still dusky and he leaned forward in his chair, clinging to Lucy's every word. At some point, he felt my stare and averted his eyes slightly to look at me. I looked for the complicity that couples are supposed to have, that unspoken communication borne of shared experience, but he was offering none of that. He looked impatient and vaguely annoyed with me.

I turned my attention to Damiano, who was still leaning toward Lucy, making a pitch-perfect show of being completely fascinated by everything she was saying. Like Malcolm, he felt my gaze and, for the briefest of moments, his eyes caught mine. Desire hit me then, with the force of a piano falling from a skyscraper. It wasn't something as simple as attraction or as ladylike as longing. It had no relation to romance. It was wanton desire so strong it was painful. And it was Damiano I desired—probably had desired from the moment I read the first page of his book. I felt the weight of this realization as a physical sensation and it threatened to suffocate me. Damiano saw everything in that second— my shock, my sudden comprehension, the nakedness of my desire— and his eyes sparked with recognition.

". . . and Angel's been working on something very interesting, haven't you, Angel? I'm going to blow their socks off with this one."

I turned to Lucy's voice, but I was well and truly lost. "The Las Vegas novel," I said, scrambling. "It's looking really good."

"Not that!" Lucy snapped. "Our mystery manuscript."

"Oh," I said. "That."

"Yes, *that*. We're taking it to New York, Angel! I have a feeling it will be the talk of the town."

I was filled with sudden, unstoppable dread. I knew Lucy had been intrigued enough by *Blind Submission* to keep pushing for more, but what I hadn't realized was how much stock she'd put into its ability to sell. Now she was taking it to New York—and me to keep it company. And I would be stuck with an anonymous author I was starting to hate and a manuscript that was probably going to drive me crazy. The worst part was that I'd brought it all on myself. I'd given her the manuscript in the first place because I wanted so desperately to please her and to give her something to sell.

"It's terribly exciting, don't you think, Malcolm?" Lucy was saying.

"Exciting?" Malcolm seemed lost.

"Angel's work," Lucy said. "Surely she—"

"I don't know," Malcolm said, flustered, his color deepening. "Angel doesn't . . . I don't know."

"Really?" Lucy said, and her eyebrows lifted in surprise. Malcolm bit his lip. Damiano leaned backward in his chair, his glass half-raised as if stopped in the middle of a toast. Lucy's expression was neutral, but her eyes glittered. I felt the tension settle inside me, clenching and twisting. The silence was becoming unbearable, a looming entity unto itself. I couldn't understand why nobody would speak. I cleared my throat and all three sets of eyes turned to me, waiting.

"I'd love another drink," I said.

⸺

I GRIPPED THE STEERING WHEEL at ten and two and stared straight ahead, petrified that I'd do something to alert the police that my blood alcohol level was way past the legal limit. Not that I was blurry, fuzzy, or felt even slightly drunk. The excess adrenaline in my body had somehow acted as an antidote to the gin, and I felt more sober than I had before my first drink. Which was a great deal more than I could say for Malcolm, who was completely potted and slouched in the passenger seat next to me. We were ten minutes from my apartment and hadn't exchanged a single word in the last twenty. The air between us was charged and smoking with resentment.

"I can fuggen drive, you know."

"You can't even fucking talk, Malcolm, let alone fucking drive, okay?"

"You've got a mouth on you, Angel," he said. "Better things you could be doing with it. Or maybe you already have."

"What are you talking about? Never mind, don't tell me. I can't believe how drunk you are."

"I'm not fuggen drunk, all right? And what if I was? How could you blame me? The way you treated me over there."

"The way I treated you? Now you have to tell me what you're talking about because you're not making any sense, Malcolm."

"You know what happened, Angel. You fuggen know."

I saw the events of the evening unfold as a series of still frames on the black night in front of me. How Lucy had moved closer and closer to me throughout dinner until our legs were touching, her cold thigh pressing into mine. How Malcolm had taken his dialogue with Lucy from shameless flattery to overt flirtatiousness to something approaching lewdness. How every time I tried to eat, I choked on the meat. How Lucy ate a good portion of several animals with gusto. How Malcolm drank and drank and how Lucy encouraged him to have still more. How Anna stood in the doorway between the living room and dining room, shooting daggers with her eyes, until uncountable minutes later, Lucy told her, "You may leave now." How Lucy presented us with dessert, a giant angel food cake in a spun-sugar basket, and explained that Damiano had baked it especially for me. How Lucy had invited us all to the deck for cigars. *Cigars!* How Malcolm had gladly accepted her offer, although he'd never smoked a cigar in his life, and left Damiano and me sitting at the table. How Damiano had leaned so close to me, I could feel the small hairs on my arms stand up with gooseflesh. How he had said, "Can I call you?" and how I knew exactly what that meant. How I told him, "I can't," and how he'd said, "I understand." How I'd watched Malcolm and Lucy through the glass deck doors. His gesturing hands, loosened with gin and vermouth, drifting ever closer to her until they touched her arm, her hand, her shoulder. How Damiano watched this tableau with me, saying nothing for a long time, then standing, telling me he had to go. How the rest of it happened very quickly—Damiano leaving, Lucy pressing foil-wrapped cake into my hands, telling me we'd be going over "our New York schedule," ushering me and Malcolm out of her big white door, my taking the keys out of Malcolm's pocket, starting the car, not believing, even now, that any of it had actually happened.

"I know you made a fool of yourself," I told Malcolm. "But I don't know why."

"*You* made me into a fool," he said.

"I didn't do anything."

He exhaled heavily, his liquor breath filling the small space inside the car. I rolled down my window. "Did you shleep with him?"

"Shleep? With who? What does that mean?"

"Angel, for fugg's sake. Don' play dumb. Did you have sssexxx? With that Italian cook. Junkie. Writer. Whatever. Did you?"

I was trembling, with anger or guilt or surprise or some combination of all three, and had to steady myself, knuckles white on the steering wheel, before I could answer him. "What are you talking about, Malcolm? Do you even know what you're saying? How ridiculous you sound?"

"You think I'm so stupid, *lover*? Think I don't have eyes in my head? *Angel* fuggen food cake? Your hair. The tail of a comet? I mean, Jeesusss. Did you think I missed that?"

"That doesn't mean anything."

"He's the one made you that CD with all the angel songs, izzen he? I knew it." He spit the last few words out with bitterness I'd never before heard in his voice.

"I edited his manuscript, Malcolm. I helped him get a lot of money. He's grateful, that's all. I didn't sleep with him. When you sober up, you're not even going to believe you said that to me."

"Edited his manuscript," Malcolm repeated slowly, his words losing their slurs. "His book. *His* book. Might as well have had sex with him. It's the same thing for you, anyway."

"That's not fair, Malcolm, and you know it. So Lucy sold his book and not yours. So what? That means I slept with him? And what were *you* doing with Lucy? Touching her, flirting—no, not flirting, *drooling* all over her. Jesus, Malcolm, she's my *boss*. And she's . . . God, she's *Lucy Fiamma*." I heard my voice go higher and higher as I went on and wondered if Malcolm would see what I thought—that I was protesting too much. He'd seen the way I'd looked at Damiano and he'd known what it meant. *Might as well have had sex with him.* Was that so far off?

I screeched to a stop. We had made it to my apartment, hydroplaning on a sea of gin, without being killed or arrested. I offered a small prayer of thanks. Malcolm and I sat in the still car for seconds or minutes, both of us lost in our own confused and tangled thoughts.

"Seems like you were pretty close to her yourself," he said finally. Suddenly he didn't sound drunk anymore, just mean and tired.

"So you think I slept with her, too? Go ahead, say it, Malcolm. That would just be the perfect end to a perfect night."

"Did you? Don't act like it's so far out, okay? I saw how close she sat to you. I think you turn her on, Angel."

"Malcolm . . ." I sighed. "That's just fucking disgusting."

I leaned back, resting my head on the seat. Malcolm was half-turned toward me, his eyes glassy, his hands lying limp in his lap like two dead birds. I remembered how handsome he'd looked at the beginning of the evening. He looked unraveled and lost now, as if he were wearing someone else's clothes. And I probably looked the same.

"Why are we doing this?" he asked.

"I don't know," I answered.

He reached over to me, his arms covering mine, his hands searching for their place in the tangles of my hair. He leaned in to kiss me, but I moved back and away from him. I couldn't do it. Not then. I gathered my purse and unlocked the car door, leaving the keys in the ignition.

"You okay to drive home?" I asked him.

Malcolm stared at me for a long moment. Even in the dark of the car, I could see the complex interplay of emotions crossing his features.

"So it's like that, is it, Angel?"

"Just for tonight," I said.

"Why? You have more *work* to do?"

"Malcolm, please." I was practically begging him. "Are you sure you're okay to drive?"

He got out of the car, came around to the driver's side, and, very formally, opened my door and gestured for me to exit. I slid out and he took my place, slamming the door behind him. He started his car and gave me a last look through the rolled-down window. "Yes, Angel," he said, "I'm okay to fu*c*king drive."

He pulled out faster than he should have, spraying gravel bits into the night behind him, but I could tell that he was in complete control. I stood there watching, purse in my hands, my eyes stinging with fatigue, until his taillights disappeared down the road.

TEN

To: angel.robinson@fiammalit.com
From: ganovelist@heya.com
Subject: Blind Submission pages

Dear Ms. Robinson:

As usual, your comments have been most useful. May I say that I am beginning to truly enjoy working with you. I understand the need to make the prose more "vivid," as you say, and, no, I don't take offense. Please review the attached pages and let me know if they fit the bill. I believe you will find them most stimulating. I do hope that they will continue to please Ms. Fiamma as well. I look forward to hearing from you as always.

G.

Blind Submission, p. 102

Alice waited naked on the bed.

The hotel was in Midtown Manhattan and nice, but not too. It wasn't so fancy that it would draw too much attention.

Nobody would suspect that Vaughn Blue would stay in a place that was just "nice." Here, disguised, he would be someone who looked like Vaughn Blue, not "the" Vaughn Blue, sex-godrockstar. And that was exactly the way Alice wanted it. She wasn't about to become some groupie slut with her face in the tabloids. She had much bigger plans than that.

Still, it was true that when they'd had that first lunch at Michael's, at Carol's request, Alice had found him almost irre-sistibly attractive. His skin was olive colored and his eyes were the color of ripe plums. He was in some twelve-step program due to an obligatory rock star addiction to heroin, so he didn't drink any alcohol and remained happily coherent. But it was his undeniable charisma that appealed to Alice the most, and her excitement grew to the point that she could hardly stand it. It was a happy coincidence that Alice found herself physically at-tracted to a man she planned to seduce. Attraction was unnec-essary but in this case it was a definite bonus.

Vaughn hadn't wanted to talk about his book at first. He seemed annoyed that Carol Moore hadn't come herself. It took little time, though, for him to warm up to Alice. Alice knew the power of her looks and how to make the best of them. But more than that, Alice knew the power of power and that power was the strongest aphrodisiac there was.

Vaughn was intelligent and he could write, which set him apart from almost every other celebrity author. Alice ignored that aspect of him—the writerly part of him that she couldn't help but detest—and focused on her growing attraction.

She soon got Vaughn off the topic of his book and on to bet-ter things, like when he might meet her again and where. He wanted some more feedback about his book, Vaughn said. Alice said, of course, and pointed out that there were several hotels where they could have such a discussion.

The first time had been amazing—a surprise to Alice, who was hard-pressed to allow herself any pleasure at all. They hadn't talked at all—they'd just gone at each other like two animals. Then there was a second time—slower, deeper, and afterward, Vaughn had talked a little about his life. There was another book, he told her. One he had written long ago. Nobody had read it. Nobody. Until he'd met Alice, he'd never felt he could fully trust anyone. Would she consider reading it?

Yes, Alice had told him. Oh yes.

Now here she was again, every bit of clothing stripped from her lithe body, her hair laid out like a golden net on the pillow, the insistent throb of anticipation in her loins.

She didn't have to wait very long.

A tapping came on the door and Alice opened it. Vaughn Blue stood in the doorway wearing a hat, sunglasses, and a false beard. He looked ridiculous, but he didn't look like Vaughn Blue. He licked his lips when he saw Alice and told her she looked like Lady Godiva. Alice asked him what he was waiting for and why wasn't he already naked?

Celebrities were always smaller than you thought when you saw them in person, Alice thought as she tore Vaughn's clothes from his body. But not Vaughn, who crashed into her larger than life.

They rolled on the bed together, their musky sweat blending and dripping onto the sheets. Vaughn bit Alice's breasts and licked her neck. Alice dug her fingernails into the flesh of Vaughn's shoulders. She pushed her hips up to meet his and he reached around to her back, pressing in with the palms of his hands, tickling her skin with his fingers. Alice moaned with pleasure. She grabbed his huge manhood and drove him inside her where she was wet and steaming. It was so good, she thought, as he plowed her like a ripe field. So very, very good as he filled her and honeyed fires coursed through her body. She wanted it to never stop, even as wave after wave of ecstasy crashed against her.

Vaughn pulled out of her trembling body and raised himself, glistening, on the pillows. He laced his fingers into her hair and held on.

"Don't stop." Alice panted.

"I have to look at you—I have to." He sighed. He ran his hands along her breasts, cupping them. He took one finger, traced it around the circle of her right nipple, and stopped.

"I never noticed this before," he said.

Alice quickly raised her hand to her breast as if to rub it off—the tattoo she'd had put there long ago when she was so much more hopeful about everything. It was a small but exquisitely detailed tattoo of Alice in Wonderland, sitting under a magic mushroom. "It's nothing," Alice said. "Nothing."

"It's beautiful," Vaughn said, "like the rest of you." He leaned down and kissed the Alice on Alice's breast.

"Let me in now," he said.

And Alice did.

So. It had been Malcolm all along.

He was due to show up at my apartment within the hour and I was finding it difficult to sit still and wait for him. I could feel anger vibrating through my body, working its way into the muscles of my jaw and shoulders, forming knots so tight they felt like bone. I watched the clock, counting off the minutes as a way of distracting myself. For perhaps the hundredth time, I felt my hand go up to my breast and curl around that cursed tattoo—the biggest mistake I'd ever made—as if I could tear it out with my fingernails. I forced my hand down but couldn't do anything about stopping my mind from going back there—to the tattoo and everything it had come to mean.

I suppose I must have known from the beginning—from its very first pages—that the literary agency in *Blind Submission* was modeled on Lucy's. It was such an obvious conclusion but I wouldn't allow myself to draw it. It could have fit the profile of dozens of other literary agencies as well, I told myself. Having only worked with Lucy, how could I be sure?

When the chapters first started coming in, I was so focused on the clumsy prose that I didn't see how clear the links were between the characters and their real-life counterparts in Lucy's office. But as the writing started to improve with my notes—and it *was* getting better—it became apparent that Carol Moore was based on Lucy, that Jewel was based on Anna, Ricardo on Craig, and Alice on me. But these were parallel-universe versions. Anna, of course, looked nothing like the beautiful and graceful Jewel. Craig was miles away from the suave sophistication of Ricardo. Like Lucy, Carol Moore was a brilliant and powerful literary agent, but in every other respect she was exactly 180 degrees removed from Lucy. Carol Moore was pleasant, even-tempered, magnanimous, gentle, and philanthropic. Lucy was . . . well, none of those things.

But it was the character of Alice that became the most disturbing to me. She was conniving, rapaciously ambitious, mean-spirited, and manipulative. And she was a writer. In all respects, she was the exact opposite of me. In my edit notes I'd been prodding the author to create a more nuanced version of Alice. It was one of the first rules of fiction that one couldn't have an entirely unlikable protagonist and expect to have a successful novel. But even as I told the author this, I started to wonder if I wasn't just trying to defend *myself*. Because my hunch was proving true: Whoever was writing the novel knew me. And not just in passing.

All this was compelling at first. Perhaps, in a narcissistic way, I even found it a little thrilling. But by the time I went to Lucy's party, the parallels were just too close and too many for comfort. And even as I tried to get in touch with Peter Johnson, I had the sinking feeling that it wasn't him after all.

I'd called Mr. Johnson at home after Jackson unearthed his number for me, only to hear the phone ring and ring, nobody picking up, no answering machine to take a message. I tried again the next day and the day after. On my fourth attempt, somebody finally answered, but it wasn't Peter Johnson, it was a woman who identified herself as Mr. Johnson's nurse. Peter Johnson had passed away, she informed me. He'd been ill for some time. She asked me who I was, and when I identified myself, she gave a sad sigh. He'd been waiting for so long for a call from my agency, she said, it was all he ever talked about. How very unfortunate that his ship had come in after he'd taken leave of this world. I offered hurried sympathies and got myself off the phone as quickly as possible. Although it was completely irrational, I couldn't help but feel that I was somehow responsible for Peter Johnson's demise. Anna's comment, "If only *all* our annoying writers would die as conveniently," only made me feel worse.

Along with regret that I hadn't been nicer to him the last time I'd spoken to him, Peter Johnson's exit left me totally confused. I told myself to just work on the manuscript like I would any other. It wasn't as if I didn't have enough going on at the office or, after Lucy's horrendous dinner party, in my own life to keep my mind occupied. Besides, *Blind Submission* was *only a book*. No, not a book, a manuscript. Hardly even a manuscript, for that matter—it was mostly a series of e-mail attachments. Plus, it needed work. It wouldn't be readable, much less salable, without my help. Whoever was writing the thing had to know that—better than he knew *me*.

But there were all those "coincidences" between the events in *Blind Submission* and the corresponding ones in my life. There was only one person who knew all the details well enough to write them. Alice's work was rejected—and so was Malcolm's. I got a raise—and so did Alice. I worked with Damiano—Alice worked with Vaughn.

Still, I wasn't sure—didn't want to admit it—until I read *that scene* and knew that Malcolm was the author of *Blind Submission*.

There could be no other explanation, no other author. Alice's torrid (and purplishly overwritten) sex scene with Vaughn perfectly mimicked Malcolm's accusation that I was sleeping with Damiano. Vaughn himself seemed like a copy of Damiano, down to the heroin and the color of his eyes. But that wasn't all—not by a long shot. What made my heart race and the tips of my fingers go cold was the description of the sex itself. Who else but Malcolm would know exactly how I—and, by extension, Alice—liked to be touched? But it was the tattoo-kissing that really got me. That little intimacy was *ours*. He'd given Alice an Alice in Wonderland tattoo to mimic my "Angel's wings" that he had kissed so many times. Reading it made me feel physically ill. If Malcolm was writing this novel—and it had to be him—everything I thought I knew about him and everything I thought I understood about our love for each other was wrong.

The funny thing was, before I read those pages I was actually feeling bad about the way I'd been treating him.

A day or two after Lucy's party from hell, Malcolm had called me, contrite. He said he was sorry, that he shouldn't have had so much to drink, he didn't know what had gotten into him, it was an awkward situation and he felt uncomfortable, surely I could understand that, couldn't I? And I could. What I *couldn't* understand was why he was suddenly so apologetic. The Malcolm I'd known before I started working for Lucy might have admitted he was wrong, might even have been conciliatory after a disagreement, but would never have groveled, especially before *me*.

He suggested that we have dinner together and I agreed. I asked him to give me a week or two and then we set a date. He seemed pleased and a little surprised, as if he hadn't expected it to be that easy.

And why *had* I made it so easy? I told myself that it was because I loved Malcolm and I wanted to mend the tears in our relationship and keep it together. But the real truth of it was simply that I felt guilty. I felt guilty that Lucy had rejected Malcolm and that I'd put him in the position of being humiliated. And I felt impossibly guilty about my feelings toward Damiano. Nothing had actually happened between the two of us or had even come close to happening, but Damiano had crept into the space inside me where only Malcolm had been for so long. I couldn't deny that attraction or its power. I'd been physically faithful to Malcolm, but the accusations he'd thrown at me the night of Lucy's party stung with the ring of truth. In my desire, I *had* cheated on him. And that was a betrayal of the man I loved.

But then I read the scene and everything I thought I believed went into a mad tailspin.

My first impulse was to call Malcolm and pour out my outrage over the phone, but I forced myself not to. I let it simmer for a couple of days, turning it around in my mind, looking, again, for reasons why he couldn't be the author, trying to recapture my trust in him. I was hoping that by the time he came over for the dinner we'd planned I'd have had some kind of revelation, but I didn't. Instead, I just felt my anger and confusion grow until my entire being was saturated with it.

This was the state I was still in as I waited for Malcolm to show up for the dinner that was supposed to mend all our fences. When, finally, I heard his knock at my door, I found my legs so stiff with tension, it was difficult to even walk across the room to open it.

The first thing I saw when I opened the door was the giant bouquet of I'm-so-sorry flowers Malcolm was holding in front of his face.

"What's the matter?" he asked before he'd even gotten both feet inside.

"Why are you doing this?" I said, sounding much more dramatic than I'd intended.

"Doing what?" he said, but his face paled immediately and he looked as guilty as sin.

"You know what I'm talking about," I said. "Don't make me go round and round with it, okay? I just want to know why. What do you think you're going to get out of this ultimately? How long do you think you can keep it going?"

"Angel . . ." He hesitated and looked down at his feet. The flowers seemed to visibly wilt in his hand. "I really don't know what you think . . . what you mean." He shrank away from me. The sight of it made me sad and furious at the same time.

"Come *on*," I said. "Stop it. When were you going to tell me? Were you going to tell me at all? She wants to sell it. She's *going* to sell it. You know that! How long do you think you can be anonymous?" My voice had risen to a screechy pitch.

I watched as Malcolm's face changed from pale to flushed. His eyes, which had been downcast and clouded, snapped and sparked. He'd been almost cowering but now stood up straight, filling his chest with air. "What the hell, Angel?" His voice was angry, no longer hesitant. "I. Do. Not. Know. What *you're talking about!* Make some sense."

"*Blind Submission*," I said. "I know you're the author. I've read that chapter, okay?"

"Say *what*, Angel?" Malcolm looked at me, his face a wild mix of competing expressions, as if he didn't know whether to laugh, cry, or throw up. He opened his hands and raised them palms up, dropping the flowers on the floor. They landed heavily, making a splayed pattern of stems and blossoms at my feet. "You're crazy," he said. "'That chapter'? Do you hear yourself? You've gone nuts, Angel."

I went on, fueled by days of compacted anger, insisting that he was the only person who could have written the manuscript. He remained adamant that he hadn't and forced me to go over every detail of it with him. He made me say it out loud—made me talk about Damiano and how I was sure that the sex scene between Vaughn and Alice was another accusation. His face grew darker when I brought up Damiano and then twisted into a grimace when I stumbled over the description of the sex scene and, finally, the irrefutable evidence of the tattoo.

"You think you're the only woman who likes it a certain way, Angel? And please, can you possibly believe that you're the only chick with a tattoo on her tit?"

I was stunned. I felt like those cartoon characters that have the floor give way underneath them but remain suspended in the air for several seconds before they fall. But Malcolm didn't need a response from me; he wasn't finished with his own commentary.

"Do you think I'd have such little pride that I'd send an anonymous novel to be edited by *you*?" he said. "Do you think I have as little faith in my own talent as you do? I'm an *artist,* Angel. You've never understood that. How could you think, even for a moment, that I'd do something like that?"

"Because—"

"How do you know it's not your boy Damiano? Maybe that's your mystery author. Seems he knows quite a bit about you, doesn't he?"

"You can't still think—"

"I'm not sure what I think anymore."

"Damiano doesn't need to sell another book!" I spat. "He's already writing a very good one for very good money."

"Unlike me, right, Angel? Isn't that what you meant to say?"

We stood staring at each other for several long seconds. I didn't know how to answer him or whether or not he was right. My eyes started to fill, but I was so confused about what was going on, so unsettled by all the strange turns my life was taking, that I didn't know whether I was crying or whether my eyes were watering at the strain of being open too wide and too long. I looked away from him, down at the mess of spilled flowers at my feet. I didn't know what to say. I didn't even know how I felt anymore.

"You think I need you, don't you, Angel?" Malcolm said. The edge of indignation in his voice was sharp and grating. "Well, I don't. I don't need your help and I don't need your pity."

"No," I said softly. "You certainly don't."

"That's right," he said, his tone growing more forceful, "and I'll tell you something else, *baby* . . ." He paused, drawing and puffing himself up, honing in. "*You* need *me.*"

"And what's *that* supposed to mean?"

"I've been carrying you since I met you, Angel."

"Carrying me?"

"Seriously, do you think you'd be where you are now without me? If I hadn't pushed you, you'd probably be out on your ass without a job, let alone a career. And then where would you be? With me, that's where. It's not like you have anyone else to support you."

"I don't remember you supporting me, Malcolm. I've been supporting myself just fine for years."

"I'm talking about emotional support, Angel. It's been only me since I've known you."

"What's that supposed to mean?"

Malcolm shrugged. "I'm just saying . . . for the last couple of years, you've had nobody but me in your corner and you haven't even looked for anyone else. And I think . . . You depend on me. That's all I'm saying."

That was all he was saying, all right. Not one word about love.

"Thanks for clearing that up, Malcolm," I said. "Maybe it's time for all of that to change." My voice was shaking.

"What do you mean?" he asked, a slight catch of doubt puncturing his self-righteousness.

"I think we should . . ." My whole body felt unbearably cold, encased in ice, but my heart was racing. I could hardly believe the step I was about to take, and I faltered on the edge of the gangplank.

"You think we should break up?" Malcolm was incredulous. "Is that what you're saying?"

"Yes, I guess that's what I'm saying." I'd started trembling. The two of us stood frozen in the chill of my words for a moment and then Malcolm took a step closer to me, leaning down so that I had no choice but to look into his angry eyes.

"I don't think you know *what* you're saying, Angel, but I'll tell you something: When you wake up and think about this for a second, you're going to realize what a huge mistake you've just made."

"I think you'd better leave now, Malcolm." I had to get him out of my apartment before I could change my mind and take everything back. I could feel myself on the edge of it as it was. It wouldn't take much to send me over.

"There's one thing you should know, Angel."

"Just *go*," I said, praying that he would before the ice melted and I dissolved in tears.

Malcolm shrugged and turned to leave. "I'm not your guy," he said as he made his exit. "You should look somewhere else."

I didn't know whether he was referring to our relationship or to *Blind Submission,* but he was long gone by the time I thought to ask him.

＿

TEN DAYS TO GO until Lucy and I left for New York. As I made my way to the office in the dawn's early light, I anticipated that every one of those days would be jammed with appointments made, canceled, and remade; memos and e-mails to various editors, assistants, and heads of houses; and endless flight and hotel reservations, again made and re-made until they arrived back at their original formula. From the moment Lucy had announced her New York trip and the fact that she was taking me with her, these booking details had become all-consuming. As we counted down to liftoff, Lucy became more and more obsessive and micromanaging about her schedule, the travel, and anything else related to the trip. Three days earlier, I had been instructed to give her a twice-daily weather report from New York ("And make sure it's the *city* of New York, Angel, I don't need to know skiing conditions in the Adirondacks") in addition to any late-breaking TSA reports about what one could or could not bring onto airplanes.

Of course, none of this work was supposed to interfere with my usual load, namely finishing my edit of Shelly Franklin's novel so that it would be ready for Lucy to sell (for a small fortune) in New York and the now-almost-impossible task of working on *Blind Submission*. The sheer magnitude of my workload did have one advantage: It kept me from thinking too much about what a shambles my personal life had become.

CRAIG'S CAR was the only one in the driveway when I pulled up to the office. I'd hoped I would be the first to arrive so I could get a jump on Lucy's endless list in relative quiet, but Craig had also been putting in crazy hours since we'd started planning our trip to New York, so I wasn't exactly surprised that he'd beaten me to work.

I steeled myself for the day ahead, gathering my bag, the endless pile of manuscripts, and my still-steaming coffee, and got out of my car backside first in order to gather everything I needed to carry in.

When I straightened up and turned around, Damiano was standing in front of me, a sudden mirage holding a vase full of calla lilies, and I jumped, a muffled yelp of shock coming from my throat, dropping my coffee and a good portion of the manuscripts I was holding.

"Damiano! You scared the life out of me!" My heart was pounding and skipping and my knees felt unsteady.

"I'm so sorry, Angel, I thought you heard me come up. Here, let me help you." He leaned over to pick up my papers at the same time I did, and the two of us bumped heads, fumbling through a scene that could have been in any number of date movies. "Sorry, sorry," he said again, and started to laugh. Our faces were very close, and when I raised my eyes to his, I was pulled in again by the sheer force of my attraction. A wave of heat rushed up my neck and into my face. I could feel myself starting to sweat. I lost my balance and started to tip over. Damiano reached out to steady me, and when his hand touched my arm, it felt like an electric shock. I had to stand up, pull myself out of this narrowing orbit of desire before I lost it completely.

"Do you have an appointment with Lucy?" I asked him when we were both standing with a comfortable distance between us and I could trust my voice again. It was a stupid question because if Damiano had an appointment with Lucy, I'd have been the one to arrange it, but it was the best I could come up with.

"No, not exactly," he said. "I have the contracts to sign and I thought to bring them in with these." He gestured to the vase of lilies, which he'd picked up again. He was wearing a white sweatshirt and blue jeans and looked as if he'd just finished shooting a Levi's print ad. I could hardly stand to look at him. It was so much easier when I talked to him on the phone and didn't have to deal with this rush of blood in my veins.

"You could have sent the contracts in," I said. "You didn't have to come all this way."

"*È vero,*" he said, and the look on his face grew clouded. "But I wanted to bring the flowers, too. I wanted to say thanks for dinner." One corner of his mouth turned up in a half-smile and he looked at me questioningly, as if there was some subtext I should understand. But it was all too dangerous and I was too exposed, and we were both within the gravitational pull of planet Lucy.

"Right, dinner," I said, trying to make my voice light and flip. "That was quite a party. I can see why you'd want to thank her for that."

Damiano knit his eyebrows in confusion and the smile faded from his face. He couldn't understand the bitter tone that had crept into my words and I couldn't blame him. I couldn't explain it myself.

"Well, I guess you'd better come in, then," I said. "No point standing out here."

"Angel," Damiano started, "did I do something to offend you? At the party . . . I'm sorry if I—"

"No, no, Dami, not at all. I didn't mean—"

"Because I didn't know you had a—"

"Boyfriend. I don't. I mean, I did, but I don't. Anymore."

I turned my eyes away from him, desperate to extricate myself from the tangled threads of the conversation.

"Okay," Damiano said finally. "Should we go in?"

"Yes," I said, feeling as if I was answering more than one question.

Craig looked up sharply as we entered, his expression changing from annoyed when he saw me, to surprised when he saw Damiano, to disapproving when he realized we'd come in together.

"Good morning," Craig said. "Good to see you, Damiano. Angel, Lucy's been waiting for you. She needs—"

"I know," I said, and made my way over to my desk. There was a note waiting on my chair, Lucy's favorite location for memos she didn't want me to miss. *GORDON HART!!!!* it screamed. *WHEN AM I SEEING HIM?!?!? PLEASE FINALIZE TODAY!!!!*

"Fine," Craig said. "Damiano, can I help you with something?"

Damiano looked from Craig to me and back to Craig again. He wore the same bemused expression I'd seen on his face the last time he'd been in the office. There was absolutely nothing about this little pig's house of bricks that intimidated Damiano in the slightest.

"I would like to see Luciana," Damiano said. "I come bearing contracts and flowers."

"Contracts, terrific!" Craig said with false brightness. "I can take those for you."

"*Bene,*" Damiano said, and shot me a sidelong glance full of amusement, "but I prefer to give the flowers to Luciana if that's okay."

I saw Craig's face redden. "Right. I'll take you in," he said, and stood so abruptly he knocked into his orderly desk, disrupting a few of his piles.

"*Grazie,*" Damiano said, and followed Craig to Lucy's door. I could hear the rise of Lucy's voice as they both entered, but couldn't make out what she was saying as Craig shut her door immediately afterward. As soon as Damiano disappeared into Lucy's igloo, I could feel some of the tension leaving my body. What had possessed me to blurt out that I'd broken up with Malcolm? My head was swimming and my intercom was already screeching.

"Oh Damiano, ha-ha, you're just a riot! Angel?"

"Lucy?"

"Gordon Hart?"

"Right now, Lucy."

"Please!" and she clicked off, still warbling over Damiano.

I fished the aspirin from my purse and picked up the phone, dry-swallowing three tablets as I dialed Gordon Hart's phone number. He wouldn't be there. He was never there unless he was the one calling, especially if Lucy Fiamma was on the line for him.

"Gordon Hart."

I was so shocked to hear his voice, I just stammered, "Uhh, uh . . . he . . . hello," into the phone.

"Ah," he said. "Angel Robinson, I presume?" I could hear the smile in his voice again—the same smile I'd heard the first time we spoke.

"I'm so sorry," I said. "I'm just surprised that you answered your phone."

Gordon Hart laughed. "Yes, we do that sometimes," he said. "Just to spice things up. What can I do for you, Ms. Robinson? Does *she* need to speak with me?"

"Um, actually, no," I said. "I'm just trying to finalize her schedule for New York. She'll . . . actually, *we* will be there the week after next, and I wanted to make sure we had a date and time settled for when the two of you will meet."

"I'd love to help you, Angel, I really would, but I have no idea when I'm meeting with her. Sarah, my assistant, takes care of these things for me. She's the keeper of my time. Frankly, I don't know how she does it."

"Of course," I said. "Sure." I was loath to let him off the phone. I had no idea when I'd be able to get him again.

"Tell you what, though," he said. "I *am* capable of writing a note, and I promise I will give Sarah one as soon as she returns. I'm expecting her back within the hour, and I'll be sure to have her call you and set the whole thing up, all right?"

"That would be great," I said. "Lucy's anxious—"

"I'm sure," he said, clipping his words. "Tell me, Angel, will we be seeing you as well when you come to New York?"

"Um . . . I don't know," I said, surprised by the question.

"Well, I hope you'll have the chance to come by," he said. "It would be nice to meet you."

"Thanks," I said. "That would be terrific."

"Take care," he said, and hung up.

I replaced the phone in its cradle. Gordon Hart wanted to meet me. One of the most important men in publishing. I couldn't stop the grin from spreading across my face.

To: angel.robinson@fiammalit.com
From: ganovelist@heya.com
Subject: Re: BS/edits

Dear Ms. Robinson,

As always, your editorial suggestions were very good; clear and to the point. I am in complete agreement with you with one exception. I don't believe that the sex scene between Vaughn Blue and Alice is, as you say, "overly graphic and cliché-ridden at the same time." You may be correct that there are one or two overly familiar tropes in my description of Alice's feelings (perhaps I'm not as adept at describing a woman's sexual response as I thought!), but I have to take issue with your assessment that it is too graphic. Alice is a voracious character—a consumer. It makes sense that she would "devour" Vaughn Blue. Alice doesn't even know exactly how Vaughn can help her, she only knows that he is a means to an end. She may fall in love with him, complicating her goal, in which case she might become slightly more tender. What are your thoughts about that? Every novel needs a good love story, doesn't it? At any rate, I will "tidy" the sex scene, but won't "clean" it, and then I'll send it back to you.

For now, I am enclosing more text for you. You'll see that I've heeded your advice to "speed things up" and now everything is starting to move much faster.

I will look forward to your comments as always,

G.

Alice was on her way into the daily staff meeting when Ricardo called her over to talk to him. Alice had big plans for this staff meeting and was mentally preparing how she was going to present "her" novel to Carol Moore for representation. This was the one Carol was going to take; the first of many moments for Alice to shine.

Alice hated having her thoughts interrupted and was annoyed to be sidetracked by Ricardo, but she kept her composure. It was very important to Alice that everyone in the office see her as calm and placid as a summer sea. Despite the fact that Ricardo would ultimately be as disposable as a kitchen sponge, Alice had to give him her attention.

"Yes, Ricky?" Alice said. Ricardo hated being called Ricky and Alice knew it. It was a game they played regularly now. Ricardo would correct Alice and Alice, affecting a Scarlett O'Hara attitude, would claim to have forgotten. Alice waited for Ricardo to play his part in the game, but this time he didn't. He looked disturbed, Alice thought. His smooth, caramel-colored skin was covered by a light sheen of perspiration and his shirt was rumpled. Normally, Ricardo was extremely careful about the way he looked and dressed.

"Alice . . ." Ricardo trailed off, looking very uncomfortable.

"Well, what is it?" Alice asked, with an impatient tone that reflected how she really felt.

"I know that Carol was very impressed after your interview for this job. Even though you didn't really have any experience, she liked you enough to hire you," Ricardo said.

Alice knit her brows together, a gesture that Vaughn had described, just this morning, as "charming." She had no idea where Ricardo was going with all of this, but his nervousness indicated it was somewhere that she wasn't going to like at all.

"Yes?" Alice said, and cursed herself for not sounding more solicitous. "I mean, of course I was thrilled when Carol hired me. But I do have experience, Ricardo."

"Do you think Carol Moore got to where she is today

because she's a stupid woman?" Ricardo asked. He was now perspiring quite heavily.

"Of course not."

"So didn't you think she would check your references and your experience?" He didn't wait for an answer. "And didn't you think that she would discover that almost all of it was made up?"

"I don't know what you're talking about," Alice said. Her fingertips were starting to feel cold and an icy sensation was starting to spread through her body like slowly melting snow.

"Of course you know what I'm talking about," Ricardo said. "The point is that Carol liked you so much that she decided to hire you even after she discovered that you'd lied at your interview." He paused and Alice waited for what was coming next, showing no expression. Her usual plan for a situation like this was to start showing some leg, some breast, or whatever part of her luscious body might appeal to a man. But Alice knew that this wouldn't sway Ricardo because there was only one woman who appealed to him, and that was Carol Moore.

"Carol told me that you reminded her of herself when she was your age," Ricardo continued. "She likes your ambition and she likes that you're motivated enough to change your circumstances in life."

Alice was growing very impatient with Ricardo's little sermon. "What are you getting at, *Ricky*?" she said.

Ricardo lowered his voice. "She trusts you, Alice. Carol Moore has been very good to me and I don't want to see her get hurt in any way."

"So who's hurting her? What are you talking about?"

"I know what you're up to, Alice. I've seen you looking through her private files. I've seen you gathering information. I've heard you talking to her authors."

"I'm not up to anything," Alice hissed, "except work. I'm doing my job." Ricardo couldn't know about the novel. Alice had been very, very careful about that. Unless . . .

"Is what you're doing with Vaughn Blue part of your job?"

Alice recoiled as if she had been slapped. She hadn't expected this. She had underestimated Ricardo and his powers of observation. This was a regrettable, but not fatal, error in judgment. He didn't know about what else Alice had been up to. Vaughn was a very small part of a much greater plan.

"Carol needs to know about this," Ricardo said. "But I'm giving you the opportunity to tell her yourself. If you come clean about it, I'm sure that she would still be willing to give you a good reference. A *real* reference."

"You're crazy," Alice said, and laughed. "I'm not going to do any such thing. And neither are you."

Ricardo stood up straight and adjusted the collar of his shirt. "Well, then, you haven't given me any choice but to talk to Carol myself," he said.

"Really?" Alice said. "And were you also planning to tell your wife about Carol?"

Instantly, all the color drained out of Ricardo's face. Alice knew she had scored a direct hit and she took real pleasure in watching the fear flood Ricardo's face like a pale ocean.

"Yes, *Ricky,* I know all about it."

"You don't . . ." Ricardo had to clear his throat and started coughing. "You don't know anything."

"Don't I?" Alice said, and tossed him a big smile.

"Hey, you two!" Jewel stopped in front of Ricardo and Alice. "There's a staff meeting happening. We'd better get going! Hey, Ricardo, what's the matter, you look awful."

Alice regarded Jewel's beautiful face with distaste. There was another one who was going to have to be dealt with soon. For all Alice knew, Ricardo might have already started shooting off his mouth.

"I think I ate some bad clams last night," Ricardo said. "But I'll be right in."

"Okay," Jewel said. "Alice, are you coming?"

"Right behind you," Alice said sweetly. She started to follow Jewel, but Ricardo grabbed her arm.

"Don't you touch me," Alice whispered, pulling her arm free.

"You don't have any proof of anything," Ricardo said hoarsely.

"Ricardo," Alice said, stretching her tongue out over the syllables. "I know everything."

"But . . . how?" Ricardo stammered.

"You said it yourself, Ricky, she trusts me. She confides in me. We're like *sisters*. I've even seen evidence of your, how do I say it, literary prowess? Carol treasures those letters of yours, by the way. I think they're a little juvenile myself, but what do I know of true love, eh?"

Alice let the effect of her words sink in.

"Now, should we go to that staff meeting?" she asked when it became clear that Ricardo was not going to respond. "Carol will start to wonder what's keeping us."

Ricardo looked utterly defeated, which was exactly how Alice wanted him. He turned to go into the staff meeting and Alice followed him. Before they could get to Carol's office, though, Alice paused and added one more little dig.

"Bad clams?" she asked. "Not likely, is it, Ricardo?"

ELEVEN

—

LUCY WAS AFRAID TO FLY. This was something she hadn't shared with anyone in the office that I knew of. If he'd been aware of it, surely Craig would have informed me before Lucy and I set out on a cross-country flight together. As I adjusted my seat belt and ignored the flight crew's halfhearted flight-safety instructions, I realized that Lucy's trepidation was probably the reason she'd never before taken anyone with her on her many business trips. Lucy hated showing weakness of any kind and never once mentioned her fear to a soul.

She hadn't exactly said anything of it to me, either, but it didn't take a genius to figure out what was going on. Before we even boarded, she started popping Xanax as if they were little candies. I'd picked up the prescription for her a few days earlier and read the Rx on the bottle, which instructed that she take one pill every six hours "for anxiety." From what I could tell, she'd taken at least eighteen hours' worth by the time we got on the plane.

Although she could have boarded before me (Lucy had purchased a first-class seat for herself and one in coach for me), she waited for my group to be called before taking her seat. Her steps were hesitant and jerky as we walked down the Jetway together, as if she were pushing against an invisible force. She fell against me at one point, gripping my arm so hard her fingernails almost punctured my skin.

"I hope you're not planning to sleep on this flight, Angel," she said through clenched teeth. "Because we've got a lot of work to do in New York and this is a perfect opportunity to get caught up."

I glanced at her, mutely nodding assent. The Xanax hadn't taken effect yet; her face was the color of a blank page and tiny beads of perspiration glistened on her forehead. I couldn't help but marvel at her ability to maintain her usual commanding tone while in the grip of a full-blown phobia. I left her in first class, where she was already ordering a hapless flight attendant to bring extra blankets, pillows, and a glass of wine "immediately," and took my seat near the back of the plane, grateful for the space between us.

But as we pulled back from the gate and began to taxi down the runway, I found myself getting nervous, and not because I was the least bit anxious about flying. It was Lucy I was concerned about. It was easy to see Lucy more as a force than a person. This was an image she cultivated. But now I'd seen that spark of naked terror in her eyes and felt compassion for her along with a weird need to protect her. It was as if her fear of flying had made her human, if only briefly, and despite the relief I felt to be sitting twenty-five rows away from her, I wanted to make sure she was all right. We lifted off the ground, all those tons of steel rising in an improbable ascent, and I could feel her fear in my own body. My stomach flipped and adrenaline made my heart race. I gripped the armrests hard enough to turn my knuckles white and attract the attention of the woman sitting to my left, who put down the paperback she was reading and smiled at me reassuringly.

"You'll be fine," she said. "Takeoff is always the hardest part."

"I'm okay," I told her.

"You look a little scared," she answered.

I relaxed my grip on the armrests. "I'm not, though," I said. "I'm not afraid to fly." I sounded like I was trying to convince myself.

"All right," she said, disbelief plain in her voice, and picked up her book. Out of lifelong habit, I looked at the cover to see what she was reading. It was the most recent edition of *Cold!*

"Good book," I said, the words falling out before I had a chance to stop them.

"What? Oh, this?" She waved the book in front of her. "Yes, it's excellent. I've already read it three times, but it's one of my favorites."

"Mine, too," I said.

"He's such an amazing writer." She sighed. "I wish he'd write another book."

"He is," I said, and bit my lip. "An amazing writer, I mean."

"Makes you wonder, though, doesn't it?" she went on as we continued our climb into the sky. She seemed pleased to have the opportunity to chat. "I mean, why *hasn't* he written another book yet? Maybe he can't. Maybe he didn't even write this one. Maybe there isn't even a real Karanuk. It's not like things like that have never happened, right?"

Not only had they happened, but they'd happened in multiples. Fake stories, lying authors, even completely fabricated identities had popped up with increasing frequency, so my seatmate wasn't off-base at all. I knew I should just agree with her, smile, and be done with it, but something seized me, some need to set her straight combined with a misguided sense of hubris, and I couldn't stem the flow of words from my mouth. "I can assure you that there is a Karanuk," I said. "And he is working on another book right now."

The woman turned her head toward me, curiosity lighting her eyes. "Do you *know* him?" she asked.

"No . . . I mean yes, but not . . ." That was it, I realized. I was screwed. And it was going to be a long flight. "I represent him," I said finally, and rather than correcting myself immediately, I let the words linger in the air for a moment, trying them on for size. She'd probably leave it at that, I thought. She was just a reader. Unfortunately, I was soon proved wrong.

"You're his literary agent?" she exclaimed.

"I work for his literary agency," I said. So much for trying things on for size.

"You work for Lucy Fiamma?" Her voice had risen to a level that threatened to alert flight attendants. I was doubly screwed. I'd managed to wind up sitting next to someone who knew enough about the world of publishing to identify Lucy as Karanuk's agent. What were the chances?

"Yes," I admitted. "Yes, I do."

"This is just the most amazing coincidence," she said, excited. "I'm a writer myself. I've recently completed my first book and I was *just* getting it ready to send to your agency."

I was triply screwed. And trapped as well. I knew what was coming next: a detailed description of this woman's manuscript, along with all the reasons it was sure to be a bestseller and probably an encapsulated version of her life story as well. And I'd have to listen politely. I'd have to outline our submissions policy and assure her that I'd pay special attention to it when she sent it in. I hoped to God she wasn't carrying a copy with her, because then I'd be forced to actually read some of it. At least she wasn't aware that Lucy was also on the flight. That knowledge could lead to a truly unpleasant situation.

"How about that?" I said, and hoped I didn't sound too disingenuous. "That really is a coincidence, isn't it?"

"Indeed," she said, and smiled broadly. She extended her hand. "Solange Martin," she said. "But everyone calls me Sunny."

"Angel Robinson," I said, wiping my damp palm on my pant leg before shaking her hand.

"Pleased to meet you, Angel," she said. I waited for her to launch into a pitch of her book, but to my surprise she stopped right there, picked up her copy of *Cold!,* and got back into her reading. I checked her out from the corner of my eye, seeing her for the first time. She was trim and tan, and everything about her was colored brown and gold, from her hair to her eyes to her loose silk pantsuit. It was difficult to determine her age because her skin was smooth and unlined, but her face had an aura of maturity about it. Mid-thirties, I guessed. I studied her more carefully and decided that she was a very attractive woman. She'd look great on a book jacket.

The pilot announced that we'd reached our cruising altitude and that FAA-approved electronic devices could now be used safely. I reached down for my laptop and Palm Pilot. I needed to give Lucy's schedule a once-over while she was far enough away from me that she couldn't change it—again—and then I needed to get back to my ongoing edit of *Blind Submission*. Lucy had been pressing me to get "fifty hot pages" of the novel ready to send to editors. She was planning to pitch it hard in New York, even though I'd told her I didn't think it was ready to go out. Since my blowup/breakup with Malcolm, there had been a few times I'd come very close to telling her that he was the likely author. But Malcolm's vehement denial, difficult to dismiss out of hand, stopped me every time.

What if he was telling me the truth and he wasn't the author of *Blind Submission*?

As difficult as it was to admit that the man I'd loved and trusted for so long could have used me in such a craven display of selfishness, it was a still more frightening prospect to consider that he hadn't. Because if it wasn't Malcolm (and, as G, he wasn't giving an inch), I couldn't think of who would know the intimate details of my life as laid out in the novel—or how that person would have obtained the information.

For her part, Lucy seemed unbothered by the fact that the author was remaining anonymous. All she cared about was that I was working on the chapters as quickly as they came in and that G wasn't going to take the project anywhere else, which I assured her wouldn't happen. I suppose, with keeping Karanuk under wraps for years, she was used to dealing with cloaks, daggers, and quirks.

"Excuse me, are you Angel Robinson?"

I looked up to see a flight attendant staring down at me. I noticed that she was wearing a St. Christopher medal and a silver airplane charm around her neck.

"Yes?" I said, adrenaline surging.

"This is for you," she said, and handed me an instantly recognizable pink memo. Clearly Lucy was wasting no time.

"Thank you," I said.

"You're welcome." The flight attendant knit her eyebrows and gave me a look that fell somewhere between annoyance and pity. I gave her a weak smile in return.

A—Need to discuss. —L.

I refolded the memo and stuck it in the seat pocket in front of me.

On the face of it, the intent of that memo was undecipherable, but I knew her so well it spoke volumes to me: *Get over to first class now and bring a notepad, my schedule, and pitch letters for every project I'm selling. We need to discuss all of it. Now. And in minute detail.*

I gathered all the necessary papers and unbuckled my seat belt. They weren't going to like a visitor from coach in the first-class cabin, but I was going to have to go, anyway. I could only pray that I'd get booted out quickly or that the Xanax would kick in and she'd pass out. I was sitting in the center seat, so I was forced to climb over Sunny to get out. She gave me a warm smile as I clambered over her with all my documents and electronic devices.

"Sorry," I said.

"No problem," she said. I got the sudden sense that she understood, that she knew what I was up against. I found it oddly comforting.

Lucy was holding the glass of wine she'd asked for and leaning against the window, a manuscript in front of her, when I made my way into the first-class cabin. She was still very pale, but the pills had made her face relax so much since we'd boarded that she was looking slightly melted.

"Angel, sit," she said, gesturing to the empty seat next to her.

"You know, Lucy, I don't think I'm really supposed to be up here," I said, sotto voce.

"Just sit, Angel . . . for God's sake. There's nobody sitting here . . . you're not going to stay long." She spoke much more slowly than usual, with big spaces between her words. I wondered if she'd taken more pills since I'd last seen her. "I paid enough for these seats, anyway," she added.

"Lucy, are you okay?" I asked her as I juggled papers on my lap.

"Why . . . wouldn't . . . I . . . be . . . okay?"

"You look a little pale."

Lucy looked down at her wineglass. "Not really much of a drinker," she said, with slightly more briskness. She handed me her glass. "Here, drink this."

I assumed she just wanted me to dispose of it, so I put it on the floor and hoped there wouldn't be any turbulence. "Sweet of you to be concerned," Lucy said, twisting her mouth into a loopy Xanax smile. I offered her one in return, unsure how to respond to this drugged version of Lucy.

"We should go over my schedule," she said.

"Right, I've got it right here," I told her, pulling out the printed version. Lucy was a Luddite when it suited her. My feeling was that she simply preferred live assistants to digital ones. The unpredictability of human emotion was what she thrived on, what she needed.

Lucy looked at her schedule and asked for a pen. But when I gave her one, she dropped it in her lap and fixed me with a look of great sincerity.

"I don't want to talk about this again," she said.

"We don't have to," I told her. "It's all worked out."

"I mean, what I really want to talk about is . . ." She leaned in very close to me. As always, I could smell her Chanel Nº5. "Why are you so far away, Angel?"

"I'm sitting right next to you, Lucy."

"But this is totally confidential," Lucy said, and raised her eyebrows in slow motion. I realized that she was probably very high, and the thought amused and frightened me at the same time.

"Okay," I said, and leaned toward her a little more. We were so close I could feel her hair tickle my forehead.

"Karanuk," she said.

"What about him?" I said, and realized that I'd lowered my voice to a whisper.

"I don't know if he's going to be able to pull it off," she said.

"Are you talking about *Thaw*?" I asked her. I'd heard Lucy on the phone, tempting editors with hints and morsels (even though, technically, Karanuk's previous publisher was supposed to get an exclusive first look at his next book), but she'd kept the actual text sealed off somewhere in her office and still hadn't allowed anyone else to read it. I hadn't really thought twice about Lucy's reticence with *Thaw*. I'd always expected that she would want to keep this particular project very private. Plus, I still didn't understand the nature of her relationship with Karanuk and wasn't sure that I wanted to.

"It's not even close to the level of *Cold!*" she said. "But that's not the problem. They'll buy it, anyway. But it's *not good,* Angel. Something's happened to him. It's as if the ability to write has been sucked right out of his being."

I flashed on Sunny, reading her crisp new copy of *Cold!* back in coach. *Why hasn't he written another book?* she'd asked. *Makes you wonder.*

"It's going to need a lot of work," she said, and fixed me in her sights. "It's going to need *you,* Angel."

"Oh." The weight of what she'd just said hit me hard. I eyed her cautiously, wondering if she knew what she was saying.

"So now you know why I haven't sold it already," Lucy continued. "If it wasn't such a mess, I'd have had the deal done the day after the first page arrived in the office."

"Of course," I said, realizing the truth of what she was saying.

"I've brought it with me," she went on, "and I want you to read it. When we get home this is going to be your first priority, Angel. And I don't need to tell you that this is a delicate situation. There's a lot of money at stake here, not to mention reputation." She inhaled deeply. "I don't know how kindly Karanuk will take to your giving him *direction,* so it's going to have to come from me. Do you get my meaning, Angel?"

Of course I got it. I'd do the work, she'd take the credit. It couldn't be clearer, really. But I didn't really care about that. I was far more concerned about Karanuk. I couldn't imagine him writing something *bad.* Not after *Cold!* I wondered if he was one of those fabled writers with just one great work inside him, a work that is almost channeled through him, and after that, it's over.

"Sure, Lucy."

"Good. As long as we understand each other." She pointed to the seat back in front of her. "There," she said. "Take it."

I reached in and pulled out the curled, worn manuscript pages. Lucy had written wild, scrawling notes all over the cover page. I could barely make out the title and Karanuk's name. Lucy leaned back in her seat, breathing very slowly. Her eyelids looked heavy and I was sure she was about to drop off. I looked up and met the eye of the flight attendant who'd brought me the memo. I could tell by her expression that my time in first class was about to get cut short.

"Lucy?" She didn't move or react in any way. "I think I'm going to have to go back to my seat now."

"He was one of the worst lovers I've ever had," Lucy said. Her voice was somnambulant. She sounded like she was reciting a passage from a novel. "Talk about cold! Ha! Great writer. Lousy lay. You wouldn't think it, would you? You'd figure an Eskimo would know how to heat things up."

I realized with horror that she was talking about Karanuk and felt my mouth drop open. I had the same feeling you get when you witness your parents fighting or when you run into a teacher outside of school. It was just wrong—and uncomfortable in the extreme.

"They don't know," she went on, "they don't understand . . . what a *privilege* it is to get published. So many of them . . . don't even deserve it."

"Miss?" The flight attendant was hovering over me, her charms dangling. "I'm going to have to ask you to return to your assigned seat, please."

"No problem," I said, and gathered my things.

"Where are you going?" Lucy asked.

"I have to go—"

"Ma'am, she needs to be in her assigned seat. If you need—"

"I'll tell you what I *need*. Now listen to me, do you know who I am?"

I'd never heard anyone actually use that phrase before and had to stifle the laugh that bubbled up in my throat. I made my exit as gracefully as possible considering the tight space and left Lucy arguing with the flight attendant. I could only hope that she wouldn't make enough of a scene to get us both detained when we arrived in New York.

I climbed over Sunny for the second time, careful to fold *Thaw* in half, and tried to settle myself back in my seat. I was already exhausted and we weren't even an hour into the flight. It occurred to me that I could make good use of Lucy's Xanax myself.

"Everything okay?" Sunny asked me, those notes of comfort and understanding in her voice again.

"Oh, yes, fine, thanks." I looked at her, still expecting her to start talking about her book, but again, she just smiled at me and went back to her reading. Perhaps she was waiting for the right time, waiting for my curiosity to be piqued. I gave a nervous glance down to first class. I hadn't seen any air marshals walking the aisles, so perhaps Lucy had quieted down. I pulled out my laptop again and turned it on. The most recent installment of *Blind Submission* stared back at me. This chapter, along with three others (G had gone into overdrive now), had come in as Lucy and I were preparing to leave, so I hadn't yet had a chance to read them.

There was no question that this manuscript was getting much better as it went along. It was as if G (or Malcolm—damn him) had had some kind of breakthrough after our last go-round and was finally finding his real voice. There was still some work to be done, of course, especially when it came to his annoying tendency to use clichéd and peculiarly awkward metaphors, but the characters were starting to come alive. Alice had found her voice as well, in a manner of speaking. The fact that this voice belonged to another author whose work she was about to steal and present as her own made for an excellent plot twist. Even as it worked on me, *Blind Submission* was getting good.

"Ms. Robinson?"

The first-class fight attendant was back at my seat. I braced myself for her wrath, sure that Lucy had stirred her up again, but was surprised to see her smiling warmly.

"Yes?"

"Would you mind coming with me for a moment, please?"

What could it be now? I wondered as I climbed over poor Sunny for a third time. I had a sudden fear that the flight attendant was only calm and smiling to avoid creating a scene before I was placed in some kind of custody at the front of the plane.

"Is there a problem?" I asked her timidly as we headed toward first class.

"No," she said, "not at all. Your mother explained the situation to me. You can stay there with her for a while if you need to." She graced me with a wide grin. "But I'd personally appreciate it if you'd return to your seat before the end of the flight."

My *mother*? Lord, but Lucy was good. I wondered if she'd promised literary representation as well.

"Thank you," I said. "She—"

"Not to worry, dear." The flight attendant actually patted my arm, which was an awkward maneuver in the tight cabin. "She's already told me everything."

I shuddered to think what "everything" might constitute.

The color and texture of Lucy's skin made her look like a wax replica of herself. She'd applied an overly generous amount of flaming-red lipstick since my last visit, which only served to heighten the effect. I sat down next to her and realized, with horror, that I hadn't brought my laptop or notes with me. I told myself it didn't matter because there wasn't a single piece of business Lucy could bring up that wasn't hardwired into my memory.

"Angel." She leaned toward me woozily, her bright green eyes clouded over. I had another pang of concern about her pill consumption. The flight attendant was attending to a passenger directly in front of us but seemed to be keeping a curious eye on us all the same.

"Mom?" I said, and realized how incredibly strange the word sounded in my mouth, and not just because I was directing it at Lucy.

"Books are like children, you know," Lucy said with great seriousness.

My hair had started to come loose and I blew a strand of it off my face. For the first time in my life, I thought it was a pity that I *wasn't* a writer. I was trapped on an airplane with my crazy-stoned boss, who was claiming to be my mother and who was now going to launch into a discussion about giving birth to literature. It was a situation that was ripe with literary possibilities. "You labor over them, deliver them, and then they're out there in the world," she continued, "and you never know what they'll become."

I'd heard this many times before. I wondered where she was going with it, if anywhere.

"I've midwifed . . . midwived . . . been the midwife for many, many books that wouldn't have been born at all without me." She ran her tongue around her lips, smearing her lipstick slightly. I thought about offering her a napkin to blot her lips.

"So true," I said, wondering why I felt the need to speak.

Lucy stared through me for a moment, her gaze on some unseen point beyond the confines of the first-class cabin. I thought she was going to zone out completely, but then she slowly brought herself back around. I could almost see the thoughts collecting behind her eyes.

"Blind submission," she said suddenly and with great force. "I need it." I looked at her, perplexed, searching her face for more information, and then it dawned on me that she was talking about the manuscript and not giving me an employment directive.

"I've just been reading it," I told her, and I could hear the skip in my voice. "It's really getting better, Lucy. I don't even think the new material is going to need much work. I'm not quite finished reading yet, but I think—"

"Really?" Her voice was in near-monotone, but I could see some animation working its way into her features. "I need to sell that book, Angel. I'd *like* to sell it as soon as possible. How close are we?"

"Close," I said. "I think with the rewrite of the last two chapters and this new—"

"I don't need the details of every sentence, Angel. I want to know *when*. We're hours away from New York. In the morning I'll be having breakfast with . . . with . . ."

"Natalie Weinstein."

"With Natalie Weinstein, and she's still upset about losing *Parco Lambro*. She's ravenous for a hot new project. From me. Can I tell her I have one or not?"

I struggled with what kind of answer to give her. "Well, I think if—"

"Do we have the pages?"

"Only on my computer. But I'm still—"

"On your computer?"

"Yes, because I'm—"

"Still *writing* it?" Lucy gave me a twisted, joyless smile, her smeared lipstick adding to it a touch of the grotesque.

"What?" I asked her.

"Are you still writing it, Angel? Is that why we don't have it yet?"

I knew that Lucy was out of it, perhaps dangerously so, but I found it difficult to imagine that she really thought I was the creative force behind this novel. Unless . . . Staring at her, unable to come up with a response, I realized in a sense I *was* writing *Blind Submission*. Hadn't I been over every word of this thing, changing it, reshaping it, doing my fairy-tale spin of straw into gold? Were the "suggestions" I was giving G starting to become more than that? Was I creating the text before he wrote it? My thoughts started to collapse on themselves in a flash of total confusion. I had the terrifying sensation that she'd found me out, that she'd caught me at something I didn't even know I was doing. I shook my head and the moment passed.

"I'm *editing* it, Lucy. Isn't that what you want me to do?"

"What I want . . ." She stared at me hard, her eyes gaining focus on mine. "What I want from *you*—" The plane gave a lurch before she could finish speaking, and the FASTEN SEATBELTS sign blinked on with its accompanying ring. Lucy cringed and seemed to shrink into herself, an expression of sheer terror flashing across her face. "Fucking airplanes," she said through clenched teeth. I was at a loss, unsure whether to try to comfort her, summon a flight attendant, or search for more Xanax. She covered her eyes with her hands and leaned forward in her seat. I waited for her to speak or change position for five minutes and then I realized that she'd fallen asleep or, more likely, passed out. I reached over and tapped her lightly on the shoulder. No response. I put my hands on her shoulders and tried to lean her back into a more comfortable position. Lucy stirred as I fumbled. Without opening her eyes, she reached up, grabbed one of my hands with her own, and held on.

"It's . . . um . . . Lucy? It's okay. Do you want me to stay here with you?"

Lucy didn't open her eyes and didn't respond. I waited another few minutes until she dropped my hand and it became apparent that she was out cold. It was as good a time as any to go back to my seat, I thought. I caught the flight attendant's eye as I headed back. She gave me a dirty look as she draped a blanket over Lucy's inert form. I knew what she was thinking. *Bad daughter.*

Nor did Sunny look forgiving when I climbed over her for what I hoped would be the last time.

"Do you want to switch seats?" she asked me. "I don't mind. And if you're going to have to get out again . . . ?"

"I hope not," I said. "But if you don't mind switching anyway, I'd really appreciate it."

We changed seats, and in the process of moving all my things, I decided I needed a break. The remainder of *Blind Submission* would have to wait. As excited as I was about how well it was progressing, every time I looked at it I was reminded of Malcolm. And I just didn't want to dwell on him, on what went wrong, or what was never right between the two of us. There were still hours to go before the end of our flight, and if I didn't manage to get back to it before we landed, there were always the wee hours to squeeze in a little work time. And to think I'd always wasted those hours in slumber before I started working for Lucy.

I turned off my laptop, shoved it under the seat, and leaned back. I took out my CD player and tried to relax. Immediately the opening chords of "Angel" by Jimi Hendrix flooded through my headphones. It was Damiano's CD. I pulled off the headphones and hit the STOP button. Damiano was another person I didn't want to think about. It was wrong, in so many different ways, to indulge the fantasies that had been hounding me since the night of Lucy's dinner party. I was upset and confused about my unraveling relationship, I told myself, and so I'd made Damiano the romantic hero Malcolm wasn't. And Damiano was a client. The attention he'd given me was probably nothing more than a gracious expression of gratitude for the work I'd done on *Parco Lambro*. To think there was anything more was to invite disaster. I hadn't spoken to him again since our dance outside the office. He hadn't called me, either at home or at the office, and that was as definite a statement as any.

I opened my eyes, which seemed to have closed of their own accord, and forced myself to focus on something other than the images in my head. Sunny had shoved her copy of *Cold!* into the seat back and was sitting with her hands folded in her lap, twiddling her thumbs. She looked like I felt—distracted and in need of conversation. I felt bad about crawling over her so many times, and I was also more than a little curious about her book, namely why she hadn't tried to pitch it to me.

"So what's your book about?" I asked her.

Sunny gave me a very sunny smile and nodded as if she'd been waiting for me to ask. "It's about astrology," she said. "And tarot."

"Oh." I was disappointed. Metaphysical textbooks weren't exactly hot sellers.

"But it's not a technical book or anything."

"Oh?"

"No, it's about an astrologer who gets involved in solving a series of ritual murders through astrology and tarot. She connects several murders of famous and powerful people through several centuries using these signs and symbols and starts being able to predict when the next ones will occur."

"Sounds interesting," I said. "Like *The Da Vinci Code*."

Sunny's brow furrowed slightly. "I keep hearing that," she said.

"You haven't read it?"

"Mm, no. But my book isn't a novel. It's a memoir. That astrologer is me."

"Really?" I said, beginning to lose interest. Another memoir. Did anyone write anything else anymore?

"I wasn't going to write about it at first," Sunny was saying. "I didn't want to be like all those other people who take advantage of their media exposure to pop out a book. I wanted to make sure it was authentic. Also, it wasn't a good time for me astrologically. Jupiter is transitting my ninth house now, so—"

"You have media exposure?" I interrupted her, my interest level ratcheting up exponentially. She was an author with a ready-made platform, something literary agents and publishers alike prayed for.

"Oh, sure," she said. "I guess you've missed me on TV, huh? I've been on *Larry King Live*, all the newsmagazines, I've even had a spot on *60 Minutes*. That was something, let me tell you."

"I can't believe I've never seen you," I said.

"Well, you've probably had better things to do than stay home and watch TV," Sunny said charitably. I stifled a laugh. If she only knew.

"So you have a real-life *Da Vinci Code*? That's fascinating. You don't have any of the book with you, do you?"

Sunny's face brightened. "I do," she said. "But I didn't want to bother you with it before. I'm sure that kind of thing happens to you all the time, doesn't it? People must throw manuscripts at you constantly. It seems as if everyone has at least one book in the drawer, don't they?"

"You don't know how true that is!" I said. I liked this woman.

"Right," she said, "and as I said before, it's just perfect that you're here. I was planning to send it your way next week."

"Well, I'm very interested," I told her. "I'd love to read it. Do you have a card?" There was something about Sunny's story that set off a flare in my head, some sort of seventh sense, and as she fished in her purse for one of her cards, I knew I wanted her to myself.

Sunny's business cards were designed to look like the night sky, with white stars and astrological symbols floating against the black background. Her name, phone number, and e-mail address were in silver. I wrote my name and cell phone number on the back of one and handed it back to her. "My direct line," I told her.

"Perfect," she said, and handed me her manuscript.

"*Balsamic Moon*," I said, looking at the title page. "I like it already."

"Thank you so much," she said. "This is just wonderful."

I glanced down toward first class. All quiet there. For how long I couldn't be sure, but for the moment I was on my own time. I turned back to Sunny. "So tell me some more about your book," I said.

TWELVE

I DIDN'T NEED THE WAKE-UP CALL I'd scheduled for seven o'clock. Lucy rang my room at six and she sounded as if she'd already been up for hours.

"I need you to come to my room now, Angel," she said. Her voice didn't reveal a trace of the grogginess or jet lag I was feeling. I wondered if she had some secret chemical rejuvenator, or if she just produced some kind of enzyme that enabled her to be so functional after a cross-country flight and all the Xanax she'd taken.

"Okay," I said, clearing the gravel from my throat, "I just need to take a quick shower—"

"You're not *awake* yet?" Lucy made impatient clicks with her tongue. "You'd better hurry, then. We've got *no time,* Angel. We'll be late. *I'll* be late. We've got very important meetings today."

"I'll be right there."

"And Angel?"

"Yes, Lucy?"

"I'm sure I don't need to tell you this, but you need to look presentable. I hope you've brought appropriate clothing. This is New York, dear, not *Petaluma*." Her emphasis on *Petaluma* made it sound like a small Third World country.

"On my way," I told her, and hung up.

Lucy's room was several floors above mine. When I entered, I could see that it was bigger and better appointed than mine. Hers had a couch and a coffee table sporting the remains of a room-service breakfast. The smell of the coffee immediately triggered hunger pangs in my stomach.

"I have an extra cup for you," Lucy said, as if she could sense what I was feeling. "But you'll have to wait to eat. I had an extra croissant, too, but I ate it while I was waiting. Early bird gets the worm."

"Right, okay, sure. Thanks." I reached for the coffee, grateful that there was anything here for me to consume at all. I remembered that Lucy's first appointment was a breakfast with Natalie Weinstein and wondered why Lucy had already eaten.

"Natalie Weinstein doesn't eat," Lucy said, reading my thoughts again. "I've never seen the woman put a molecule of food past her lips. Breakfast is just a term she uses for an early meeting." She gave me a blinding-white smile. "There's so much you don't know, Angel." She paused, hands on hips, and assessed my attire. "You look all right," she said. "Unimaginative, but all right."

"Mm," I said, sipping the lukewarm coffee and instinctively smoothing a crease on my pants. Lucy herself was dressed like a stylish undertaker. She was wearing fitted black pants and a black blouse with a mandarin collar. A matching black duster was thrown across the back of a chair. Her hair was pulled back in a tight chignon and a turquoise dream-catcher pendant hung from her neck. Despite the sepulchral quality of her ensemble, she actually looked very good.

"Now," she continued, "I need you to call the office and get Craig on the phone."

I was already punching the numbers on my cell phone when I remembered the time difference. "Do you want me to leave a message?" I asked her. "There won't be anyone in right now. It's four o'clock in the morning in California."

Annoyed impatience danced across Lucy's features. "Very inconvenient," she said. "Well, then, send a fax or an e-mail or something. I need numbers." Lucy's requests were always missing vital pieces of information. What numbers did she need, for example? Where was Craig supposed to send them? I'd stopped asking Lucy for details about these kinds of things long ago, choosing instead to make educated guesses and hope for the best. The longer I worked with her, the easier it got to figure out what she wanted. Still, she was prone to throw a spanner in the wheel just when I thought I'd reinvented it for the last time. I sent a text message to Craig's e-mail address telling him that Lucy needed numbers and that he should call me on my cell phone as soon as he had them. I hoped that would cover all the bases.

"He'd better have that handy. He's been so distracted lately," Lucy was saying. "Must be having problems at home again. That wife of his . . . You should see—" She cut herself off and stared at me hard. "Marriage is a curse, Angel. You should really think about that before you make any big moves with that *fiancé* of yours."

I debated telling her about Malcolm. Although I didn't know why exactly, I was sure it would please her to know that we were no longer together. Fortunately, she didn't give me a chance.

"Get the new one on the phone as well," she said. "Make sure he knows what he's doing with the submissions."

"I've shown him—" I started, knowing that she was referring to Jackson, who apparently hadn't been part of the staff long enough to warrant a name in Lucy's eyes. I supposed it was better than being called "Nora." I wondered, fleetingly, what had become of Kelly.

"Just make sure he knows," Lucy interrupted me.

I looked up at Lucy, who was hovering over me like a dark cloud, and the edge of an image pressing against my brain. I had a feeling of déjà vu, as if something she'd said had triggered a memory, but I couldn't quite grasp it.

"Now," she said, "tell me what I'm doing today. I can't find that annotated list of editors and projects, which was very annoying, by the way, Angel, because I could have gotten a jump-start this morning if I'd been able to *look* at my schedule."

I knew that Lucy had several versions of her schedule with notes and lists attached, but I didn't bother to tell her this. Instead, I reached for one of the many extra copies I had handy and handed her one.

"Now, what about *Elvis*?" she asked me.

"I've got two copies."

"*Two?* What the hell can I do with two copies, Angel?"

"Um, you didn't want to bring more? You said we could—"

"Fine! We'll just make copies as we go, but really, Angel . . ."

It went like this for the better part of an hour—Lucy chastising me for following directives that she'd given me specifically, and me pretending that she hadn't and allowing her to come up with "solutions" to nonexistent problems. I had to wonder, though, how she had managed these trips without an assistant in the past. I was reannotating her schedule for what must have been the twentieth time when she said, "Angel?"

"Yes, Lucy?"

"What are you waiting for? We have to go."

She loaded me up with canvas bags full of manuscripts and lists until I looked like a pack mule. "You should have a briefcase," she said as I struggled under the weight.

I patted my laptop carrying case, which was buried under a *Book Lovers Never Go to Bed Alone* tote bag, and said, "This is it."

"Well," Lucy said, and adjusted the strap of her large black purse on her shoulder, "you should get something more like this." She picked up a small black alligator briefcase and held it out for me to see. "I'm paying you enough now, Angel. Really. You can't cry poverty."

"Right."

"Unless you've spent all that money I've given you already? Have you?"

The question so took me by surprise I was rendered speechless. How could she have known that I had indeed spent a large portion of my "raise" paying off my student loans and accumulated credit-card debt? I'd left enough to cover the taxes I was going to have to pay on her generosity and a little that I planned to send to my mother, who was perpetually without funds and a reliable phone.

But Lucy wasn't waiting for an answer to her question. "We ought to take you for a haircut and maybe a makeover while we're here—spruce you up a bit. I'd be willing to help you with that, Angel. You do represent me, after all."

"Oh. Well, I—"

"Come on, Angel, let's go."

I gazed longingly at the crumbs of food on her coffee table and followed her out the door.

"You should know I don't like taking taxis unless it's absolutely necessary," Lucy said, marching ahead of me in the echoing marble lobby of the hotel. She pushed herself through the revolving glass door at the entrance, leaving me and my bags caught hopelessly between the rotations. I struggled to free myself and I could hear her saying, "Nobody walks in California. Here you can walk!"

I finally freed myself from the revolving doors and broke out onto the street, into Midtown Manhattan. My senses were all immediately overloaded with every kind of sensory information—honking, exhaust, yelling, smoke, perfume, garbage, music, garlic, laughter, daylight, and the vast shadows of tall buildings. It was impossible to take it all in at once.

"Angel!" Lucy's voice reached me through waves of sound and air. "Let's get moving."

THE TRIAD PUBLISHING GROUP was located ten city blocks from our hotel. I knew this because I counted every single one as I struggled to keep up with Lucy's pace. She was right, this was the ideal city to walk in—every square foot jammed with activity and something to look at—but I couldn't stop to see any of it. I followed as close behind Lucy as possible with all the weight I was carrying. If I lost her, I'd lose myself in a matter of seconds.

I was short of breath and sweating like a horse by the time we arrived. There was a giant concrete obelisk outside the building engraved with the Triad name and colophon, which was the symbol for infinity within a circle, within a triangle, within a square. I stared up at it and felt a chill run through my entire body—the same chill I'd felt the first time I walked into Lucy's office and knew, unequivocally, that I was in the right place, the place in which I was meant to be. This was the center, the beating heart of publishing, the place where everything was about letters, words, books. I loved this world so much it took my breath away. Lucy must have sensed my sudden sense of book-geek awe because she turned to me, eyebrows raised, one corner of her carmine-stained mouth turned up in a sardonic half-smile.

"What?" she said.

"It's ... um ... exciting," I answered.

"Yes, this is your maiden voyage, isn't it?" she said. "Well, don't get too carried away, Angel, we've got a lot of work to do." She was all business as usual, but there was a glimmer of recognition in her eyes and her smile broadened. Wasn't my love of this business and everything it entailed the reason she had hired me in the first place? It was a love she had to have felt—had to still feel—herself.

Like the other large publishing houses, Triad had swallowed several smaller publishers over the years, most of which now had their offices in the same building. I was surprised by how sparse and unbooklike the lobby appeared when Lucy and I walked in. Gabriel Press, where Natalie Weinstein ran Weinstein Books, was located on the eighth floor. Over the course of the next couple of days, though, Lucy would have many more meetings here on different floors. C&P Publishers was on the sixth floor, First Wave on the eleventh, and so on. These smaller publishers all had specific types of books they put out (C&P published literary works, for example, whereas First Wave only published mass-market paperbacks—the kind one found in supermarkets and drugstores), but they were all ultimately answerable to and dependent on Triad.

"One has the illusion that there are many options when it comes to selling books," Lucy had once said, "but that's all it is—an illusion." She often bemoaned the current state of publishing, claiming the book business had been so much "spiritually richer" in the old days before massive corporations took it over, but then this kind of complaint was almost de rigueur for anyone who had been in the business for longer than five minutes, from booksellers to literary agents to editors. None of it was stopping Lucy from selling books, however, and none of it was stopping publishers from buying them.

"Don't speak to her unless she asks you a question," Lucy said as we rode the elevator to the eighth floor. "She's very particular about that kind of thing. She's also quite prickly, so just steer clear of her and don't attempt conversation."

"You mean Natalie Weinstein?" I was baffled. I'd spoken to Natalie several times from the office, and unless she was in a state of high dudgeon over something Lucy had done or not done, she was extremely personable and always polite.

"Well, who the hell else would I be talking about? Honestly, Angel, sometimes I worry about the speed of your thought processes."

There wasn't really a need to respond to that statement, so I just followed Lucy out of the elevator. We stepped through glass doors etched with the Gabriel Press colophon (a trumpet) into a waiting area that was as lush and literary as the lobby had been sterile.

There is something about the aroma of fresh books that is totally intoxicating. When I'd worked at Blue Moon, I loved to unpack the cartons when they came in. A new book has a certain clean, crisp smell full of promise that is difficult to define. Sort of like the scent and feeling of just-washed bed linens at the moment you slide your legs between them. The air in Gabriel Press was full of this fragrance—the halls were lined with books, paper, and bound galleys. There were blown-up book jackets on the walls and thick cream-colored carpeting on the floor. And it was quiet—peaceful—the sounds of computer keyboards, phones, and voices all muted in some kind of literary hush. It was, I thought, very much like my idea of a personal heaven.

As we marched through the corridors, Lucy tossed greetings through every open door and cubicle, sending ripples of sound through the calm. It was still early, so the offices were only half-full from what I could see, but Lucy managed to announce her presence to everyone who was there:

"Daniel, I can't wait to show you this scrumptious novel," was followed by, "Susan, I have one that practically came in with your name on it," and then, "Jason, be sure to tell your boss that I am simply dying to see her as soon as she gets in," winding up with, "You're going to love it. . . . You'll love it. . . . You will fall in love. . . ."

Natalie Weinstein was at the far end of the floor, occupying a large corner space. Several semienclosed cubicles, the largest of which belonged to her assistant, encircled her office. The assistant was not at her desk when we arrived and Lucy made *tsk-tsk* noises. "She's had a lot of trouble with assistants," Lucy said. "Personally, I can understand why. She can't be an easy boss, if you know what I mean."

I shrugged so as to give her some kind of response, but again, I was perplexed. Natalie's assistant, Wendy, and I had also spoken on the phone several times, and she'd always seemed not only efficient, but pleasant. She had none of the strain in her voice that I knew *we* all had at the agency.

"Naaaatalieeee," Lucy called. "Helloooo?"

"Come on in, Lucy," came the voice from behind the door, but Lucy was already halfway in and I came trailing behind her.

I assumed that Natalie Weinstein was sitting behind her large lacquered desk, so when she moved away from it to greet us, I was stunned to find she'd been standing. She was minute. Not just short or small-boned, but tiny in every way. I watched as Lucy leaned over and swallowed her in an embrace. She had to be under five feet, I guessed, and her body looked like an assembly of twigs covered with skin. Her hair was platinum blond and cut so short it had a military look to it. She had huge light-blue eyes and her skin was extremely tan. She looked, I thought ungenerously, like an alien.

"Always a pleasure to see you, Lucy," Natalie said. "You look well."

"As do you, my dear," Lucy responded. Lucy continued on with pleasantries for a few moments and I hung back behind her, directing my gaze out Natalie's large corner windows, which offered a spectacular view of the city.

"And you must be the famous Angel," Natalie said, moving away from Lucy and fixing me with her extraterrestrial eyes.

"Famous!" Lucy snorted.

"It's a pleasure to meet you in person," I said, shaking Natalie's small bony hand.

"Likewise," Natalie said, and tipped her head to one side, assessing me in some way I couldn't figure out. Behind her, Lucy was looking at me and shaking her head as if to tell me not to speak.

"Shall we get down to business, my dear?" Lucy said sharply. "I know how valuable your time is."

"And yours, of course," Natalie said. "But wouldn't you like a cup of coffee or something?"

"I think my assistant can handle that," Lucy said, waving her hand in my direction. "Also, if you don't mind, Natalie, I have a manuscript here. . . . I was planning to go out with this in the next couple of weeks, but I know you're going to fall in love with this one. It's the perfect cross between literary and commercial, and I know you've been looking for something Las Vegas–oriented, yes? Anyway, I've just decided now that you must have it. My assistant can make a quick copy for you if you'll direct her to the copy machine?"

"Sounds intriguing," Natalie said, and looked up at me. "Wendy can help you find everything, Angel. Thank you."

"Do you . . ." I started. I could feel that my face was flushed and my ears were burning with the mortification of being reduced to coffee/copy girl by Lucy. "Would you like some coffee?"

"No thanks," Natalie said. "I'm on a green tea diet at the moment. No coffee allowed."

"Well, then, I'd be happy to get you a green tea," I said, and left her office before Lucy could speak to, at, or about me again.

—

MY CELL PHONE RANG as I was negotiating how to get back into the building while balancing the coffee, the green tea, the *Elvis* manuscript, and the muffin I'd bought for myself. I was forced to put everything on the ground to dig into my purse and pull the phone out. The caller ID listed a 212 area code.

"This is Angel."

"We're growing old here, Angel. What could be taking you so long?"

She was calling me from Natalie's office phone. The memory of that old horror flick—*the calls are coming from inside the house!*—flitted through my head and I had to stifle a wild giggle. Kill the babysitter. Kill the assistant.

"On my way now," I said, and snapped the phone shut. It rang again before I could put it back in my purse.

"This is Angel."

"It's Craig. I got your message."

I looked at my watch. It wasn't even seven o'clock in California. "Are you in the office?" I asked him.

"Of course I'm in the office," he said. "How else would I— Can you put Lucy on the phone?"

"I'm downstairs. I mean, she's upstairs. . . . I'll have to have her call you back, Craig. She's in a meeting with Natalie Weinstein."

"Take down these numbers," he said. "Then you can give them to her and she can call me back."

"I can't do that right now, Craig. I'm kind of standing on the street."

"Just tell her 'seventeen without,' then. But she needs to call me back."

"Okay, thanks. Listen, Craig, I need to speak to Jackson when—"

"WHY WOULD JACKSON BE HERE," he screamed into the phone, "AT THIS HOUR OF THE DAY?!" and hung up.

Craig was obviously losing it. Could it be that he was suffering from Lucy-withdrawal and didn't know what to do with his slavish self without her? I mean, really, *seventeen without.* It was like something from *The Rule of Four.* The world was going mad. My corner of it at least.

———

NATALIE WAS ALONE in her office when I finally made it back upstairs, and she beckoned me to come in and sit down. I looked around for Lucy and I wondered if she'd left me behind to go on to her next appointment.

"Your boss is using the restroom," Natalie said in the same tone that someone would tell a lost child, *Don't worry, your mother will be right back.* "Thank you so much for the tea."

"It's a pleasure," I said. "You have a beautiful office." She smiled at me. "And I just want to say I think that your books are fantastic." I pointed to her bookshelf, which was stacked with Weinstein Books titles. Her books *were* exceptional; they won a disproportionate number of literary awards, but they rarely made it onto bestseller lists. *Parco Lambro* would have been perfect for her. She was exactly the kind of editor Damiano needed, but she hadn't been able to come up with enough money to satisfy Lucy.

"I've known Lucy Fiamma for a long time," Natalie said.

"So she's said." Lucy had also told me, "I knew Natalie Weinstein before she was *Natalie Weinstein*—when she was still taking messages for Gordon Hart."

"She's never brought anyone to New York with her before," Natalie went on. She paused a moment to let this sink in. "You must be something very special," she said, and let out a mirthless laugh. "Either that or you've got something on her."

I laughed politely.

"I'm betting on the former," Natalie said. "That Italian book . . . Lucy hasn't come through with anything like that for a long time. I think you had something to do with that one, didn't you?"

I laughed again. It seemed like the thing to do.

"And I think you have a hand in whatever it is she's got today."

I shrugged.

"Ever thought about moving to New York, Angel?"

"No," I said. "Not really."

"Maybe you should. Think about it, that is. So tell me, should I get excited about that manuscript you're holding?"

I looked down at *Elvis,* which was getting damp and curled from the sweat of my palms. I knew I should tell her that she'd *fall in love* with it, but I was thinking about Sunny Martin and her memoir, *Balsamic Moon.* I'd read part of it the night before when I was too wired to sleep and I really liked it. I knew that it was exactly the kind of book that Natalie Weinstein wanted. "Well, it's . . ." I hesitated, my mouth still open around the words.

"Come on, Angel," she said. "Let's see what you've got. Pitch it to me."

I looked into Natalie Weinstein's freaky eyes and made a decision. I hoped I wouldn't live to regret it, because once the next words were out of my mouth, I'd never be able to take them back. I was taking a big chance. Lucy could walk in on us at any moment and I'd be caught in literary flagrante delicto.

"This is a terrific book," I said, holding up *Elvis,* "but I think I should let Lucy tell you about it. She's so excited about it and I'd hate to ruin it for her. But I have something else. It just came in and Lucy's not— I mean, I'm sort of handling it right now and . . ." My nerve was fading and I looked at Natalie for a sign that I should proceed.

"I get it," she said, giving me one. "Go on."

"The title is *Balsamic Moon,*" I said in a quick rush, frantic to get it all out before Lucy came back. "It's a memoir by an astrologer, but with a great twist. It's a real-life *Da Vinci Code,* which is perfect since everyone wants a new *Da Vinci Code,* but nobody wants another imitator. I think we all know *that* ship has sailed. The subject matter is fascinating— hasn't been done before that I can tell—and the writing is excellent. She's a natural. I know the kind of books you publish and I know you'll love this one."

"Indeed," she said. "And what is the author's name?"

"That's the best part," I said, going in for the close. "She already has great media visibility. Her name is Sunny—Solange—Martin. I'm sure you're familiar with her."

"In fact, I am," Natalie said. "Is there a finished manuscript?"

I was about to answer her when Lucy glided back into Natalie's office on a wave of freshly applied Chanel Nº5. The three of us froze in a weird little tableau for a moment, Natalie looking like the cat that ate the canary, Lucy glowering when she saw me seated in front of Natalie's desk, and me, slack-jawed and speechless. It was Natalie who spoke first.

"Well, Lucy, your assistant has just been telling me what beautiful weather you've been having in California. Sounds divine." She looked over at me, smiled, and winked.

"Like Valhalla," I said, and stood to give Lucy my chair.

To: anna.anderson@fiammalit.com
From: angel.robinson@fiammalit.com
Subject: manuscripts/editors/questions

Hi Anna,

Hope all's well. We're back at the hotel for a minute before we head
out again for dinner—well, before Lucy has dinner with Susie Parker
and I wait for her in the bar—so I've got a minute to send you a note.
I know I've already spoken to you about 50x today, but Lucy keeps
adding more editors for every project, so I've been continually up-
dating all day. I guess the most important one is *Elvis Will Dance at
Your Wedding*. She's been pitching that to everyone, and since I can't
copy it everywhere we go, please send a copy overnight to the following editors: Susan Jones (C&P), Lydia Smith (Long, Greene), and
everybody who bid on *Parco Lambro* (you have a copy of that list,
right?). I'm sure there will be more tomorrow, but that's it for now.

She's really been talking up *Blind Submission* and they're getting excited. It's not ready to go yet, but Lucy wants you to start generating
a list. Just put every editor in New York on it and I'm sure you'll be
fine. Speaking of *BS*, Lucy wants to know if everybody's read the material. If you could let me know, or maybe send me reader reports,
that would be great.

Some random questions from Lucy (I'm reading my scribbled notes
here, so bear with me—I had to write this stuff down while I was running along next to her on the way to appointments!):

—Film interest for *Parco Lambro*?
—Permissions backlog for *Cold!*?
—Reading cycle while we're gone? (I think she means is Jackson
   picking up more submissions?)
—Change hold music. Lucy would like you or Craig to change the
   hold music in the office (but she also said that she doesn't want
   anyone to ever *get* the hold music—she called a couple of times

today and the phones went right over to hold and she wasn't happy). Anyway, she wants the music changed to "Some Girls" by the Rolling Stones. (I don't know why.)

I think that's it for now. I'll be here for about another forty-five minutes and plugged in, so if you can e-mail back, I know Lucy would appreciate it.

Thanks!
Angel

To: angel.robinson@fiammalit.com
From: anna.anderson@fiammalit.com
Subject: Re: manuscripts/editors/questions

Hi Angel,

That is GREAT news about *Blind Submission*!!!! Please tell Lucy that I will be MORE THAN happy to put together a list immediately. Does she need a pitch letter? I can do that too. And if she wants me to put the pages together, it's no problem.

As for the list of editors who bid on *Parco Lambro,* of course I have it. I put it together. Anyway, I will get those manuscripts off to the editors ASAP. Although I think you should know that since you've been on vacation, we're seriously short here, so I'm picking up a lot of the slack, including the reading, and I might not get that out until tomorrow morning. I guess that answers one of your other questions about Jackson. He really doesn't seem to be "getting it." Maybe you can retrain him when you get home. Because of this, I haven't been able to get to the permissions (I thought you were supposed to be covering this?) or the film interest for *PL* yet. But please tell Lucy that I am working on it and will hope to have very good news for her when she returns.

Re: hold music. Can you tell Lucy that *Exile on Main Street* is considered by many critics to be one of the Rolling Stones's best albums? If she likes, I can prepare a folder with some of the important reviews for both that album and *Some Girls* and then she can make a final decision.

So, are you having a good time in New York? Have you eaten at Michael's yet? That's where all the literary muckety-mucks hang out. You should go. It must be so exciting to be there—you should live it up, do something outrageous and different. You go, girl, as Oprah would say.

Give Lucy my love.

See ya!
AA

P.S. Speaking of Oprah, can you please tell Lucy that I just learned that my aunt's stepdaughter's friend's cousin is a producer there! Please tell Lucy that I'd be happy to use my connection to try to get our authors on the show.

To: anna.anderson@fiammalit.com
From: angel.robinson@fiammalit.com
Subject: Re: Re: manuscripts/editors/questions

Anna,

I don't think Lucy wants a report on which Rolling Stones album was better received—I'm pretty sure she just wants you to change the hold music, okay?

By the way, I'm not on vacation. I haven't done anything except work since we got here (and sleep—although not very much). Just so we're clear on that.

I'll pass your Oprah news on to Lucy. And I'll get back to you on everything else tomorrow. Have to go now.

Thanks,
Angel

To: angel.robinson@fiammalit.com
From: anna.anderson@fiammalit.com
Subject: one more thing

Hi Angel,

You're probably off having drinks or whatever now, but I wanted to send you a note before I forget to tell you that someone named Sunny Martin called for you today. She was calling about a book. She said you met on the plane? She said you had given her your "private number" but that she "lost" it. She was calling here because she said you told her you worked with Lucy. I must have gotten confused because it sounded like you were offering to represent her. . . . Anyway, I told her that you would be back in the office on Friday and that she could send in the first 50 pages and you would pass it on to Lucy. Just thought you'd like to know.

Also, your old boss from the bookstore called looking for you. I didn't tell her where you were. She said she has your home phone number.

That's it for now. Hope you're having fun! Make sure you take care of Lucy!

AA

To: solange@sunstar.com
From: angel.robinson@fiammalit.com
Subject: BALSAMIC MOON

Dear Sunny,

I just wanted to drop you a note to tell you how wonderful it was to meet you on the plane the other day. What good fortune for both of us! I also wanted to offer you my thanks for being so gracious about having to get up and down so many times—that was really very nice of you. Finally, I must tell you how excited I am about your book. I've read quite a bit of it already and I think it's terrific. I've been meeting with several editors here in New York and I think that many (if not all) of them would be most interested in a book such as yours. I've already mentioned it to one of the most talented editors I know and she's extremely interested—sight unseen! This is the right time for a book like *Balsamic Moon*.

Speaking of sight unseen, I understand you spoke with Lucy Fiamma's assistant, Anna, today? My apologies if she didn't understand who you were. As I'm sure you can imagine, we get scores of submissions daily and many of the authors claim to "know" us to get a foot in the door. Anna may have been a little aggressive in her screening today—my apologies again.

I'll look forward to discussing all of this with you very soon. I'm including my personal phone number, which Anna said you'd misplaced, so please feel free to call if you have any questions.

Many thanks again, Sunny.

Best,
Angel

To: angel.robinson@fiammalit.com
From: jackson.stark@fiammalit.com
Subject: Anna

Hey Angel—

Hope all's well with you. I'm sure you're super busy and I might be totally out of line here, but I thought you should know that Anna's been going through your desk a lot since you've been gone. Well, actually, she's been sitting *at* your desk. And also—I know this sounds a little weird—she's answered the phone a couple of times by saying "This is Angel." She said she just got confused because she's sitting at your desk and that she had to sit at your desk because she has to do all your stuff now that you're gone, but I don't know. Like I said, it's a bit weird. Also, she's been feeding your fish—A LOT. He doesn't look good, Angel. I told her to stop but she said she promised to take care of him for you. I didn't think that sounded right. I think the only thing Anna knows to do with fish is eat them. Anyway, maybe you don't want to know any of this and maybe I'm just overreacting, but I thought I should tell you.

Thanks,
Jackson

To: jackson.stark@fiammalit.com
From: angel.robinson@fiammalit.com
Subject: Re: Anna

Hi Jackson,

I don't think you're overreacting and I appreciate your telling me all of this. Would you do me a big favor and just take my fish over to your desk before she kills it? Tell her I asked you to do it to take some of the load off her. As for the other stuff, yes, please keep me posted about what she's doing. And, not that I have to tell you this, but it's just between you and me, okay? And please make sure that you delete this e-mail after you've read it, okay? Thanks, Jackson.

Angel

To: angel.robinson@fiammalit.com
From: jackson.stark@fiammalit.com
Subject: Re: Re: Anna

Hey Angel,

Not to worry re. deleting and keeping things on the QT. I'm glad you're not mad. You never know around here. . . . One more thing. I heard her on the phone (but don't worry, she didn't know I was listening) having an argument and then crying. Well, weeping actually. Anyway, she was talking to someone named Malcolm. She seemed pretty upset. Isn't your boyfriend's name Malcolm? Not that there's only one Malcolm in the world but still . . .

Speak to you soon,
J.

THIRTEEN

To: angel.robinson@fiammalit.com
From: ganovelist@heya.com
Subject: ?

Dear Ms. Robinson,

I'm wondering if you've received my most recent installment? You
are usually very prompt, so I'm a little concerned about what might
have become of you! And may I ask what are Ms. Fiamma's feelings
about the manuscript to this point? One final thought: I am wondering if either you or Ms. Fiamma have discussed the possibility of film
for this book?

Looking forward to your reply,
G.

To: ganovelist@heya.com
From: angel.robinson@fiammalit.com
Subject: Re: ?

Dear G,

I'm sorry that I haven't been able to respond for the past few days, but I've been in New York City with Lucy Fiamma on business and am only intermittently on e-mail. I'll be back in the office on Friday.

I have received your pages and I've just finished reading them. I think that they're very good. This set is really in the best shape of all that you've sent so far. I think the direction you've taken is a good one and I also think you've really hit your stride. I'll be sending back my notes as soon as I return to the office. For now, though, here are a couple of questions I had:

I'm not totally clear on why Carol likes Alice as much as she does. It seems to me that Alice hasn't really offered Carol much to like? I guess the question is, what is Alice giving Carol Moore?

What has happened to Alice's own writing? Is her ultimate goal to publish her own work or just to have her name on a book? I'm not sure where you're heading with this and, while I like the underlying comment you're making about the "business" of books and the role of the writer within that business, it's important that we have an actual story here. Does this make sense? If not, it's probably because I'm getting kind of punchy. It's been a long day.

At any rate, I've shown the pages to Lucy and she's gone over them as well, although she'll be giving a closer read when we return home. But she's very enthusiastic about this book—so enthusiastic, in fact, that she's been talking about *BS* to editors while we're here and are all very excited about it. The sooner you can get it all to us, the sooner we can get it out there! We haven't discussed film in any depth yet (it's a bit early for that), but Lucy has, as I'm sure you know, an excellent track record as far as selling her projects in that arena.

I'll have to sign off now as it's extremely late and my day will begin again in a few hours. Just one more thing . . . Between friends (because I do consider you and I to be friends at this point and I hope you feel the same), who are you? I promise not to tell anyone! Well, maybe Lucy! Seriously, G, do you think you might consider revealing yourself pretty soon? It's not like this book is giving away any national secrets or anything. It's a book about books, right? I guess the secrecy thing is kind of fun, but I don't really understand it. We're getting pretty close to the wire here, and if you want us to represent you, we're going to have to know a LITTLE bit more about who you are. Have to know where to send those checks, right?

Soon,
Angel

To: angel.robinson@fiammalit.com
From: ganovelist@heya.com
Subject: Re: Re: ?

Dear Ms. Robinson,

I am quite thrilled on all counts.

I'll look forward to your notes (and I do look forward to them—it's so refreshing to read them—you have an excellent way of identifying exactly what I mean to say, quite a talent), but in the meantime, let me address your questions. What does Carol see in Alice? As Ricardo stated, Carol sees *herself* in Alice and she likes the reflection. As I wrote in Chapter 2, Carol's rise to the top wasn't exactly without some questionable moves, but that was what she had to do to reach her goal. Carol sees the same drive and ambition in Alice. Of course, Alice is possessed by something that Carol is free of and that is the need to write. Alice is a self-loathing writer and clearly not very good at her craft. So her plan is just to take over, to attain as much power as possible, and then take the publishing world by storm. The catch, as I pointed out in Chapter 1, is that Alice wants to be a *legitimate* writer. She wants to write a bestseller, but she wants the accolades, too. She knows that Carol Moore is the key to all of this. As for her own writing—well, I thought I'd made it clear that she didn't deal with rejection very well. Of course, if you're not getting any of this, then I'm not doing my job, am I? Back to work I go.

To answer your last question about my identity, "all in good time," as they say. I have my reasons for remaining anonymous, and as long as Ms. Fiamma is satisfied with my progress, I shall remain so for just a little while longer. As to your considering me a friend—I think we are both more and less than that now.

Here's to you, Ms. Robinson; coo coo coo-choo.

With best wishes,
G.

I was too exhausted to move. I lay on my hotel bed, where I'd fallen a half hour earlier, without enough energy to even pull back the cover, which I knew was laden with the filth of every person who'd lain there before me. I'd pulled back the heavy purple drapes before I'd collapsed on the bed and I could see a sliver of gray-blue New York City sky behind the crowd of brick and concrete walls. My feet and head were throbbing, but the thought of going downstairs to the lobby to buy an eight-dollar bottle of aspirin was overwhelming. It was my last night in New York and my first nonsleeping break from Lucy in days.

She'd gotten herself invited to a cocktail party that HartHouse was throwing in conjunction with HBO for a series based on a book by one of its authors and was going *alone*. In fact, she'd been adamant about keeping me away from any function or meeting that might involve Gordon Hart. And as much as I wanted to meet Gordon Hart, I wasn't disappointed that Lucy left me out of the meetings. I could only imagine the embarrassing things she'd think to say, and would rather never meet the man at all than be humiliated in front of him.

"Why don't you go get yourself some dinner in the Big Apple?" she'd suggested when I left her room after reorganizing her notes, responding to her messages, and preparing her for the next day's meetings. "If you can't find a good place to eat in New York City, you don't know what food is. Or better yet, you can order something in your room and get caught up. I'm sure you've got a lot of work to do." As if any work I had to do was unrelated to her. "Anyway, enjoy yourself—this is your vacation! But don't get carried away. We've got a long day tomorrow and then you'll have to get yourself to the airport."

Lucy had decided to take an extra day in Manhattan without me (which had entailed at least two hours of phone time for me, rearranging her flight and negotiating an extra night at the hotel at the same rate) and had given me no information about why or what she was planning to do. Which was fine with me. I'd never worked as hard as I had in the last two days or been as connected to another human being for such an extended period of time. I marveled at Lucy's energy level. She was unstoppable. She had to tire, had to feel the effects of her mad pace, but she never seemed to show it. I had begun to wonder if she was sucking that energy from me. Despite my suspicion that she was some kind of psychic vampire, though, I was impressed, almost awestruck, by her performance in New York. They didn't always seem (or even pretend) to like her, that much was certain, but every editor and publisher gave her their undivided attention for as long as she was with them. From what I could see, Lucy had no "pals" in New York. Nobody ever spoke to her as if she were a girlfriend or a buddy. Nobody asked about her hobbies, her family, or the details of her life. But every one of them, including the elusive Gordon Hart, wanted to know what she *had*.

And Lucy had something for everyone. She had an encyclopedic knowledge of every editor's history, exactly what kind of books they liked, and exactly how far out on a limb they could go to buy. Often, that limb didn't seem to extend very far, but I only saw Lucy express anything less than brisk confidence once.

We were marching out of Long, Greene, where she'd just finished a meeting with Julia Swann, an editor with a number of adjectives on her stationery (executive, vice president, senior, etc.), but a very limited allowance for what she could buy. Julia had sighed when Lucy told her about *Elvis,* said that it sounded wonderful but that she doubted she'd be able to get it past her board. She was looking for the next *Da Vinci*

Code, Julia said—didn't Lucy have one of those? And what was happening with Karanuk, for heaven's sake? Now, there was something she'd have carte blanche to bid on.

"This is a very difficult time to be in publishing," Lucy said as we hit the street and headed down Fifth Avenue to her next appointment. "Nobody has any imagination anymore and they're all scared to buy anything that isn't incredibly safe or has been done before. I mean, really, how many celebrity children's books do we need? Or prizewinning authors writing *cookbooks*?"

This rare moment of doubt passed as quickly as it had come, though. Lucy was back on her game by the time we reached her next meeting, busily pitching her own celebrity children's books and literary cookbooks (because, of course, she *had* them) along with everything else on her list. It was really quite a sight to behold. Lucy must have known this, too, because, despite insisting that I fetch coffee and make copies almost everywhere we went, she seldom excluded me from her meetings. She wanted me to see her in action. At all times, Lucy made it very clear that I was her assistant, but as we circled New York City like hungry sharks in search of prey, I began to get the sense that she also wanted my admiration. She had it, of course.

After being attached to her at the hip for almost three days, though, I couldn't stand the sight of Lucy anymore. I was sick of her relentless rudeness, of the way she managed to make me look like an ignorant hick at every office we visited, never giving me an iota of credit for doing anything other than the most basic of clerical tasks, and I was sick of carrying her crap, literally and figuratively. But mostly, I was weary and unsettled by how *close* I was to her—of how she seemed to occupy every space of my being, under my skin and inside my head.

I also had the feeling that somehow she knew about my conversation with Natalie Weinstein and was just waiting for the right moment to drop some kind of bomb on me. Although Natalie had indicated that she wasn't about to tell Lucy, my anxiety wasn't entirely irrational. Anna had spoken to Sunny Martin and, for all I knew, had gone straight to Lucy with that information. If Jackson was to be believed (and I did believe him—I had decided that I had to trust somebody), Anna had been acting strangely enough to justify those suspicions and more.

I hadn't figured out what I would do if Lucy confronted me about Sunny Martin. I hadn't even worked out how I was actually going to *sell* Sunny Martin's book with or without Lucy knowing about it. All I knew was that I wanted to sell it. That book was *mine*. The last thing I wanted to do was to give it to Lucy.

I rolled over on the bed and faced the door. My laptop sat on a tiny desk, plugged in and wired into the phone jack, awaiting e-mail messages. The screen threw an eerie blue light onto my suitcase, which looked like it had exploded, spewing paper and clothing everywhere. Keeping Lucy organized required the constant pulling out and reordering of my own things. Taking the time to make neat piles had not been a priority. *Balsamic Moon* sat on the floor next to my copy of *Thaw*. I'd read all of those pages as well, and they were every bit as bad as Lucy had said they were, but I had ideas about how Karanuk could fix them. Despite the scattered story and disconnected paragraphs, Karanuk's prose still held grains of the genius that had made *Cold!* great. I knew I could work with that and I knew Karanuk could work with me. Maybe that was the answer, I thought. I'd try to trade my work with Karanuk and *Blind Submission* for a shot with *Balsamic Moon*.

But, no, she'd never go for it.

After all she'd done for him, Karanuk would never take me over Lucy in any way. And while it wouldn't be as good, *Blind Submission* could probably survive without me. It was likelier that Lucy would just fire me. No, she wouldn't do that, either. If the last few days had taught me anything, it was that I was valuable to Lucy. Not *in*valuable, mind you. Nobody is ever invaluable. But I was valuable enough not to fire if she didn't have to. She'd rather try to make me so miserable that I'd want to quit, and if I quit I'd have to pay back all the money she'd given me in that hellish contract I now knew I never should have signed. And I couldn't afford to do that. So I couldn't quit and she wouldn't fire me. In all scenarios, Lucy came out ahead.

I thought if I could get up and tidy some of the mess in my room, it might help me to gain some clarity, but I was just so tired. It occurred to me that the hollow feeling in the center of my being was probably due to hunger and that I should eat something. I decided I would order room service as soon as I checked my messages. I reached over to the bedside table for my cell phone and dialed my home number first. There was one message:

"Hi, Angel, it's Elise. You never called me back. Are you okay? Have you been eaten by wolves? Or should I say *wolf*? I tried you at work, but that weirdo who answered the phone wouldn't tell me where you were. Listen, Angel, I've been doing a lot of thinking and planning and, well, you always knew that I wouldn't be able to stay out of the book business, didn't you? Anyway, I've decided to go for it again. I want to reopen Blue Moon but"—there was a long sigh—"smaller, more upscale. More, I don't know, geared to a specialty market, although I don't know what that is. I'm still thinking. But the thing is, I was wondering if you'd be interested in putting this together with me. I couldn't afford— I don't know how much you're making now, Angel, but I'd love to have you with me on this. Think about it. I miss it, Angel. And I miss you! I'm going on and on here, listen to me, I'm going to fill up all the room on your machine. Please call me when you can, okay? And I've *still* got something I want to show you. I won't tell you what it is—I'll leave it a surprise, okay? You'll find it very interesting, I can tell you that. Call me! Bye, Angel."

I listened to the message one more time and then erased it. I was in no state to think clearly about what Elise was offering. Part of me was thrilled that she was going back to bookselling, but another part of me was frustrated that she was doing it *now* and offering me an opportunity that I would have jumped at only a few months ago. I missed her as well, but in the way you'd miss a halcyon period in childhood you know you can never return to. The truth was, no matter how difficult it was to deal with Lucy, one day in her office was more exciting than all my years at Blue Moon combined, and I'd become addicted to that rush. I knew that going back to what I'd been doing before I started working for Lucy would feel like a huge letdown. I'd need some kind of rehab to get back to normal—although, now, I wasn't even sure what "normal" was.

Despite this ambivalence, I decided to consider Elise's offer anyway. It was reassuring to know that I could still count on her, and if my behind-the-scenes maneuverings blew up in my face, I knew she would help me pick up the pieces. I made a note to call her as soon as I got home.

I closed up my phone and laid it down on the bedside table. I felt sweaty and covered with grime. What I really needed was a shower, I thought. At least that was one thing that was easily done. With great effort, I lifted myself from the bed, pulled back the cover so that the clean sheets were exposed, and stripped off my clothes. I was almost there, almost under the hot running water, when I heard a knock at my door. Lucy. She'd found something else for me to do or had suddenly decided I needed to come with her to hold up the hem of her dress while she mingled. Typically, she'd found the most inconvenient moment to come looking for me. I grabbed a towel from the bathroom and wrapped it around my body as best I could.

"Lucy?" I said, placing one hand on the door handle. I hoped I sounded as exhausted and unable to muster enthusiasm as I felt.

"Angel? Is that you?"

My heart leaped into my throat. I'd heard and read that phrase so many times, but I'd never really understood it—never truly felt it—until that moment, when I realized that it was Damiano on the other side.

I pulled the door open and the towel fell to the floor. I froze, unable to make any kind of move to pick it up. Damiano walked in and closed the door behind him, and I stood in front of him completely naked. For a long moment, he just stared at me and said nothing. When I raised my eyes to meet his, I saw them shining with frank admiration and desire. But there was so much more behind that. There was empathy, the whisper of sadness, and deep longing. It was as if I were looking into my own heart. It was Damiano I needed. Of course.

He moved toward me until we were almost touching, then stopped. Without taking his dark eyes off mine, he reached out his right hand and slowly traced the curve of my hip as if he were carving it out of soft clay. He moved his left hand up to cup the side of my face and drew me close enough for me to feel his breath on my lips. We stood like that for a small eternity, his hands warm on my skin, the moment before the kiss suspended in anticipation between us. I wanted to stay like that forever and I wanted to grab him and pull him into me. My tension turned to trembling and I felt myself start shaking.

"*Angelina mia,*" Damiano whispered. He put both arms around me and held me tight. He kissed me, his lips light and soft, savoring the taste. I pressed against him, opening my mouth to his, my hands moving wild across his back and arms in a frenzy of exploration. I pulled at his shirt, desperate to feel the smoothness of his skin beneath it. Our arms tangled, our mouths pressed together hard. He lifted me as if I were weightless and carried me to the bed. He tripped, stumbled, and we both fell heavily onto the sheets. He landed on my hair and pulled it out from under him. Something that sounded like a curse fell from his mouth and I laughed. He sat up, yanked off his shoes, and started fumbling with the buttons and buckles on his clothes.

"*Vieni qua,*" he said, pulling me up. "Help me."

I reached around him and lifted his shirt over his head as he managed to free himself from his jeans. There was a moment of awkwardness then, the hesitation that falls between new lovers when they see each other naked for the first time. But he leaned over, softly kissed the racing pulse in the hollow of my throat, and suddenly the entire room seemed to ignite.

Sensation took over, pushing every thought out of my head. I felt myself give way to the weight of his body on mine, felt the softness of his skin and the taut muscles beneath it. I felt my body rise up to meet his lips wherever they touched me—on my thighs, breasts, and belly. I felt myself open and heard myself sigh with satisfaction. I felt Damiano's breath in my ear, heard him whisper, "*Che ricco,*" tasted the salt of his sweat as it mingled with my own. I closed my eyes, using my fingertips and tongue to see. I felt him deep inside me and I lost myself there, buoyed up and away on a long swell of pleasure that went on and on and on.

The room was dark when I opened my eyes again. I couldn't see any sky at all through the narrow space between the drapes, just the reflection of artificial light against the buildings. Damiano lay melded to me, his arms fastened around me. I blinked my eyes to adjust to the dimness and realized that I was covered in sweat and that the sheets and pillows felt damp. Damiano's back was slick and wet under my hands. His breathing was soft and even against my chest, so slow that I thought he'd fallen asleep. I moved my arm, which was pinned under his shoulder, and he raised his head and kissed my mouth.

"Thank you," he said. He traced one finger along my eyebrow, down my cheekbone, and to my lips. "You are so beautiful," he said. "Here." He stroked the inside of my thigh. "Here." He rested his hand on the skin of my abdomen. "And here." He laid his hand gently on my forehead.

"I don't . . ." I began, and had to clear my throat of all the passion that had accumulated there since I'd last spoken. "I don't usually open the door stark naked for men who come knocking."

Damiano laughed, sending a merry echo through the room. "But it was very convenient," he said. "Thank you for that also. I've never been greeted in such a way. I think it is something I'll remember for my whole life."

"I was going to take a shower," I said. "I thought you were Lucy."

"You can still take a shower," he said. "But not yet. Please don't go away from me yet. I have . . . ahh, *Angelina* . . ." He sighed and kissed me again. "I was wondering . . . I didn't know if you would be pleased to see me. The last time, you were so strange. I thought maybe I did something wrong or said something. I don't know. But . . ."

"But?"

"I knew we would be here before I saw you for the first time. I felt you inside me, Angel. Didn't you know, too?"

If I could have spoken, I would have told him that I did, but my lips were trembling too much for me to get the words out. I had started crying, without even knowing why, and the tears were coming fast, spilling down the sides of my face and wetting my hair. I tried to stop, tried to strangle the sobs that were forming inside my chest, but that only made them come harder.

"No, no," Damiano said. He brushed my cheeks with his fingers. *"Non piànge.* What did I say? Why are you crying?"

"I d-don't kn-know," I said. "I'm s-sorry."

"No, no," he said. "Shh. Don't be sorry."

He wrapped me in his arms again, whispering words I couldn't understand into my hair. He stroked my back and my shoulders. And then he leaned over me and kissed the tears off my face.

"*Angelina,*" he whispered. "You see? I drink your tears. Don't cry."

I thought that if I had to die right then, wrapped in his arms, his lips on my cheek, I'd die happy.

I must have fallen asleep, although it couldn't have been for long, because when I opened my eyes again, the lights were on and Damiano was propped up against the pillows next to me, smiling down at me.

"I wanted to look at you," he said. "You are so beautiful, I can't believe it."

I smiled back at him.

"Are you okay?" he asked.

"Yes," I said, and reached out for him, pulling him close to me again.

"I want to make love with you, Angel," he said, "here in this room. Again and again."

I rolled on top of him and stared down into his wine-brown eyes. They were alive with desire. *For me.* "I think I can help you with that," I said, and placed my hands on either side of his head, feeling the bristly ends of his hair under my fingertips. "But first tell me, how did you know I was here? Why are you in New York?" I wanted—no, I *needed*—him to tell me that he couldn't stop thinking about me, that his desire for me had driven him to search me out, to drop everything and cross the country to find me.

"I spoke to Luciana," he said. "She told me the hotel."

"*Lucy?*"

"*Sì.* What's the matter?"

I slid off him and sat up. Out of some belated and now-unnecessary sense of modesty, I drew the sheets up around my waist. "Why would *Lucy* tell you where I was?"

"She told me where *she* was going to be. But I knew you were with her, Angel. I was there at the famous dinner party, remember?" Damiano was looking up at me with a bemused expression, as if he couldn't understand why any of this would be of concern to me. He lifted a strand of my hair and stroked it between his thumb and forefinger. "That was the first time I saw this beautiful hair all free like fire."

"I still don't really understand, Damiano. You called Lucy to ask her where we were staying in New York? Didn't she wonder why you wanted to know?"

"*Bella,*" he said patiently, and raised himself so that we were sitting side by side on the bed. "I didn't call Lucia— Lucy. She called me a week . . . maybe two weeks ago. She told me she was coming to New York. She said it would be a good idea for me to come as well. She said for me to meet my editor? *Capisce,* no? I thought you would know about this. She ask if I can get a ticket to New York and of course I can. We made a meeting with my editor for the day after tomorrow and today I am here with you."

The day after tomorrow—Lucy's extra day in New York. Without me. I'd wondered why Damiano's editor hadn't been on Lucy's list of appointments when I'd scheduled this trip for her, and I'd even asked Lucy about it. "No need," she'd said at the time, and now it made sense.

"I'm going home tomorrow," I said.

"Yes, I know," he said, "that's why I came early." He shrugged as if all of this should be totally obvious to me and started pulling me gently toward him, his eyes sparkling with undisguised lust. "*Ècco. Vieni qua,* Angel. Come here, *amore.*"

"Wait," I said, instinctively moving away from him until I was on the far corner of the bed. There was something about this scenario that was starting to feel frighteningly wrong, some sense that I'd been expertly manipulated into being the butt of an elaborate and cruel practical joke. "How did you know what *room* I was in? Did Lucy tell you that, too?"

"No, no, of course not. I spoke to Anna. She was very sweet. She told me where you were."

"*Anna knows?*"

He missed the alarm in my voice and went on, a smile curving the corners of his mouth. "Don't worry," he said. "I came in very quiet," he said, and chuckled. He lowered his voice to a conspiratorial stage whisper. "Nobody saw me, I promise. I wore dark glasses." He laughed again. "Like a rock star."

"Like Vaughn Blue," I said. My voice sounded distant and hollow, as if it were coming from across the room.

"*Che?*" A worried and ever so slightly annoyed expression passed across Damiano's face and was replaced by renewed desire. He moved over to my side of the bed. "Ahh," he breathed, "so beautiful." He cupped my breasts in both of his hands, leaned over, and formed a kiss on my angel-wing tattoo.

I leaped off the bed, pulling the sheet with me and wrapping it tightly around my nakedness. I backed up as far from him as I could get until I was pressed against the window.

"Why are you over there, Angel? What are you doing?"

I stared at him and tried with all the powers of reasoning I had left to convince myself that I was in the middle of a bad dream. *Who was this man?* He'd become a complete stranger in a matter of seconds. No, he'd been a stranger all along. I knew his words on a page—I didn't know *him* at all. But he knew me, didn't he? Knew just what I'd do, how I'd be, what I wanted, and he *had kissed my tattoo*. He knew everything. It was worse than a bad dream, I decided—it was a bad dream that belonged to *someone else*.

"Angel?"

"I think you should go." I sounded weak and slightly hysterical. In the remote corner of my brain that wasn't full of frightened confusion, it occurred to me that I'd just delivered one of those lines that only works in the movies.

"What? Why? *Che cosa c'é?*"

"I . . . my . . ." I raised my hand to my right breast, instinctively covering my tattoo. "You knew about this. How did you know?"

"Know? I don't understand. Excuse me . . . Angel?"

"Can you just— Can you *please leave*?" The note of hysteria in my voice had sharpened.

Damiano searched my eyes with his. His face went from light to dark with surprise, confusion, disbelief, and finally something that looked like a kind of sad acceptance. He shook his head slightly and started to speak again, but caught himself and closed his mouth, compressing it into a tight line. He got up, more gracefully than I would have expected under the circumstances, picked up his clothes from the floor, and put them on in less than a minute.

He was at the door, one hand on the handle, before he turned to me again. "Angel?" I shook my head, tightening my grip on the sheet, and looked away. *"Mi dispiace,"* he said, and then he was gone.

I waited, suspended, for what could have been seconds or minutes and listened to the sounds of voices and traffic coming from outside the window. The room had gone cold and I was shivering. It was suddenly essential that I be clothed. I didn't want to look at my own naked, traitorous body for another second. I walked over to my suitcase, dragging the sheet with me, and saw that I had an e-mail message waiting on my computer. I was going to wait—to get dressed and read it afterward—but then I saw who had sent it.

To: angel.robinson@fiammalit.com
From: ganovelist@heya.com
Subject: Alice

My dear Ms. Robinson,

A quick question for you.

I've just realized that since Alice's steamy encounter with Vaughn early on, we haven't seen much of the two of them together in the flesh as it were. I'm wondering if I shouldn't write in a quick scene of Alice and her stud getting down and dirty in their favorite hotel (which, incidentally, is the Whitman on East 54th Street—is it a problem if I use the real name of the hotel in my manuscript? I thought it had a nice literary feel to it). What do you think? Personally, I believe it would add a little heat. Sex sells, doesn't it? And the two of them could be very, very hot together, no? But you're the boss—I'll only add it in if you think it would be a good idea.

Looking forward,
G.

I looked from my laptop to the small hotel pad and pen next to it. The curling script on each said *Whitman Hotel*. He knew where I was.

He was watching me.

I stood over the computer, my body paralyzed by fear but my mind alive and swarming with wild thoughts. I had been such a fool to believe, even for a second, that Damiano was involved in *Blind Submission* in any way. My paranoia was justified—the e-mail was hard evidence of that—but I'd made the terrible mistake of directing it at the wrong person. I'd kicked Damiano out, a move as cold as anything Alice could have come up with, after he'd given me so much, and now he was gone. I'd become so unbalanced by this novel that I could no longer tell what was real and what was fiction. I was Alice, all right, and I'd gone right through the looking glass. But my feelings for Damiano had to be genuine. I hadn't dreamed what had happened between us. I'd had him and lost him in the space of an hour and now I didn't know if I'd ever get him back. He was probably thinking about what a mistake *he'd* made at this very moment. And all of this was because of a book—*Malcolm's* book. Of course Malcolm would know where I was. Anna had seen fit to share all those details with Damiano, hadn't she? It would make perfect sense that she'd shared them with Malcolm as well. Like me, Damiano had just been a pawn in the game Malcolm was playing. The game he'd been playing with Anna's help. Anna, who had been sitting at my desk, going through my things, talking to someone named Malcolm on the phone . . .

Was it possible that Malcolm and Anna were working on this thing *together*?

I looked at the clock and subtracted three hours. It was only five o'clock on the West Coast. Everyone should still be in the office.

To: jackson.stark@fiammalit.com
From: angel.robinson@fiammalit.com
Subject: <no subject>

J—

Are you still in the office? Is Anna? What is she doing? Need to know.

A.

While I waited for Jackson's answer, I tried to figure out what I should write back to G. It was clear that I was *supposed* to respond in some way, but I didn't want to risk playing into whatever scenario G was setting up for me next. I didn't have time to get very far, though, because Jackson's response came over within minutes.

To: angel.robinson@fiammalit.com
From: jackson.stark@fiammalit.com
Subject: Re: <no subject>

Hi A—

I'm here, but Anna's gone. She left work early (a couple of hours ago, maybe?)—said she was feeling sick. Why? What's up? What do you need?

J.

Anna hadn't missed a day of work since I'd started and had never taken off early. Feeling sick, was she? If my not-so-far-fetched suspicions were true, she really *was* sick. I didn't take the time to write back to Jackson, reaching instead for my cell phone and dialing the office number.

"Lucy Fiamma Agency, this is Jackson."

"Jackson, hi, it's Angel. Just act like I'm calling about a submission, okay?"

"I'm sorry, she's unavailable at the moment. May I help you with something?" He was good. I felt a small twinge of relief that I hadn't dismissed his intelligence before it was too late.

"I need Damiano Vero's cell-phone number. Can you get that for me?"

"Yes, we'd be happy to look at it," he said. "Anything else I can help you with?"

"That's it for now. Thanks, Jackson."

"No problem," he said.

"I'll fill you in later," I said. "I know you're wondering. . . . Anyway, I'll be back in the office soon and we can talk then."

"Well, we'll look forward to reading that," he said, and as he spoke, an e-mail message from him containing Damiano's phone number appeared on my computer screen.

"Got it," I said. "Thanks again."

As soon as I'd hung up with Jackson, I dialed Damiano's number. I was desperate to find him. I needed to explain everything to him, which I should have done before I threw him out. I had to tell him how sorry I was and beg him to come back. My heart was beating so hard as I dialed the numbers that the phone vibrated in my hand. His name was on my lips, ready to fall, when an automated operator came on the line informing me that the wireless customer I was trying to reach was out of the area. Damiano was gone—just gone—and I was the one who had sent him away.

For the second time that night, my eyes spilled over with tears. But this time the tears were angry ones. I'd been feeling so sorry for myself, as if I'd been the victim of some master manipulation. But what had really happened was that I'd allowed myself to become a character in somebody else's story. The realization that I'd been facilitating it all along made me furious with myself. It might be too late to save what I could have had with Damiano, I thought, but this—I turned back to my computer— I could still control.

It was time to smoke out the author of *Blind Submission*.

To: ganovelist@heya.com
From: angel.robinson@fiammalit.com
Subject: Re: Alice

G—

I don't want to play anymore. I'm done. I've discussed it with Lucy and she agrees. She'll be in touch to let you know how we proceed from here.

Angel

I sat in front of my computer and waited. I didn't know exactly who G was, it was true, but in a strange sense I *knew* G—the entity behind *Blind Submission*—quite well. I knew what kind of notes to give him and how he'd respond to them. Editorially, at least, I knew what he wanted from me—and that was for me to keep going. He liked our little arrangement very well. I sent the e-mail because I knew G would be quite disturbed by the thought that I was quitting *Blind Submission* and would quickly write back to me with some kind of concession or maybe an apology for going too far. Either way, my e-mail would get to him enough for him to reveal himself—I hoped. I was taking a risk, of course. It was possible that he'd contact Lucy himself and tell her and then I'd have to answer for it, but I didn't think he would. G needed me.

When there was no response after a half hour, I got up, put on a pair of pants and a sweater, and sat back down again. After another half hour of staring at the screen, I picked up the hotel phone and ordered a sandwich from room service. It took forty-five minutes to be delivered and twenty for me to eat it and place the tray outside my door. Still there was no response from G. I sat, and then lay down on the bed. I could smell Damiano on the sheets and I buried my face in the pillow to breathe what might be the last of him into my body. I wasn't even aware of falling asleep until the hotel phone rang at midnight, jolting me out of unconsciousness. I was still half in a dream when I picked it up.

"He-hello?"

"Angel! Are you awake?" Lucy's voice shredded the remnants of my sleep and pulled me into full, glaring alertness.

"Um, I am now."

"Good! What's on tomorrow's schedule?"

"Well, you've got . . . um . . ." I couldn't remember the details of her day, and I started to slide off the bed to pull out my copy of her schedule when she stopped me.

"I need you to rearrange my morning, Angel. I want you to move all my appointments to the afternoon."

"But I can't do that, Lucy. It's too late to call—"

"You'll find a way, Angel—you're a bright girl and this isn't rocket science."

I sighed into the phone. It was senseless to argue with her. "Okay," I said. "And is there something you'd like me to schedule instead?" Like a meeting with the mayor, I thought, or something equally impossible.

"We're taking a spa morning, Angel! Hair, nails, the works!"

"What?"

"It just occurred to me that tomorrow is your last day here in Gotham and I promised to get you made over when we arrived. So voilà, Angel, I'm true to my word."

I was sure that, like all of Lucy's "generous" gestures, this one had a catch buried in it, but she sounded genuinely excited at the prospect of taking me with her to a salon and I was too unstrung to try to figure out why.

"Okay," I said. "Great. I'll see you in the morning, then."

Lucy hung up without saying good-bye, something I'd gotten used to from her. It saved time and skipped over any finality. If she hadn't said good-bye, she was still present in some form and one would have to stay at the ready, waiting for the next command. I placed the receiver back in its cradle and got out of bed. The wise thing to do now was to leave messages for the editors Lucy would now not be seeing in the morning, but instead of reaching for the schedule, I sat down once more in front of my laptop. It was still on and plugged into the phone line.

There were no new e-mails waiting for me.

FOURTEEN

MY FLIGHT ARRIVED in San Francisco so late it went over into the next day. By the time I got out of the airport, through the city, and on the road to my apartment, it was close to five o'clock in the morning. I'd been able to sleep a little on the plane, but that only served to stave off total exhaustion. What I really needed was a long night in my own bed. I was so tired I didn't know if I could even stay awake for the long drive home. If you counted the time change, I was twenty-four hours into what had become an endless day.

It had started, as so many of my days now did, with Lucy. After obsessively checking my e-mail only to find my in-box empty and G now apparently playing possum, I collected Lucy, who actually sprang for a taxi to take us to one of New York's finest salons.

"This is where I always come when I'm in the Big Apple," Lucy told me. "They are beyond fabulous here. I've pulled quite a few strings to get you in as well. What they do here is *better* than plastic surgery. You won't believe it. You're going to be *transformed,* Angel Robinson!"

"What am I transforming exactly, Lucy?" I softened my question with a bright smile, but I was starting to get a very uneasy feeling about Lucy's plans for our spa day.

"Well, among other things, your hair," Lucy said.

"What's wrong with my hair?"

"The *color,* for one thing. You shouldn't *be* a redhead in the first place, Angel, that's the problem right there. And the length is an entirely different issue. Mature women don't have long hair, Angel, it's a rule."

I had a painful flashback to Damiano and how he'd run his hands through my hair, how genuinely he'd admired it and how beautiful he'd made it seem. Lucy saw the memory reflected in my face and gave it an entirely different interpretation.

"Don't worry about how to style it, Angel. I've instructed them to cut your hair like mine. This is a brilliant cut and very versatile. And I think my color—well, maybe a shade or two darker—would be *perfect* for you."

That was when I decided that our bizarre girlfriend-bonding moment was over.

"That's extremely generous of you, Lucy," I said, "but I'm kind of attached to my hair the way it is."

"You're not *serious*?" she asked. "If it's the cost you're worried about, don't—I'm buying. Now, let's go, shall we?"

"No, really, Lucy, I don't want to color my hair. I'm not going to color my hair. Or cut it."

She gave me a long look, her irises bright green against her pale skin. "You don't want to look like me, is that it?"

"No, that's not it. I just . . ." I didn't know what to say. Her eyes were begging me to tell her that I would love nothing more than to look exactly like her and that I was overwhelmed with gratitude. I sensed that anything less would actually wound her. But I couldn't find it in myself to give her what she wanted. "I just don't think it would suit me," I said.

"That's where you're wrong," she said. "You don't know what suits you. That's why you look the way you do. I thought I could help you with that, but clearly I'm mistaken."

"I'm sorry, Lucy, I didn't mean—"

The daggers flying from Lucy's eyes cut me off mid-sentence. She moved away from me and toward the salon. I followed her, preparing to go in with her, but she put her arm out to stop me.

"We're done for the day, Angel. You're on your own. Make sure you don't miss your flight."

This, I realized, was Lucy's way of showing that she was hurt.

I stood bewildered on the street for a minute after that, wondering what she expected me to do. Was I supposed to follow her? Apologize? For a second, I toyed with the idea of doing just that. But a second was all it took to realize that I was actually *free* of her for the first time in days, released from servitude and able to go wherever I wanted. I hailed my own cab and went to the hotel. I was going to pick up my things and then I was headed directly to the airport. Because the only place I wanted to go was home.

DAWN WAS BREAKING as I dragged my suitcase up the stairs to my apartment. I'd never craved the comfort of my own bed with such a single-minded intensity. It was all I could think about as I dropped my bags, locked the door behind me, and fell down onto my covers.

Something was wrong.

I sat up and looked around my apartment. All the objects around me were still, familiar, the way I had left them. But there was something different in the air. I got the distinct feeling that things had been moved and then put back in their place. There was a just-settled feeling all around me, a displacement of ions, a faint odor I couldn't place—as if someone had been there very recently. I got up and flipped on the light, although the sun was starting to filter through the window. The feeling of intrusion got stronger even as I failed to find anything that would confirm it. My unrinsed coffee mug was exactly where I had left it in the kitchen. The piles of papers and manuscripts next to my bed were in exactly the same state of disarray. The sink in my bathroom was dry. My bed was made, exactly the way I'd left it. Had I made my bed before I'd left? I searched my memory for the details of that morning and couldn't find them. I'd always been inconsistent about making my bed in the morning, leaving it rumpled half the time when I couldn't be bothered. I grabbed the covers and threw them back, expecting I didn't know what to jump out at me, but of course there was nothing there except the sheets and pillows.

I was very tired, I told myself. This was a reasonable explanation for why I was suddenly so paranoid. Sleep deprivation was the quickest way to get to hallucinating twitchiness. But I'd operated just fine on less sleep. I'd only started feeling this pervasive sense of intrusion since *Blind Submission*.

It took only a minute to pull my laptop from its bag and power it up. There was one e-mail waiting for me. From G.

> To: angel.robinson@fiammalit.com
> From: ganovelist@heya.com
> Subject: An excerpt
>
> Dear Ms. R—
>
> I find myself with an excerpt and I'm looking for a place to insert it. Ideas?
>
> Cheers,
> G.

Alice's bed was her sanctuary. She loved the feel of rich cotton sheets and plump down. She took her bedding very seriously. She'd read somewhere that Jackie Onassis had said that people with real wealth and taste only used pure white cotton sheets and Alice had never forgotten it. It had been difficult, in the early days, to provide herself with a bed, let alone white cotton sheets, but as soon as Alice had the means, she'd gone shopping for linens of gradually increasing thread counts.

It wasn't easy to keep such high-quality sheets looking good. They had a tendency to wrinkle at that level. But Alice was willing to sacrifice for her luxury. She ironed her sheets with steam, focused to the point of meditation, until every wrinkle vanished from their surfaces. Then she took great care to lay them on the bed and tuck them in tightly. It was then that Alice could slide herself between those tight, soft sheets of white. In this, Alice's bed resembled nothing so much as a book. The bedsheets became clean white sheets of paper that she slid herself between, insinuated herself against. And Alice became the text written upon them.

Soft white sheets for her hard dark thoughts.

I looked over at my bed, at my white down comforter and my white five-hundred-thread-count cotton sheets that, until this moment, I had been dying to lie down on and I started to cry.

He was gaslighting me and it was working.

Blind Submission was starting to make me crazy just as Alice was becoming crazy in it.

It was time to tell Lucy. She'd read the manuscript and she'd seen my notes, but she had no idea of the extent of G's personal game with me. I'd kept it from her out of . . . what? Pride? The illusion that I could control both the book and its author? Or was it fear? Fear that Malcolm, my bitter ex-boyfriend, was the real author. It was time to come clean— to tell her about Malcolm and to fill her in on my suspicions about Anna. I didn't know exactly how I was going to do this, but I had a little time to plan it out. By the time she got back from New York, I'd be ready.

I realized that my telephone was ringing. Damiano! I'd tried his cell phone at least a dozen times over the last day and got the same out-of-area message every time. I lunged for the phone, catching it before it had a chance to go to voice mail.

"Hello?" I sounded, both breathless and anxious.

"Angel? It's Jackson." He was whispering.

I checked the time. It was 8:15 A.M.

"Jackson, what is it? What's the matter?"

"Are you coming in?" he asked.

"I just got in," I said. "My plane was delayed. I was going to come in later. . . ."

"I think you should come in now," he said.

"What's the hurry?" I asked. "What's going on?"

"Lucy's about to have a staff meeting. I've only got a second here—Craig's in the bathroom. But Anna's in there already, Angel. She told Lucy that you're not coming in and she's—"

"But how can Lucy have a staff meeting?" I said stupidly. "She's still in New York."

"She's not in New York, she's here."

"But she's staying an extra day—today—in New York. She's not coming home until tonight." *So she can take Damiano to meet his editor and whatever else she's planning to do with him,* I added to myself.

"No," Jackson said insistently. "She's here. And Julia Swann came in with a preemptive offer for the *Elvis* book and Lucy's looking to maybe have some kind of mini auction for it. Didn't you know that?"

"Today? But Julia Swann said— I thought she wasn't even going to offer on it. How can Lucy have an auction *today?"*

"I don't know, Angel, but she's going to. I thought you knew. Lucy was expecting you to be here. There's a note on your desk from her."

"What does it say?"

"Angel, I have to go. I'll tell her you're on your way."

How was it possible that Lucy was back in the office when I'd barely landed myself? And where was Damiano?

———

THE OUTER OFFICE WAS EMPTY when I walked in a half hour later. I could hear voices coming from Lucy's office and assumed the staff meeting was already in progress. I dropped my purse and manuscripts next to my chair and was overwhelmingly relieved to see my angelfish alive and swimming in its bowl. There was a yellow sticky note stuck to the side. *Welcome back,* it said in Jackson's handwriting. Lucy's note sat next to it, waiting for me on my desk. I grabbed it and scanned it as I headed toward her office.

Angel—

Today's top priorities:

1. *Get "Elvis" author on the phone asap—we need to discuss her new direction with her novel!*

2. *Karanuk—see me!!!*

3. *My NY notes are on your desk—please sort!*

4. *What is going on with Blind Submission?!?!*

5. *Prepare list and status of all option books!*

—LF

I was trying to figure out where she'd found the time to even think about the items on the list, let alone organize them as tasks for me, when I walked into her office and saw all eyes in the room immediately turn to me.

"Well," Lucy said, "glad you could join us, Angel. Anna said that you were ill, which I found difficult to believe since I just saw you yesterday and you were fine." Lucy delivered this statement with her usual crispness but didn't seem at all annoyed. She looked well rested and surprisingly chic in a black pin-striped pantsuit. Her hair, a white mist around her head, looked exactly the same as it had the day before.

"That's interesting," I said, shooting quick daggers at Anna, "because I never said any such thing."

"Um, well, I guess I just assumed," Anna said. There was something different about Anna, and it took me a second or two to figure out that she was wearing makeup—too much of it, in fact, and she'd chosen exactly the wrong color (powder blue) to layer on her eyelids. She'd used some kind of greasy product to slick back her hair and was squashed into a pair of khaki overalls. I had no idea what kind of look she was going for, but whatever it was, it wasn't working. She looked like painted lunch meat wedged between Craig and Jackson on Lucy's couch.

"As fascinating as the semantics of your conversation are, Anna, there is business at hand," Lucy said. "Do I need to reiterate that we are extremely short on time today?" Anna's face flushed and she looked down at the floor. Craig, who seemed more sallow and shapeless than usual, was staring intently at the pad of paper on his knees, and Jackson simply looked relieved to see me. I sat down in the only available chair, which happened to be right next to Lucy.

"Weren't you planning to stay in New York today, Lucy?" I said.

Lucy raised her eyebrows and gave me a half-smile. "My plans changed," she said. "If that's all right with you, Angel?"

"I was just wondering," I said, "because—"

"In fact, I was due to meet with an author," Lucy interrupted. "Your Italian man." She gave me one of her laserlike stares. I felt my heart flip and beat erratically against my chest. I couldn't control the flush I could feel spreading to the roots of my hair. I looked down at my notepad in a weak effort to conceal it.

"Damiano Vero," Anna squeaked from her position on the couch.

"Yes," Lucy said. "Damiano Vero. But he never showed up. Which is either the height of disrespect or an indication that something's happened to him."

"But how . . . ?" I began. My overtired brain was trying to work out how Lucy could have been in New York waiting for Damiano a couple of hours ago and be sitting here now. I scrambled for options, but the only ones I came up with were witchcraft and time travel. "Weren't you meeting with him *today*?" I asked before I realized that I wasn't supposed to know anything about their meeting at all.

"Actually," Lucy said, plucking a speck of lint off her pants, "we were supposed to meet for drinks yesterday." She shrugged dramatically. "I gave him an hour and a half. I think that's plenty of time. It was obvious that he wasn't going to make an appearance. I'm assuming he didn't contact you, Angel?"

"Um . . . no." I didn't have to see my face to know that it was beet red.

"Heeey," Anna said, as if something important had just occurred to her. "Didn't you talk to him the other night, Angel?"

I was a deer stuck in headlights and couldn't speak, couldn't move away from the oncoming impact. A look of genuine surprise spread slowly across Lucy's face, and behind that I thought I detected a glimmer of satisfaction. I needed to say something, but my words were frozen and unyielding in my throat.

"What's this?" Lucy asked.

I could actually see Anna puffing herself up like a hideous popover. Clearly, she'd been waiting a long time for this moment. "He called here the other day looking for Angel. He wanted to know what room she was staying in. In New York. I thought he had, you know, a meeting or something." Anna gave Lucy a big fat grin. I wanted to kill her—put my hands around her doughy neck and squeeze until she choked. "Did I do the wrong thing?" Anna said sweetly.

"Did you talk to him, Angel?" There was an echo in Lucy's voice, as if she were speaking to me through a tunnel. I couldn't focus. My heart was beating so hard, my vision was jumpy and blurred.

I cleared my throat and with all the self-control I could muster, I said, "No. I haven't spoken to Damiano Vero for weeks."

"Really," Lucy said. "Well, I can't imagine what happened to him."

"Isn't he, like, a heroin addict or something?" Anna said. "Maybe he, you know . . ." Every one of us turned to Anna then, our faces showing varying degrees of surprise and disgust. Anna sensed that she'd taken her little riff too far and her color rose slightly. "I'm just saying—" she started, but Lucy finally cut her off.

"Find him, Angel," Lucy said. There was firmness and finality in her tone. "But not now. Right now we need to discuss the *Elvis* book. You saw my note? Have you spoken to the author yet?"

"Not yet, no. I haven't had a chance."

"Well, that might be better, actually, although I can't imagine what you have to do that would be more important. The point is this: Julia Swann is very interested in this project. She's offering us a one-hundred-and-twenty-thousand-dollar preempt." Lucy took a dramatic pause and tapped her Waterman pen on her knee.

"That is so great," Anna interjected.

"I thought Julia said that she wasn't likely to get a book like this past her board," I said. "What happened to change that?" I was flooded with relief that we were off the topic of Damiano, and intended to keep steering the conversation away from any other verbal land mines.

"*I* happened," Lucy said. "I see you were paying attention, Angel, but not closely enough. This book has certain elements that are irresistible to Julia Swann and to Long, Greene, and they want it badly enough to offer us a lot of money."

"But what elements?" I pressed.

"Poker," Lucy said.

"*Poker?*"

Lucy sighed as if my question was very tiring to her. "Yes, Angel, poker. And if it's Texas No Limit Hold 'Em poker, that's even better. I don't remember if that's the specific game she's writing about."

"That's because she wasn't writing about poker at all. It's a literary relationship story about modern love, trust, and marriage set against the backdrop of Las Vegas. It's about a road trip. It has nothing to do with poker."

Lucy looked at me, and perhaps it was some trick of light in the room, but I could swear her eyes were twinkling. Her mouth, however, remained set and determined.

"It does now," she said.

"So that's the new direction you want me to discuss with the author?" I said after a pause.

"Exactly," Lucy said.

"But Lucy . . ." I couldn't stop, although I wanted to. After all, it wasn't *my* book, and what did I care if Shelly Franklin rewrote her entire novel to include the game of poker as a central theme? But I couldn't let it go. I didn't particularly care for Shelly Franklin herself and thought she could use both a primer on social skills and a few visits to a good therapist, but I loved her novel and I'd worked very hard to get it in the shape it was in. The thought of dumbing it down and tearing it apart to make it fit the commercial flavor of the moment was revolting to me.

"What if the author doesn't want to take this book in a different direction?" I asked Lucy. I heard the strident note in my own voice and did nothing to soften it.

Lucy waved her hand in the air and smiled. "Please," she said. "Of course she'll *want* to. That's not the concern here. Look, Angel, you know as well as I do that poker is very hot right now. There are plenty of instructional books and collections of fiction, but there isn't really anything out there *like this*. Honestly, do you think this author would rather sell her book to Long, Greene—who, by the way, have plenty of literary cachet if that's what she's after—or some tiny little press with no money to give her and no way to give her book wide distribution? There's a reason she came *here*, Angel."

"I don't know, Lucy, I've been working with her for a while now. I don't know if she can change this book so radically."

Lucy tilted her head to the side and gave me an appraising look. I'd never challenged her this way before and we both seemed to realize it at the same time. What came as a surprise to me, though, was that Lucy didn't seem to mind. In fact, she seemed invigorated by it.

"Well, you'll call her in a minute, Angel, and we'll see, won't we?" Lucy crossed her legs slowly and tucked an errant wisp of hair behind her ear. I noticed that she was wearing a brand-new pair of black alligator pumps that matched the stylish briefcase I'd seen her carry in New York. "But the consideration now," she went on, "is do we accept Julia's preempt or do we take it out and possibly get more? Or possibly less? Julia's advised me that she won't use her offer as a floor, so we'd be starting lower. I've got substantial interest for this book, but you never know how that's going to play out. Especially these days. So which way do we go?"

Lucy's question had a rhetorical flavor, but I answered, anyway. "Shouldn't we ask the author?"

This was, perhaps, one question too many. "Again, Angel, why did she come here? If she could make these decisions for herself, she wouldn't need an agent, would she? She wouldn't need *me*. Does anyone *else* have any thoughts on this? We need to get it settled immediately."

"It would be so cool to have another auction," Anna said. "You're so amazing with those, Lucy."

"Okay," Lucy said. "Any other thoughts?"

"It's a very solid offer from Long, Greene," Craig said. "And I think that if you limit the rights to North America, we could get some decent sales on the foreign side. Then there are the other subsidiary rights. It could do well as an audio book. Then, of course, there are the paperback rights. You could try to work some magic with royalty rates there."

How had Craig gotten this job in the first place? I wondered. He lacked anything resembling a spleen. His little speech was so dull and devoid of passion, he risked boring all of us into a collective coma. Perhaps sensing this, Lucy moved on.

"What about you, Jason? Any thoughts?"

Jackson, clearly unused to being called by a name that wasn't his, hesitated for a moment before answering. I could almost *hear* Lucy's irritation increase.

"Well?" she barked.

"Um . . ." Jackson looked over at me as if for support. "I kind of think Angel's right. Maybe we should ask the author what she wants to do."

"Well, what do *you* know?" Lucy said, dismissing Jackson. "It's after noon in New York. This meeting is over. Let's get to work, people. Angel, you stay here. Get the author on the phone."

Lucy seated herself at her desk as everyone else beat a hasty retreat out of her office. "Use my phone," she said. "And put her on speaker." I punched the numbers and Shelly Franklin picked up after the first ring.

"Hi, Shelly, it's Angel Robinson."

"Hi?"

"I've got Lucy on the phone for you."

"Okay?" On speakerphone, Shelley Franklin's verbal tics were more annoying than usual. The woman was hopeless. There was no way she'd be able to turn *Elvis* into a book about poker. Lucy was in for a surprise and I was going to enjoy it wholeheartedly.

"Hello, dear," Lucy boomed. "We've been working extremely hard for your book. Angel and I have just returned from New York, where we blanketed the landscape with the fruits of your labor." I winced inwardly at Lucy's mixed metaphor. "What do you think of that?"

"Oh?" Shelly giggled nervously. "That's great?"

"So listen, dear, I've got some very exciting news for you. Are you sitting down?"

"Sitting down?"

Lucy looked at me, gestured to the phone, and rolled her eyes. I shrugged. Lucy lifted her hands, palms up, and I nodded my agreement. Just like that, without either of us uttering a word, we'd been able to have an entire conversation.

"We have a lot of interest in your little novel, my dear," Lucy sang into the speaker, "but here's the best part: I have received an offer from Julia Swann, an editor at Long, Greene. I'm assuming you've heard of them?"

There was a long pause before Shelly came back with, "Long, Greene? Oh, yes, I've heard of them. They're . . . that's wonderful!"

"But wait," Lucy said. "The best part is the kind of money they're offering. One hundred and twenty thousand dollars, my dear. That kind of money is almost unheard of in publishing these days. Do you understand what I'm saying?"

"Oh . . ." Shelly said. "Oh, oh, oh . . ." She sounded as if she were swooning.

"Indeed," Lucy said. "But now I want you to listen carefully, all right? We have two options. I can accept the Long, Greene offer right now or you can wait and we take our chances trying to sell it elsewhere. Of course, there are no guarantees that I could get the same kind of money from another publisher. Not to mention the fact that Long, Greene will undoubtedly do a wonderful job of publishing this novel. They are the kind of house that builds their authors. Do you understand what I'm saying? You'd have a future there."

"I want to take their offer," Shelly said without hesitation, the shy, faltering tone completely absent from her voice.

"You don't have to rush into anything," Lucy said. "Although I do have to tell you that I promised Julia Swann I would get back to her today, and well . . . We do have an excellent opportunity here. But would you like to consider the other option and give me a call back?"

"No!" Shelly gasped. "Please call her and tell her that I want to take her offer."

"You're sure?" Lucy asked. She looked up at me and smiled.

"Yes!" Shelly said. "I'm sure. Oh, please call her before she changes her mind."

"I'm thrilled," Lucy said. "Nothing would make me happier. Now listen, dear, there's one thing."

"What? What is it?" Shelly now sounded frantic.

"Julia Swann, who, by the way, is an *excellent* editor, would like you to play up the poker element in your novel. This is very important to her, dear. It's sort of a deal-breaker. Do you think you'll be able to do that?"

"The . . . what? I'm sorry," Shelly said, "I don't think I heard you?" Here it was, I thought, and formed a smile of my own. I doubted Shelly Franklin had ever played the game of poker, let alone considered making it a part of her novel.

"*Poker,*" Lucy said firmly. "The novel needs poker. Texas No Limit Hold 'Em, to be specific." Another long pause on the other end. "Have I lost you?" Lucy said. "Are you already spending your money?" She barked out a laugh. "I do need to call her back, dear, so keep that in mind."

"Okay," Shelly said. "It's no problem. I can do that. I can write about poker."

I felt my heart sink with disappointment and mourned the untimely death of Shelly Franklin's artistic integrity.

"Wonderful," Lucy said. "And really, I think that it's a wonderful new direction to take the novel in. When I speak to Julia, I'll be sure to let her know that you're very excited about it. You're going to love working with her, dear. She's even come up with a fabulous new title. Hold on a second, I have it written down here somewhere." Lucy leaned back in her chair, making no attempt to find anything, written or otherwise, on her desk. After a few seconds had passed she said, "*White Aces and Promises.* That's it. As in 'white lace and promises.' That way you keep the wedding theme."

I heard something that sounded like a stifled groan or a grunt on the other end of the line. Lucy ignored it and went on. "Really, dear, the more I think about it, the more impressed I am with this offer. I hope you know how fortunate you are?"

"Oh yes, yes. I am so very lucky."

"Indeed. Lady Luck has certainly been looking over your shoulder," Lucy said, taking the poker metaphor to its nauseating end.

"Yes, I know, but . . ." Shelly was faltering.

"What is it, my dear?" I noted that Lucy's *my dear* had the same emphasis as *you bitch*.

"I don't . . . I don't know ANYTHING ABOUT POKER!"

Lucy and I both cringed at the sound of Shelly's outburst. What the hell had happened to her? Five seconds before she'd been willing to sell her firstborn for a book deal.

"It's not a difficult game," Lucy said, disgust creeping into her voice. "Just turn on the damn TV and you'll see some tournament on every other channel. Better yet, get a book on the subject."

"But I don't know how to do it. I don't know how to make it a book about poker. I don't know what to dooooo. . . ." Shelly Franklin had started weeping. I was embarrassed for her. Lucy was having a very different reaction.

"You know, my dear, I worked very hard to put this deal together, and as with every deal I make, my reputation is on the line. I didn't sweat my ass off in Manhattan so that you could sit around feeling miserable when a *million talented authors* are out there waiting for me to discover them. So am I to call Julia Swann and accept the offer or am I to tell her that the author has fallen apart and will not be able to write about a game that any eight-year-old can play?"

"Ah, unhh, baa, haaa . . ." Shelly Franklin was falling apart and so was her deal. But I had an idea.

"Shelly?" I said. "Can you hear me?"

"A-A-Angel?"

"Yes. Listen, Shelly, I've been thinking. You know how Michael is hiding his alcoholism from Jennifer and she's hiding her pregnancy? Well, why can't he—or she—also be addicted to gambling—poker, specifically—and then when they get to Las Vegas, of course it all comes out? Michael could leave her to go to a tournament. Or she could leave him and go play. Then he goes to the bar, gets drunk—again—and then they try to hash out their problems, but she's winning and they both get caught up in it. Then you can make poker the central motif. You can have both characters thinking about it all the way to Las Vegas along with all the other things they're keeping from each other. Because—

here's a thought—perhaps they *both* have a secret passion for this game. Can you see it, Shelly?"

There was a crackling silence from the speakerphone. Lucy was staring at me, her eyebrows forming perfect arrows, her lips folded into a thin line.

"I can do that," Shelly said finally. "I can definitely do that."

"So I can call Julia Swann?" Lucy had taken it down several notches now that Shelly was back on the line.

"Yes, I'm so happy," Shelly said. "Please accept. I can do it. I can do what they want."

"They want to publish you!" Lucy exclaimed.

"Of course, of course. Thank you, Lucy. Thank you so much for making this happen."

"Thank *you,* dear. But listen, you'd better let me go so that I can call Julia. Again, I'm just thrilled. Enjoy! I'll have Angel call you when we wrap this up, yes? Bye, dear." Lucy hung up before Shelly could say good-bye and immediately turned to me, her eyebrows still raised.

"Well, that's done."

"Yes. Congratulations."

"Thank you," Lucy said. She waited a moment before delivering her next words, which sounded as if they'd been torn from her. "And kudos to you, Angel. Nice work at the end. You have, indeed, been paying attention." That was clearly all the praise or acknowledgment I was going to receive, and it seemed to have cost her substantially to give it to me. I folded my arms and tried to keep my disgust from working its way onto my face. I'd finally understood why so many of Lucy's authors never wrote second books—she hated writers. And she probably hated me because I didn't.

Lucy stood, brushing the folds out of her pants, looked over at me, and completely misread my thoughts. "I hope you weren't expecting *her* to thank you," she said, gesturing to the phone. "Not that one. Another one who doesn't deserve what's falling into her lap. To think *I* had to convince *her.* It's a disgrace how many of these self-obsessed narcissists get published, get acclaim, while so many deserving writers *never get heard.*" She took a deep breath. "They'll let you down if you allow them to. I knew you were an author advocate when I hired you, Angel. It helps. But you get much too involved. You can't separate the writers from their writing. That's your problem." She shrugged and placed her hands flat on the surface of her desk. Her fingernails were painted with a pale opalescent polish. "It's a great pity that one can't excise the author from the book once it's written," she said. "But there you are."

Lucy seemed to drift for a moment, caught up in thoughts she chose not to share, before she bristled, her shell hardening once more.

"Speaking of authors," she said, "I need you to get Karanuk on the phone. You've read his pages, yes?"

"Yes."

"So you've seen the shape they're in?"

"Yes, but Lucy, I think—"

"But I know how we're going to fix this." Lucy paused, forming her hands into a steeple and placing them under her chin. "Karanuk is going to write *Cold!Cooking*." She smiled broadly. "Prose recipes from Alaska. It's a brilliant idea."

She looked at me for confirmation. I tried, and failed, to muster any kind of enthusiasm. It was a god-awful idea, worse than turning *Elvis* into a novel about poker. She could sell it, of course, but it would permanently damage Karanuk's career. Lucy saw the disapproval in my face and said, "What? What is it, Angel?"

"I know that *Thaw* doesn't look good right now," I said, "but I think I can work with him. It's got so much potential, Lucy—he's an amazingly talented writer."

"Fuck *Thaw*!" Lucy snapped. "Get him on the phone for me. He'll write *Cold!Cooking* if I tell him to."

"Okay," I said, and turned to leave her office.

"Wait," she said. "Get me Julia Swann first before she *does* change her mind."

"Okay," I said.

"And Angel?"

"Yes?"

"We've got a lot to do today, so you'd better get going."

FIFTEEN

AS SOON AS I CONNECTED Julia Swann with Lucy, I felt myself breaking into a cold, crawling sweat. Chilled and overheated at the same time, I put my hands to my forehead and pressed. Bouncing between the extremes of lack of sleep, the absolute creepiness of *Blind Submission,* Shelly Franklin's deal, and worry over the missing Damiano, I was on the verge of having a panic attack. Damiano would never intentionally stand Lucy up. It just wasn't his way. Plus, such disrespect wouldn't exactly be a good career move. He was already in New York and planning to meet with her when I saw him. What could have happened between then and the following evening? I glanced at Anna, snake in the grass that she was, and thought about her heroin addict comment. What if my throwing him out had driven Damiano to . . . but no, I was giving myself *way* too much credit there.

So where was he?

"Find him," Lucy had said, and that was good enough for me. I tried his home phone number first. I let it ring ten times before I hung up. I'd discovered during our all-night editing sessions that Damiano had no answering machine or voice mail for his home phone. I tried his cell phone again, but it was still out of area. The last number I had for him was a work number, but even as I dialed it, I knew I wasn't going to find him there.

"Dolce and Pane." At least someone had answered at this number. Someone who might have a clue as to where Damiano could be, even if the gruff male voice on the other end didn't exactly sound like it belonged to a rich conversationalist.

"Good morning. Is Damiano there?"

"Damiano? No."

"Do you know if he's coming in? Do you know when?"

"Damiano? No."

"Damiano Vero, yes. He works there, right?"

"Damiano? Yes, yes. Work here."

"Do you know where he is?" I asked.

"Damiano? No. You try later," the voice said, and the line went dead.

I turned to my computer so that nobody in the office could see the tears stinging my tired eyes. Damiano, wherever he was, did not want to be found. At the very least, I thought, he didn't want to be found by me. I was going to have to get control of myself. My blushing and stammering during the meeting had surely tipped my hand, but becoming a sobbing wreck at my desk would expose me entirely. As if on cue, my computer chirped with the sound of an instant message from Anna.

Are you ok?

I turned around in my chair to face her and saw that she had her fingers on her keyboard and her eyes fixed intently on her computer screen. I stared at her long enough for her to notice me, but she kept up with her ridiculous pretense of looking busy. Behind me, my computer chirped again.

You seem a little upset.

I debated whether or not to send a message back. Somehow Anna had managed to become entangled in every aspect of my life. I wondered when all of that had happened and how I'd missed it. Perhaps *missed* wasn't the right word. *Underestimated* was more like it.

We need to talk, I wrote back. I heard the electronic ping of an incoming e-mail and welcomed the distraction.

To: angel.robinson@fiammalit.com
From: solange@sunstar.com
Subject: Re: BALSAMIC MOON

Greetings, Angel!

Thank you so much for your note. I apologize for not writing back to you sooner, but my computer's been on the blink for the last few days and I've just gotten it back up and running (this always happens to me when Mercury goes retrograde, so you'd think I'd be used to it by now)! At any rate, I'm so glad you got in touch with me. I believe our meeting was most fortuitous—and destined to happen. Of course, destiny and the stars are my business, so my belief in them both isn't so surprising.

I am "over the moon" (ha-ha) that you are so excited about my book and can't wait to discuss the next step. I look forward to hearing from you again.

Regards to you and Ms. Fiamma,
Sunny

P.S. If you're interested, I would be delighted to send you a copy of your astrological birth chart. All I need is your date, place, and time of birth. Think about it—it might prove to be quite illuminating!

SM

I'd almost forgotten about Sunny's book in all the madness of the last twenty-four hours. This was something else to add to the "tell Lucy" list, which was starting to become very long and complicated. I started to send Sunny a reply, something that would hold her off until I figured out a way to keep her from the fate of Shelly Franklin, but the sound of another incoming e-mail completely sidetracked me.

To: angel.robinson@fiammalit.com
From: ganovelist@heya.com
Subject: Re: Re: Alice

Dearest Angel Robinson,

I fear I've offended you, but I can't imagine why. It seemed that we were working so well together. I've just read your last e-mail (apologies about the delay) and I've taken it to mean that you don't agree with the direction I was thinking of taking here, so after giving it much thought, I've decided to rewrite. I'm attaching the fruits of my labor. I'm sure you'll give it your best consideration, Ms. Robinson. I can hardly believe that you wouldn't want to know what becomes of our Alice.

With my very best,
G.

I leaped out of my chair like an insane woman, ran the few steps over to Anna's desk, and turned her computer to face me before she had a chance to quit out of what she was doing.

"Hey!" Anna yelled, and recoiled as if I'd struck her. The sound was loud enough to alert both Craig and Jackson, who looked at us with matching stares of alarm. I gripped Anna's computer screen and peered into it. Solitaire. She was playing Solitaire.

"What are you *doing*?!" Anna squealed.

I searched for open windows on her computer, for any indication that she'd just sent me that e-mail, and found none. She'd been sitting there all along playing an electronic card game. It was no wonder she never got anything done.

"Is there a problem, Angel?" Craig's voice rumbled through my consciousness and forced me to turn around.

"No, no problem," I said, and walked back to my desk, where my intercom was shrieking.

"Angel!"

"Lucy?"

"My office, please!"

"On my way." I quit out of my e-mail program and grabbed the folders on my desk before heading over. I wasn't about to leave anything behind.

"Angel," Anna hissed as I passed her desk.

"What?"

"What's the matter with you?"

"Nothing," I said in a stage whisper. "Thanks for asking!"

"Well, that's done," Lucy said as I entered her office. "Elvis has left the building."

I smiled. I had to give her credit for that one. "Viva Las Vegas," I said, playing along.

"Indeed," she said. "One hundred and fifty thousand later." She looked at my surprised expression and nodded. "That's right, I got her to go higher. And I got our girl a bestseller bonus, too. Let's hope that the *poker* is still *hot* by the time it's published." Lucy was clearly on a roll.

"Have you called the author back to tell her?"

"Angel, I'm an extremely busy woman. If I spent all my time listening to the billing and cooing of grateful authors, I'd have none left to actually sell their books. Now, *what's next*?" She was moving with her usual sharklike speed, swallowing up everything in her path.

"Karanuk?" I offered.

"Yes, but first we need to talk about *Blind Submission*." Lucy walked around her desk to her couch and sat down. She patted the space beside her. "I can't have a conversation while you're standing there like that, Angel. Come and sit down."

I took a seat on the couch as far away from her as I could get, and placed my papers on her coffee table. A wave of dizziness hit me and I had to steady myself to keep from falling forward. I realized that the overload of adrenaline that had been keeping me awake had just run out. It didn't help that the temperature in Lucy's office, which was usually brisk at best, was quite warm, hovering between sultry and somnolent.

"Aren't you exhausted?" I asked her. "With the flying and the time change and all?"

Lucy smiled at me, showing an excessive number of her gleaming white teeth. "I slept on the plane," she said. I wondered if her remaining Xanax had anything to do with that. "The time change never bothers me. It's only three hours and, as you know, I live on New York time, anyway."

"But you must have taken a red-eye, right? I mean, that's the only—"

"Angel, I appreciate your concern for my health, but onward we go, yes? *Blind Submission*. What's going on with it?"

The very sound of the title made my throat constrict. But I had to tell her. "Yes, I need to talk to you about that," I said. "It's gotten a bit complicated."

For the second time that morning, Lucy seemed surprised. It wasn't an expression I was accustomed to seeing on her face, and it made me very uneasy.

"Really?" she asked. "In what way?"

She waited for me to answer, another anomaly, and I reached for the right words.

"I can't work on it anymore," I said at last.

"And why is that?" Lucy asked.

"Because I think I know who's writing it and I know why."

"Well, I'm most interested to hear about the *why*," Lucy said, "but first, do tell me the *who*." She seemed to be enjoying the conversation immensely. There was none of the usual clipped sharpness in her tone. For once, she seemed content to stay on one topic for longer than five seconds.

"It's Malcolm," I said, and held my breath, waiting for her reaction. I'd prepared myself for several—anger, annoyance, a lack of surprise— but not for what I saw, which was complete and authentic confusion.

"Malcolm who?" she said.

"My ex-boyfriend, Malcolm."

"Your *what*?" I watched as she puzzled it out in her head. Was it really possible that she didn't know who I was talking about? Lucy and I faced each other with mirrored expressions of bewilderment until a lightbulb finally went on in some corner of her brain. "Ohhh, *Malcolm*. The *fiancé*." Her expression changed to one of distaste. "The *writer*," she said with cruel emphasis. "Really, Angel? You're telling me that your fiancé is the author of a novel you've been working on for—how long now?—and that I've been pitching all over New York?"

"He's not my fiancé," I said. "He's not even my boyfriend anymore."

"Is this your way of trying to get me to represent him, Angel?" she said. "Because I can assure you it's not going to work."

"And I can assure you that I'm not," I said.

For a moment I thought I saw the flicker of a smile on her face, but I couldn't tell. Her eyes had gone very bright and clear and were staring right through me. I had the sudden sensation that we were on opposite sides of a seesaw and that the balance between us was about to shift.

"An-gel," she said, stretching the syllables of my name, "you're saying your— Malcolm told you he was the author of this novel? Why on earth wouldn't you have told me sooner?"

"Because I wasn't sure. I'm still not one hundred percent positive, but it *has* to be him."

"And why is that?"

"I think this was his plan all along," I started. I looked at Lucy, trying to gauge her receptiveness. She was waiting patiently for me to continue, with what seemed like genuine concern on her face. That look gave me strength and my words started tumbling out. "He wanted me to work here in the first place," I said. "He figured I'd give you his novel and then you'd represent him. But when that didn't work, he started writing this one, anonymously, so that we wouldn't know it was him and automatically reject it. His writing is all he's ever cared about, not me. And then I broke up with him. That was not part of his plan."

Lucy tapped her fingers lightly on her leg, her impatience returning. "But how is that connected to *Blind Submission*, Angel?"

I hesitated for a fraction of a second while I debated whether or not to tell her about Damiano. That was all it took to decide not to. "Lucy, you've read that manuscript," I said. "Don't you think it's more than a coincidence that the characters and plot are so much like us and this agency?"

Lucy shrugged. "Maybe," she said, "but that's part of what makes it interesting. Part of what makes it *different* from all the other crap out there. But Angel, I still don't know what makes you think it's your—Malcolm."

"There are aspects of Alice," I began, and stopped, searching again for the right words. "There are some very personal details of that character that are identical to me. Nobody but Malcolm would know about those."

"And how would *Malcolm* know about what goes on in a literary agency?"

"Well, I told him things he could have used," I said. "But I also think he had some help from . . ."

"From *whom*, Angel?"

"Anna," I said. "I think he and Anna . . . I think they are or were involved in some way."

"What?" Lucy looked revolted.

"I don't know," I said. "For sure."

"Well, Angel, I have to say I'm very disappointed in you." Lucy shook her head as if to punctuate her point.

"You're . . . ?"

"If you'll recall, you assured me when I hired you that your *personal* life would not infringe on your professional life. This is exactly the kind of scenario I was trying to avoid. You were not honest with me, Angel. And I have to say this hurts me. Really, I feel that I've offered you much more than a job here. I've given you a career, not to mention a salary that is astronomical by publishing standards. And I feel, frankly, like I've been a mother to you, Angel."

I remembered how on our flight to New York Lucy had convinced the flight attendant that I was her daughter. As absurd as it seemed, perhaps she'd convinced herself as well. For an instant, I thought about what it would be like to be Lucy's daughter and found it vaguely terrifying. I promised myself I would call my own mother as soon as I had the chance.

Lucy was still talking. "Do you know how many aspiring writers have come through this office in the guise of employees?" she asked me.

"But Lucy," I told her, "I am *not* a writer."

Lucy raised her hand to stop me. "No," she said, "what you've done is less honest than that. This is a business, Angel. I sell books here. And I now have a book that I have a tremendous amount of interest in, a book that I have staked my reputation on, and now, because of your personal involvement in it, I am supposed to abandon it?"

"No, that's not what I'm saying," I said, grasping for whatever it was that I *was* saying. "I just don't want to work on it anymore."

"Angel, do I need to remind you that you were the one who 'found'"—she made quotation marks in the air—"this novel in the submission pile?"

"Yes, but—"

"Has it suddenly become a bad book?"

"No, it hasn't."

"So the only reason that you don't want to work on it is that your ex-boyfriend is writing it? Because you *did* want him to get published, and that's why you took advantage of your position here, but now that you've broken up with him, you *don't* want him to get published, so you've decided to try your best to destroy his book? Is that right?"

"No," I said. I had to admit it to myself, Lucy's argument was starting to sound perfectly valid. It was true that *Blind Submission* had become a much better book. It was true that I had wanted to help Malcolm. And it was true that I no longer wanted to have anything to do with him. With a few well-aimed verbal strokes, Lucy had managed to make me doubt all of my own motivations.

"I wouldn't have thought you'd want to represent this novel now," I said, "knowing that he's writing it."

"But why wouldn't I, Angel? It's not about *him*, it's about the book."

As soon as the words were out of her mouth, I realized the truth in them. It was always about the book for me. In one form or another, I'd been living inside a book for as long as I could remember. And now I was living inside *Blind Submission,* a book about books, which *was*, in its own perverse way, about me. I'd been living on its pages, shaping it to suit myself. She was right: It wasn't about him at all—for her or for me.

"Do you really think it's that good?" I asked her.

"It will be when you get through with it, Angel. You were there with me in New York. You heard them. They want it."

"They haven't seen it," I said.

Lucy shrugged. "That doesn't matter," she said. "They're going to buy this one and they're going to spend a lot of money. It's going to be big, Angel."

"But what about Malcolm?" I asked her.

Lucy gave me a tight smile and folded her arms. "What if you're wrong, Angel? What if he's not the author? Are we going to let it get away because of your personal problems?"

"Well—"

"But let's assume that he is for a moment. Why don't we let him remain anonymous? Since that's the way he chose to come in. And now that I think about it, that may be the best way to sell him as well, as an industry insider who has to keep his identity concealed." She ran her fingers along the crease in her pant leg, sharpening it. "It's fitting, no? He gets his book sold, but he doesn't get any glory. Everybody wins. What do you think?"

I liked the idea more than I wanted to admit, and I thought that Malcolm would never go for it, which made it even better because he'd have to. And I was the one who was going to deliver the news to him.

"Okay," I said.

"Good," she said. "I'm glad we've got that settled. Now, is there anything else you'd like to get off your chest?"

"No," I said.

"Good," she said. "Then get Karanuk on the phone. No, don't leave, Angel. Use my phone and put him on speaker. You need to hear this."

I was halfway to her desk when I decided to take one more leap into the deep end. "Actually, there is one more thing, Lucy."

"What?" All of Lucy's trademark impatience was back.

I took a deep breath. "I've been thinking, and I know you like us to take initiative, Lucy, you know, be *proactive*." I tried to smile, although my heart was beating double time at the thought of what I was about to say. "I've learned so much from you, Lucy. I'm sure I could never be as good as you, but I was wondering if . . . you'd consider giving me a shot at selling a project on my own. For this agency, of course."

Lucy was amused. "At what point did I give you the impression that I was interested in adding another agent to my staff, Angel?"

"You've said I've got a good eye, Lucy. I could still do what I'm doing now, but I'd be better, more productive."

"How can you possibly think you've learned enough to be a successful agent, Angel? You're a baby in this world."

I swallowed the insult and moved forward. Still smiling, I said, "I've had an excellent teacher. The best."

Lucy paused, weighing the options. "I'll have to think about it," she said finally.

"That would be great." And enough to move forward with Sunny Martin, I thought.

"This is a good day for you, Angel. Now, if you don't mind, get Karanuk on the phone."

I was halfway to her phone when Lucy stopped me again. "Go get everybody else," she said. "I need everyone to hear this. It's not often one gets to witness the birth of a seven-figure book idea."

"Karanuk!" Lucy shrieked into the speakerphone once we were all assembled once more in her office.

"Yes, Karanuk," he said with his characteristic deadpan.

"My dear, I've got some fabulous news for you," Lucy said, sweeping her eyes over the four of us.

"News," Karanuk repeated.

"I know you've been torn as to what to write next, dear," Lucy said, "and I'm just thrilled to tell you that I've just been to New York and I have come up with a brilliant idea for you."

"I'm writing *Thaw*," Karanuk said. "I sent it to you."

"*Cold!Cooking!*" Lucy yelled into the speaker, unable to contain herself any longer. "Recipes in prose. Or essays and recipes. A new kind of cookbook. It will be stunning, K, just stunning."

The static hiss was the only indication that Karanuk hadn't hung up. Flushed with anticipation, Lucy leaned closer to the phone. "Karanuk? Are you thrilled?"

"I'm writing *Thaw*," Karanuk said finally. "I am working with your assistant, Angel. I'll talk to her. She understands."

Lucy leaped at the phone and picked it up so that Karanuk's voice would no longer be audible to the rest of us. All eyes, I noticed, were now on me. "Listen, K," Lucy said, "this is a good idea. You should consider it. What? Well, in all honesty, *Thaw* needs some work, K. Yes. Yes, she is. Yes, I do. *I'm* your agent, Karanuk, not her. No. Well, I hope you'll reconsider."

Lucy hung up the phone and looked across her office at the four of us. It was impossible to get an exact read on her expression. "He wants to write *Thaw*," she said quietly. "Angel, you'll need to work with him on that."

Nobody spoke or got up for a moment. I got the sense that we were all afraid that if we moved she'd explode.

"Why the FUCK is everyone still sitting here?" she said finally. "Have we run out of work to do?"

Within seconds, every one of us was back at our desks.

SIXTEEN

To: ganovelist@heya.com
From: angel.robinson@fiammalit.com
Subject: Blind Submission

Hello G,

I thought you'd like to know that we've decided that we now have enough text to take your novel out for sale. However, we won't be able to do that until you sign an agency contract. I know you want to remain anonymous, but I'm afraid it's time to "come out." Lucy and I both know who you are, so there's no need to keep this up. There's no harm done, okay? Just give me a call—you know the number—and we'll get this thing going the way it's supposed to.

Thanks,
Angel

It was almost noon on Saturday when I turned on my computer and prepared to check my e-mail. As my laptop booted up, I dialed Damiano's number one more time and listened to it ring a half-dozen times before I placed the phone back in its cradle. It was the fifth time I'd tried to reach him since I'd left work. I'd brought my angelfish home at last and had placed the bowl next to my computer. I ran my hands over the glass as if it were a crystal ball and tried to make myself believe that I hadn't lost Damiano forever. But as I connected with the server and logged onto my e-mail program, I could see immediately that it wasn't going to be a day for faint hopes and half-baked beliefs. There waiting for me was another missive from my author from hell.

To: angel.robinson@fiammalit.com
From: ganovelist@heya.com
Subject: Re: Blind Submission

Dear Ms. Robinson,

Well, it seems we are in the home stretch, doesn't it? I am racing toward the finish—with your help, of course. I don't have time to write you a long note (need to get back to work, don't I?), but I wanted to tell you this:

It's time for a murder, Ms. Robinson.

I've given this a great deal of thought, and while there is certainly merit in writing a bloodless tale, a look at the bestseller list will show you that public taste runs to killing. Death seems to sell. So, a murder. You'll find it within the enclosed chapters. I am working both backward and forward, incorporating your notes and hurrying to finish. My hope is that the next installment will be the last.

Enjoy!
G.

P.S. We'll talk soon.

BLIND SUBMISSION

Chapter 9

Alice was dreading her meeting with Carol Moore. Alice knew what it was about and, although she had plenty of alibis at the ready, she was still a little anxious about making sure that Carol didn't suspect her. Not that there was anything to suspect, really. Carol wouldn't have known anything about her affair with Vaughn from Ricardo—Alice had seen to that. As far as Jewel went, Alice's assessment of her was that whatever intelligence that woman had didn't translate into anything like street smarts. Alice, of course, had plenty of street smarts, having trolled them herself for quite some time. All that time in dark alleys had come in most useful recently when she'd gone looking for the drugs. She'd known exactly where to go and within hours she'd had exactly what she'd needed.

But she wasn't going to think about any of that now. What she needed to do was focus on her meeting with Carol. The agent was distressed and Alice thought she'd even seen Carol wiping tears from her face when she'd heard the news. Well, it was understandable, Alice thought. Carol had barely signed him and hadn't even had a chance to pitch his book and now he was permanently out of the picture.

Vaughn Blue's death represented a substantial loss of potential income for Carol Moore.

Alice pondered this. It was possible, even likely, she thought, that Carol actually liked the man. This was something she couldn't understand about Carol—how she seemed to have genuine feelings for her clients. She got involved with them, suffered through their stupid writer's blocks with them, listened to their asinine complaints about having to sacrifice themselves for their art (as if!), paid attention when they came to her with tales of husbands and wives gone astray, ungrateful children, alcoholism, and on and on. They were impossible, Alice thought, always wanting to talk, talk, talk. And yet Carol had unlimited patience with them and a seemingly endless flow of compassion for their plights.

Maybe she was faking it, Alice thought. If so, she admired Carol even more than she did now, and she *did* admire Carol. You couldn't not admire what Carol had accomplished in the world of publishing. But Alice would have preferred to think that Carol made a show of being so emotionally involved with those writers. Like Vaughn Blue. Could Carol really be that upset over his death? Really, if anyone should be crying it should be her. It had to be the loss of Vaughn's book that was bothering Carol. Well, that was all right, too, Alice thought, because her own book would provide just the remedy.

Alice had made a big mistake with Vaughn—she'd trusted him. Foolishly, she'd told him that the "idea" for her novel had come from another author. Then Vaughn had developed a very unfortunate sense of moral outrage. Damn writers—they were all the same! She had to come clean, Vaughn told her. She was better than this, he insisted. He would stand behind her, help her. He loved her, he said.

Alice had played at being sorry. Fine, she said, she would tell Carol. And then she would tell Carol about the two of them. They'd announce themselves as a couple. They should celebrate, Alice told him. They should do something . . . wild.

Alice shook her head. It had been so easy to convince him. It was as if he'd just been waiting for the opportunity to fall back into the arms of Morpheus. If you thought about it, she hadn't really done anything that he wouldn't eventually have done himself. And she hadn't exactly twisted his arm to expose the vein.

One of the silly office girls, Brie—or Sarsaparilla or whatever her ridiculous name was—nervously approached Alice's desk, interrupting her thoughts.

"What?" Alice said. She'd given up the pretense of being nice to the underlings. Now that she'd become more valuable to Carol, it was no longer necessary, or fitting, to treat them as equals.

"Carol's waiting to see you," the girl said. "She asked me to come get you."

"Get me?"

"Asked you to come see her."

"Tell her I'll be right there," Alice said.

The girl hesitated. Alice gave her a look of impatience. "What is it?"

"It's so sad about Vaughn Blue, isn't it?" the girl said.

"Terrible," Alice said without hesitation. "Very sad."

"He was so talented."

More than you know, Alice thought. "Yes, he was," Alice said.

"And he was so gorgeous," the girl said, sighing.

"Yes," Alice agreed, but, in reality, she couldn't remember. The last time she'd seen Vaughn Blue he'd been the same color as his name and quite dead.

"Tell Carol I'll be right there," Alice said, and dismissed the girl with a wave of her hand.

No, I thought. No, no, no. It was too cruel. Why did he want to torture me like this? He wouldn't—couldn't—do anything to Damiano. The fact that Damiano was missing had nothing to do with this fictional murder and everything to do with the fact that he thought I was crazy. Maybe that was what he meant. Maybe the murder was supposed to be metaphoric. By making me as crazy as Alice, he'd made me "murder" my relationship with Damiano. Had he— Oh God, had he *spoken* to Damiano? Had he found Damiano before I'd had the chance?

There was more—much more, judging from the size of the document—but I had to stop reading. Barely concentrating on what I was writing, I fired off a response and sent it.

To: ganovelist@heya.com
From: angel.robinson@fiammalit.com
Subject: Re: Re: Blind Submission

Look, Malcolm, I know you're writing this book, okay? What are you
trying to prove now? Are you trying to scare me with this "murder"? It
doesn't even make sense in the context of the book. Don't be an idiot.
Are you trying to get back at me? Lucy knows, okay? She knows.

Within moments, a reply appeared in my in-box. He was obviously
online just waiting to see how I'd react. I couldn't get over the sheer gall
of him—I didn't know where he found his nerve.

To: angel.robinson@fiammalit.com
From: ganovelist@heya.com
Subject: Re: Re: Re: Blind Submission

The question, Ms. Robinson, is not what I'm trying to prove, but
whether or not this is good fiction. What's your opinion? If you're
scared by my murder, it must mean you think it works.

To: ganovelist@heya.com
From: angel.robinson@fiammalit.com
Subject: Re: Re: Re: Re: Blind Submission

I didn't say it scared me, I asked if it was supposed to scare me. I
know who "Vaughn" is supposed to be and I know what you're trying
to imply here. Don't ask me to believe that he's dead and that I'm
somehow responsible, because that's not going to work. I was going
to play along—I have been playing along all this time—but I don't
want to do this anymore. I'm finished with your charade.

I punched the SEND key with so much force that my laptop slid
backward on my desk. I waited for Malcolm to send me another poisonous e-mail and dialed Damiano's home phone number one more

time. No answer. I told myself that it didn't matter, that this manuscript was merely the product of Malcolm's clearly bitter mind. It had nothing to do with reality. I had to stop, had to pull myself out of the pages of this book and . . . It was a *book,* that was all. "You're nothing but a book," I said out loud, and wondered where I'd heard the same line. The memory floated just out of reach for a moment and then I grabbed it. *Alice in Wonderland.* That was it. *Who cares for* you, Alice says at the end of the story, *you're nothing but a pack of cards.*

I got up and stretched my legs, trying to ease some of the tension in my muscles. I tried not to stare at the computer, tried not to hit the REFRESH icon more than once a second, and tried to keep the edge of fear from cutting into my consciousness. Finally, after several more minutes of waiting and watching, I couldn't stand it anymore and took a long, almost scalding shower. I toweled my hair dry and got dressed. Still no response from G.

"This is ridiculous," I said out loud, and grabbed the telephone. I was sick of playing along—I was just going to call him.

"AANNGGELLL!!!"

There was an inhuman wailing coming from outside my apartment, along with fists pounding on the door. "Damn it, bish! Open the fuggen door!" It was Malcolm—not on my computer but at my doorstep—and by the sound of it, he was out-of-his-mind drunk. "Aaannngel! Open it!" He pounded again. As I got up and walked over to unlock the door, it occurred to me that *now* was the time to be frightened. The crazy-drunk-ex-boyfriend-pounding-at-the-door story never had a happy ending. I opened the door knowing that legions of women who'd done the same before me often wound up as statistics. But I was completely calm. There was desperation, not violence, in Malcolm's voice. And he was making an infernal scene outside. If I didn't let him in, there would be police at my door within minutes.

Malcolm looked like the wreck of the Hesperus. Bedraggled didn't even begin to cover it. His hair was matted and dirty and plastered to one side of his head. He was wearing a pair of baggy torn jeans I'd never seen before and a stained gray T-shirt that said *Canada* in faded red letters. His clothes looked as if they'd been wet and then had dried on him while he slept in them. He was unshaven and unwashed and there was a still-raw scrape down the side of one cheek, as if he'd slid his face along a gravel road. His eyes were bloodshot and dark with patent misery. And if all that wasn't enough, he stank—of liquor and cigarettes and a few other substances I didn't want to identify.

"What happened to you?" I said.

Malcolm looked at me, fists still raised to hit the door I'd just opened, and started to cry. "Bish," he whimpered. "You ruined my life."

I stood aside and let him stumble through the door. "What is this?" I asked him after I'd closed the door behind him. "What have you done to yourself?"

Malcolm staggered toward my desk to sit down, but he was too drunk to negotiate something as complicated as lowering himself onto a chair. He missed it, sliding to the floor, catching my computer cord on his way down so that I had to leap over him to save my laptop from crashing onto his head. When I replaced the computer on the desk, I saw that I had another e-mail. It was the response I'd been waiting for.

To: angel.robinson@fiammalit.com
From: ganovelist@heya.com
Subject: Re: Re: Re: Re: Re: Blind Submission

Are you so sure it's a charade?

Doesn't art imitate life?

Malcolm was sprawled out on the floor, making feeble motions to try to right himself. "Annnggel," he moaned. "I fugged up."

I leaned over him, peering into his face. The fumes coming off him were toxic and I had to stop myself from gagging. "Malcolm! Listen to me. How long have you been here?" Even as I asked the question, I knew that the answer didn't matter. He was here now and couldn't possibly have sent me that e-mail. My hands and feet had gone cold and a chill was spreading up my legs and arms to my spine.

"I dunno," he said. "I had shome drinksh."

"Some drinks?" I said. "You think?" I stood up, reached over to my laptop, and hit REPLY. *Who are you?* I typed. *What are you doing?* I pressed SEND and waited.

"Anngggellll," Malcolm wailed at my feet.

"Malcolm, get up and tell me what's going on."

Malcolm raised himself to a sitting position. "You ruined my life," he repeated. "Why, Annggell? Why'dja have to do that?" He hiccuped and put his hand to his head. "I think I'm gonna be sick," he said.

"No!" I yelled at him. "Don't you *dare* throw up in my house now! Malcolm, for God's sake, tell me what the hell you're talking about."

Malcolm covered his mouth with his hand and hiccuped again. "You told her . . . she told me . . . never going to have a career . . . gonna be a waiter for the resht of my life . . . your fault, Angel. No angel. Thass you. No fuggen angel."

As he was finishing his slurred diatribe, another message appeared on my computer.

To: angel.robinson@fiammalit.com

From: ganovelist@heya.com

Subject: Blind Submission

Angel Robinson wrote:

Who are you? What are you doing?

Dear Ms. Robinson,

I am writing a book, which you've been editing (quite well, I might add) for literary representation by Ms. Fiamma. And while it's obviously that you've read *some* of what I've recently sent you, I don't think you've finished. I urge you to continue—I think you'll enjoy it. And while our little flurry of messages has been most entertaining, I think it would be remiss of me to take up any more of your time with pleasantries. We both have work to do, don't we? I'll sign off now, but

I promise to be in touch soon. I'm almost certain that I'll be able to finish the book within the next day or two.

Until then,

G.

"Never should've got you that job," Malcolm was saying. "Woulda had better luck on my own . . . My angel . . . left me for a guy with a book deal. Ruined my career . . ." He started to laugh and started coughing. "Really bad country song," he said. "She warned me . . . I shoulda listened."

"Who warned you?" I asked him. I kept my voice quiet and calm but firm enough to get through his drunken haze. "Who warned you about what?"

"Lucy," he said. "Told me you didden really care about my career."

"When did Lucy tell you this? *Why* would she tell you?"

Malcolm whimpered. "I screwed up, Angel. I never shoulda . . . I thought she believed in me."

"Never should have *what*, Malcolm?"

"Don't you get it?" he asked me miserably. "I screwed her. She's the one who told me about you and that Italian guy. I knew it, but I didn't wanna believe it."

"You *had sex* . . . with *Lucy*? Is that what you're saying?"·

"She told me I had talent," Malcolm wailed. "She told me you were cheating on me."

I looked at him and knew he was telling the truth. I thought about how flustered and familiar he'd been with her at her dinner party and how she'd looked at him as if he were another piece of meat at her table. He'd known how to get to her house not because he'd followed me to work but because he'd been there before. Then there were the flowers, asking forgiveness for things he'd never felt the need to apologize for before. It all made sense. I was starting to feel sick. Bile rose in my throat.

"How long—" I started, and had to swallow the bitterness in my mouth. "You're not still . . . ?"

"It was a mis-mistake," he hiccuped. "I love you, Angel. Always loved you."

"Sure, Malcolm. That's why you screwed my boss."

"She wasn't anything like you, Angel."

"That's disgusting, Malcolm."

"I know," he said. "I'm disgusting. Take me back."

I looked at my computer and then back down at Malcolm. "Anna . . ." I said, more to myself than to him. "Malcolm," I said, leaning over once again so that I could see into his eyes, "did you have sex with Anna, too?"

Malcolm stared up at me, my question working its way through a sea of alcohol to his brain. I saw it register and watched as a look of shame cut through the bleariness in his eyes. "Sort of," he said.

"Sort of?"

"I was drunk," he said. "She tried to . . ." He shook his head slightly and winced at the pain the motion caused him.

"She was nice to me," he said finally.

"Lucy?"

"Anna. She understands . . . what it's like."

"Are you working on this book together, Malcolm?"

"What book?"

"*Blind Submission.*"

"She told me—" He stopped and tried to lick the dryness off his lips. "You shouldn't be so mean to her, Angel. She just wants to *be you*. You gotta feel sorry for her."

"I should feel *what*?"

"You don't know, Angel," he said. "You think you do, but you don't know *anything* about what it takes to be a writer." He fell over again and attempted to pound the floor with his fists. I could tell that it was supposed to be a dramatic gesture, but it was just a weak slap against the wood. "Angel," he said, "I loooove you." He wrapped his arms around my legs, throwing me off balance.

"Listen to me, Malcolm. Let go of me and get up. I'm going to get you some coffee now and you're going to drink it and sober up. We're going to talk. And then I'm taking you home. Do you understand?"

He lay still for a moment, his head resting on my feet. Then he sighed and released his grip on my legs. "Okay," he said.

"GOOD LORD, ANGEL, I thought I'd never see you again!"

Elise stood in the doorway of her small, shaded San Anselmo house and regarded me with a look of kind concern.

"Can I come in?" I asked her, smiling.

"Oh hell, I'm sorry, honey, I didn't mean it to come out that way. I'm so pleased to see you." She wrapped me in a tight hug. "Come on in. Let's get you something to eat. Have you had lunch?"

"You know, I haven't," I said, following her into the house. "It's been quite the morning."

"Honey, you're gonna have to tell me about it." Elise looked better than I'd ever seen her. She'd cut her long hair into a short, loose style that made her look ten years younger, and she'd traded her bookstore pallor for a light golden tan. She'd obviously been exercising, something she'd never had time to do before, because her body was toned and tight. All around, she looked the picture of health. Not working— or at least not working at the bookstore—seemed to be agreeing with Elise.

"You look good, Elise."

"Thanks, honey, but I have to say you've looked better. Well, maybe *healthier* is a better word. You're a little pale."

"Yes, well, I don't get out much these days," I said.

"I imagine you wouldn't," she said, "working for *her*. Come into the kitchen. We'll get you something to eat and then you'll tell me all about it. Best room in the house, the kitchen. It's the heart and soul of a home, don't you think?" She led me by the hand as she prattled on. "Nourishment, the nurturing that comes with cooking. Women used to have their babies on the kitchen table in the old days."

"Elise," I said, smiling, "women did *not* have babies on the kitchen table in the old days."

"How do you know?" she said, sitting me down in a comfortable cushioned chair at her own kitchen table. "It's a little-known fact. Good things happen in the kitchen."

I pushed the hair out of my face and sighed. I could believe good things happened in Elise's cheerful kitchen. I felt comforted and safe and I could see myself sitting there forever.

"Elise," I said as she took a tin of loose tea from her pantry and filled the kettle with water, "it's so good to see you. I've missed you."

"Me, too, honey," she said. "I'm very glad you called."

"I should have called you long ago. You know, before you left me that message. I'm sorry about that. It's unforgivable."

"Angel, please don't apologize. There's nothing to be sorry for at all. I can imagine how busy you've been. . . ." She stopped and stole a glance at me. "Anyway, you're here now, that's the important thing." She opened the fridge and cupboards, clattering plates, cups, and silverware.

"Thanks for letting me come over today," I said. "I know it was short notice."

"Don't be silly, Angel. You can come over any time you like. Hang on a minute now, I'm going to get you set up here."

As Elise busied herself putting food on plates and preparing tea, I felt my body begin to relax. It wasn't the sleepy kind of unwinding that comes at the end of a hectic day, but a kind of yogalike awareness. It was as if I were slowly coming back to myself.

"There," she said, placing a steaming mug in front of me, "drink that. It has great restorative powers."

"What's in it?" I asked.

"Plain old ordinary English Breakfast," Elise said. "Nothing like it." She pointed at the mug. "Remember those?"

I turned the thick white ceramic mug around and saw the words *Blue Moon Books* written underneath a cobalt gibbous moon. Years ago, in one of her efforts to increase sales, Elise had ordered several cases of those mugs for the store. We'd sold very few of them, as I remembered, but almost all of them had disappeared.

"You managed to save one," I said. "I haven't seen these in forever."

"I thought you'd get a kick out of it," Elise said, and put a full plate and fork next to the mug. "And here's some *homemade* carrot cake for you. That's right, I made it. Been doing a lot of cooking lately, actually. All that time selling cookbooks and I hardly ever checked them out. Anyway, eat, Angel." Elise sat down next to me with her own cup of tea and watched as I picked up my fork and started eating. I hadn't realized how hungry I was until the first delicious bite, and then I couldn't stop, wolfing it down as if it would vanish if I didn't get it into my mouth as fast as possible.

"Good?" she asked.

"Amazing," I answered, my mouth full of cake and raisins.

"Well, there's plenty more," she said, "so keep eating."

In the middle of my second slice, I took a breath and leaned back. I traced my fingers over the moon on my mug. "So you're really going to try this again?" I asked her.

Elise shrugged. "The bookstore? I have to. You always knew that, didn't you, Angel? It's in my blood. What can I do?"

"But you seem so relaxed. I mean, it must be nice not having to worry about the store all the time. The books . . ."

"Yes, that's true, it's been great. I wasn't intending to get back into all of that mess again, Angel, that's the truth. But . . . Well, here's what tipped me over the edge. I was in a certain bookstore, which shall remain nameless," she said with mock seriousness, and then laughed, "and I was just snooping around. You know, old habits die hard. Anyway, here's this kid who obviously needs a book for school and he asks the clerk, who, by the way, can't be much older than the customer and looks as if he'd rather be anywhere else, doing anything else, than wandering around a bookstore, if it could even be called a bookstore—I mean, they've got everything but plumbing supplies, I could practically do my grocery shopping there. . . . Anyway, the kid's got a piece of paper with the name of the book written down and he says to the clerk, 'I'm looking for a book by Victor Hugo called *Less Miserable.* Can you tell me where to find it?' And the clerk, in his infinite wisdom, says, 'Uh, I've never heard of it. But why don't you try the self-help section?'"

I chuckled and Elise joined in. "We laugh, Angel," she said, "but really, it's so sad. I mean, there's dumbing down and then there's *dumbing down,* you know?"

My laughter turned into a long sigh. "Ah, Blue Moon," I said. "Those were the days."

Elise smiled at me. "I'd love to try it again with you, Angel. I don't know if you've given that any thought. You know, after I left you that message I realized how presumptuous it was to ask you to even think about giving up your job to take a chance on something as foolhardy as a bookstore. I just thought, well . . . I guess I've really missed you, Angel."

"I've missed you, too," I said. "I've been thinking about it, Elise. Looks like I'm going to need a job, actually, and probably a loan, too." I looked down at the table, at my crumb-filled plate and my empty Blue Moon mug, and I could feel angry tears brimming in my eyes. I blinked hard and folded my hand into a fist. Elise reached out and gently covered my hand with her own.

"What's going on, Angel?" she asked. "Is it Malcolm? Is he okay?"

He would be, I thought, once he cleaned himself up and slept off his drunkenness. I'd taken him home right before I'd called Elise and driven over to her house. After several cups of coffee, he'd been sober enough to get himself into his apartment, but he was still wasted, ugly, and ranting about how I'd ruined his life. Out of some vestigial need to take care of him, I waited in my car until I saw him unlock his door and go inside. But as I watched him disappear, I found myself wondering how it was possible that I'd wanted to marry him, that I ever believed I loved him.

"We've broken up," I told Elise.

"Oh, honey, I'm so sorry," she said.

"Don't be," I told her. "It's definitely for the best. He . . . God, Elise, I don't even know where to start."

Elise got up and put more water in the kettle. "Why don't you start at the beginning, Angel? There's no hurry now, okay? We've got as long as you need."

I opened my mouth then and the words came pouring out. I left nothing out, no detail about Lucy, Malcolm, or Damiano or anything that we'd done with or to one another. I told her about the books, the sales, and what went on in the office. I told her about Lucy's hellish contract with me, which I'd have to break because I couldn't possibly work for her anymore after what had happened. And I told her, chapter by chapter, about *Blind Submission*.

I didn't stop talking until the daylight faded and the kitchen grew dark. Elise turned on the light and I blinked, my eyes adjusting to the electric glare. The table was littered with cups and glasses from the unending rounds of tea, coffee, and water that Elise had prepared for both of us. She pushed them together in the center of the table and started to carry them to the sink.

"So you think *Anna's* the one who's been writing this mystery manuscript?" she asked.

"I'm not sure what I think anymore, Elise. I'm thinking now that it has to be the two of them. That's the only way it makes sense—the only way either one of them would have enough information." I told Elise how, after two cups of Italian roast, Malcolm had been coherent enough to tell me that he and Anna had spoken on several occasions. Somewhere in there Anna took Malcolm's selfish attempts to extract information as some kind of romantic attention and made a play for him. Then he'd dumped her as quickly as Lucy had dumped him, which explained the tearful phone call Jackson had told me about.

"It's not even so much what Malcolm did," I told Elise, "as how she sat there while I told her that whole story about Malcolm with that disapproving look on her face. Butter wouldn't melt in her mouth, Elise—it would freeze."

"Let me say this first, Angel. I'm not upset that you're through with Malcolm. I'm sorry for your sake that it got so ugly, but I never liked him. Never thought he was right for you."

"I wish you'd told me," I said. "Why didn't you?"

"Some things you have to discover for yourself, Angel. You know that." She paused, taking time to formulate her words. "I could have told you about Lucy, too. I've always known that she was a . . . difficult woman."

"Putting it mildly," I said.

"Well, I didn't really know the extent of it, that's for sure. There have always been rumors, but you know . . . But what good would it have done to discourage you, anyway, Angel? And I'm glad I didn't."

"You are? Why?"

"You don't see it yet, do you?"

"See what?"

"How good you are at what you do. Look how far you've come in such a short time. You've found your true calling, Angel, even if it came at a certain cost. I mean, Karanuk! Would you ever have thought you'd have a . . . a literary relationship with one of our most famous authors?"

That stopped me short and I couldn't think of how to reply to her. Elise washed her hands and dried them with a bright lemon-colored dish towel. She walked over to me and put her hand on my shoulder. "Damiano sounds like a good man," she said. "Much better for you than Malcolm. I'm so glad you found him, Angel. And I can't wait to read his book." She paused, considering something. "Maybe you can get him to consider appearing at my new store when it comes out."

"But . . . you don't think . . ."

"That you've scared him off? That he really is Vaughn Blue?" Elise gave a breathy delivery to the character's name and grinned.

"Well, when you put it that way . . . I know it sounds ridiculous, Elise, but I've been trying to reach him. . . ." I couldn't stop the quick sob that escaped from my throat. "What if . . . if . . ."

"He'll turn up, Angel," Elise said. "And sooner than you think. I'm quite sure of it."

"How do you know that? Have you also got some special information I'm not aware of?" I smiled at her as I said it to let her know that I was kidding, but her face had become very serious.

"What?" I said.

She took a deep breath. "Angel, do you remember I told you I had something to show you?"

"Oh, right," I said as it came back to me. "Now I do. What is it?"

"Hold on," she said. "Let me go get it."

"Is it bigger than a breadbasket?" I joked as she left the kitchen. I waited, rubbing out the wet circles of condensation on the table, until she came back a minute later holding an old, beaten-up paperback book.

"I thought this was just funny when I found it," Elise said, "and that's why I didn't make a big deal out of it. I thought you'd get a kick out of it. But it's taken on a whole new meaning now. You'll have to decide what you want to do with it. Here." She handed me the book.

I looked at the cracked spine first and noticed that the book was so old its publisher no longer existed. I turned it around and saw that the cover, probably once a garish purple, had faded over time to a grayish puce. The title, *Flaming Heart,* was printed in large block type and surrounded by orange flames. Below that, in hot-pink script, were these words:

A novel by Lucy Fiamma.

I held it in my hands for what seemed like a very long time, staring at the letters until they blurred, and then I turned it over again and read the back cover.

> *She was born to a life on the streets but was destined to rise above them to the mansions she saw every day. . . .*
>
> *Eden Summer was no ordinary prostitute. With the face of a goddess and the sex appeal of a centerfold, she was desired and pursued by rich and powerful men from around the world. Using her wiles and wisdom, Eden played her men for money and position. She was poised to marry the wealthiest man in the world and live a life of power and influence, and then came the day when she was betrayed . . . by her flaming heart.*

I opened the book and found a small black-and-white photo of a much younger but instantly recognizable Lucy on the inside cover. The title page had been torn or had fallen out, leaving the dedication as the book's first page.

> *For the Eden inside every woman.*

I flipped through the brittle, faded pages and stopped at random.

> *Eden used her body like a knife to cut through the heart of a man's desire. She loved to hold them hostage, to withhold, then give of her sex until they were trembling and helpless with passion.*

I closed the book and looked up at Elise, who had been standing statuelike over me. I pointed to the cover.

"Well, they certainly got the color right, didn't they?" I said. "Prose doesn't get any more purple than that. Where did you find this?"

"Buried in Blue Moon," Elise said. "I found it when I cleaned out. Angel, I hope you know that if I'd known what was going on with you, I would have found a way to get this to you much sooner."

"Of course you would have," I said. I looked again at Lucy's name on the cover to make sure that it was still there. "Obviously pre-Karanuk," I said.

"Obviously. *Way* pre-Karanuk. She has no idea I have this . . . this opus of hers. I'm quite sure she'd want it back if she did."

"*Goddamn* her!" I spat. "I should have seen it, Elise. I should have been able to figure it out."

"How?" Elise said. "How could you have put yourself in *that* mind?"

"And to think I was worried about getting fired," I said. "Can I keep it?" I asked, holding the book up.

"Of course," Elise said. I stood up and, very carefully, placed the book in my purse.

"You know, Angel," Elise began, "*Blind Submission* really does have quite an intriguing concept behind it." Her voice was sly and conspiratorial, as if she were sharing a particularly juicy secret.

"Well, she's certainly got a lot of interest in New York," I said. "But Elise . . ."

"With the right pitch," Elise went on, "and of course, with your editing . . . You could sell it, Angel." I looked up at her and saw her nodding sagely. "You can make this work for you, Angel."

"But I can't work for Lucy anymore. And if I quit, I have to pay—"

"Honey, you're not going to have to pay a thing. Think about it, Angel. I mean really think about it this time. I'd love to work with you again, but I don't think that's really what you want, is it?"

I looked up at her and smiled. "What an amazing piece of luck it is that you're in my life, Elise."

"And I'll always be, honey. Now, you should go home, take a hot bath, and read that manuscript again. You'll be looking at it with fresh eyes. It's all going to come to you, Angel. You'll see."

I stood and picked up my purse, holding it gingerly as if it contained a bomb. In a sense, it did. I leaned over and hugged Elise hard. "Thank you," I whispered into her hair, "for everything."

"You're okay, right?" she asked me. She reached over and tucked a strand of hair behind my ear. "I don't need to worry about you?"

"I'm fine," I said, and kissed her lightly on the cheek. "In fact, I'm better than I've been for a long time."

But Elise still seemed unconvinced. "You sure about that? You seem a little too . . . calm."

"Really, I'm okay, Elise," I told her. "I'm going to go home. I'm going to call my mother. I'm going to take that hot bath. And then we'll see what happens after that."

SEVENTEEN

BLIND SUBMISSION

Chapter 13

Alice sat down at Carol's desk and laid her tools in order. There wasn't much to contemplate: a bottle of fine, single-malt Scotch, an unopened package of razor blades, and a small sheaf of correspondence from one of the country's most prestigious publishers. Although Alice knew the contents of this file better than she cared to admit, she opened it one more time and leafed through. There was the original letter of interest in "her" novel. Alice read that again for the slight thrill it could still give her, despite her growing numbness.

"We are very excited about this book," the letter read, "and feel that the author's voice is truly unique. This novel is certainly one of a kind."

That Alice knew the truth behind the novel's creation mattered not a bit to her. She felt the same slow flush of triumph that had come the very first time she'd laid eyes on that letter. Below the letter were several handwritten notes describing the details of the sale. Alice read through those carefully as well. She marveled again at Carol Moore's ability to put together the perfect deal. A copy of the actual book contract lay beneath the notes. Carol had made sure that this contract had been drawn up and signed in record time. Alice couldn't bring herself to look at it again. What did it matter if she, as the author, had gotten everything Carol had asked for? It was all over now. The contract had been canceled, nullified. Not only was the publisher refusing to print the book, but they were taking legal action against Alice and Carol both. That was the final piece of paper in the file that Alice held in front of her.

"We are deeply shocked and disturbed," the letter read. Alice scanned the page, which practically burned her fingers with the heat of its outrage. "Literary theft is egregious in itself," the letter went on, "but to abuse the good faith of this publisher is beyond heinous."

Alice felt no hint of remorse. Everything she had done had been justified in her mind. What really hurt, what tore at her soul, and why she was sitting at her desk with Scotch and razor blades, was that her book was not going to be published. Now she would never see her name on the spine of a book. She would never be able to walk into a bookstore and gaze at her own image on a dustcover. Not now, not ever. And worse still than that, she would never, ever be able to bask in the glow of legitimacy that came with being a bestselling author. And it would have been a bestseller, Alice knew. As had Carol.

Carol could have played this differently, Alice knew, but the bitch was caught up in her own damn ethics. Carol had been the one who discovered that the novel belonged to another writer. She'd been sly, as had Carol. She hadn't told Alice about her discovery until after she'd contacted the publisher.

Bitch!

Of course, Carol was a smart bitch. She didn't know, could never prove, that Alice had had anything to do with Vaughn's death, but she suspected something foul. Clever. Had Carol confronted Alice before this all became a publishing scandal, Alice would have seen to it, somehow, that Carol never opened her mouth.

"I'm deeply disappointed in you," Carol had said. "I put such trust in you. To think I even made you an associate agent in this office. You had such a promising career, Alice, and now you've thrown it all away."

Carol had been "kind," allowing Alice to take her things and leave the office without making a scene. Well, Alice had plans for a much grander exit.

Alice closed the file and placed it neatly in Carol's in-box. It was time. She uncorked the Scotch and took a long slug from the bottle. The liquid flamed as it ran down her throat, but Alice kept it down. She needed the warm courage the booze would provide as soon it hit her stomach. As Alice opened the razor blades and held one in her slightly trembling fingers, she was struck with a final inspiration. Rising unsteadily from Carol's chair, Alice plucked a sheet of paper from the fax machine. Using a fat, permanent marker, Alice wrote, "I did it for Vaughn. I loved him and he loved me. Now we'll be together in heaven." Let the bitch find *that* when she stumbles on my body in the morning, Alice thought.

Alice took one more slug from the bottle and sat down heavily. The office was quiet and dark. Alice smiled to herself. Carol had had no idea that Alice had an extra key made. Nobody knew that she was here, in the middle of a Sunday night. Tomorrow morning would provide a real Monday surprise for the famous Carol Moore.

How strange it was, Alice thought as she dragged the razor blade up each wrist, it didn't even hurt. But there was more than enough blood to make a fabulous mess of Carol's office. Alice was surprised at how much. She held her arms up slightly and moved around in the chair, coloring Carol's carpet crimson. Soon, very soon, Alice was no longer able to move. Her eyes were closing and her thoughts floated, disconnected. She remembered something, dimly, as she began to slip away, and it made her want to laugh.

It was something someone had once said about writing . . . that it was so easy . . . all you had to do was sit down . . . and open a vein. That was it, open a vein. Alice's lips curved into a half-smile. Who was it who had said that? It was clever, Alice thought as the darkness closed in on her. So very, very clever.

IT WAS THE BRIGHTEST, clearest Monday morning I'd ever seen. The sky held a deep range of blues, from cool sapphire in the west to golden azure where the sun was just rising. Heading north on the Golden Gate Bridge, I could see the greens, reds, and browns of the Marin Headlands ahead of me. The bridge stretched out, a perfect design of flame-colored lines and curves, so beautiful in the clean light of morning.

The traffic on the bridge was surprisingly light for a Monday morning and I was making good time. I considered this a positive sign of things to come. I planned to get to the office early enough to beat the rest of the staff, but it wouldn't make any difference when they showed up. I was going to have my time with Lucy regardless.

My fingers went to the hollow of my throat and I touched the small golden angel hanging there. I smiled as I felt the tiny points of its wings under my forefinger. "For protection," Damiano had said when he'd fastened it around my neck. "An angel for an Angel."

When I'd left him less than an hour before, at the door of his North Beach apartment, he'd kissed my throat just above the charm. "I knew it would be perfect," he said, touching the chain with his fingers. "It was made for you."

"I'm going to need it today," I said, kissing his lips, soft and warm from sleep.

"Are you sure you don't want me to come with you?" he asked me then, concern creasing his forehead. "I can be ready in five minutes. *Dai,* Angel, let me come with you."

"It's okay," I told him. "It will be fine."

"You will call me?" he asked.

"I will."

"And I will see you?"

"Later," I said. "You're going to meet me there, right?"

"*Sì,*" he said. "I come early."

"Okay."

"I don't want to let you go again," he said, holding fast to my hand.

"And I don't want you to," I said. "But it's not going to be for long."

"Okay," he said, and pressed his cheek against mine in a gesture more intimate than a kiss. "Angel," he whispered, "*ti vòglio bene.*"

"What does that mean?" I asked him. "It sounds so lovely."

"I'll tell you later," he said, and then he let me go.

I touched my guardian angel again, drawing strength from its small weight. He'd given it to me late Saturday night as we sat in the bay window seat in his living room. We were drinking small glasses of dessert wine and eating almond biscotti that he'd baked himself. The sweet taste of the fruit was heavy in my mouth. He reached into the pocket of his jeans and pulled out a small red box. The angel was inside.

"I got it in New York," he said. "After . . . I never should have left you there. It was a mistake."

"You didn't know," I told him. "You couldn't have known."

Elise had been right about Damiano, although I'm sure she didn't expect him to reappear as soon as he did.

I'd come straight home after I left her house. I'd called my mother and the two of us had talked for the better part of an hour. Then, as Elise had suggested, I'd taken a long, hot, full bath. I put Damiano's CD of angel songs in my stereo, turned it up loud, and submerged myself in bubbles up to my neck, holding the pages of *Blind Submission* above the edge of the tub so as not to get them completely soaked. I couldn't remember when I'd last taken a bath. Since Lucy, I hadn't allowed myself time for anything as luxurious. Elise was right about *Blind Submission*, too. Now that I knew who was writing her, Alice finally made sense to me. And as I read the last few chapters, it became clear to me how I was going to change the ending, not just of the book, but of my own story.

Halfway through the third rotation of Damiano's CD, as if summoned, my phone rang and he was on the other end.

"Angel, it's Damiano. Please don't hang up."

"Oh, Dami . . ." I could feel tears of relief stinging my eyes. "I tried to call you so many times. I didn't get an answer. I didn't know where you were."

"I was in New York," he said. "I just got back this afternoon. I was afraid to call you. . . ."

"You stayed . . . in New York," I said. I couldn't stand up anymore, my knees had gone liquid and weak, so I sat down on the edge of my bathtub, the phone pressed against my wet ear. "I'm so glad to hear your voice."

"But Angel . . . *Non capisco.* I don't understand."

"Lucy said you never showed up for your meeting with her," I said, the words coming fast and high. "She said you never called her, that you just didn't show up. It was right after we . . . and I thought . . . but now I know . . . oh, Dami . . ." I sighed deeply.

"She said I didn't show up?" Damiano sounded confused. "I had a meeting with my editor in New York. *Porca misèria,* Angel, I wish you were there with me. I didn't know what I was doing." He blew out a short puff of air in irritation. "I had to go by myself," he said, "because Luciana wasn't there. She called me to tell me that she had to go home early. She said she had an emergency." I pressed the phone to my ear as if I could push him through it. "I was worried about you," he said finally. "You were so upset. . . ."

"I'm sorry," I said to him. "I'm so sorry about that. I need to explain it to you."

"*Sì,*" he said. "Can I . . . Can I come to see you?"

I looked around at my unmade bed, stacks of manuscripts, and unwashed cups on the table. I hadn't even washed out the coffeepot from the last round I'd made for Malcolm.

"No," I said. "Let me come to you this time. Tell me where you are."

It was late by the time I arrived at his apartment, set amid a throng of restaurants. The air smelled like garlic, rain, and espresso and was bright with neon. The noise of diners, revelers, and car horns echoed off the street. Damiano waited for me outside his building, leaning against a wall, a cigarette in his hand.

"I didn't know you smoked," I said by way of greeting. It was suddenly awkward to be seeing him in the flesh after what had happened between us. I didn't know where we were supposed to pick up or what level of intimacy we'd reached. And I suspected he didn't, either.

"Only sometimes," he said, grinding the cigarette out under his shoe. "When I'm nervous."

When we got upstairs, Damiano poured the wine and we talked, hesitantly at first, then comfortably, gradually moving into a conversation that was quiet and tender. I told him everything I could about the events of the past week and everything I should have told him in New York. Damiano spoke little while I told my story, saving his own thoughts and feelings until I stopped. He didn't touch me until he clasped the angel around my neck. We'd been talking for hours.

"It's so late it's early," I said then, looking out the window at the violet lines starting to break in the sky.

"You should sleep," he said, and led me into his bedroom. In the center of the room was a king-size bed covered with a simple olive green comforter and two large pillows in matching fabric. There was one bedside table with a lamp and a shallow dish of change. On the far wall, there were three floor-to-ceiling bookshelves filled with books of every size and shape in English and Italian. I wanted to study them right then, to look at every title, but I was suddenly so weary I could barely stand up.

Damiano sat me down on his bed and leaned over to take off my shoes. *"Vieni qua,"* he said, patting a pillow. "Lie down, Angelina." I did and he lay down next to me, taking me gently in his arms and resting his head close to mine. I was asleep in seconds. When I woke up the window was flooded with daylight and Damiano was smiling at me.

"Shall I make you breakfast?" he asked me.

"No," I said. "Make love to me." And then neither one of us spoke again for a very long time.

Much later, the two of us ate dinner together by candlelight.

"So, of course I am going to fire her," Damiano said. "Don't you think?"

"You can't fire her, Dami. I mean, you *can,* but she'll always be the agent on *Parco Lambro.* She sold it. It's hers."

"No," he said. "It's your book as much as mine."

"It doesn't matter," I told him, covering his hand with my own. "There will be other books. She doesn't own the rights to *you.* Or to me."

"But I have to do something," he said.

"I have a plan, Dami," I told him. "But let's not talk about that now. Let's . . . I'm sure we can find better things to do until I have to leave in the morning."

"*È vero,*" Damiano agreed. "I think we can."

I SIGHED CONTENTEDLY as I followed Highway 101 to the San Rafael exit. I could still feel the touch of his fingertips stroking my face and could still smell the faint scent he'd left on my skin. Neither one of us had gotten very much sleep the night before, but I felt as refreshed as if I'd gotten a full eight hours. When I checked my reflection in the rearview mirror, I saw that my skin was fresh and glowing, as if I'd spent the day in a spa. *But love can do this, too,* I thought, and wondered where I'd heard the line before. It took me a minute to realize that it came from Shelly Franklin's novel.

As I wended my way through the streets of lovely San Rafael, I felt the familiar flip in my stomach that I got every time I got close to Lucy's house. But this time it was anticipation, not fear, that was giving me butterflies.

I pulled in to Lucy's driveway and saw that I'd judged my time well. I was the first to arrive. I took a moment to gather my wits and take a few long, deep breaths, and then I picked up my things and went inside.

The office was cool and much neater than we'd left it on Friday afternoon. Lucy had obviously spent some time over the weekend going through everybody's desk. Periodically, she was wont to do this kind of "cleaning up" after we left for the day, and we'd come back to our desks in the morning to find them completely rearranged. It was another way of letting us know that everything in her domain, including her staff, was controlled by and belonged to her alone.

I had a flash of my first day in the office, a visceral memory of how I felt in those initial moments. I felt again the fight-or-flight response I'd had standing there, surrounded by the sound of telephones and voices and the silent, pressing demands of all those words, written, typed, and printed, coming at me all at once. I'd thought I was in over my head then, like Alice falling into Wonderland. Alice. There was that name again. It turned out I'd been closer to the truth then, on that first day, than I would get until this moment.

I walked past my desk and went straight to Lucy's office. Her door was open and I stood at the threshold, looking in. She wasn't there, but the lights were on and a cup of still-steaming coffee sat on her desk. Behind it, the door that led into the main part of her house had been left ajar. I looked at the slice of white light coming through the crack and realized that never once had I seen Lucy leave this door open. I walked over to Lucy's side of her desk and sat down. She'd see me as soon as she walked in, but I would see her first.

I didn't have to wait long.

"Angel!"

I'd expected her to jump or startle at the sight of me, and I was slightly disappointed that while I'd certainly caught her unaware, my sudden presence in her office hadn't given her any kind of fright.

"How nice to see you here so early," she said. "At my desk, too. Very industrious of you. I hope your colleagues don't think you're trying to kiss up to the boss, hmm?"

"Hmm," I answered. Lucy sat down in the chair opposite me, the chair that I normally sat in, and reached over for her coffee. She took a sip. I noticed that she hadn't taken the time to style her hair this morning. It was pulled back and pinned up behind her, giving her face a severe, slightly strained effect. She was wearing a black catsuit, the kind that had become so popular in yoga studios of late, over which she'd thrown a filmy white duster that tied in a bow at her décolletage. Her feet were clad in a pair of shiny silver ballet flats. All in all, a ridiculous outfit, I thought. Classic Lucy.

"Well, I assume that you've been checking my call list for the day," she said, "since you're sitting at my desk." She gave me a pointed look tinged with curiosity. "Shall we discuss?"

"Actually," I said, "what I'd really like to talk about is the reading I did this weekend."

"Oh?" Lucy leaned back in her chair, an enigmatic smile spreading across her lips. I couldn't tell what she meant by it. My heart was beating wildly and my mouth felt dry. I lifted my hand to my throat and ran my fingers across the angel. I could feel warmth and confidence returning to me. The gesture caught Lucy's eye and she said, "That's an interesting little charm, Angel. Is it new?"

"Yes," I said, and I could hear new strength in my voice. "A friend gave it to me when he came back from the dead."

Lucy's eyes narrowed to emerald slits as she studied me, waiting to see what I'd come up with next.

"I found a fascinating little book over the weekend," I said. "A real gem." I leaned over, reached into my purse, and pulled out *Flaming Heart*. I held it up for her to see. *"Les jeux sont faits,"* I said. *"You're* the author of *Blind Submission."*

Lucy's face was a study in conflict. Surprise, discomfort, relief, and excitement all battled one another in her eyes. She started to speak several times but kept stopping herself, the words dying in her throat before they had a chance to escape her mouth. For the first time since I'd met her, she was tongue-tied. I knew it couldn't last long because, surprise or no, Lucy was still Lucy, and so I stayed silent, savoring the moment, until she folded her arms across her chest and said, "Well, I must say, it took you long enough, Angel."

"That's true," I said. "There were enough clues along the way, but I suppose I just chose to ignore them. It was so much easier to believe that Malcolm had set this all up, but I know now that I was giving him much more credit than he could ever deserve. At one point, I even thought that *Anna* had authored the book, if you can believe that." I took a breath and went on. "The tattoo was a nice touch, Lucy." I raised my hand reflexively to my breast. "I suppose you saw mine that night at your party. Unless Malcolm told you . . ." I shuddered at the grotesque images that appeared in my mind's eye and went on. "It was the *why* of it I didn't get, though. Why me? Why paint *me* as Alice when Alice is so clearly you?"

Lucy regarded me with interest so intense it bordered on lust. "And?" she said, expectantly. "You worked it out?"

"Your dedication in this book is what did it," I said, holding up *Flaming Heart*. "'For the Eden in every woman,'" I read, and gave Lucy a long, searching stare. "Alice is both of us, Lucy. You needed me in order to write her and I needed you in order to become her. No, to become the *better* part of her."

"The better part of her?" Lucy asked.

"Well, I'm not a writer," I said. "If you think about it, that's what really screws Alice up, isn't it? That's her fatal flaw."

"You're more like Alice than you know," Lucy said. "You've been shaping her in your own image."

"I'm not you, Lucy," I fired back.

Lucy's eyes were glittering. She placed her hands, palms down, on her desk and pushed herself up to a standing position. "And I'm no *angel*, is that it? Let me tell you something, my dear, you can't get to where I am by being a sweet little angel. Success isn't about being *liked*, it's about being tough. If you haven't learned that by now, you never will." Lucy leaned over me, her face darkening. "This has all been very illuminating," she said, "but it's time to get to work. Unless you've got something else you want to say?"

I stood up and walked around to meet her on the other side of her desk. "I'm not going back to work for you, Lucy."

"Really?" Lucy didn't sound at all surprised. This was something she'd prepared for. "You're so morally outraged that you're going to quit? Planning to take off into the sunset with your Italian man—yes, I know all about it—and live happily ever after on his royalties?"

"Not quite," I said.

"I'm very disappointed, Angel, but then I'm often disappointed in people." She gave an exaggerated sigh. "So be it," she said. "You'll owe me some money, of course, as per the terms of your contract. You can see Craig about that. And I expect to be paid immediately. In addition, you may not use any of the contacts you've made in this office in the future. If you think you're going to continue your relationships with any authors or editors you've met through me, you are mistaken. I will sue you, Angel. I will ruin you. In fact, if I were you, I would consider an entirely new career because it will be *impossible* for you to work in publishing again." Lucy paused to let her words take effect. "But," she said, "I am a magnanimous person. I'll allow you to reconsider, Angel. Do you want to change your mind?" Lucy gave me a big smile. She was expecting that I'd fold in fear and awe. No, she was *counting* on it. Out of the corner of my eye, I could see two figures in her doorway. Jackson and Anna had come in and were hovering, listening to every word.

"No," I said, "but I'll allow *you* to reconsider."

"What?"

"*Blind Submission,*" I said. "I've finished it. It needs a lot more work, Lucy, but I can get it to where it needs to be. It could sell now, but you and I both know that it wouldn't be the kind of success you want it to be. It can be a great book, Lucy, but not without *me,* and you know it." I picked up *Flaming Heart* and held it in front of her. "Of course, you could always write a sequel to *this.* But I don't think that's what you want. I don't want your authors, Lucy, or any part of your"—I gestured to the expanse of white in her office—"empire. I only want what's mine. You're going to release me from that contract and you're not going to stand in my way." I heard a quick gasp coming from the doorway.

"Is that so?" The color had drained from Lucy's face, but her voice was still strong and vibrating with anger. "And what makes you think I'll do that?"

"Because you need me, Lucy. And, as a gesture of goodwill, I'll even help Karanuk finish *Thaw.*"

"You can't touch Karanuk!"

"I don't want to touch him, Lucy. I said I'd help him—help you."

"Clearly, I'm going to have to think about this," Lucy said.

"I really need to know now," I answered.

Lucy clenched her fists and set her jaw. She strode over to her desk and fell heavily into her chair, slamming into her desk and rattling her collection of pens and notepads. "Well, then, you'd better get over here now, Angel, so we can work out the terms of this—whatever this agreement is."

A faint but unmistakable sound of soft clapping came from the doorway. Lucy and I turned our heads to look at the same time, but they'd vanished into the recesses of the outer office. Lucy turned to me and glared.

"When did you become this *person*, Angel?" she asked. "How did you get the nerve?"

I walked over to her desk and sat down opposite her. "Like I told you before, Lucy, I had an excellent teacher."

EPILOGUE

BOOK NEWS WEEKLY
JUNE 13–JUNE 19

Real Deals

Hot deal for Cold! *author:*

The biggest news in publishing this week, and no doubt for many more to come, is the sizzling sale of a new book by reclusive, elusive **Karanuk,** author of the award-winning, mega-selling phenomenon *Cold!* Quelling the seemingly endless speculation as to what Karanuk might do for an encore, **Gordon Hart** announced early this week that **HartHouse** will publish *Thaw* next spring as (no surprise) a lead title. Hart won what he described as "a stunning follow-up" from Karanuk's longtime literary agent, **Lucy Fiamma,** after a heated auction involving at least ten publishers. "We are absolutely thrilled," Fiamma said from her Marin County office. "Second acts are always challenging, but Karanuk had an especially difficult task after the enormous success of *Cold!* He took his time and he has created a unique, inspiring book that was well worth waiting for." Fiamma has good reason to be thrilled; the sale is reported to have topped out at seven figures. "We are extremely excited to be working with Gordon Hart," Fiamma added, "and we are confident that HartHouse will do a beautiful job with this very important book." No word yet on whether or not the mysterious Karanuk will make any appearances to promote this book when published, but Fiamma won't rule out the possibility. "We are discussing options at the moment," Fiamma said. "Expect the unexpected."

BOOK NEWS WEEKLY

JULY 11–JULY 17

Real Deals

An "angel" gets her wings with first book by star-watcher:

Astrologer and first-time author **Solange Martin** got news this week that even she couldn't have predicted. That news was that her memoir, **Balsamic Moon,** had been sold to **Natalie Weinstein** of **Weinstein Books** at **Gabriel Press.** Weinstein bought world rights for the book with a six-figure preemptive offer. Weinstein described the memoir as a "real-life *Da Vinci Code* with an astrological twist" and hails the author as "a major new voice in nonfiction." What is perhaps bigger news than this, though, is *who* Weinstein made the deal with: brand-new literary agent **Angel Robinson,** formerly of the **Lucy Fiamma Literary Agency.** "She has a great eye and a wonderful book sense," Weinstein said of Robinson. "I'm really looking forward to working with her." Could Robinson be a major new voice in the world of agents? It seems that she's well on her way. Although Robinson isn't naming names, her assistant, **Jackson Stark,** claims that the agency is inundated with submissions and recently signed at least one "very big" author.

Book News Weekly

JULY 18–JULY 24

Bookselling News This Week

Blue Moon rises again:

When **Elise Miller** closed the doors of her well-known but often-struggling bookstore, **Blue Moon,** last year, she planned to "relax, garden, and forget about the high-stress world of bookselling." Fortunately for her devoted customers and the authors she helped support, Miller just couldn't stay away. This week she announced the grand opening of **Blue Moon 2,** a smaller but no less diverse store nestled in the heart of Marin County, California. "Our goal is to carry titles that are varied enough to attract readers looking for a change from the same old thing," Miller said. "I've found that most people are hungry for recommendations beyond the bestseller lists. There's no substitute for human exchange. We want to provide a place where people feel comfortable asking questions." The original Blue Moon was a popular stop for both touring and local authors, and Miller plans to continue that with the new store. "We've got an amazing lineup of authors already," said **Anna Anderson,** the store's events coordinator. "This is going to be a really exciting year." Anderson claims to have booked several well-known authors as well as some hot newcomers, including **Damiano Vero,** whose forthcoming book, *Parco Lambro,* is already garnering rave reviews. Anderson also hinted about "a very major literary event" to come but remained mum about what that might be.

BOOK NEWS WEEKLY

AUGUST 15–AUGUST 21

Real Deals

Fiamma's Angel agents the agent:

It's a story that could only happen in publishing, folks. Hot on the heels of her first big sale, **Angel Robinson** of the **Robinson Literary Agency** scored again this week with the phenomenal sale of ***Blind Submission,*** a novel by none other than her ex-boss **Lucy Fiamma.** In a further literary twist, the novel is about, yes, a literary agent and her assistant-turned-writer. Who said the book world was self-absorbed? Robinson generated enough enthusiasm to cut short several summer vacations for what she called "a very lively auction." **Triad** was the winner of this one, with publisher **Julianne Davis** personally making the deal with Robinson for an undisclosed sum. "It's a fabulous book," Robinson said, "written by a talented and deserving author who obviously knows the territory well." Triad plans to publish in the spring.

Book News Weekly
NOVEMBER 14–NOVEMBER 20

Real Deals

Robinson gives thanks:

The unstoppable **Angel Robinson** announced the sale of an important project this week, just in time to make Thanksgiving a very happy one. Robinson's special deal was for an author who is, literally, very close to home for the agent. The book, sold on a proposal, is titled ***Fringe: A Study of Witches, Goddesses, and Other Women on the Edge of Normal,*** and the author is **Hillary Robinson,** the mother of her own agent. **Gordon Hart** made the deal for **HartHouse,** outbidding two other publishers. **Kate Small** will edit. *La mère* Robinson was unavailable for comment, but her daughter told us this: "Hillary has an encyclopedic knowledge of these groups as well as direct experience. This is going to be a stunning book on an extremely important topic but will be accessible to all readers."

Spoken like a good daughter.

BOOK NEWS WEEKLY
MARCH 13–MARCH 19

Bookselling News This Week

Surprise appearance makes Blue Moon 2 the hottest ticket in town:

Patrons of **Blue Moon 2** bookstore were rewarded for their loyalty last Monday when none other than renowned *Cold!* author **Karanuk** gave an impromptu lunchtime reading of his new, already mega-selling book, *Thaw,* to a lucky crowd of readers. Because Karanuk has been so reclusive in the past, he was able to browse unrecognized in the stacks until store owner **Elise Miller** made the announcement that he was there. Wearing a baseball cap, blue jeans, and a Lakers sweatshirt, Karanuk took a seat on the small stage at the far end of the store and read for thirty minutes to a rapt audience. Word spread quickly that Karanuk, who has never before given a public reading, was in Blue Moon 2, and by one o'clock the store was full to capacity.

"We knew he was coming," events coordinator **Anna Anderson** said, "but of course we respected his request that we not broadcast this information to the media. This is a once-in-a-lifetime event and we wanted to do it the way he wanted." Anderson reported that she'd ordered "hundreds" of both of Karanuk's books, but that the store sold out almost immediately.

Karanuk's publisher, **HartHouse,** denies that he will be touring for *Thaw.* So what was behind Karanuk's surprise appearance? And why Blue Moon 2? San Francisco power-agent **Angel Robinson** may have something to do with it. After his reading, Karanuk thanked Robinson for "beginning the thaw that led to my vernal equinox." Robinson, a long-time friend and colleague of Miller's, was in attendance with her husband, author **Damiano Vero.**

"She can read the heart of a writer," Karanuk said of Robinson, "and understand what she finds there. And that is something only an angel can do."

ACKNOWLEDGMENTS

FOR THEIR LOVE, encouragement, support and patience, I would like to offer huge thanks to: my family, especially my sister Maya, who gets an additional lifetime thank-you for being the only person to have read everything I've ever written; G, Gabe, and Gabriel; Shaye Areheart (and everyone at Shaye Areheart Books), for giving this book such a welcoming home; my literary agent, Linda Loewenthal, for taking such good care of me; my inestimable editor, Sally Kim, for making so many wonderful things possible.

ABOUT THE AUTHOR

Angel Robinson hadn't been working for the well-known literary agent Lucy Fiamma for very long when the first pages of a mysterious manuscript by an anonymous author arrived at the office. Although juggling Lucy's colossal ego and seemingly neverending list of demands kept her busy, Angel was pulled in by the plot. Set in a New York literary agency, the novel, titled *Blind Submission*, centered on the ambitious assistant to a successful literary agent. As the story unfolds—with chapters e-mailed one by one—it becomes clear that the mystery author is writing the story of Angel's own life, turning her initial curiosity to panic. Someone is watching her, even plotting against her. Could it be her backstabbing coworker, her jealous boyfriend, or her seductive new client? When the novel's plot turns to murder, Angel knows that if she doesn't discover the author's identity before the final chapter is written, more than just her career will be cut short. This guide is intended as a starting point for your reading group's discussion of this thrilling tale of assistant lit.

1. How long would you have lasted as Lucy Fiamma's assistant? Who was the worst boss you ever had? How does that person compare with Lucy?

2. Describe Angel's relationship with her mother. With Malcolm. What do these relationships have in common? How do they impact her relationship with Lucy?

3. What was your impression of Angel's coworkers Anna and Craig? Why does Kelly/Nora allow Lucy to rename her? What kind of atmosphere does Lucy's attitude create in the office? Why would a boss pit her staff against each other? What does Lucy have to gain?

4. Lucy takes credit for turning *Cold!* into a bestseller by adding the exclamation point to the end of the title. What do you think this says about Lucy in light of what we discover at the end of the novel?

5. What was your first impression of Malcolm? Both Angel's mother and Elise dislike him. Why? Do you think his motivations for showing Angel Lucy's ad were selfish?

6. Who did you think was the mystery author? Why?

7. Why does Lucy bring Angel to New York? Does she have reasons other than selfish ones for doing so? How does this trip set up Angel for success on her own?

8. How is Damiano different from Malcolm? Do you think Angel's love of books—and writers—plays into her attraction to him? If so, is Malcolm's mediocre talent a turnoff for her?

9. Angel gives Lucy Malcolm's book without reading it herself? Why? Why does Angel tell Lucy the manuscript was written by her boyfriend? Was she trying to hurt Malcolm's chances of getting published or was it an innocent misstep?

10. Lucy's dinner party is painfully awkward. Why have it? Why hire Anna, Angel's coworker, to serve? Why serve only meat?

11. Lucy offers Angel a spa day during their trip to New York, but the whole event is canceled when Angel refuses to cut and color her hair to look exactly like Lucy's. Why would Lucy suggest this style change in the first place? Is this about control or creating a protégé?

12. Why is Angel convinced that *Blind Submission* is about her life? How does her growing paranoia about it affect her life?

13. Why does Lucy follow Angel home from New York and then lie about it?

14. Why does Lucy seem to hate writers even though she's supposed to be working on their behalf?

15. At the end of the novel within the novel, the main character, Alice, recalls a famous line about writing: "It was something someone had once said about writing . . . that it was so easy . . . all you had to do was sit down . . . and open a vein" (page 313). What does that phrase mean? How does it relate to the experiences of the writers in *Blind Submission*?

16. On page 320 Angel says that Alice is part her and part Lucy. In what ways is she like Angel? How is Angel like Alice? What aspects of Lucy's character are evident in Alice?

17. Why does Lucy give in to Angel's demands at the end of the novel? When does the balance of power between the two begin to change? How much control over the outcome of the novel did Lucy have?

An excerpt from the
upcoming novel by Debra Ginsberg

THE GRIFT

August 2005

Marina Marks had been sweating for weeks. Constant, skin-crawling perspiration ran in tiny rivers across her body. Sweat started at the base of her skull and ran down her neck and back, traveling the length of her zodiac tattoo, sliding over the ram's head symbol for Aries between her shoulder blades and finishing with the swimming fish symbol for Pisces at the very base of her spine. In front, the moisture condensed on her chest, disappeared in droplets between her breasts and pooled in the marsh between her legs. It didn't matter how many showers she took in a day or how long she stood under the water. By noon, she was wrung out and flattened.

They said the body was better equipped to deal with the dry bake of a desert than with the wet heat of a swamp. Meteorologists pointed to this fact when they talked about the heat index. It might be only eighty-five degrees outside, but when the air scorched wet and heavy, the temperature *felt* as if it were over a hundred. Babies, the elderly and the infirm were all at risk in this kind of heat, they said. Weak bodies might just give up and give out and even the healthy ones would struggle with discomfort. And they were right, Marina thought. She was one of the strong ones, but this relentless, steambox humidity was killing her. This morning had been the worst yet in a season that had already offered more than its share of bad days. She'd slept hard but badly, as if she were being slowly suffocated. At dawn, she'd startled into full consciousness, hot, gritty and thinking about her mother, a clear indicator of just how uncomfortable a night she'd spent. Marina never thought about her mother voluntarily and when visions of that woman—always the horrible way she'd looked the last time Marina had seen her—managed to press their way to the surface from deep in her unconscious, Marina knew that her life was stressed and uneasy.

Marina lifted her heavy hair away from her neck and angled herself toward the standing fan next to her table even though it helped very little and served mostly just to move the heat around. Three weeks earlier, her air conditioner had groaned as if it were in pain, spat ice for the length of an afternoon and then died. Living without an air conditioner in Florida at the height of summer was ridiculous, even crazy, but Marina hadn't fixed hers or replaced it. Either option would have required much more money than she was willing to spend for a couple months' worth of relief. She had calculated that two months—three at the very outside—was all the time she needed to clear out and get herself set up in California and there was no room in her budget for any expenses that weren't strictly necessary. But it wasn't just the money, because Marina could have found that if she'd really wanted to. Fixing the air conditioner would have made it too easy to stay longer, might even have implied a kind of permanence. The constant sticky discomfort was an ongoing reminder and incentive to leave as soon as possible.

Marina bent closer to the warm stream of air. What small relief the breeze provided was canceled out by the thought that she'd have to turn the fan off and move it before Mrs. Golden arrived, which would be within the next fifteen minutes. Appearances counted for so much more than people ever imagined. Marina could not have a plastic fan on display in her house where it would clash badly with her crystals, tarot cards and delicate silk scarves. Nor could she be seen as a person who suffered the effects of heat, humidity or any other physical indignity. She needed to be perceived as above and beyond the pains and ills of the flesh. This was the package her clients were buying and the likely reason why nobody had yet complained about how hot it was in her house.

She could have played it straight—just your average work-at-home woman dressed in casual cottons who also happened to be a psychic—but Marina knew how well most minds responded to subliminal advertising. Looking the part without going over the top into some kind of caricature was one of her key selling points. This was why Marina wore more dark makeup on her green eyes than she would have liked (Witches Brew eye shadow and Voodoo eyeliner, no less), dressed in a collection of flowing skirts and gauzy blouses vaguely reminiscent of Stevie Nicks in her "Gypsy" heyday, and had dyed her hair Midnight Black for so long she couldn't remember its natural color. Marina would have cut that long, thick, *hot* hair short—even shaved it off—long ago had it not been such an important element of her image.

But for this godforsaken place, Marina thought, none of it would matter. Florida, especially this piece of it, felt to her like hell on earth. It was no wonder the word "muggy" was used to describe weather that seemed to attack you every time you exposed yourself to it. No wonder, too, that the elderly, the ill and the spiritually lame all converged in this hot soupy trough—misery coming to misery. She should have known better, or at least earlier, that she'd never find happiness here.

When she'd arrived in Florida, the end of her slow drift down the eastern seaboard, Marina hadn't intended to stay long. She traveled light but even so it took weeks before she unpacked all her clothes and longer before she started adding new items to the small house she was renting. Gradually, almost in spite of herself, Marina bought a lamp to go here or a chair to go there until her place looked more like a home than the temporary box she'd moved into. She started making money quickly as almost all of her early clients became regulars and before she knew it she was settled in, making appointments for the months ahead, her feet firmly planted on the Florida ground. But the further entrenched she became, the more Marina wanted to leave. And it wasn't just the weather or the general malaise of the place that was pushing her out. Underlying those things—and the real reason Marina had decided to head as far west as possible—were the *others;* those who were making it impossible for her to get on with her business.

Slowly, and not very subtly, Marina was being squeezed. She had landed in a community where Gypsies, *santeros* and *voodooiennes* existed in a delicate, mutually wary balance. Marina was an outsider and she played by her own rules. It wasn't her way, for example, to go for a big score with a client and then never see that client again. Hers was a slow build of confidence and a fostering of need. Many of her clients saw her as frequently as their doctors and with the same deference to authority. Marina had always believed that it took more skill to develop trust than inspire fear. It paid better in the long run too and was much less likely to end in angry clients who felt they'd been shafted. That she held herself to her own set of standards wasn't really the problem, though; it was her refusal to ally herself with or pay her respects to any particular group. She didn't try to make nice and it wasn't long before she discovered that she wasn't welcome.

She noticed little things at first: a few cold stares, the barely perceptible clicking of tongues. But then the friendly neighborhood cop stopped by, just wanting to make sure she was "okay," telling her that there'd been "some trouble" in the area, that she should keep her eyes open just in case. Oh, and if she were doing any kind of business out of her house, she should make sure that her licenses and permits were in order because she wouldn't want to be on the wrong side of the law in case she needed help of any kind. . . .

After that, she started hearing whispers everywhere, started seeing eyes in the bushes. She didn't like to admit it, but she'd allowed herself to become spooked. How she hated Florida. She couldn't wait to get out of this backwards swamp with its ignorance and heavy superstitions. Two more months and she'd be breathing in the light California air and making some real money without having to contend with sacrificed chickens, zombies and pinholed dolls. Californians loved the weird and the illusory as much if not more than anyone, but never seemed to take anything too seriously, least of all themselves. And the further south you traveled in California, the easier it was to reinvent yourself and live comfortably in whatever persona suited you. This was certainly what Marina was after but wasn't the only reason she had chosen California as her destination. She'd lived there once, so long ago it seemed a recollection from another life. She was only a little girl and it had been a very short stay, too short for Marina to attend school or to remember now which beach city in southern California it had been. But Marina recalled it as a brief, bright moment in an otherwise hard and miserable childhood. That shining memory beckoned her now like a lighthouse glow across the darkness.

Marina flicked the fan off and pushed it into a storage closet behind a bead-covered doorway. Sweat formed instantly, trickling down her ribs. The crawling sensation made her shiver and Marina closed her eyes. There was a quick flash of light behind her closed lids and she flinched. Marina stared at nothing for a moment wondering if the heat was short-circuiting her brain. She closed her eyes again and focused. The flash came again, but this time Marina could see its form—a fork of lightning illuminating rain—and then she remembered. This storm behind her eyes was the echo of a dream she'd had. . . . Was it last night? She'd woken up so abruptly with the damp and tangled sheets strangling her and her mother in her mind. Had her mother been in the dream? Maybe there had been thunder outside—a real storm. But no, the day was cloudless, no sign of rain. Marina prickled with irritation at herself, not wanting to recall her dreams; good, bad or otherwise. The heat was now driving her mad as well as making her uncomfortable. She needed to pull herself together because she could hear knocking at the door. Mrs. Golden, usually punctual to the minute, had inexplicably chosen this day to come early. If only it were just five degrees cooler, Marina thought as she made her way to the door.

Marina pulled her front door open to the bright wet air and the smell of rot hit her like a wave. Mrs. Golden, however, was nowhere in sight. It took only a second for her to look down, away from the empty rectangle of light in her doorway, and see the dead snake, stuffed with foul dark matter, coiled on her front step. Even as she was slamming the door shut, adrenaline shooting through her veins, Marina knew she had to open it again and get rid of the thing. Sweat sprang from every pore in her body as she moved fast to the closet to pull out a broom and a rolled up grass mat. No time to make this neat. Perspiration pooled like still tears under her eyes. Marina opened the door again, breath held and eyes averted, and hit the thing hard with the broom, sweeping it off the step and into a shallow dip filled with half-dead birds of paradise. One more swipe at the grimy black smear it left behind and Marina threw the broom after it. There wasn't time for a hose or bucket. She unrolled the mat and tossed it on the step. She could still smell it but at least she couldn't see it.

Marina scrubbed her hands until her palms were red and throbbing. She wiped the slick sweat from her neck and pulled her thin shirt away from where it had become glued to her back. She laughed; a hard crazy sound that had nothing to do with amusement. So now they'd decided to leave their voodoo trash at her doorstep. Curses, spells and hexes—Marina believed in none of them. She could produce her own set of tricks that were just as impressive. But she believed in the power of bad intentions. The snake was a particularly crude warning and Marina suspected there wouldn't be many more. She couldn't afford to wait two more months. She had to find a way to get out now.

Once more there was knocking. Mrs. Golden had arrived exactly on time. Marina pictured her client standing on the grass mat and knew she needed to answer the door before the old woman smelled what was hiding in the flowers. But if I make her wait, Marina thought, she'll be frantic and desperate by the time I let her in. Frantic and desperate were good for business and exactly what Marina needed right now. She had no time and had to think, calculate, speed up her mental process. She glanced at her table where she'd laid out the cards for Mrs. Golden, and a decision began forming in her mind.

This would be Mrs. Golden's last reading and it would be very expensive. Mrs. Golden knocked again. "Hello? Are you there? Hello?" The voice was high and urgent. Yes, Marina thought, Mrs. Golden was ready. The old woman was on the edge anyway and hardly even needed a push. Her worries had been escalating over the last few readings. Concerns over the state of her own health had turned to irrational fears that her dead husband was unable to rest in peace. Wishes for her sick neighbors to get well had turned to morbid curiosity over the nature of her own death; when and how it would happen. Mrs. Golden's need for bad news had been increasing with every appointment and she'd been scheduling her sessions closer and closer together. *Tell me something bad, Marina. Tell me something terrible.* Her eyes begged for it—searched for it every time she came for a reading. Today her search would be over. It wasn't Marina's business to understand why Mrs.

Golden or any of her clients had such a powerful need for calamity. But it *was* her business to give it to them.

Marina smoothed the folds of her skirt and wiped the beads of moisture from her lip. She willed herself into stillness for a few seconds, controlling her breath and allowing her professional mask to drop and settle over her. She could feel her face relax, her back straighten and her eyelids fall. When finally she made her way over to the door, Marina had, by sheer force of will, transformed herself from a frazzled, ordinary woman in her thirties to an ethereal, ageless psychic.

Appearances counted for a great deal indeed.

"Hello, Mrs. Golden."

"Marina . . . I was worried that you . . . you . . ."

Marina fixed her eyes on Mrs. Golden with the careful, studied gaze she'd perfected over years of training. Mrs. Golden's usually well-maintained auburn hair was showing white roots and her cheekbones were sharp against the glare of the afternoon sun. Her fingernails, digging into the tired beige leather of her handbag, were unpolished and uneven in length. The coral lipstick she had hastily applied was dry and feathery, long past its prime. She was wearing polyester taupe slacks and a matching blouse. The outfit was old and too warm for the weather. Nor did it go with the shoes, child-size clear jelly sandals available for $1.99 at any drugstore. She was letting herself go, Marina thought, and it wasn't for lack of money. Marina knew she had plenty of cash on hand and much more in the bank. So either dementia was setting in or the woman was just sick of keeping up the façade. Marina could certainly relate to that.

"Not to worry, Mrs. Golden. Please come in." Marina's voice was low and even, but friendly and familiar.

The old woman stepped inside and blinked in the dimness of Marina's small shuttered house. "I thought you . . . when you didn't answer—"

"Don't be silly," Marina interrupted. "You know I'll always be here for you."

Mrs. Golden smiled, showing the perfect white teeth available only to those who could afford them, and loosened her grip on her handbag. "Yes, dear, of course you are."

Marina offered the smallest of smiles in return and gestured toward her table. Today she would be the daughter Mrs. Golden never had—one of many roles she was able to adopt. She was sometimes the best friend, sometimes the mistress, the child or the parent. The medium became the message—and it was all the same to Marina as long as they paid in cash.